Transmission Lines and Wave Propagation

This book is part of
The ALLYN AND BACON series
in Electrical Engineering

Consulting Editor
Norman Balabanian
Syracuse University

Transmission Lines and Wave Propagation

PHILIP COOPER MAGNUSSON

Professor of Electrical Engineering
Oregon State University

Allyn and Bacon, Inc. *Boston, 1965*

Printed in the United States of America.
Library of Congress Catalog Card Number:

65-19812

To

Evelyn / Barbara / John / Elizabeth

Preface

A transmission line is more than a set of long, parallel wires. To the electrical engineer it is a distributed-parameter physical system, one in which voltage and current, whether moving bulk power or conveying communication signals, must be regarded as continuous functions of location along the given line. This is in contrast to lumped-parameter networks of resistors, inductors, and capacitors, in which a discrete number of currents and a discrete number of voltage drops describe fully the system behavior.

Electrical analysis of a transmission line involves two independent variables, time and distance, and thanks to linearity, mathematics may be applied advantageously. This presentation will be a mathematical one, but physical interpretation will be emphasized. Voltage and current functions on a transmission line have the form of *finite-velocity traveling waves*, a concept which will be introduced almost immediately. The lossless line with sinusoidal excitation provides a direct demonstration of the traveling-wave properties and so is considered first, in Chapter 1. It is followed, in Chapter 2, by the lossy line.

Reflection phenomena are of key importance; standing waves, which result, are examined both from the viewpoint of voltage and current functions (Chapter 3) and from that of impedance or admittance (Chapter 4).

The propagation of transient wave fronts (Chapter 5) is studied by means of the Laplace transform. Electrical-engineering students usually receive an introduction to this subject before their senior year, and they profit by using it in diverse applications. Advantages of the transform approach are (1) the derivation of such functions as the reflection coefficient by the transform method parallels closely that for a-c phasors; (2) the unit step function is admirably suited to describe traveling waves; and (3) the Laplace transform has the scope to accommodate the more complicated problems, such as wave front propagation on a general lossy line.

A transmission line may be simulated, over a stated frequency range, by means of a lumped-parameter network of the two-terminal-pair type. This, and other networks of that type which are used in connection with transmission lines, are analyzed in Chapter 6.

Electric and magnetic fields (Chapter 7) serve as mechanisms to relate voltage and current to the cross-sectional geometry of the physical transmission line. They further serve to describe the propagation of electromagnetic energy in free space (Chapter 8) and in hollow metallic tubes, or *wave guides*. Differential equations for the dynamic electromagnetic field were derived by Maxwell, and they form a starting point for particular problems.

Two transmission-line cross sections which are commercially important and also mathematically tractable are the coaxial cable and the parallel-wire pair; these are examined in Chapter 9. Wave guides of rectangular and circular cross sections are used in ultra-high-frequency installations, and their fields and properties are analyzed in Chapters 10 and 11.

Situations involving more than two conductors (Chapter 12) arise in three-phase power transmission, in the consideration of coupling between two lines, and when account is taken of the physical ground.

Antennas, devices by which the field configuration of electromagnetic power is changed from one which fits a two-conductor line or a wave guide into that for free space, or vice versa, are much less susceptible to theoretical analysis than lines, wave guides, or free space individually. An introduction to antennas, emphasizing elementary electromagnetic theory, is given in Chapter 13.

This book differs from many on the general subject in that extensive use is made of the form in which alternating-current quantities are stated as explicit functions of time. The phasor form is introduced in the middle of Chapter 2 and used frequently thereafter in derivations because of its brevity. The explicit form, on the other hand, has advantages for the display of results in that the average student is aided thereby in making correct interpretations.

The problems at the end of each chapter have been chosen in the philosophy that application and extension of the ideas developed in the text is essential to understanding. Worked-out numerical examples have in general been used only for topics which, in the author's experience, are common foci of misunderstanding, or which cannot be accommodated by the "leading question" type of problem.

The content of this book is based largely on a two-term course on transmission systems required of seniors in electrical engineering at Oregon State University. The author has taught the lecture portion of this course since 1956; it was originally taught by Professor Arthur L. Albert, whose encouragement with respect to this project has been greatly appreciated.

P. C. M.

Contents

Introduction

"A system of conductors suitable for conduction of electric power or signals between two or more termini."[10] This is one definition, and a concise one, among many which have been written for the noun "transmission line."[2,7,11] From the standpoint of applications, one will find that the term covers a tremendous range in power level, frequencies, line lengths, and modes of construction.

This text deals with transmission lines and wave propagation primarily from an engineering-mathematical point of view. But such study is enhanced if one considers aspects of the growth of the surrounding technological pattern, and that will be the theme of this introduction.

Invention and development within a given sector of knowledge have commonly begun with simple applications of basic concepts and, gradually, proceeded to more exacting forms, as related physical behavior has become better understood and as technology in general has advanced. The word "technology" includes, notably, (1) the development of materials which excel, in specific properties, materials previously available; (2) the devising of less expensive and more precise means of fabricating parts; and (3) the development of better techniques and devices for observing and measuring all manner of physical phenomena.

Thus the earliest device to use electrical transmission lines was one which required little power to make it function, could be built of simple and rather crudely fashioned mechanical parts, and was modest in terms of the frequency spectrum needed. It was the telegraph; Morse sent the first public message in

1844. Wire telegraphy over land was followed by submarine-cable telegraphy. The English Channel was crossed in 1851; a successful cable was laid across the Atlantic Ocean in 1866.[4,6]

Telephony, far more demanding in the complexity and minimum quality of sending-end and receiving-end instruments, and requiring a much wider frequency band, came several years later. Bell's patent was dated 1876.

Soon afterward, thanks to the development of generators and motors, in particular to the polyphase-induction motor invented by Tesla in 1886, the transmission of electric power became a commercially relevant objective. Since both voltage and current levels are much higher in power transmission lines than for telegraphy or telephony, the improving of insulation, the development of suitable switchgear, and the reduction of losses became foci of importance in this field.

Radio, or "wireless," followed. Marconi sent signals across the Atlantic Ocean in 1901. At first glance radio would seem to have dispensed with transmission lines. But, because of the short wavelengths used, physically short sections of radio-frequency line, such as those joining transmitters to their antennas, are electrically long. By this is meant that their lengths are in the order of a quarter wavelength or more. Thus radio systems included, inadvertently, transmission lines.

A continuing tendency in radio and, in turn, television, has been to utilize higher and higher frequencies. The microwave spectrum (approximately 3000 megacycles per second and above) was entered during the development of radar. In this frequency range a single, hollow, metallic tube, or *wave guide*, proved to be a practical, low-loss means for the transmission of energy. Since that time other variations have been tried, including the use of dielectric media for guide structures.

Having named some principal techniques with which transmission lines are associated, one may list some of the continuing problems which have arisen and note some plans of solution which have been evolved. The communication-line aspect will be emphasized.

I-1. LINE LOSSES VERSUS DISTANCE OF TRANSMISSION

The resistance of a line will reduce or attenuate a signal passing along it by converting part of the signal energy into heat. Inasmuch as some minimum amount of energy is necessary to actuate positively a telegraphic receiving-end instrument or to produce an intelligible output from a telephone receiver, attenuation tends to limit the practical distance of transmission. Two basic countermeasure approaches are (1) to reduce the attenuation per unit length of line, and (2) to regenerate or amplify the signal at intervals along the line.

Samuel Morse pioneered the latter course when, as part of his original development of the telegraph, he devised the repeater. This is essentially an amplifier which uses electromechanical coupling; a weak incoming signal on one circuit actuates, through an electromagnet, the transmitting key for an electrically separated outgoing circuit. The power level may be increased markedly thereby.

A substantial reduction in attenuation was made possible next by a change in the usual conductor material. Iron wire had been used in the early telegraph systems because it had the necessary tensile strength for stringing, whereas copper wire then available was less suitable. The development of hard-drawing of copper wire (1877) made practical the use of this higher-conductivity material for overhead transmission-line conductors.

Submarine-cable development was marked by many problems from the standpoint of mechanical strength, techniques of handling and laying, and ability to withstand an unfavorable environment. Attenuation too was troublesome, and the use of repeaters at intermediate points was impractical. The development of extremely sensitive receiving-end instruments (siphon recorders), combined with use of a low-resistance conductor and a sea return, was the initial solution.

Vaschy in 1889, and Heaviside in 1893, had concluded from mathematical study of the general transmission line that an increase in the inductance of a cable should reduce its attenuation. *Loading* is the rather incongruous name which has come to designate the increasing of line inductance by ferromagnetic means. Pupin and Campbell independently developed (1899) *lump-loaded* lines, in which ferromagnetic-cored coils were inserted in series with the line conductors at regular intervals. About the same time (1902) Krarup produced a *continuously loaded* cable by winding a small-diameter soft-iron wire around a copper conductor in a closely spaced helix, which was then covered with insulation.[6]

Lumped loading found immediate use in telephony, for attempts to adapt the telegraph repeater to operation at the frequencies required for voice communication had been disappointing. By means of lumped loading, voice communication over increasingly long distances was realized; in 1914 calls were made from New York to Denver, although under the handicap of attenuation amounting to a ratio of more than 3000 between input and output powers, and severe distortion or change in speech quality.[8]

The commercial potentiality of continuous loading was not fully realized until some years later, after ferroalloys such as *permalloy* and *mumetal*, with permeabilities 10 or more times that of soft iron had been developed. A telegraph cable continuously loaded with permalloy tape was laid from New York to the Azores in 1924.[3] Because of cost, continuous loading has been limited largely to submarine cables.

The development of the vacuum-tube amplifier provided a workable technique for signal amplification on telephone lines over land. Transcontinental telephony was achieved in 1914, and the use of loading on open-wire lines was soon discontinued. In the years that followed, vacuum-tube amplifiers were made more reliable and were so reduced in size and in power requirements that they could be installed in submarine cables. Trans-Atlantic telephony was realized in 1957. The name "repeater" has been retained for amplifier units in telegraphy and telephony, even though electromagnets and moving levers have been replaced by control grids and varying streams of electrons.

In the field of power transmission, losses were reduced and transmission over long distances was made economically feasible by using progressively higher voltages. Prior to World War II, 230-kv lines had become common, and during the decade 1950–60 many lines were built for 345-kv operation. Considerably higher voltages are employed in some recently-built systems. Cables which are insulated for voltages of this order of magnitude are costly, hence overhead-line construction is usual.

I-2. RATE OF CONVEYING MESSAGES

Better utilization of plant is a means to greater profits in any business. Increased utilization of communication transmission lines has been achieved in two principal directions: (1) decreasing the time required to transmit a given message, and (2) making possible the simultaneous transmission of larger numbers of messages on a given circuit.

Telegraph-message handling shifted from mechanized transmission and reception to manual and then back to mechanized. Morse's original telegraph system included a mechanical transmitting unit, and the output was in the form of an ink or pencil trace on a paper strip. It was soon found that human operators could transmit much faster with a manual key, and that they could interpret the message at the receiving end at an equally higher speed if the dot and dash pulses of current and voltage were put into audible form with an electromagnetic vibrator or sounder. Some years later the printing telegraph or teletypewriter was devised; it was put into general use on trunk telegraph lines in 1914. Teletypewriter installations have typewriter-like keyboards for message input and print the received messages in letters. Code-punched paper tape or magnetic tape may be used as an intermediate storage means for the message at either end of the telegraph line. The transmitting speeds attained are considerably above those at which human operators' muscles and nerves can function.

Simultaneous transmission of more than one message per pair of wires has been achieved by three principal techniques: (1) *duplexing*, whereby messages can be sent in both directions simultaneously; (2) *phantom* connections, by means of which three channels are made available within a set of four wires; and (3) *carrier-frequency* transmission.[1] The first two of these methods use bridge circuits at the terminals to separate the signals which share given conductors. Repeater units for such lines are more complicated than those for single-channel lines.

Carrier telephony employs techniques similar to those of radiotelephony. The signal is combined with a sinusoidal wave of much higher frequency, the *carrier*, by the process of *modulation*; a band of frequencies close to the carrier is transmitted, and, at the receiving end of the line, the audio-frequency form of the signal is recovered by *demodulation*, also known as *detection*. Many signals, modulated with differing carrier frequencies, may be transmitted simultaneously. Appropriate *filters*, or frequency-selective networks, are needed to separate the individual modulated signals from the composite received wave. Lump-loaded lines are not suitable for transmission of carrier-frequency signals because the coils cause the line to act as a low-pass filter or attenuate heavily all components above some *cutoff* frequency. At coil spacings that are economically practical the cutoff frequency, although ample for audio-frequency transmission, is well below the minimum required for carrier-frequency transmission. With continuously loaded cables, hysteresis and eddy-current losses limit the usable frequency range. Carrier-frequency transmission was used commercially in 1918, and the trend since has been to obtain more and more channels by utilizing progressively higher frequencies.

An interesting sidelight of the last several decades has been the widespread use of power transmission lines as carrier-frequency communication channels for telemetering, dispatching, and control.[5] In recent years microwave-radio links have tended to displace such installations.

I-3. INTERCIRCUIT COUPLING AND SPURIOUS SIGNALS: LIGHTNING

When two or more current paths are in proximity to one another, coupling will ordinarily exist. Inductive and capacitive couplings are most common, but resistive coupling may also be present. The resultant signal in a communication line may be influenced by coupling with other communication circuits ("cross talk") and by coupling with power transmission lines.

Lightning involves an intense electric current of brief duration. A surge may be induced in any nearby transmission line and the lightning path may actually strike one or more conductors.

a. Ground currents and resistive coupling

Resistive coupling is characteristic between circuits that have ground returns. The latter form of construction has, for economy, been used commonly in telegraphy and, to a limited extent, in telephony. The nautical variation, a sea return, was used for many years for submarine telegraph cables.

Current in the ground-return portion of a circuit has available a path of enormous cross section, but the actual diffuseness of ground-current flow depends on frequency. The higher the frequency, the higher the concentration in the proximity of conductors carrying current in the opposite direction. The resulting variability in propagation and intercircuit coupling characteristics becomes increasingly objectionable in communication applications as the frequency range is increased. Hence the trend has been toward all-metallic telephone and telegraph circuits. The same is true of submarine cables intended for carrier-frequency operation. Here the return conductor consists of a number of parallel strips of copper laid over the insulation which surrounds the center conductor. Additional insulation and armoring is placed over the outer conductor.

Power systems may cause troublesome ground currents even though their load currents are supposedly confined to metallic conductors. In any event they are capacitively coupled to ground and, for safety reasons, they may also be grounded at the neutral points of transformer banks and similar locations, either directly or through a resistor or reactor. Substantial ground currents may flow briefly during short-circuit faults; continuing ground currents, usually at third-harmonic frequency, occasionally result during steady-state operation of power utilities.[5]

b. Inductive and capacitive coupling

Attempts to reduce inductive and capacitive coupling effects follow two general philosophies: (1) to arrange the geometry of the parallel conductors of the circuits so that interfering voltages induced in one section of conductor will be exactly offset by corresponding voltages induced in another portion of the circuit, and (2) to *shield* the circuit, that is, to surround it with a highly conducting sheath or jacket, so that the magnetic and electric fields associated with the interfering signals do not reach it.

Procedures following the first of these approaches are the use of *balanced-circuit* construction and the use of *transpositions* (open-wire lines) or spiralling (cabled conductors). By "balanced line" is meant one in which the corresponding series elements of the two conductors and the shunt effects of each conductor to ground or to other circuits are as nearly equal as is economically practical. These requirements must be observed with respect to each loading coil, repeater, and terminus, as well as the line itself, if the system as a whole is to be balanced. A system of paralleled lines is *transposed* by interchanging the conductors in each of the circuits at stated intervals of distance in accordance with a repetitive sequence. This reduces drastically, on a distance-averaged basis, inductive and capacitive coupling between lines.

Cabling a number of conductor pairs together and enclosing them in a conducting sheath largely eliminates coupling with exterior circuits. At the same time it yields a far more compact cross section than open-wire construction, and for that reason has been generally adopted for telephone circuits. Accurate balance among the conductor pairs within the cable is necessary, though.

The coaxial cable, consisting of a hollow cylindrical conductor with a smaller cylindrical conductor centered within it, is an unbalanced line, but at high frequencies it is self-shielding. It is an excellent form of transmission line for frequencies from about 1 megacycle per second up to the microwave range. At those frequencies the electric and magnetic fields are confined to (1) the space between the two conductors, (2) a thin conducting layer at the outside surface of the inner conductor, and (3) a similar layer at the inside surface of the outer conductor. The remainder of the outer conductor forms an effective shield from external fields of those frequencies. Hollow metallic wave-guide structures similarly confine the fields of the signals which they transmit, and they likewise shield out interference.

c. Protection from lightning

Lightning is a source of danger to personnel and equipment, and protective devices are an important part of any transmission system.[5,9] So-called *protectors*, consisting of fuses and carbon-block discharge gaps, are ordinarily used on telephone circuits where exposure to dangerous extraneous voltages is anticipated. To shield aerial power-transmission conductors from contact by lightning strokes, one or more *ground wires* are sometimes strung parallel to and above a set of power-carrying wires. Such ground wires are electrically connected to the ground. In territory where ground resistivity is high, *counterpoises* or buried conductors leading outward from the tower bases may be used to aid the dissipation of the concentrated energy of a lightning surge. Lightning arrestors are installed at the terminals of line sections to protect transformers and similar terminal equipment by shunting surges of excessively high voltage to ground.

I-4. CLOSURE

The purpose of the foregoing has been to introduce, partly in historical perspective, some of the principal engineering aspects of transmission lines and their applications. The body of this book is concerned with the mathematical analysis of the electromagnetic circuit and field phenomena on transmission lines which make those applications possible.

REFERENCES

1. Albert, Arthur Lemuel, *Electrical Communication.* New York: John Wiley & Sons, Inc., 1950.
2. *American Standard Definitions of Electrical Terms, Group* 35, *Generation, Transmission and Distribution*, p. 16, paragraph 35.40.215; *Group* 65, *Communication*, p. 14, paragraph 65.04.005. New York: American Institute of Electrical Engineers, 1957.

3. Buckley, Oliver E., "High Speed Ocean Cable Telegraphy," *Bell System Tech. J.*, 7 (1928), 225–67.
4. Dibner, Bern, *The Atlantic Cable*. Norwalk, Conn.: Burndy Library, Inc., 1959, 2nd ed., New York: Blaisdell Publishing Company, 1964.
5. *Electrical Transmission and Distribution Reference Book*. East Pittsburgh, Pa.: Westinghouse Electric Corporation, 1950.
6. *Encyclopædia Britannica*. Chicago: Encyclopædia Britannica, Inc., 1960. Articles on "Telegraphy" and "Telephony."
7. *I.R.E. Dictionary of Electronics Terms and Symbols*, pp. 154, 164. New York: The Institute of Radio Engineers, Inc., 1961.
8. Jewett, Frank B., "The Technical Significance of the First Transcontinental Telephone Line," *General Electric Rev.*, 42, No. 12 (1939), pp. 510–19.
9. Lewis, Walter W., *The Protection of Transmission Systems Against Lightning*. New York: John Wiley & Sons, Inc., 1950.
10. *McGraw-Hill Encyclopædia of Science and Technology*, Vol. 14, p. 47. New York: McGraw-Hill Book Company, Inc., 1960.
11. *Webster's Third New International Dictionary*, p. 2429. Springfield, Mass.: G. and C. Merriam Company, 1961.

CHAPTER 1

Transmission-Line Parameters and Propagation on a Lossless Line

Electromagnetic-energy propagation along transmission lines will be considered initially in terms of voltage and current waves traveling on two uniform conductors. This is the distributed-parameter-circuit point of view, in contrast to the more general one of electric and magnetic fields. (The second approach will be detailed in Chapter 9.)

Analysis in terms of voltages and currents which vary sinusoidally with time will receive primary emphasis because of the simplicity and utility of steady-state a-c theory. The propagation of wave fronts and pulses is, in general, more complicated and will be examined in an introductory fashion in Chapter 5.

Voltage and current on a transmission line may be regarded at this stage simply as quantities measurable with conventional instruments such as voltmeters, ammeters, and oscilloscopes. They are functions of two independent variables, time t and distance along the line z.* Whatever the length of the line and the type of termination, and whatever the wave form or time-varying character of the energy source or sources, those functions, $v(z,t)$ and $i(z,t)$, are constrained to follow differential equations based on Kirchhoff's laws.

* The lower-case letter z was chosen for the distance coordinate because the distributed-circuit equations about to be derived will be supplemented with field equations. Some of the latter will be written in terms of cylindrical coordinates, and z, the axial coordinate, is the direction of movement of the fields. In no instance will lower-case z represent an impedance.

1-1. LINE PARAMETERS

The two-conductor line may be described for this purpose by means of four parameters: l, the distributed inductance in henrys per unit length of line; c, the distributed capacitance in farads per unit length of line; r, the distributed resistance in ohms per unit length of line (the sum of the resistances of the separate conductors per unit length); and g, the distributed shunt conductance (leakage from one conductor to the other through the insulation) in mhos per unit length of line.*

In practical transmission lines these parameters are approximately constant with respect to time and with respect to the magnitudes of voltage and current. They will be assumed to be constant for the basic traveling-wave analysis; this makes the system, for mathematical purposes, *linear*. Differential equations descriptive of the voltage and current functions along the line will then be of the linear, constant-coefficient type.

Inductance is primarily a function of the spacing between conductors and their cross-sectional dimensions, but it is also influenced by any ferromagnetic materials present, such as the high-permeability metallic tape used in some submarine cables.

Capacitance is, like inductance, a function of the spacing and of the conductor cross-sectional dimensions, but it also depends on the permittivity of the medium around the conductors, and varies somewhat with frequency.

Resistance is a function of the conductor material, the conductor cross-sectional area, and the temperature. Conductor resistance to alternating current (or to current changing in any manner) is dependent on the frequency. This variation, known as *skin effect*, arises because varying magnetic flux within the conductor renders the current density nonuniform (see Appendix "B").

An "effective" value is used for shunt conductance in most calculations—one which will account for the loss associated with the insulation. Such loss has been observed to increase with frequency and, in open-wire lines, to vary appreciably with humidity.

Formulas for l and c will be derived in Chapter 9, with the aid of field theory, for two important cross sections, the coaxial cable and the parallel-wire pair. All four parameters may be thought of as circuit quantities susceptible to experimental measurement.

1-2. PARTIAL DIFFERENTIAL EQUATIONS OF LOSSLESS LINE

A lossless line, extending toward infinity in both directions, will be considered first. This choice will, with minimal algebraic distraction along the way, give results which emphasize the propagation properties.

* Lower-case italic letters will be used to designate distributed parameters; capital letters will be used for lumped parameters.

Let the positive directions of current, voltage, and distance along the line be assumed as indicated in Fig. 1-1. It is essential that the positive directions of all three quantities be specified if ambiguity is to be avoided.

The voltage at location $z_1 + \frac{1}{2}\Delta z$ differs from that at location $z_1 - \frac{1}{2}\Delta z$ whenever the current flowing through the incremental inductance $l\,\Delta z$ is changing. Here Δz is assumed to be short compared to the wavelengths of interest, and hence the current at point z_1 may be considered to be the average

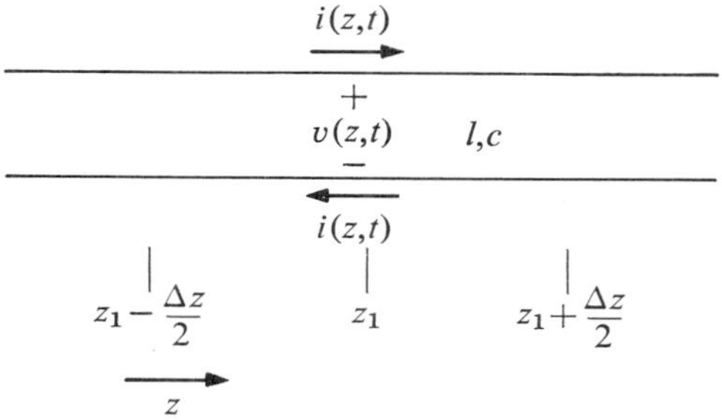

Figure 1-1 Coordinate system for two-conductor transmission line

of the actual current function over the interval from $-\frac{1}{2}\Delta z$, to $\frac{1}{2}\Delta z$. (The difference between the current at z_1 and the true average consists of terms proportional to the second and higher powers of Δz, and is neglected. This is customary in linearized analysis in classical mathematical physics; it is justified mathematically on the basis of the limiting process by which finite-difference terms are reduced to derivatives.) Thus

$$v(z_1 + \tfrac{1}{2}\Delta z, t) = v(z_1 - \tfrac{1}{2}\Delta z, t) - l\,\Delta z\,\frac{\partial i(z_1,t)}{\partial t} \qquad (\Delta z \to 0) \qquad \textbf{(1-1)}$$

In like manner, the current at location $z_1 + \frac{1}{2}\Delta z$ differs from that at location $z_1 - \frac{1}{2}\Delta z$ whenever the voltage impressed across the incremental capacitance $c\,\Delta z$ is changing:

$$i(z_1 + \tfrac{1}{2}\Delta z, t) = i(z_1 - \tfrac{1}{2}\Delta z, t) - c\,\Delta z\,\frac{\partial v(z_1,t)}{\partial t} \qquad (\Delta z \to 0) \qquad \textbf{(1-2)}$$

It will be assumed that

$$\frac{\partial^n v(z,t)}{\partial z^n}(\Delta z)^n \ll \frac{\partial v(z,t)}{\partial z}\Delta z \qquad (n > 1)$$

Then the voltage difference can be expressed in terms of the rate of change of v with respect to z:

$$v(z_1 + \tfrac{1}{2}\Delta z, t) = v(z_1 - \tfrac{1}{2}\Delta z, t) + \Delta z\left[\frac{\partial v(z,t)}{\partial z}\right]_{z=z_1} \qquad (\Delta z \to 0) \quad \textbf{(1-3)}$$

The corresponding result for current is

$$i(z_1 + \tfrac{1}{2}\Delta z, t) = i(z_1 - \tfrac{1}{2}\Delta z, t) + \Delta z\left[\frac{\partial i(z,t)}{\partial z}\right]_{z=z_1} \qquad (\Delta z \to 0) \qquad \textbf{(1-4)}$$

Substitution of Eqs. 1-3 and 1-4 into Eqs. 1-1 and 1-2 yields

$$(\Delta z)\left[\frac{\partial v(z,t)}{\partial z}\right]_{z=z_1} = -l\,\Delta z\,\frac{\partial i(z_1,t)}{\partial t} \qquad (\Delta z \to 0) \qquad \textbf{(1-5)}$$

$$(\Delta z)\left[\frac{\partial i(z,t)}{\partial z}\right]_{z=z_1} = -c\,\Delta z\,\frac{\partial v(z_1,t)}{\partial t} \qquad (\Delta z \to 0) \qquad \textbf{(1-6)}$$

The subscripts 1 may be omitted, since these relationships apply at all locations on the line, and Δz may be divided from both sides, yielding

$$\frac{\partial v(z,t)}{\partial z} = -l\,\frac{\partial i(z,t)}{\partial t} \qquad \textbf{(1-7)}$$

$$\frac{\partial i(z,t)}{\partial z} = -c\,\frac{\partial v(z,t)}{\partial t} \qquad \textbf{(1-8)}$$

The function $i(z,t)$ may be eliminated from the set by differentiating Eq. 1-7 with respect to z and Eq. 1-8 with respect to t:

$$\frac{\partial^2 v(z,t)}{\partial z^2} = -l\,\frac{\partial}{\partial z}\left[\frac{\partial i(z,t)}{\partial t}\right] \qquad \textbf{(1-9)}$$

$$\frac{\partial}{\partial t}\left[\frac{\partial i(z,t)}{\partial z}\right] = -c\,\frac{\partial^2 v(z,t)}{\partial t^2} \qquad \textbf{(1-10)}$$

The order of differentiation of $i(z,t)$ with respect to z and t in Eqs. 1-9 and 1-10 is immaterial if $\partial i/\partial t$, $\partial i/\partial z$ and the second-order derivatives of i in those equations are continuous.[2] The solutions which will be examined in this chapter meet these conditions*; hence

$$\frac{\partial}{\partial z}\left[\frac{\partial i(z,t)}{\partial t}\right] = \frac{\partial}{\partial t}\left[\frac{\partial i(z,t)}{\partial z}\right] \qquad \textbf{(1-11)}$$

By substituting Eq. 1-10 in Eq. 1-9, the following is obtained:

$$\frac{\partial^2 v(z,t)}{\partial z^2} = lc\,\frac{\partial^2 v(z,t)}{\partial t^2} \qquad \textbf{(1-12)}$$

In like manner, an equation in terms of current may be derived:

$$\frac{\partial^2 i(z,t)}{\partial z^2} = lc\,\frac{\partial^2 i(z,t)}{\partial t^2} \qquad \textbf{(1-13)}$$

* Wave functions with discontinuities will be treated in Chapter 5 with the Laplace transform.

Equations 1-12 and 1-13 are identical except for replacing v by i. When one of those functions has been found, the other may be found from it by means of either Eq. 1-7 or 1-8.

1-3. TRAVELING-WAVE FUNCTIONS

These results (Eqs. 1-12 and 1-13) are known in classical physics as *wave equations*. The general theory of solutions to a wave equation is recondite,[1] but particular solutions may be readily tested by direct substitution. That procedure will be followed in this text, using specific forms of the following *traveling-wave* solutions: $f_1(t - z\sqrt{lc})$ and $f_2(t + z\sqrt{lc})$. Here f_1 and f_2 may be any functions of the given arguments, but attention will be directed primarily to the sinusoidal function because it is also applicable (with minor modification) to the line with losses. The *traveling-wave property*, which characterizes those solutions, will be examined (Sec. 1-4) after an assumed voltage function of each type (f_1 and f_2) has been tested and the accompanying current function for each has been found.

A particular form of f_1 will be postulated first; let

$$v_1(z,t) = V_{1M} \sin\left[\omega(t - z\sqrt{lc})\right] \tag{1-14}$$

Here V_{1M} will be understood to be simply a magnitude in volts, and ω is the angular frequency in radians per second. Forming the second derivatives leads to

$$\frac{\partial^2 v_1(z,t)}{\partial z^2} = -V_{1M}\omega^2 lc \sin[\omega(t - z\sqrt{lc})] \tag{1-15}$$

$$\frac{\partial^2 v_1(z,t)}{\partial t^2} = -V_{1M}\omega^2 \sin[\omega(t - z\sqrt{lc})] \tag{1-16}$$

Substitution of these into Eq. 1-12 yields an identity; hence $v_1(z,t)$ is a valid solution.

From Eqs. 1-7 and 1-8 it appears that every voltage function which varies with z and t is necessarily accompanied by a current function; $i_1(z,t)$ may be found by differentiating $v_1(z,t)$ with respect to z and substituting in Eq. 1-7. Integration of the result with respect to t will yield the following:

$$i_1(z,t) = V_{1M}\sqrt{\frac{c}{l}} \sin[\omega(t - z\sqrt{lc})] \tag{1-17}$$

Comparing this result with the assumed voltage function, Eq. 1-14, indicates that the current wave $i_1(z,t)$ is in phase with $v_1(z,t)$ at all times and at all locations and also that it differs dimensionally from v_1 by the factor $\sqrt{c/l}$.

A second voltage function, this one a form of f_2, will be defined as follows:

$$v_2(z,t) = V_{2M} \sin[\omega(t + z\sqrt{lc})] \tag{1-18}$$

This function also satisfies Eq. 1-12 identically, but the expression for the accompanying current function differs from that for $i_1(z,t)$ in its algebraic sign as well as in the argument of the sine function, as can be found by duplicating the above analysis:

$$i_2(z,t) = -V_{2M}\sqrt{\frac{c}{l}} \sin[\omega(t + z\sqrt{lc})] \tag{1-19}$$

In a linear system, such as has been assumed here, any linear combination of solutions to the differential equations is itself a solution. In other words, $v_1(z,t)$ and $v_2(z,t)$ may exist simultaneously on the line.

1-4. PROPERTIES OF THE SINUSOIDAL-TRAVELING-WAVE SOLUTIONS

Interpretation of mathematical results in terms of the given physical situation is essential in engineering analysis. Items to be examined here include the voltage-current relationship of each solution and the nature of the traveling-wave arguments.

a. Characteristic impedance: a derived parameter

Dimensionally the term $\sqrt{l/c}$ is an impedance, and in the mks system it has the units ohms. This term relates the magnitudes of voltage and current for each basic traveling-wave solution of the differential equation; accordingly it is called the *characteristic impedance* and is designated by the symbol Z_0:

$$Z_0 = \sqrt{\frac{l}{c}} \qquad \text{(lossless line)} \tag{1-20}$$

It should be noted that, since both l and c include the dimensions of "per unit length" and one is divided by the other, the dimensions of the quotient do not involve "per unit length." This is as one would expect, because dimensionally $v(z,t)$ is simply volts and $i(z,t)$ is simply amperes.

b. Velocity and direction of propagation

Dimensional homogeneity of the argument $t - z\sqrt{lc}$ requires that the quantity $1/\sqrt{lc}$ have the dimensions of velocity. Such proves to be the case, since the product of henrys per unit length and farads per unit length yields

seconds squared per unit length squared. The Greek letter ν will be used to designate this quantity, which thus far has not been named:

$$\nu = \frac{1}{\sqrt{lc}} \tag{1-21}$$

Equations 1-14 and 1-18 may be rewritten

$$v_1(z,t) = V_{1M} \sin\left[\omega\left(t - \frac{z}{\nu}\right)\right] \tag{1-22}$$

$$v_2(z,t) = V_{2M} \sin\left[\omega\left(t + \frac{z}{\nu}\right)\right] \tag{1-23}$$

The traveling-wave property of $v_1(z,t)$, $v_2(z,t)$ and their accompanying current functions can be readily visualized if one fixes his attention on one point of the sinusoidal function—in other words, keeps the argument constant, and then notes what changes δz must take place in z as t increases by δt. This fixed value of the argument might be zero, corresponding to voltage passing from negative to positive with increasing time, as indicated in Fig. 1-2.

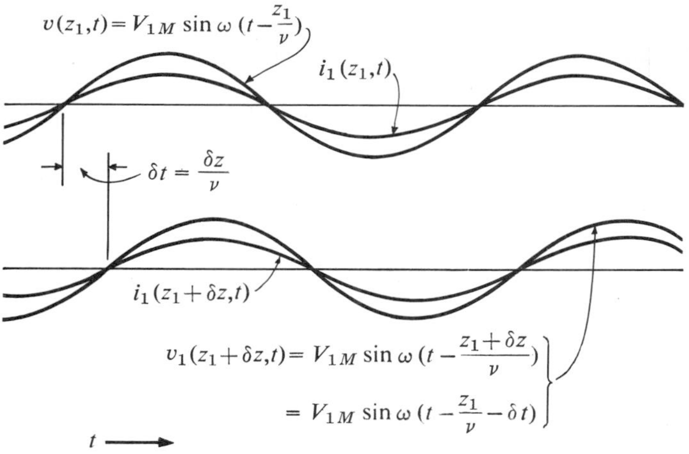

Figure 1-2 Sinusoidal traveling waves observed as functions of time at two locations on lossless transmission line

In the case of $v_1(z,t)$ and $i_1(z,t)$, a shift of δz equal to $\nu\,\delta t$ will maintain the same value of the argument. Thus constant-phase points on the waves described by $v_1(z,t)$ and $i_1(z,t)$ would progress or travel at a velocity of ν in the increasing, or positive, z direction with increasing time. It should be noted that (1) since this is a steady-state analysis, the given functions are assumed to be applicable over the range $-\infty < t < \infty$; and (2) because the line is assumed to extend in both directions an infinite distance, the functions are valid over the range $-\infty < z < \infty$.

Examination of $v_2(z,t)$ and $i_2(z,t)$ from this point of view indicates that for a point of constant phase, the shift δz is equal to $-v\ \delta t$, or, in other words, the waves travel at velocity v in the decreasing or negative z direction as t increases. On this basis the quantity v is given the name *phase velocity*, or, more loosely, velocity of propagation.

c. Generalizing of solutions by superposition

The principle of superposition, which is applicable to a linear system, may be used to bring out a corollary to the preceding paragraphs. Only the sinusoidal traveling wave has been studied thus far, but the characteristic impedance (Eq. 1-20) and the phase velocity (Eq. 1-21) on the lossless line are independent of ω. Accordingly any number of component sinusoidal voltages, differing in frequency but traveling in the same direction, may be superposed to yield a wave of arbitrary shape. Such a wave will maintain its shape as it travels along the line, and it will be accompanied by a current wave which is in direct proportion to it at all combinations of z and t (see also Chapter 5).

d. Power and the direction of energy transfer

The preceding results may be studied from the standpoint of direction of power flow. Instantaneous power is the product of instantaneous voltage and instantaneous current, and when only $v_1(z,t)$ and $i_1(z,t)$ are present this becomes

$$p_1(z,t) = v_1(z,t)i_1(z,t) \tag{1-24}$$

Substitution of Eqs. 1-14 and 1-17 yields

$$\begin{aligned} p_1(z,t) &= V_{1M}^2\sqrt{\frac{c}{l}}\sin^2\left[\omega\left(t-\frac{z}{v}\right)\right] \\ &= V_{1M}^2\sqrt{\frac{c}{l}}\frac{1}{2}\left\{1-\cos\left[2\omega\left(t-\frac{z}{v}\right)\right]\right\} \end{aligned} \tag{1-25}$$

Similarly, if only $v_2(z,t)$ and $i_2(z,t)$ are present, the instantaneous power is, with substitution of Eqs. 1-18 and 1-19,

$$p_2(z,t) = v_2(z,t)i_2(z,t) \tag{1-26}$$

$$p_2(z,t) = -V_{2M}^2\sqrt{\frac{c}{l}}\frac{1}{2}\left\{1-\cos\left[2\omega\left(t+\frac{z}{v}\right)\right]\right\} \tag{1-27}$$

Corresponding time-averaged values $P_1(z)$ and $P_2(z)$ are easily obtained:

$$P_1(z) = \frac{V_{1M}^2}{2}\sqrt{\frac{c}{l}} \tag{1-28}$$

$$P_2(z) = \frac{-V_{2M}^2}{2}\sqrt{\frac{c}{l}} \tag{1-29}$$

In terms of the polarity convention adopted in Fig. 1-1, a positive value of power, which arises when the instantaneous current and voltage at a given location are both positive or both negative, corresponds to a movement of energy in the increasing direction of z. Thus the fact that $P_1(z)$ is positive indicates that energy is moving in the positive direction of z, the same as the direction of travel of the $v_1(z,t)$ and $i_1(z,t)$ waves. On the other hand, $P_2(z)$ is negative for the reason that the instantaneous voltage $v_2(z,t)$ at a given location is positive only when the instantaneous current $i_2(z,t)$ is negative, and vice versa. This indicates a movement of energy in the negative direction of z, which is the direction of travel of the $v_2(z,t)$ and $i_2(z,t)$ waves.

e. Significance of coordinate-direction designation

It should be noted that the speed of propagation and the magnitude of the characteristic impedance are each the same for both directions of travel. This is reasonable because physical phenomena may be expected to proceed independently of any observer's choice of coordinate system, and the properties of the line appear to be the same when viewed from either direction.

On the other hand, the algebraic signs associated with the mathematical descriptions of such quantities as voltage, current, and power may be expected to differ if changes are made in the coordinate scheme (see Problem 1-3). In any event a sketch, such as Fig. 1-1, in which the assumed positive polarities and directions have been marked, is necessary for physical interpretation of mathematical results.

1-5. CONCLUSIONS

A uniform electrical transmission line may be described, for linear distributed-parameter analysis, by the following four constants, each stated on a per-unit-of-length basis: inductance l, capacitance c, resistance r, and shunt conductance g.

On a lossless line, the voltage and current functions must satisfy the following differential equations (the coordinate system is shown in Fig. 1-1):

$$\frac{\partial v(z,t)}{\partial z} = -l\frac{\partial i(z,t)}{\partial t} \tag{1-7}$$

$$\frac{\partial i(z,t)}{\partial z} = -c\frac{\partial v(z,t)}{\partial t} \tag{1-8}$$

Either current or voltage may be eliminated from this set to yield a *wave equation* in terms of the other function:

$$\frac{\partial^2 v(z,t)}{\partial z^2} = lc \frac{\partial^2 v(z,t)}{\partial t^2} \tag{1-12}$$

$$\frac{\partial^2 i(z,t)}{\partial z^2} = lc \frac{\partial^2 i(z,t)}{\partial t^2} \tag{1-13}$$

Traveling-wave functions satisfy these equations. In such functions the argument has the form $t - z\sqrt{lc}$ or $t + z\sqrt{lc}$; any identified point on the function for which the argument value is fixed will appear to move at *phase velocity* ($v = 1/\sqrt{lc}$) in the $+z$ or $-z$ directions, respectively.

The magnitude of a voltage wave traveling in one direction is at all times and locations equal to $\sqrt{l/c}$ (the *characteristic impedance*) times that of the accompanying current traveling wave. This is in accordance with Eqs. 1-7 and 1-8.

Energy is transferred in the direction in which the voltage-and-current wave pair travels.

PROBLEMS

1-1. An open-wire line with negligible losses has the following parameters: $l = 2.80 \times 10^{-3}$ henry per mile, $c = 10.6 \times 10^{-9}$ farad per mile. What is the velocity of propagation, and what is the characteristic impedance?

1-2. Let $v_3(z,t) = V_3\epsilon^{-(t-z\sqrt{lc})^2/T^2}$. This would represent a nonrecurrent surge with continuous derivatives of all orders. Verify by differentiation that it satisfies Eq. 1-12, and find the corresponding current function. Use the same polarity convention as in Fig. 1-1. Do the same for the function $v_4(z,t) = V_4\epsilon^{-(t+z\sqrt{lc})^2/T^2}$. Sketch $v_3(z,t)$, $i_3(z,t)$, $v_4(z,t)$, and $i_4(z,t)$ as functions of z for a constant value of t, using the same abscissa scale throughout.

1-3. Let the polarity-and-direction convention shown in Fig. 1-3 be adopted. Rewrite Eqs. 1-7 and 1-8 so as to be consistent with this convention. Note which of the succeeding equations are altered thereby, and compare the

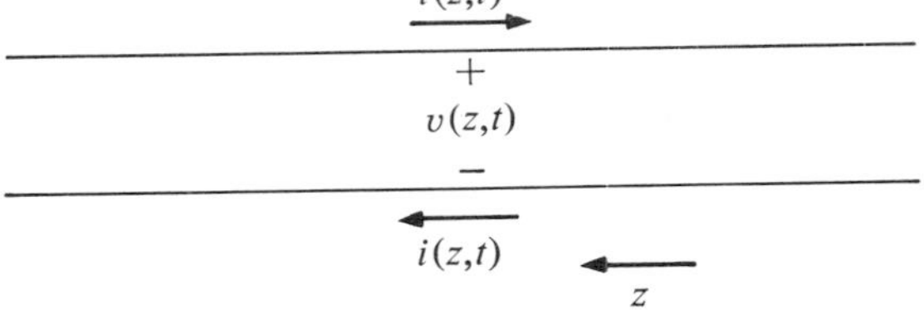

Figure 1-3 Alternate coordinate system for two-conductor transmission line

various mathematical results with those obtained with Fig. 1-1. Comment on the agreement or disagreement when each set of mathematical results is interpreted in terms of the polarity-and-direction diagram from which it was derived.

1-4. Write expressions for instantaneous power and time-averaged power [$p(z,t)$ and $P(z)$] if traveling-wave pairs $v_1(z,t)$, $i_1(z,t)$ and $v_2(z,t)$, $i_2(z,t)$ are both present on a lossless line.

REFERENCES

1. BATEMAN, H., *Partial Differential Equations of Mathematical Physics*. London: Cambridge University Press, 1932; New York: Dover Publications, Inc., 1944.
2. WOODS, FREDERICK S., *Advanced Calculus*, pp. 68–9. Boston: Ginn and Company, 1934.

CHAPTER 2

Sinusoidal Traveling Waves on a Line with Losses

Practical line conductors have nonzero resistance; this affects propagation phenomena. Shunt conductance too should be included in a general study. These parameters alter the results just found, in that many current and voltage functions do not travel, with wave shapes intact, at a single, clearly defined velocity; instead, they change in appearance progressively as they move along the line. Fortunately the sinusoidal functions of $\omega(t - z/v)$ and $\omega(t + z/v)$ (where v may be a function of ω), if multiplied by exponential functions of distance, are exceptions to this discouraging generalization. Steady-state analysis of the general transmission line is built around those two functions.

Propagation behavior of the sinusoidal traveling waves may be described concisely with the aid of two complex quantities, the propagation function and the characteristic impedance. Each is derivable in terms of the four line parameters and the frequency, a total of five variables.

Certain limiting cases yield much simpler results than the general expressions for the propagation function and characteristic impedance. The lossless line, described in the preceding chapter, is one such limiting case. Another is the distortionless line, to be introduced in this chapter. The asymptotes approached as frequency approaches zero or infinity are other limiting-case solutions. These limiting-case results are helpful reference points from which to survey the multiparameter, general transmission line. Series expansions prove useful in showing quantitatively the effects caused by small deviations from the respective limiting-case conditions.

Explicit functions of time and distance will be used for the initial presentation. In the interest of making the mathematical manipulations and the physical interpretations of the basic propagation phenomena as elementary as possible, introduction of phasor representation of traveling-wave alternating-current functions will be postponed until Sec. 2-2.

2-1. MATHEMATICAL SOLUTION FOR TRAVELING-WAVE PROPERTIES

The same general plan will be followed here as in Chapter 1, that of deriving the applicable partial differential equations, testing a postulated solution for the voltage function, and determining the accompanying current function. This will be followed by interpretation in terms of direction and speed of wave propagation.

a. Partial differential equations of general line

The derivation of the differential equations for the line with loss closely parallels that for the lossless line, so only the differences will be emphasized here. The polarity-and-direction convention given in Fig. 1-1 will be followed.

Equation 1-5, for the change of voltage along the line because of current flowing through the series inductance, is altered if one allows for the incremental conductor resistance $r\,\Delta z$:

$$\Delta z\left[\frac{\partial v(z,t)}{\partial z}\right]_{z=z_1} = -r\,\Delta z i(z_1,t) - l\,\Delta z\,\frac{\partial i(z_1,t)}{\partial t} \qquad (\Delta z \to 0) \qquad \textbf{(2-1)}$$

In like manner, shunt conductance will alter Eq. 1-6, because of current through the incremental shunt $g\,\Delta z$:

$$\Delta z\left[\frac{\partial i(z,t)}{\partial z}\right]_{z=z_1} = -g\,\Delta z v(z_1,t) - c\,\Delta z\,\frac{\partial v(z_1,t)}{\partial t} \qquad (\Delta z \to 0) \qquad \textbf{(2-2)}$$

Again the subscripts 1 may be omitted, and Δz may be divided out:

$$\frac{\partial v(z,t)}{\partial z} = -r i(z,t) - l\,\frac{\partial i(z,t)}{\partial t} \qquad \textbf{(2-3)}$$

$$\frac{\partial i(z,t)}{\partial z} = -g v(z,t) - c\,\frac{\partial v(z,t)}{\partial t} \qquad \textbf{(2-4)}$$

Except for the added terms in r and g, these parallel Eqs. 1-7 and 1-8. By appropriate differentiations and substitutions, which the reader should carry out in detail, $i(z,t)$ may be eliminated from the set:

$$\frac{\partial^2 v(z,t)}{\partial z^2} = rg v(z,t) + (rc + lg)\,\frac{\partial v(z,t)}{\partial t} + lc\,\frac{\partial^2 v(z,t)}{\partial t^2} \qquad \textbf{(2-5)}$$

Similarly, $v(z,t)$ may be eliminated from Eqs. 2-3 and 2-4 to yield:

$$\frac{\partial^2 i(z,t)}{\partial z^2} = rgi(z,t) + (rc + lg)\frac{\partial i(z,t)}{\partial t} + lc\,\frac{\partial^2 i(z,t)}{\partial t^2} \tag{2-6}$$

These equations are known in classical physics as the *equations of telegraphy*. They will reduce to wave equations (Eqs. 1-12 and 1-13) if r and g are set equal to zero. Some points of dimensional homogeneity may be commented upon. Each term in Eq. 2-5 has the dimensions of voltage divided by length squared, and each term in Eq. 2-6 has the dimensions of current divided by length squared. The product rg has the dimensions of the inverse of length squared. The products rc and lg each have the dimensions of time divided by length squared, and the product lc has the dimensions of time squared divided by length squared.

b. Traveling-wave solutions for voltage

One might suspect that a traveling-wave type of function could satisfy Eq. 2-5, as was true of the wave equation, 1-12, but from physical reasoning one would expect the amplitude to be reduced with distance because of losses in the resistance and shunt conductance. Let the following solution be assumed, in which α and β are unknown coefficients:

$$v_1(z,t) = V_{1M}\epsilon^{-\alpha z}\sin(\omega t - \beta z) \tag{2-7}$$

Direct differentiation and substitution into Eq. 2-5, paralleling the procedure followed for the lossless case, will yield cumbersome expressions and is unsuitable. A better plan is to replace the sine function with exponentials with complex arguments:

$$\begin{aligned} v_1(z,t) &= \frac{V_{1M}}{2j}\,\epsilon^{-\alpha z}[\epsilon^{j(\omega t-\beta z)} - \epsilon^{-j(\omega t-\beta z)}] \\ &= \frac{V_{1M}}{2j}\,[\epsilon^{j\omega t}\epsilon^{-(\alpha+j\beta)z} - \epsilon^{-j\omega t}\epsilon^{-(\alpha-j\beta)z}] \end{aligned} \tag{2-8}$$

Equation 2-8 is differentiated to give the various partial derivatives called for in Eq. 2-5, and the results are substituted there. If all the coefficients of $\epsilon^{j\omega t}$ are gathered on the left side of the equality mark, and all the coefficients of $\epsilon^{-j\omega t}$ are gathered on the right side of the equality mark, and the denominator quantity $2j$ is multiplied out, the following is obtained:

$$\begin{aligned} &V_{1M}\epsilon^{j\omega t}\epsilon^{-(\alpha+j\beta)z}[(\alpha + j\beta)^2 - rg - (rc + lg)j\omega - lc(j\omega)^2] \\ &= V_{1M}\epsilon^{-j\omega t}\epsilon^{-(\alpha-j\beta)z}[(\alpha - j\beta)^2 - rg - (rc + lg)(-j\omega) - lc(-j\omega)^2] \end{aligned} \tag{2-9}$$

If the postulated solution is to be valid, Eq. 2-9 must be satisfied for all combinations of values of t and z. V_{1M} and $\epsilon^{-\alpha z}$ may be cancelled from both sides, and the left-hand side reduced to a constant by dividing the remaining equation by $\epsilon^{j\omega t}$ and $\epsilon^{-j\beta z}$. The result is an equation of this form, in which A is a constant and A^* is its conjugate:

$$A = A^* \epsilon^{j2\omega t} \epsilon^{-j2\beta z}$$

This equation can be satisfied for independently chosen values of t and z only if A and A^* are zero. Hence

$$(\alpha + j\beta)^2 - rg - (rc + lg)j\omega - lc(j\omega)^2 = 0 \qquad \textbf{(2-10)}$$

$$(\alpha - j\beta)^2 - rg - (rc + lg)(-j\omega) - lc(-j\omega)^2 = 0 \qquad \textbf{(2-11)}$$

Because Eqs. 2-10 and 2-11 are conjugates, the same values of α and β will satisfy both equations (see Problem 2-1). The complex sum γ is given the name *propagation function*:

$$\gamma \doteq \alpha + j\beta$$

From Eq. 2-10

$$\gamma = \sqrt{rg + (rc + lg)j\omega + lc(j\omega)^2}$$

$$= \sqrt{(r + j\omega l)(g + j\omega c)} \qquad \textbf{(2-12)}$$

Thus the postulated solution $v_1(z,t)$, Eq. 2-7, satisfies the equation of telegraphy, 2-5, provided α and β are chosen in accordance with Eq. 2-12.

In like manner, the following function $v_2(z,t)$ may be shown to satisfy Eq. 2-5.

$$v_2(z,t) = V_{2M}\epsilon^{\alpha z} \sin(\omega t + \beta z) \qquad \textbf{(2-13)}$$

The values for α and β prove to be the same as those in Eq. 2-12.

c. Properties of the propagation function

The real and imaginary parts of the propagation function are called the *attenuation function* and the *phase function*, respectively. Numerical values for particular problems are usually found by solving Eq. 2-12 for γ in polar form and then resolving it into rectangular components.

(1) DIMENSIONS AND UNITS. The term $r + j\omega l$ has the units ohms per unit of length, whereas $g + j\omega c$ has the units mhos per unit of length. Accordingly, the dimensions of γ are the inverse of length, and the same is true of its real and imaginary components.

The products αz and βz, as used in Eqs. 2-8 and 2-9, are exponents of the natural logarithmic base ϵ. Both products are dimensionless, as every exponent must be; αz is measured in units of *nepers*, while βz is measured in units of *radians*. Thus α and β, as found directly from Eq. 2-12, have the units of nepers per unit of length and radians per unit of length, respectively. Unfortunately, no unit name for γ, the complex sum of those two quantities, has been generally accepted.

For numerical work the phase constant β is often stated in degrees per unit of length, and the attenuation constant α in *decibels* per unit of length. To introduce the latter unit and to relate it to nepers, the maximum values of $v_1(z,t)$ at two locations, $V_M(z_1)$, and $V_M(z_2)$, where $z_2 > z_1$, will be compared. From Eq. 2-7,

$$V_M(z_1) = V_{1M}\epsilon^{-\alpha z_1}$$
$$V_M(z_2) = V_{1M}\epsilon^{-\alpha z_2}$$

Dividing the first of these equations by the second, and taking the natural logarithm of both sides, yields

$$\alpha(z_2 - z_1) = \ln\left[\frac{V_M(z_1)}{V_M(z_2)}\right] \quad \text{(nepers)}$$

The same attenuation may be stated in decibels by means of the following equation:

$$\alpha_{\text{db}}(z_2 - z_1) = 20 \log_{10}\left[\frac{V_M(z_1)}{V_M(z_2)}\right] \quad \text{(decibels)} \qquad \textbf{(2-14)}$$

[See Sec. 6-3*b* and the accompanying footnote regarding (1) the definition of decibels in terms of the ratio of input to output power, and (2) the calculation of attenuation of impedance-transforming networks.] The ratio of the root-mean-square voltage values is, of course, the same as that of the maximum values.

The conversion factor between nepers and decibels may be derived as follows:

$$\log_{10} u = (\log_{10} \epsilon)(\ln u)$$
$$= 0.4343 \ln u$$
$$20 \log_{10} u = 8.686 \ln u$$

Hence an attenuation constant in nepers per unit length of line may be converted into decibels per unit length by multiplying it by 8.686.

Probably the decibel unit gained early acceptance largely because base-10 logarithms seemed more familiar than natural logarithms. The latter are awkward to work with in tabular form, but the log-log scales on slide rules make them as convenient as logarithms to the base 10 as far as computational effort is concerned. When studying the phenomena of propagation on transmission lines, the reader is urged to reason in terms of natural logarithms, nepers, and radians because those units are directly related to the operations of calculus and the solution of differential equations.

(2) VELOCITY OF PROPAGATION. Phase velocity was defined in Sec. 1-4*b* for the unattenuated waves on a lossless line by noting the change δz which should accompany a change δt to keep the argument of the sinusoidal function constant. The same definition may be extended to the attenuating wave, as that is the velocity with which any point on the voltage or current

wave, defined as a stated fraction of the maximum value at each location on the line, will appear to move. Comparison between Eqs. 2-7 and 1-22 indicates that the velocity of propagation is related to the frequency and the phase function as follows:

$$v = \frac{\omega}{\beta} \tag{2-15}$$

For the lossless line, β is equal to $\omega\sqrt{lc}$. In general, if β is directly proportional to ω, the velocity of propagation will be independent of frequency.

(3) CONSTRAINT FOR DISTORTIONLESS TRANSMISSION. Study of the propagation function, Eq. 2-12, with a view toward finding particular solutions suggests examining the effect of the following constraint:

$$\frac{r}{l} = \frac{g}{c} \tag{2-16}$$

This proportionality simplifies the propagation function as follows, if g is replaced by rc/l:

$$\begin{aligned}\gamma_{\text{dl}} &= \sqrt{(r + j\omega l)\left(\frac{rc}{l} + j\omega c\right)} \\ &= \sqrt{\frac{c}{l}(r + j\omega l)^2} \\ &= r\sqrt{\frac{c}{l}} + j\omega\sqrt{lc}\end{aligned} \tag{2-17}$$

Thus a line for which Eq. 2-16 is applicable has an attenuation function which is independent of frequency and a phase function which is directly proportional to ω. Furthermore, the phase velocity is equal to $1/\sqrt{lc}$ and independent of frequency, the same as for the lossless line.

The principle of superposition may be applied advantageously here, too, and it follows that a voltage or current wave composed of components of several frequencies, when observed with oscilloscopes located at successive positions along the line in the direction of wave travel, would appear the same except for an ordinate scale factor (attenuation effect) and successively greater delays from a common "zero time" (result of a finite velocity of propagation). The same is true of nonrecurrent pulses.

Such a line is known as a *distortionless line*, and Eq. 2-16 is the criterion which distinguishes it. It may also be noted that β and the velocity of propagation are independent of the particular values of r and g, as long as the constraint of Eq. 2-16 is observed.

For economic reasons the distortionless proportioning of line parameters is not realized in any practical line; r/l is always considerably greater than

g/c. Nevertheless, the distortionless line is an important concept mathematically as a limiting case, for the resulting solution is almost as simple as that of the lossless line.

For lines in which r or g or both are not zero and are not proportioned with respect to l and c as stipulated by Eq. 2-16, the attenuation and the velocity of propagation are functions of frequency.

d. Voltage-current relationship: complex characteristic impedance

Expressions should be found for the current functions which accompany voltages $v_1(z,t)$ and $v_2(z,t)$. An expression for $i_1(z,t)$ may be found by differentiating $v_1(z,t)$, Eq. 2-8, with respect to t and substituting in Eq. 2-4. Integration of this result with respect to z yields

$$i_1(z,t) = \frac{V_{1M}}{2j}\left[\frac{g + j\omega c}{\alpha + j\beta}\,\epsilon^{j\omega t}\epsilon^{-(\alpha+j\beta)z} - \frac{g - j\omega c}{\alpha - j\beta}\,\epsilon^{-j\omega t}\epsilon^{-(\alpha-j\beta)z}\right] \tag{2-18}$$

Substitution of Eq. 2-12 and its conjugate for the denominator terms $\alpha + j\beta$ and $\alpha - j\beta$ yields

$$i_1(z,t) = \frac{V_{1M}}{2j}\left[\sqrt{\frac{g + j\omega c}{r + j\omega l}}\,\epsilon^{j\omega t}\epsilon^{-(\alpha+j\beta)z} - \sqrt{\frac{g - j\omega c}{r - j\omega l}}\,\epsilon^{-j\omega t}\epsilon^{-(\alpha-j\beta)z}\right]$$

The quantity $\sqrt{(g + j\omega c)/(r + j\omega l)}$ has the dimensions of admittance, and its reciprocal will be designated by the following complex quantity:

$$|Z_0|\,\epsilon^{j\theta_0} = \sqrt{\frac{r + j\omega l}{g + j\omega c}} \tag{2-19}$$

Then

$$|Z_0|\,\epsilon^{-j\theta_0} = \sqrt{\frac{r - j\omega l}{g - j\omega c}}$$

$$i_1(z,t) = \frac{V_{1M}}{2j\,|Z_0|}\left[\epsilon^{j(\omega t-\theta_0)}\epsilon^{-(\alpha+j\beta)z} - \epsilon^{-j(\omega t-\theta_0)}\epsilon^{-(\alpha-j\beta)z}\right]$$

$$= \frac{V_{1M}}{|Z_0|}\,\epsilon^{-\alpha z}\sin(\omega t - \theta_0 - \beta z) \tag{2-20}$$

It appears from comparison of Eq. 2-20 with Eq. 2-7 that, in a general line with losses, the current and voltage traveling waves are not in time phase at any value of z. The relationship between current and voltage waves of a single frequency may be expressed by a complex quantity $|Z_0|\,\epsilon^{j\theta_0}$, which, by analogy with the lossless line (see Eqs. 1-14 and 1-17 through 1-20), will be called the *characteristic impedance*.

Similarly, the current accompanying $v_2(z,t)$ may be shown to be the following:

$$i_2(z,t) = -\frac{V_{2M}}{|Z_0|}\,\epsilon^{\alpha z}\sin(\omega t - \theta_0 + \beta z) \tag{2-21}$$

In general the magnitude $|Z_0|$ and the angle θ_0 are both functions of frequency; the one exception occurs for the distortionless line, for which the parameters are proportioned in accordance with Eq. 2-16:

$$Z_{0d1} = \sqrt{\frac{r + j\omega l}{(rc/l) + j\omega c}} = \sqrt{\frac{l}{c}} \tag{2-22}$$

e. Direction of travel: consistency with attenuation function

The functions $v_1(z,t)$ and $i_1(z,t)$ describe sinusoidal waves which travel in the positive z direction with increasing t, as indicated in Fig. 2-1. The maximum value which each function can attain at any particular z is progressively reduced as the location considered is moved in the positive z direction, because of the attenuation function. This is to be expected physically because the flow of conduction current through the conductor resistance and of leakage current through the shunt conductance converts a part of the

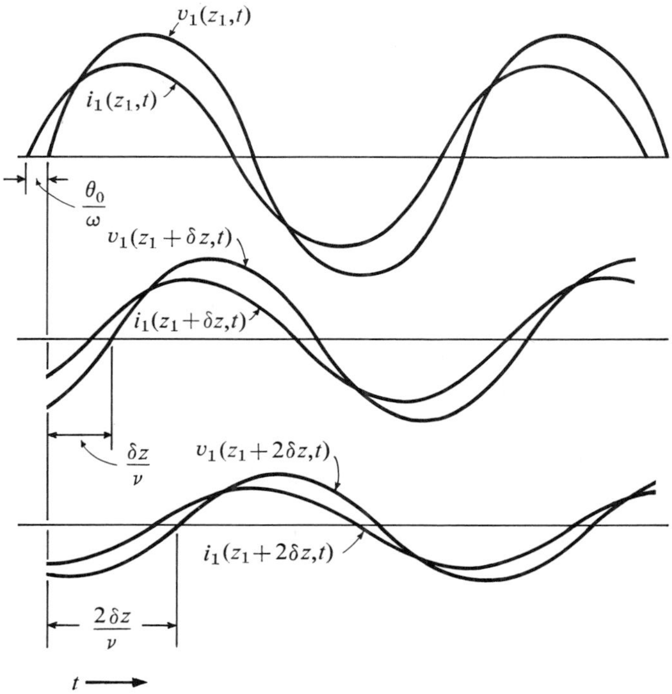

Figure 2-1 Sinusoidal traveling waves observed as functions of time at three locations on a transmission line with losses

electromagnetic-field energy associated with the current and voltage waves into heat.

The functions $v_2(z,t)$ and $i_2(z,t)$, on the other hand, represent sinusoidal waves traveling in the negative direction of z. Since an increase in time is accompanied by a *decrease* in z for any reference point on the moving wave, the factor $\epsilon^{\alpha z}$ becomes progressively smaller for any such traveling point, corresponding to reduction in the amount of electromagnetic-field energy remaining in the wave system.

Thus the three aspects of direction of wave travel, (1) the direction of movement of a constant phase point with increase of time, (2) the direction of average power flow (Sec. 1-4*d*), and (3) the direction in which reduction in wave-pattern magnitude takes place, are consistent for both cases considered here.

2-2. PHASOR NOTATION FOR TRAVELING-WAVE FUNCTIONS

Up to this point the current and voltage functions have been written out in "long hand," with the functional relationship to both z and t explicitly stated. This was to make the operations of differentiation and integration as obvious as possible and free of any unwritten "understandings." For brevity in the analyses to follow, and to enable the concept of impedance to be used freely, the phasor notation will be introduced here. It should, of course, have long been familiar to the student in the analysis of lumped-constant networks under steady-state conditions with alternating-current excitation (see Problem 2-3).

Let
$$v(t) = V_M \sin(\omega t + \phi) \tag{2-23}$$
$$v(t) = \frac{V_M}{2j}\left[\epsilon^{j(\omega t+\phi)} - \epsilon^{-j(\omega t+\phi)}\right] \tag{2-24}$$

As was indicated in the solutions for propagation function and characteristic impedance in Secs. 2-1*b* and *d*, the coefficients of $\epsilon^{j\omega t}$ and $\epsilon^{-j\omega t}$ in those procedures are conjugates of each other at every step. This is true of the voltage-and-current relationships in linear circuits generally; hence it suffices to perform the calculations on the coefficient of $\epsilon^{j\omega t}$, and the corresponding coefficient of $\epsilon^{-j\omega t}$ for the result could be written immediately (in practice the latter step need not be performed).

The two exponentials in Eq. 2-24 may be expanded in rectangular form:

$$\epsilon^{j(\omega t+\phi)} = \cos(\omega t + \phi) + j\sin(\omega t + \phi)$$
$$-\epsilon^{-j(\omega t+\phi)} = -\cos(\omega t + \phi) + j\sin(\omega t + \phi)$$

The imaginary part of $\epsilon^{j(\omega t+\phi)}$ is $\sin(\omega t + \phi)$, the same as $1/(2j)$ times the sum of the last two equations. This may be stated in mathematical form by introducing the operator Im; it means "imaginary part of."* Thus

$$v(t) = \mathrm{Im}[V_M \epsilon^{j(\omega t + \phi)}] \tag{2-25}$$

The equivalence between Eqs. 2-25 and 2-23 may be shown explicitly:

$$\begin{aligned} v(t) &= \mathrm{Im}[V_M \cos(\omega t + \phi) + jV_M \sin(\omega t + \phi)] \\ &= V_M \sin(\omega t + \phi) \end{aligned} \tag{2-23}$$

Thus Eq. 2-25 carries the same information as Eq. 2-24. The phasor function for the indicated voltage is derivable from Eq. 2-25.

In steady-state analysis one ordinarily deals with a single frequency at one time, and root-mean-square (rms) values of voltage or current are more meaningful than maximum values. Hence the voltage described by Eq. 2-25, which is mathematically complete, is commonly written in "shorthand" as follows:

$$V = \frac{V_M}{\sqrt{2}} \epsilon^{j\phi}$$

For convenience in routine work, the complex exponential is often abbreviated as shown below:

$$V = \frac{V_M}{\sqrt{2}} \underline{/\phi} \tag{2-26}$$

The function V, known as a *phasor*, is related to $v(t)$ as follows:

$$v(t) = \mathrm{Im}[\sqrt{2} V \epsilon^{j\omega t}] \tag{2-27}$$

It will be understood that the subscript M attached to V or I designates the maximum value of a sinusoidal wave, which value is a magnitude, a pure real number. The capital letters V and I without the subscript M will be understood to be phasors. In transmission-line problems the voltage and current phasors are functions of line location z; thus $V(z)$, $I(z)$.

The traveling-wave voltage $v_1(z,t)$, as given in Eq. 2-7, may be rewritten in phasor form as $V_1(z)$:

$$v_1(z,t) = V_{1M} \epsilon^{-\alpha z} \sin(\omega t - \beta z) \tag{2-7}$$

$$V_1(z) = \frac{V_{1M}}{\sqrt{2}} \epsilon^{-\alpha z} \epsilon^{-j\beta z}$$

$$= \frac{V_{1M}}{\sqrt{2}} \epsilon^{-\gamma z} \tag{2-28}$$

$$v_1(z,t) = \mathrm{Im}[\sqrt{2} V_1(z) \epsilon^{j\omega t}] \tag{2-29}$$

The capital letter Z will be understood to represent an impedance as a complex quantity:

$$Z_0 = |Z_0| \epsilon^{j\theta_0} \tag{2-30}$$

* Correspondingly, Re indicates "real part of."

This may be illustrated in expressions for $i_1(z,t)$:

$$i_1(z,t) = \frac{V_{1M}}{|Z_0|} \epsilon^{-\alpha z} \sin(\omega t - \theta_0 - \beta z) \tag{2-20}$$

$$I_1(z) = \frac{V_{1M}}{Z_0\sqrt{2}} \epsilon^{-\gamma z} = \frac{V_1(z)}{Z_0} \tag{2-31}$$

$$i_1(z,t) = \text{Im}[\sqrt{2} I_1(z) \epsilon^{j\omega t}] \tag{2-32}$$

The derivations of the differential equations of telegraphy and of the propagation function and characteristic impedance may be condensed considerably by the use of phasors rather than explicit functions of time, but at the expense of less detailed statements. Broader understanding of the transmission-line problem is needed than that which comes from the mere *rote* use of phasors, even though the latter may suffice for some repetitive calculations in circuit analysis. Both forms of notation, phasor and explicit, will be used in the remainder of this text, the phasor form where mathematical manipulation will be expedited thereby, and the explicit form for the display and examination of results.

2-3. PROPAGATION CHARACTERISTICS AS FUNCTIONS OF FREQUENCY

The transmission of intelligence is characterized by a signal which varies in a nonrepetitive fashion. Theoretically, in accordance with the Fourier integral, the complete frequency spectrum (except possibly some discrete values) is present in such a signal. Actual transmission processes will distort a composite wave or change the proportions and relative phases among its frequency components, but in practice the intelligence put into the signal is recoverable if distortion is kept small within some limited band of frequencies, even though distortion elsewhere in the spectrum is severe. On the other hand, a single-frequency sinusoidal wave by itself carries no intelligence. The variation in propagation characteristics of transmission lines with frequency is therefore a relevant subject.

Voice communication may be satisfactorily accomplished with a frequency range of about 100 to 3600 cps,[4] and this will be designated as the *audio-frequency range* for order-of-magnitude purposes. (Better fidelity may be obtained in sound transmission if the usable range is wider.)

Commercial two-wire lines may be grouped into two general classifications, which have rather different quantitative values for their propagation properties: (1) open-wire lines, in which the spacing between the wires is commonly of the order of 100 times the conductor diameter, and the medium surrounding the conductors is air; and (2) cables, in which the center-to-center spacing is of the order of twice the conductor diameter, and the conductors are surrounded with a solid insulating medium. Coaxial cables have parameter values which logically associate them with the latter group.

Two-wire cable circuits in turn may be subclassified according to whether they are continuously loaded or lump-loaded, as mentioned in the Introduction, or unloaded. The reduction of attenuation by loading is discussed in Sec. 2-4, and the filter property of lumped loading, in Sec. 6-4.

The low-loss, open-wire line will be the subject of probing by the technique of series expansions in this section; the unloaded cable will be inspected more briefly as an interesting limiting case.

a. Characteristic impedance as a function of frequency

Some general observations on the functional relationship between characteristic impedance and frequency may be made, and afterward series expansions developed to indicate the effect of small changes in frequency in situations of principal interest.

(1) LIMITING VALUES. The limit approached by Z_0 as frequency approaches infinity is found from Eq. 2-19 to be

$$Z_0(\infty) = \sqrt{\frac{l}{c}} \tag{2-33}$$

This result is applicable at radio frequencies as an excellent approximation for Z_0 for the usual open-wire line and is a good approximation at audio frequencies for such lines. Sometimes referred to as the "surge impedance," it is used for analysis of traveling-wave transients on power transmission lines.

For frequencies approaching zero, Z_0 approaches the following limit:

$$Z_0(0) = \sqrt{\frac{r}{g}} \tag{2-34}$$

This result is largely of theoretical interest as an asymptote.

(2) OPEN-WIRE LINE. The deviation of Z_0 from the infinite-frequency asymptote of $\sqrt{l/c}$ for a low-loss open-wire line (r small compared to ωl; g small compared to ωc) may be readily described with Taylor series. Two basic expansions will be used:

$$\sqrt{1 \pm u} = 1 \pm \frac{u}{2} - \frac{u^2}{8} \cdots \qquad (|u| < 1) \tag{2-35}$$

$$\frac{1}{\sqrt{1 \pm w}} = 1 \mp \frac{w}{2} + \frac{3w^2}{8} \cdots \qquad (|w| < 1) \tag{2-36}$$

Equation 2-19 may be rearranged as follows:

$$Z_0 = \sqrt{\frac{j\omega l\left(1 + \dfrac{r}{j\omega l}\right)}{j\omega c\left(1 + \dfrac{g}{j\omega c}\right)}}$$

Let u equal $r/j\omega l$ and w equal $g/j\omega c$, and substitute Eqs. 2-35 and 2-36:

$$Z_0 \approx \sqrt{\frac{l}{c}}\left[1 + \frac{1}{2}\frac{r}{j\omega l} - \frac{1}{8}\left(\frac{r}{j\omega l}\right)^2\right]\left[1 - \frac{1}{2}\frac{g}{j\omega c} + \frac{3}{8}\left(\frac{g}{j\omega c}\right)^2\right]$$

One precaution to be observed in multiplying series together is that all terms involving small quantities of a given order be carried, if the approximation is to be valid to that order. Here terms up to and including those of second order have been written for both component series; the product of those expressions will be a valid approximation for terms up to and including the second order but not for higher-order terms:

$$\begin{aligned} Z_0 &\approx \sqrt{\frac{l}{c}}\left[1 + \frac{1}{2}\frac{r}{j\omega} - \frac{1}{2}\frac{g}{j\omega c} - \frac{1}{8}\left(\frac{r}{j\omega l}\right)^2 - \frac{1}{4}\frac{r}{j\omega l}\frac{g}{j\omega c} + \frac{3}{8}\left(\frac{g}{j\omega c}\right)^2\right] \\ &\approx \sqrt{\frac{l}{c}}\left[1 + \frac{1}{2}\frac{r}{j\omega l} - \frac{1}{2}\frac{g}{j\omega c} - \frac{1}{8}\left(\frac{r}{j\omega l} - \frac{g}{j\omega c}\right)\left(\frac{r}{j\omega l} + \frac{3g}{j\omega c}\right)\right] \\ &\approx \sqrt{\frac{l}{c}}\left[1 - \frac{j}{2\omega}\left(\frac{r}{l} - \frac{g}{c}\right) + \frac{1}{8\omega^2}\left(\frac{r}{l} - \frac{g}{c}\right)\left(\frac{r}{l} + \frac{3g}{c}\right)\right] \end{aligned} \tag{2-37}$$

Let:

$$Z_0 = R_0 + jX_0$$

$$R_0 \approx \sqrt{\frac{l}{c}}\left[1 + \frac{1}{8\omega^2}\left(\frac{r}{l} - \frac{g}{c}\right)\left(\frac{r}{l} + \frac{3g}{c}\right)\right] \tag{2-38}$$

$$X_0 \approx -\sqrt{\frac{l}{c}}\frac{1}{2\omega}\left(\frac{r}{l} - \frac{g}{c}\right) \tag{2-39}$$

Examination of those terms which cause the characteristic impedance to deviate from $\sqrt{l/c}$ within the designated range ($r \ll \omega l$ and $g \ll \omega c$) indicates that substitution of Eq. 2-16, the proportionality which defines the distortionless line, would cause those deviation terms to vanish. Thus the approximation of Eq. 2-37 checks with the exact solution (Eq. 2-22) in this limiting case.

For the usual line in which $(r/l) > (g/c)$, the reactive component of the characteristic impedance is capacitive. The deviation of Z_0 from $\sqrt{l/c}$ in the high-frequency range may be computed from Eqs. 2-38 and 2-39 more easily than from the original equation, 2-19. Likewise the principal modes of variation in that range, $1/\omega$ for X_0 and $1/\omega^2$ for R_0, are clearly brought out in those equations.

Series approximations for the polar form of Z_0 are also of interest:

$$\frac{X_0}{R_0} = \tan \theta_0$$

Division of Eq. 2-39 by $R_0 = \sqrt{l/c}$ (simplification of Eq. 2-38 by neglecting the $1/\omega^2$ term) yields a first-order approximation for the angle θ_0:

$$\theta_0 \approx \tan \theta_0$$
$$\approx -\frac{1}{2}\left(\frac{r}{\omega l} - \frac{g}{\omega c}\right) \qquad \textbf{(2-40)}$$

Derivation of a series expression for the magnitude of Z_0 is left as Problem 2-5.

The exact computed values of R_0, X_0, $|Z_0|$, and θ_0 (Eq. 2-19) of a typical open-wire line are shown in Fig. 2-2 as functions of frequency. The approximations given in Eqs. 2-38, 2-39, and 2-40 and in Problem 2-5 are shown on the same plot.

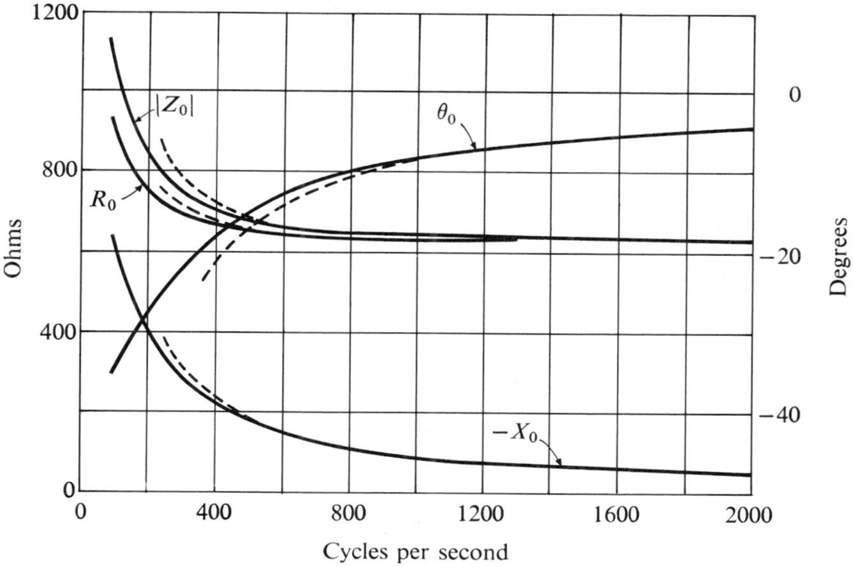

Figure 2-2 Characteristic impedance of an open-wire line as a function of frequency. $r = 6.74$ ohms per mile of line, $l = 3.53 \times 10^{-3}$ henry per mile, $c = 8.71 \times 10^{-9}$ farad per mile, and $g = 0.29 \times 10^{-6}$ mho per mile. Solid lines represent exact computed values according to Eq. 2-19; dashed lines represent series approximations, Eqs. 2-38, 2-39, and 2-40, and the answer to Problem 2-5 [data are for 128-mil hard-drawn copper wires with 12-in. spacing at 1000 cps; taken from Harold Pender and Knox McIlwain, *Electrical Engineer's Handbook, Electric Communication and Electronics* (New York: John Wiley & Sons, Inc., 1950), Table I, p. 10-03, by permission]

(3) UNLOADED CABLE. At the other extreme from the low-loss open-wire line is the unloaded cable, which at the lower audio frequencies will satisfy simultaneously the conditions $g \ll \omega c$ and $r \gg \omega l$. A low value of inductance arises because of the close spacing of the conductors; this same factor, combined with a higher-than-unity relative permittivity for the insulating material, increases the capacitance. If both inductive reactance and shunt conductance are neglected, a simple approximation for characteristic impedance results:

$$Z_0 \approx \sqrt{\frac{r}{j\omega c}}$$

$$\approx \sqrt{\frac{r}{\omega c}}\, \epsilon^{-j(\pi/4)} \qquad \textbf{(2-41)}$$

Computed values of $|Z_0|$ and θ_0 (Eq. 2-19) of a typical unloaded cable, together with the approximate functions from Eq. 2-41, are shown in Fig. 2-3. The range of applicability of the approximations should be checked, particularly because the inductance of an actual cable cannot be zero. For the

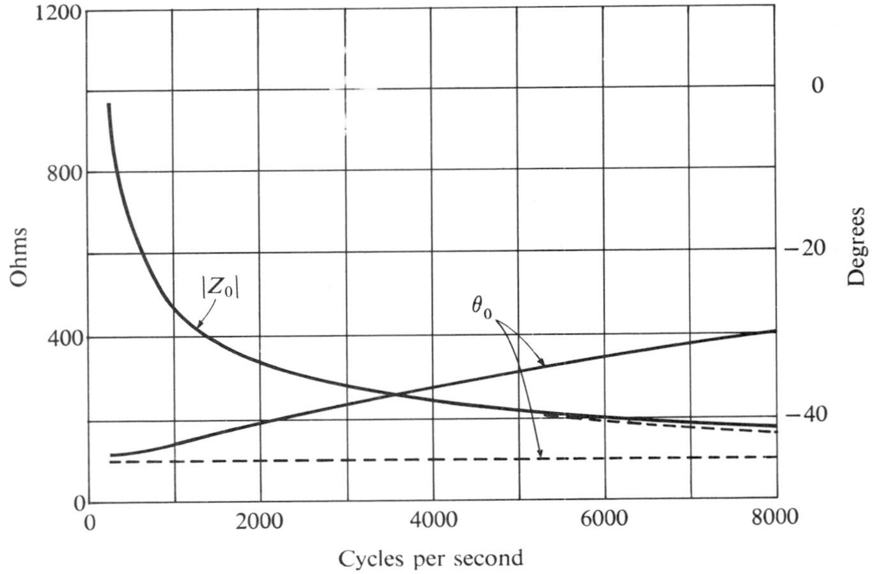

Figure 2-3 Characteristic impedance of an unloaded cable as a function of frequency. r = 85.8 ohms per mile, $l = 1.0 \times 10^{-3}$ henry per mile, $c = 62 \times 10^{-9}$ farad per mile, and $g = 1.5 \times 10^{-6}$ mho per mile. Solid lines represent exact computed values according to Eq. 2-19; dashed lines represent series approximations from Eq. 2-41 [data are for #19 A.W.G. unloaded cable at 1000 cps; taken from Pender and McIlwain (see Fig. 2-2), by permission]

specific parameters used in Fig. 2-3, ωl is equal to r at 13,700 cps, and this severely limits the frequencies for which Eq. 2-41 is useful. This is shown in Fig. 2-3 by the progressive change in θ_0 from the $-\pi/4$ approximation. On the other hand, ωc is equal to g at 3.85 cps, and hence g has slight influence on Z_0 at communication frequencies.

The term "ideal cable" is sometimes used in connection with approximate calculations in which g and ωl are neglected. It should be understood that the word "ideal" refers to the resulting mathematical simplification, not to electrical transmission properties.

b. Attenuation and phase velocity as functions of frequency

The propagation function may be expanded in series to show the high-frequency and low-frequency asymptotes of the attenuation function and the phase velocity under the usual condition of $r/l \neq g/c$.

(1) OPEN-WIRE LINE. For investigation of the high-frequency region, r will be assumed small compared with ωl and g small compared with ωc. The expansions in this instance will be carried through the third-order terms:

$$\sqrt{1 \pm u} = 1 \pm \frac{u}{2} - \frac{u^2}{8} \pm \frac{u^3}{16} \cdots \qquad (|u| < 1) \tag{2-42}$$

Equation 2-12 may be rearranged as follows:

$$\gamma = \sqrt{j\omega l\left(1 + \frac{r}{j\omega l}\right) j\omega c\left(1 + \frac{g}{j\omega c}\right)}$$

The terms $1 + (r/j\omega l)$ and $1 + (g/j\omega c)$ are both replaced by the series expansion of Eq. 2-42:

$$\begin{aligned}
\gamma &\approx j\omega\sqrt{lc}\left[1 + \frac{1}{2}\frac{r}{j\omega l} - \frac{1}{8}\left(\frac{r}{j\omega l}\right)^2 + \frac{1}{16}\left(\frac{r}{j\omega l}\right)^3\right] \\
&\quad \times \left[1 + \frac{1}{2}\frac{g}{j\omega c} - \frac{1}{8}\left(\frac{g}{j\omega c}\right)^2 + \frac{1}{16}\left(\frac{g}{j\omega c}\right)^3\right] \\
&\approx j\omega\sqrt{lc}\left[1 + \frac{1}{2}\frac{r}{j\omega l} + \frac{1}{2}\frac{g}{j\omega c} - \frac{1}{8}\left(\frac{r}{j\omega l}\right)^2 + \frac{1}{4}\frac{r}{j\omega l}\frac{g}{j\omega c} - \frac{1}{8}\left(\frac{g}{j\omega c}\right)^2\right. \\
&\quad \left. + \frac{1}{16}\left(\frac{r}{j\omega l}\right)^3 - \frac{1}{16}\left(\frac{r}{j\omega l}\right)^2\frac{g}{j\omega c} - \frac{1}{16}\frac{r}{j\omega}\left(\frac{g}{j\omega c}\right)^2 + \frac{1}{16}\left(\frac{g}{j\omega c}\right)^3\right]
\end{aligned}$$

The various terms of like order may be grouped together and factored as follows:

$$\begin{aligned}
\gamma \approx j\omega\sqrt{lc}&\left[1 + \frac{1}{2}\left(\frac{r}{j\omega l} + \frac{g}{j\omega c}\right) - \frac{1}{8}\left(\frac{r}{j\omega l} - \frac{g}{j\omega c}\right)^2\right. \\
&\left. + \frac{1}{16}\left(\frac{r}{j\omega l} - \frac{g}{j\omega c}\right)^2\left(\frac{r}{j\omega l} + \frac{g}{j\omega c}\right)\right]
\end{aligned}$$

The real and imaginary parts may be grouped together to indicate the nature of variation of the attenuation and phase functions:

$$\gamma \approx \left(\frac{r}{2}\sqrt{\frac{c}{l}} + \frac{g}{2}\sqrt{\frac{l}{c}}\right)\left[1 - \frac{1}{8\omega^2}\left(\frac{r}{l} - \frac{g}{c}\right)^2\right] + j\omega\sqrt{lc}\left[1 + \frac{1}{8\omega^2}\left(\frac{r}{l} - \frac{g}{c}\right)^2\right]$$

$$(r \ll \omega l;\ g \ll \omega c) \qquad \textbf{(2-43)}$$

If the line parameters were proportioned as specified in Eq. 2-16 for the distortionless line, the coefficients of the $1/\omega^2$ terms would vanish, and hence attenuation would no longer be a function of frequency, and the phase function would be in direct proportion to frequency. These results correspond to those obtained previously, and give a limiting-case check. Substitution of Eq. 2-16 for g in the remaining expression for attenuation function indicates that one-half the loss associated with a traveling wave on a distortionless line takes place in the conductor resistance and one-half in the leakage conductance.

For a well-insulated open-wire line, r/l is much greater than g/c. Within the frequency range for which $r \ll \omega l$, the attenuation function, represented by the real part of Eq. 2-43, reduces to the following:

$$\alpha \approx \frac{r}{2}\sqrt{\frac{c}{l}} \qquad \textbf{(2-44)}$$

This, it should be noted, is just one-half the value of α for a distortionless line with the same values of r, l, and c, Eq. 2-17.

Owing to skin effect, r is a function of frequency, as was mentioned in Sec. 1-1. In general the attenuation of a physical open-wire line increases with frequency throughout the carrier-frequency range (approximately 5000 to 150,000 cps) and beyond. (Problem 2-6 deals with the applicability of skin effect within the frequency ranges shown in the plots of characteristic impedance, attenuation function, and phase velocity in Figs. 2-2, 2-3, and 2-4.)

An approximation for the phase velocity may be found from Eq. 2-15 and the complex part of Eq. 2-43:

$$v \approx \frac{1}{\sqrt{lc}\left[1 + \frac{1}{8\omega^2}\left(\frac{r}{l} - \frac{g}{c}\right)^2\right]}$$

The following approximation will be used:

$$\frac{1}{1 \pm a} = 1 \mp a \cdots \qquad (|a| < 1) \qquad \textbf{(2-45)}$$

$$v \approx \frac{1}{\sqrt{lc}}\left[1 - \frac{1}{8\omega^2}\left(\frac{r}{l} - \frac{g}{c}\right)^2\right] \qquad \textbf{(2-46)}$$

The attenuation-function asymptote as frequency approaches zero is

$\sqrt{rg}$, as may be seen by inspection of Eq. 2-12. The velocity of propagation at frequencies approaching zero is the subject of Problem 2-7.

(2) UNLOADED CABLE. The propagation function of an unloaded cable may be approximated at low frequencies by a simple expression. As was done in deriving the corresponding approximation for the characteristic impedance, Eq. 2-41, ωl and g are ignored in comparison with r and ωc:

$$\gamma \approx \sqrt{j\omega c r} \approx \sqrt{\frac{\omega c r}{2}} + j\sqrt{\frac{\omega c r}{2}} \tag{2-47}$$

The corresponding velocity of propagation may be found with the aid of Eq. 2-15:

$$v \approx \sqrt{\frac{2\omega}{cr}} \tag{2-48}$$

Computed values of attenuation and phase velocity are shown in Fig. 2-4 for an unloaded cable. It is apparent that these vary widely over the

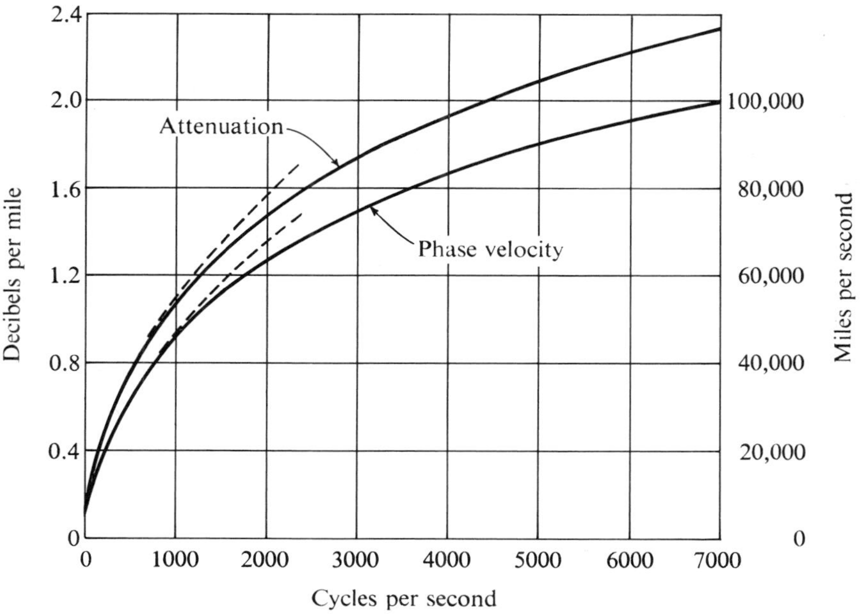

Figure 2-4 Attenuation and phase velocity for an unloaded cable as functions of frequency (parameters same as for Fig. 2-3); solid lines represent exact computed values from Eq. 2-12, dashed lines represent series approximations from Eqs. 2-47 and 2-48

audio-frequency range. The comments following Eq. 2-41 (approximate function for Z_0) regarding the assumption that $r \gg \omega l$ are also applicable to the approximate results in Eqs. 2-47 and 2-48.

c. Distortion

Changes in signal wave shape with distance traveled along a linear transmission line may be classified as *attenuation distortion* and *phase distortion*. Attenuation distortion is the result of variation of the attenuation with frequency (see the real part of Eq. 2-43 or 2-47), and phase distortion is the result of variation of phase velocity with frequency (see Eq. 2-46 or 2-48). Dependence of the characteristic impedance on frequency is not referred to as distortion, although it results in a difference between a voltage wave and the accompanying current wave which, if components of more than one frequency are present, is more pronounced than a mere phase shift. These three effects are necessarily all present if any one is present; only if the line is lossless or distortionless are they absent. Attenuation-distortion and phase-distortion effects are cumulative with distance of travel, and they reduce the quality and intelligibility of a signal.*

The use of loading to reduce attenuation, as described in the next section, will at the same time reduce attenuation distortion and phase distortion, but in practice will introduce distortion of another type, *nonlinear* distortion. This is because the ferromagnetic materials used to increase the series inductance have nonlinear magnetization characteristics which will create harmonics of each sinusoidal component of driving current present. If two or more sinusoidal driving components are present, sum-and-difference frequency components will be created as well.

2-4. LOADING: GENERAL COMMENTS

Low attenuation is a desirable attribute for a transmission line, but it may be had only at a price. In the pioneer days of telephony, which preceded by some years the practical development of the vacuum-tube amplifier, the signal energy thrust onto the line by the sending-end instrument could not be replenished. Transmission losses had to be kept low enough so that whatever energy remained when the signal reached the receiving-end instrument could

* A common method of correcting attenuation distortion and phase distortion is by use of terminal networks known as *equalizers*.[1,2,3,4] An *attenuation equalizer* has an attenuation characteristic which, ideally, complements that of the transmission line; it attenuates as little as possible those frequencies which are heavily attenuated by the line, but attenuates more heavily the frequencies which are transmitted with little attenuation. The overall attenuation of the line and equalizer is almost independent of frequency over the selected band. *Phase* or *delay equalization* is based on a similar concept; it retards the high-velocity components with respect to the lower-velocity ones so as to give very nearly the same resultant delay time (line plus equalizer) for all frequencies within the given band.

produce an intelligible sound. Loading coils were of decisive value in improving the quality and increasing the potential distance of transmission. With the steady improvements that have been made during the past several decades in the performance and reliability of amplifiers, the significance of line attenuation as a controlling design parameter has diminished. The problem of line design has become one of economic balance, in which the costs and performance limitations of amplifying equipment must be compared with those of loading coils in terms of the particular application.

a. Possible means of reducing attenuation

All four line parameters contribute to the attenuation function, the real part of Eq. 2-12. Loss is caused directly by the conductor resistance and by the leakage conductance, and it may be correctly surmised that a reduction in either will reduce attenuation. Leakage conductance is at a low level in any case if the insulation meets minimum requirements. Reduction in conductor resistance may be achieved by using conductors of larger cross-sectional area, but an economic limit is rapidly approached. The influence of inductance and capacitance on attenuation is not obvious from Eq. 2-12, but the approximation for the low-loss, open-wire line given in Eq. 2-44, which is repeated below, puts the matter into clearer perspective:

$$\alpha \approx \frac{r}{2}\sqrt{\frac{c}{l}} \qquad \textbf{(2-44)}$$

It appears that an increase in l or a decrease in c will reduce the attenuation function. As is shown in Chapter 9 for two specific types of line (coaxial cable and two parallel wires), inductance is proportional to the logarithm of the spacing, whereas capacitance is inversely proportional to the same logarithm. In open-wire construction, the possibility of decreasing attenuation by increasing the spacing has a practical limit, because this also increases inevitable but unwanted couplings between the given circuit and other nearby circuits.

The remaining possibility for reducing attenuation is that of increasing the inductance by ferromagnetic means, or "loading" the line. For an open-wire line, only a modest reduction in attenuation is practical by loading. Loading was used on early long-distance, open-wire circuits, but such applications were discontinued soon after vacuum-tube amplifiers had become practical. Loading produces more decisive reductions in the attenuation of cables, and it is used today, although less generally than it was some years ago.

Continuous loading, in which a highly permeable ferroalloy tape is wound around the conductor, is used in some submarine cables and yields a continuously distributed inductance. It is more expensive than lumped loading, but a mechanically uniform structure (longitudinally) has merit for a cable from the standpoint of handling during laying.

Lumped loading increases the average inductance per unit length of line, but it does not do so uniformly. This causes heavy attenuation of all components above a certain *cutoff frequency*, which is determined in part by the spacing between loading coils. The propagation properties of a lump-loaded line are more complicated than those of a continuously loaded one and will be considered briefly in Chapter 6 with lumped-parameter networks. Land cables, which may be either in conduits in the ground or suspended aerially, may be lump-loaded if they are to carry audio-frequency signals but not carrier-frequency signals.

b. Changes in characteristics caused by loading

By means of a series expansion of the general expression for γ, Eq. 2-12, it may be shown that, as long as r/l is greater than g/c, an incremental increase in distributed inductance should decrease the attenuation function. Concurrent effects of loading are to increase the characteristic impedance and to decrease the velocity of propagation.

Let l in Eq. 2-12 be replaced by $l_0 + \Delta l$, where l_0 is the average inductance of the line (unloaded or loaded) to which an incremental inductance Δl is to be added:

$$\gamma = \sqrt{(r + j\omega l_0 + j\omega\,\Delta l)(g + j\omega c)}$$

$$= \sqrt{(r + j\omega l_0)(g + j\omega c)\left(1 + \frac{j\omega\,\Delta l}{r + j\omega l_0}\right)}$$

The series approximation given in Eq. 2-35 may be used to advantage here:

$$\gamma \approx \sqrt{(r + j\omega l_0)(g + j\omega c)}\left[1 + \frac{j\omega\,\Delta l}{2(r + j\omega l_0)}\right]$$

$$\approx \sqrt{(r + j\omega l_0)(g + j\omega c)} + \frac{j\omega\,\Delta l\sqrt{g + j\omega c}}{2\sqrt{r + j\omega l_0}} \qquad \textbf{(2-49)}$$

Let

$$\gamma_0 = \sqrt{(r + j\omega l_0)(g + j\omega c)} \qquad \textbf{(2-50)}$$

$$\Delta\gamma = \frac{j\omega\,\Delta l\sqrt{g + j\omega c}}{2\sqrt{r + j\omega l_0}} \qquad \textbf{(2-51)}$$

The angles of $r + j\omega l_0$ and $g + j\omega c$ will lie between 0 and 90 degrees, and their geometric mean, γ_0, will necessarily have an angle between 0 and 90 degrees. Hence α_0, the real part of γ_0, will necessarily be positive. If the addition of the incremental inductance Δl is to be beneficial, the real part of $\Delta\gamma$ should be negative. By referring to Eq. 2-51 one can see that the angle of $\Delta\gamma$ will be greater than 90 degrees, and hence the real part of $\Delta\gamma$ will be negative, if the angle of $g + j\omega c$ is greater than that of $r + j\omega l_0$, or, in other words, if r/l_0 is greater than g/c.

Actually the practical limit to loading is considerably lower than has just been indicated. This is because lumped-inductor windings necessarily have some resistance which adds to that of the conductors, and the ferromagnetic material used for coil cores or continuous-loading tape will add hysteresis and eddy-current losses.

That loading should increase the characteristic impedance is apparent from the basic equation for Z_0, 2-19. This leads to a physical explanation as to why loading should decrease the attenuation. The increased characteristic impedance will cause a signal of a given power level to be transmitted at a higher voltage and lower current than otherwise. With satisfactory insulation, the increase in shunt leakage loss (v^2g) will be negligible compared with the reduction in series resistance loss (i^2r). Thus the power loss per unit length of line for a given transmitted power will be reduced, as will the attenuation.

If the imaginary part of Eq. 2-51 is examined as the real part was, it may be seen that the imaginary part of $\Delta\gamma$ is positive, as is β_0. From Eq. 2-15 one may see that an increase in phase constant at a given frequency will result in a decrease in phase velocity.

2-5. CONCLUSIONS

The general uniform transmission line with unconstrained values of inductance, capacitance, resistance, and shunt conductance will propagate sinusoidally varying voltage and current waves in either direction. These waves are reduced in magnitude in proportion to the exponential of the product of the distance traveled and an attenuation factor.

Phasor notation is derivable from the complex exponential form of the sine function. It may be adapted to the traveling-wave function readily, and the functional variation with respect to distance becomes $\epsilon^{-\gamma z}$ or $\epsilon^{\gamma z}$, depending on the direction of travel. Here γ is the *propagation function*, a complex quantity of which the real part is the *attenuation function* α and the imaginary part is the *phase function* β:

$$\gamma = \sqrt{(r + j\omega l)(g + j\omega c)} \tag{2-12}$$

The phase function is related to the *phase velocity* v (also known loosely as the velocity of propagation) in the following manner:

$$v = \frac{\omega}{\beta} \tag{2-15}$$

The *characteristic impedance* Z_0 relates the voltage and current phasors of a traveling-wave pair:

$$Z_0 = \sqrt{\frac{r + j\omega l}{g + j\omega c}} \tag{2-19}$$

At any given location, corresponding voltage and current sinusoidal traveling waves are, in general, not in time phase with each other.

Several special cases yield simple, concise expressions for the characteristic impedance, attenuation function, and phase velocity; these results are summarized in Table 2-1.

Table 2-1 TRANSMISSION-LINE PARAMETERS

Type of line	*Identifying feature*	*Characteristic impedance*	*Attenuation function*	*Phase velocity*
Lossless	$r = 0$ $g = 0$	$\sqrt{\dfrac{l}{c}}$	0	$\dfrac{1}{\sqrt{lc}}$
Distortionless	$\dfrac{r}{l} = \dfrac{g}{c}$	$\sqrt{\dfrac{l}{c}}$	$r\sqrt{\dfrac{c}{l}}$	$\dfrac{1}{\sqrt{lc}}$
Low-loss	$r \ll \omega l$ $g = 0$	$\sqrt{\dfrac{l}{c}}\,\epsilon^{-j(r/2\omega l)}$	$\dfrac{r}{2}\sqrt{\dfrac{c}{l}}$	$\dfrac{1}{\sqrt{lc}}$
"Ideal" unloaded cable	$\omega l \ll r$ $g = 0$	$\sqrt{\dfrac{r}{\omega c}}\,\epsilon^{-j(\pi/4)}$	$\sqrt{\dfrac{r\omega c}{2}}$	$\sqrt{\dfrac{2\omega}{rc}}$

The addition of series inductance to a transmission line by inserting ferroalloy-cored coils or by wrapping a cable conductor with ferroalloy tape is known as *loading*. Within a suitable frequency range it reduces the attenuation, increases the characteristic impedance, and also decreases the phase velocity.

PROBLEMS

2-1. Expand Eqs. 2-10 and 2-11 and solve for α and β separately.

2-2. Write expressions for the instantaneous and time-averaged power of a traveling-wave pair $[p_1(z,t)$ and $P_1(z)]$ using Eqs. 2-7 and 2-20.

2-3. Your study of traveling waves on transmission lines is interrupted by a call for help from a friend, an engineering student who is majoring in a branch other than electrical engineering. Your friend is taking a "service" course for nonelectrical students; he was told in lecture today that the differential equation for a resistance-inductance series a-c circuit is as follows:

$$Ri + L\frac{di}{dt} = V_{\max}\sin(\omega t + \alpha)$$

(Your friend has doubts as to the logic of the di/dt term but will accept it tentatively.) He was also told that the solution to this equation is

$$I\underline{/\phi} = \frac{V\underline{/\alpha}}{R + j\omega L} = \frac{V\underline{/\alpha - \tan^{-1}(\omega L/R)}}{\sqrt{R^2 + (\omega L)^2}}$$

He asks the following questions in one breath: (1) What does the expression $I\underline{/\phi}$ really mean physically? (2) What became of the t's in the original equation? (3) How did the j get into the first form of the answer, and how did it disappear in going to the second form? (4) How good an approximation is given by this method? (5) Do students majoring in electrical engineering really understand a-c steady-state theory? Your friend has a working knowledge of trigonometry and differential calculus but would probably be confused by special operators such as Im. Prepare a reasonably brief but convincing mathematical demonstration which will explain the points raised by questions 1 through 4, and cause your friend to answer question 5 affirmatively.

2-4. Given a 30-mile length of transmission line which is terminated with an impedance equal to the characteristic impedance of the line. (As is shown in Sec. 3-2*a*, only a single traveling-wave pair approaching the termination could then exist.) The input and terminal voltages and currents are

$$V_{\text{in}} = 10.0\underline{/0^\circ} \text{ volts}$$
$$V_{\text{out}} = 6.0\underline{/-150^\circ} \text{ volts}$$
$$I_{\text{in}} = 0.20\underline{/7.5^\circ} \text{ amp}$$
$$I_{\text{out}} = 0.120\underline{/-142.5^\circ} \text{ amp}$$

Find the characteristic impedance and evaluate the attenuation function (in nepers per mile and in decibels per mile) and the propagation function.

2-5. Write an expression for the magnitude of Z_0 which involves no j's or other complex quantities. Expand this in a series under the simultaneous conditions that $r \ll \omega l$ and $g \ll \omega c$.

Answer:
$$|Z_0| \approx \sqrt{\frac{l}{c}}\left\{1 + \frac{1}{4\omega^2}\left[\left(\frac{r}{l}\right)^2 - \left(\frac{g}{c}\right)^2\right]\right\}$$

2-6. In the discussion of skin effect in Appendix "B" it is shown that the ratio between effective resistance of a solid, homogeneous, circular conductor and the d-c resistance is but little greater than unity if the frequency is less than the skin-effect-demarcation frequency f_{skd} as given in Eq. B-62 and Fig. B-6. Above that frequency the resistance ratio increases approximately as the square root of frequency. Find f_{skd} for the following conductors: (*a*) Copper wire of 128 mils diameter (used for Fig. 2-2); (*b*) Copper wire, AWG #19, 1.0 mm diameter (used for Figs. 2-3 and 2-4); (*c*) Solid copper conductor, AWG #2, 0.258 in. diameter. Compare the results of (*a*) and (*b*) with the maximum abscissa values shown in the corresponding figures.

2-7. Expand the propagation function in a series for the low-frequency-limit conditions of $r \gg \omega l$ and $g \gg \omega c$. From the complex part of the series, find a first-order approximation for velocity of propagation for frequencies approaching zero.

Answer:

$$v \approx \frac{2}{l\sqrt{\dfrac{g}{r}} + c\sqrt{\dfrac{r}{g}}}$$

Show that this result cannot exceed $1/\sqrt{lc}$. (HINT: Let $r/l = kg/c$, paralleling Eq. 2-16 for the distortionless line, and eliminate r and g from the result just derived for v.)

2-8. When $\log |Z_0|$ and θ_0 are plotted versus $\log \omega$, properties of symmetry exist with respect to the abscissa value $\omega_{sy} = \sqrt{rg/lc}$. Investigate these. Also compute ω_{sy} for the open-wire line parameter values given in Fig. 2-2 and the cable parameter values given in Fig. 2-3.

REFERENCES

1. CREAMER, WALTER J., *Communication Networks and Lines*, pp. 132–54. New York: Harper & Brothers, 1951.
2. EVERITT, W. L. and G. E. ANNER, *Communication Engineering*, pp. 505–38. New York: McGraw-Hill Book Company, Inc., 1956.
3. National Association of Broadcasters, Inc., *NAB Engineering Handbook*, 5th ed., A. PROSE WALKER, ed. pp. 4-3 to 4-60. New York: McGraw-Hill Book Company, Inc., 1960.
4. *Transmission Systems for Communications*, Technical Staff, Bell Telephone Laboratories. New York: Graybar Electric Company, Inc., 1964.

CHAPTER 3

Discontinuities, Reflections, and Standing Waves

The infinitely long uniform line is a fiction of mathematics; practical lines are uniform over only finite distances. Such lines are necessarily terminated; in addition they may branch, and frequently they are interrupted by lumped impedances inserted in series with each conductor or connected in shunt from one conductor to the other.

Ohm's law and Kirchhoff's laws must be obeyed at each such transition point, and in general the voltage-to-current ratio at such a point does not correspond to that for a single pair of voltage and current waves traveling in one direction. To meet all impedance requirements simultaneously, a set of voltage and current waves departing on each of the lines joined to the discontinuity is usually necessary.

3-1. INCIDENT AND REFLECTED WAVES

The elementary situation illustrated in Fig. 3-1, that of a uniform line terminated with a lumped impedance, will be examined first. Energy is assumed to be originating in the source at the left; waves traveling to the right and impinging on the terminating impedance are known as *incident* waves, whereas those leaving the terminating end and traveling to the left are called *reflected* waves.

In accordance with the polarity-and-direction convention indicated in Fig. 3-1, the following expressions for postulated voltage and current may be

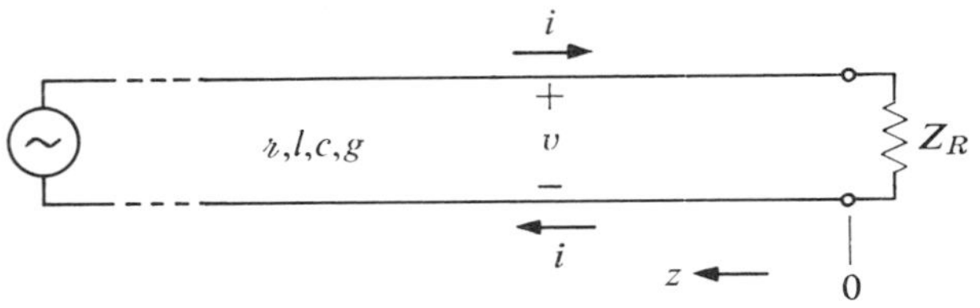

Figure 3-1 Transmission line terminated with lumped impedance

written

$$v_{\text{inc}}(z,t) = V_{IM}\epsilon^{\alpha z}\sin(\omega t + \beta z) \tag{3-1}$$

$$i_{\text{inc}}(z,t) = \frac{V_{IM}}{|Z_0|}\epsilon^{\alpha z}\sin(\omega t - \theta_0 + \beta z) \tag{3-2}$$

$$v_{\text{ref}}(z,t) = V_{RM}\epsilon^{-\alpha z}\sin(\omega t + \theta_K - \beta z) \tag{3-3}$$

$$i_{\text{ref}}(z,t) = -\frac{V_{RM}}{|Z_0|}\epsilon^{-\alpha z}\sin(\omega t - \theta_0 + \theta_K - \beta z) \tag{3-4}$$

The angle θ_K allows for a time-phase difference between the incident and reflected components of voltage at the terminated end where z equals zero. The foregoing expressions may be rewritten in phasor form as follows, in which $V_{\text{inc}}(0)$ has been taken as the reference phasor:

$$V_{\text{inc}}(z) = \frac{V_{IM}}{\sqrt{2}}\epsilon^{\gamma z} \tag{3-5}$$

$$I_{\text{inc}}(z) = \frac{V_{IM}}{Z_0\sqrt{2}}\epsilon^{\gamma z} \tag{3-6}$$

$$V_{\text{ref}}(z) = \frac{V_{RM}}{\sqrt{2}}\epsilon^{j\theta_K}\epsilon^{-\gamma z} \tag{3-7}$$

$$I_{\text{ref}}(z) = -\frac{V_{RM}}{Z_0\sqrt{2}}\epsilon^{j\theta_K}\epsilon^{-\gamma z} \tag{3-8}$$

As in Sec. 2-2, the explicit functions are related to the phasors in the following manner:

$$v_{\text{inc}}(z,t) = \text{Im}[\sqrt{2}V_{\text{inc}}(z)\epsilon^{j\omega t}] \qquad \text{etc.} \tag{3-9}$$

a. Relationships at termination

By superposition, the voltage across Z_R and the current through it are related to the traveling-wave components as follows:

$$v_{\text{ter}}(t) = v_{\text{inc}}(0,t) + v_{\text{ref}}(0,t) \tag{3-10}$$

$$i_{\text{ter}}(t) = i_{\text{inc}}(0,t) + i_{\text{ref}}(0,t) \tag{3-11}$$

Stated in terms of phasors these become

$$V_{ter} = V_{inc}(0) + V_{ref}(0) \tag{3-12}$$

$$V_{ter} = \frac{V_{IM}}{\sqrt{2}} + \frac{V_{RM}}{\sqrt{2}} \epsilon^{j\theta_K} \tag{3-13}$$

$$I_{ter} = \frac{V_{IM}}{Z_0\sqrt{2}} - \frac{V_{RM}}{Z_0\sqrt{2}} \epsilon^{j\theta_K} \tag{3-14}$$

In accordance with Ohm's law,

$$V_{ter} = I_{ter} Z_R \tag{3-15}$$

Substitution of Eqs. 3-13 and 3-14 in Eq. 3-15 yields

$$V_{IM} + V_{RM}\epsilon^{j\theta_K} = Z_R\left(\frac{V_{IM}}{Z_0} - \frac{V_{RM}}{Z_0} \epsilon^{j\theta_K}\right)$$

Both sides have been multiplied by the factor $\sqrt{2}$. Terms involving V_{IM} may be gathered together on the left-hand side of the equality sign, those involving V_{RM} gathered on the right-hand side, and the resulting equation multiplied by Z_0:

$$V_{IM}(Z_R - Z_0) = V_{RM}\epsilon^{j\theta_K}(Z_R + Z_0)$$

Let

$$K = |K|\, \epsilon^{j\theta_K}$$

$$= \frac{V_{RM}\epsilon^{j\theta_K}}{V_{IM}} \tag{3-16}$$

Substitution of Eq. 3-16 in the preceding expression yields the following:

$$K = \frac{Z_R - Z_0}{Z_R + Z_0} \tag{3-17}$$

The complex quantity K is known as the *reflection coefficient*. As an example, let

$$Z_0 = 600\underline{/-20.0^\circ} \text{ ohms}$$

$$Z_R = 500\underline{/35.0^\circ} \text{ ohms}$$

From Eq. 3-17,

$$K = 0.528\underline{/102.8^\circ}$$

A phasor diagram relating the voltages and currents at the terminal of the line is sketched in Fig. 3-2. In drawing such a diagram it is convenient to start with $V_{inc}(0)$. The reflected component of voltage leads it by angle θ_K and is in proportion to $|K|$. The incident current phasor is related to the incident voltage by angle θ_0; here it leads by 20 degrees. Reflected current leads the

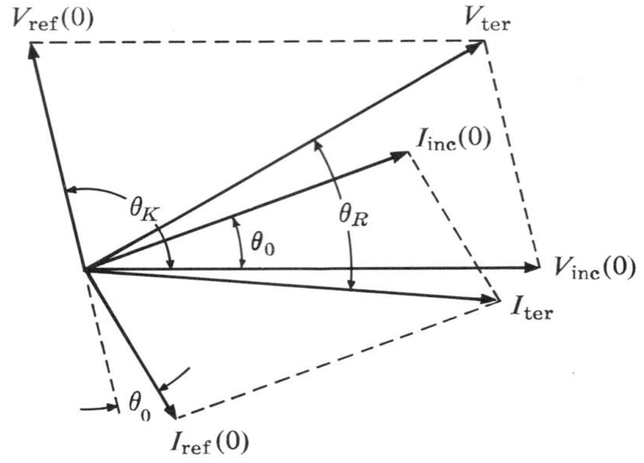

Figure 3-2 Phasor diagram at termination of transmission line: $Z_0 = 600\underline{/-20.0^\circ}$ ohms, $Z_R = 500\underline{/35.0^\circ}$ ohms

negative of reflected voltage by the same amount. The two voltage components add to form V_{ter}, and the two current components add to form I_{ter}. Load current should lag the load voltage by the angle of Z_R, in this instance 35 degrees.

b. Resultant voltage and current away from termination

A phasor diagram relating voltages and currents at the termination may be generalized to show those quantities at any desired point on the line by adding traveling-wave phasor loci as shown in Fig. 3-3. It was assumed in the construction of that diagram that the ratio α/β is 0.1 neper per radian. The phasor for the incident component of voltage at distance z_1 (meters, miles, etc.) from the termination is positioned on the diagram by drawing a line radially from the origin at an angle of βz_1 radians counterclockwise from the phasor of incident voltage at the termination. The phasor for the reflected component of voltage is positioned in direction by drawing a radial line at angle βz_1 radians clockwise from the phasor of reflected voltage at the termination. The lengths of both phasors are determined by the spirals, which start at the respective terminal phasors and progress outward and counterclockwise in the case of incident voltage and inward and clockwise for the reflected voltage. After one full revolution the spiral intersects the radial line from which it started, and the ratio of its larger intercept to its smaller one is $\epsilon^{2\pi\alpha/\beta}$—in this case $\epsilon^{0.628}$, or 1.873. The same principle applies for current components. Resultant voltage and current, including their phase angles relative to the reference voltage, may be found by phasor addition of the respective incident and reflected components drawn for the appropriate βz_1.

Plots of rms magnitudes of resultant voltage and current with respect to

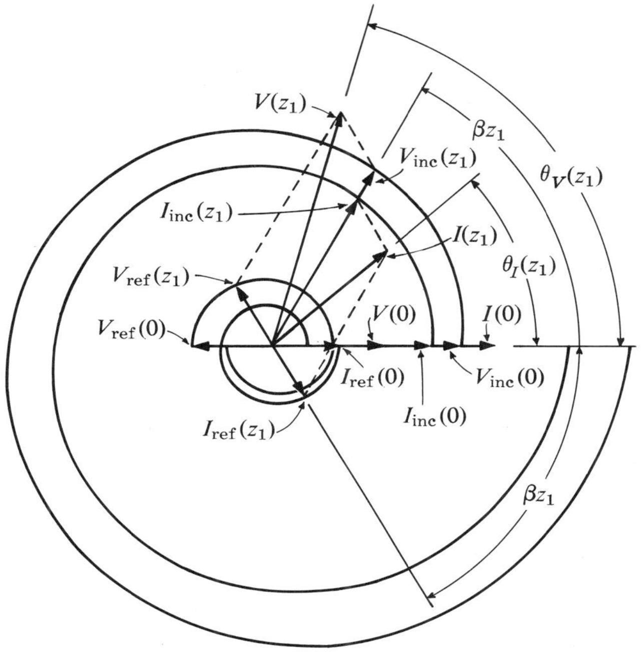

Figure 3-3 Phasor loci for distortionless transmission line with resistive termination: $Z_0 = 600\underline{/0°}$ ohms, $Z_R = 250\underline{/0°}$ ohms, $\alpha/\beta = 0.1$ neper per radian

distance from the termination, and also of their phase angles relative to the terminal voltage, are instructive and are given in Fig. 3-4 for the situation studied in Fig. 3-3.

Mathematical expressions paralleling the procedures followed in Fig. 3-3 may be found from Eqs. 3-13, 3-14, and 3-15:

$$V(z) = \frac{V_{IM}}{\sqrt{2}}(\epsilon^{\gamma z} + K\epsilon^{-\gamma z}) \tag{3-18}$$

$$I(z) = \frac{V_{IM}}{Z_0\sqrt{2}}(\epsilon^{\gamma z} - K\epsilon^{-\gamma z}) \tag{3-19}$$

These functions may be stated in instantaneous form as follows:

$$\begin{aligned} v(z,t) &= v_{\text{inc}}(z,t) + v_{\text{ref}}(z,t) \\ &= V_{IM}[\epsilon^{\alpha z}\sin(\omega t + \beta z) + |K|\,\epsilon^{-\alpha z}\sin(\omega t + \theta_K - \beta z)] \end{aligned} \tag{3-20}$$

$$\begin{aligned} i(z,t) &= i_{\text{inc}}(z,t) + i_{\text{ref}}(z,t) \\ &= \frac{V_{IM}}{|Z_0|}[\epsilon^{\alpha z}\sin(\omega t - \theta_0 + \beta z) - |K|\,\epsilon^{-\alpha z}\sin(\omega t - \theta_0 + \theta_K - \beta z)] \end{aligned} \tag{3-21}$$

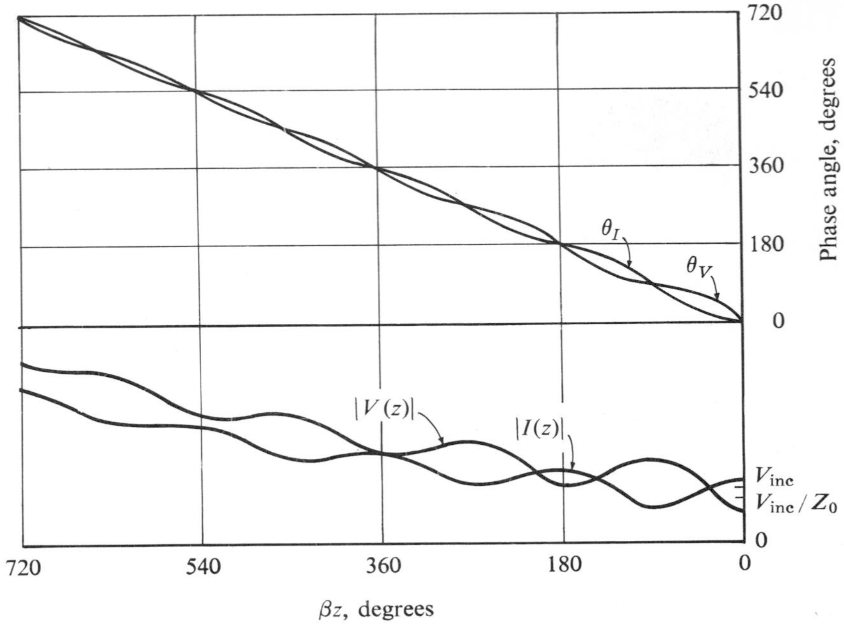

Figure 3-4 Magnitudes and relative phase angles of voltage and current on distortionless transmission line with resistive termination: $Z_0 = 600\underline{/0^\circ}$ ohms, $Z_R = 250\underline{/0^\circ}$ ohms, $\alpha/\beta = 0.1$ neper per radian

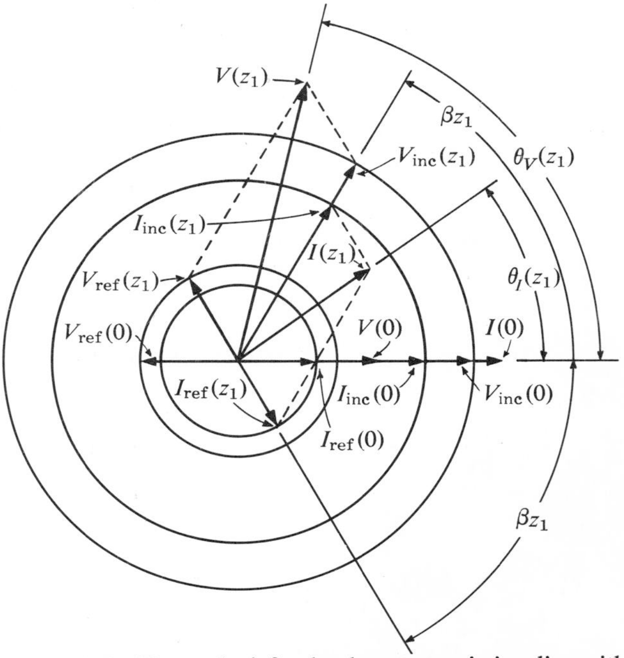

Figure 3-5 Phasor loci for lossless transmission line with resistive termination: $Z_0 = 600\underline{/0^\circ}$ ohms, $Z_R = 250\underline{/0^\circ}$ ohms

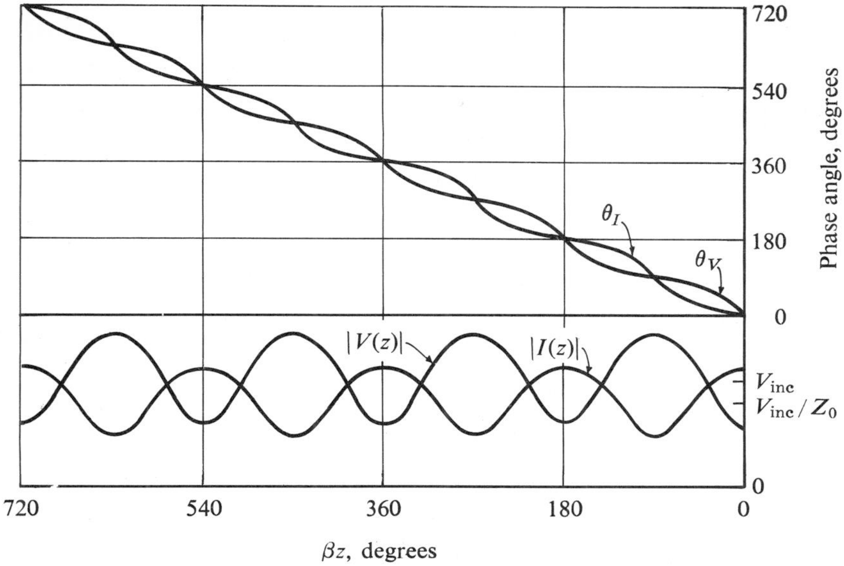

Figure 3-6 Magnitudes and relative phase angles of voltage and current on lossless transmission line with resistive termination: $Z_0 = 600\underline{/0°}$ ohms, $Z_R = 250\underline{/0°}$ ohms

If the line is lossless, the loci of the magnitudes of the components become circles and the results become recurrent, as shown in Fig. 3-5. Plots of magnitudes of resultant current and voltage then repeat every 180 degrees in βz, as shown in Fig. 3-6. Such variations in rms values with distance are described as *standing waves*; the concept is most meaningful for a lossless line or one with very low losses, such that each undulation differs but little from those adjacent to it.

3-2. LIMITING-CASE REFLECTION SITUATIONS

Certain special cases yield much simpler results than the general examples just given.

a. Terminating impedance equal to characteristic impedance

Should the terminating impedance be equal to the characteristic impedance, the numerator of Eq. 3-17 would vanish and the reflection coefficient would be zero. Root-mean-square voltage and current would be uniform along a lossless line under these circumstances; they would increase exponentially with distance from the termination toward the source on a line having losses. Relative phase angles would increase linearly in the leading direction with distance from the termination.

b. Open-circuited end: lossless line

Letting Z_R approach infinity will reduce the reflection coefficient to unity. In terms of instantaneous quantities, taken from Eqs. 3-20 and 3-21, with α and θ_0 both set equal to zero,

$$v(z,t) = V_{IM}[\sin(\omega t + \beta z) + \sin(\omega t - \beta z)]$$

$$= 2V_{IM} \sin \omega t \cos \beta z \tag{3-22}$$

$$i(z,t) = \frac{V_{IM}}{Z_0}[\sin(\omega t + \beta z) - \sin(\omega t - \beta z)]$$

$$= 2\frac{V_{IM}}{Z_0}\cos \omega t \sin \beta z \tag{3-23}$$

In terms of phasors, from Eqs. 3-18 and 3-19,

$$V(z) = \frac{V_{IM}}{\sqrt{2}}(\epsilon^{j\beta z} + \epsilon^{-j\beta z})$$

$$= \sqrt{2}V_{IM} \cos \beta z \tag{3-24}$$

$$I(z) = \frac{V_{IM}}{Z_0\sqrt{2}}(\epsilon^{j\beta z} - \epsilon^{-j\beta z})$$

$$= j\sqrt{2}\frac{V_{IM}}{Z_0} \sin \beta z \tag{3-25}$$

Plots of rms magnitudes and relative phase angles are given in Fig. 3-7. It should be noted that resultant voltage and current are in time quadrature with each other at all locations; in the quarter wavelength of line nearest the open-circuited end the current leads the voltage, and in the next quarter wavelength the current lags the voltage. This pattern is repeated every half wavelength. It should also be noted that the resultant current and resultant voltage each dip to zero every half wavelength, but the standing waves are displaced a quarter wavelength such that the resultant current is a maximum at those locations at which voltage is zero, and vice versa.

c. Open-circuited end: line with finite loss

When losses are present, the simplifications which result from substituting the open-circuit reflection coefficient in Eqs. 3-18 through 3-21 are slight:

$$V(z) = \frac{V_{IM}}{\sqrt{2}}(\epsilon^{\gamma z} + \epsilon^{-\gamma z}) \tag{3-26}$$

$$I(z) = \frac{V_{IM}}{Z_0\sqrt{2}}(\epsilon^{\gamma z} - \epsilon^{-\gamma z}) \tag{3-27}$$

$$v(z,t) = V_{IM}[\epsilon^{\alpha z} \sin(\omega t + \beta z) + \epsilon^{-\alpha z} \sin(\omega t - \beta z)] \tag{3-28}$$

$$i(z,t) = \frac{V_{IM}}{|Z_0|}[\epsilon^{\alpha z} \sin(\omega t - \theta_0 + \beta z) - \epsilon^{-\alpha z} \sin(\omega t - \theta_0 - \beta z)] \tag{3-29}$$

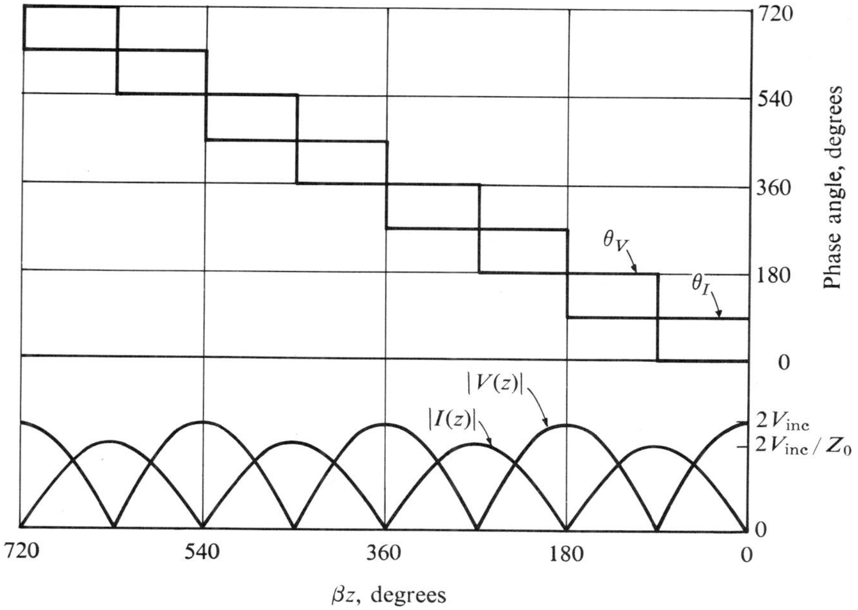

Figure 3-7 Magnitudes and relative phase angles of voltage and current on open-circuited lossless transmission line

Plots of the magnitudes and relative phase angles of the resultant voltage and current on an open-circuited lossy line, computed from Eqs. 3-28 and 3-29, are given in Fig. 3-8. Significant differences between these curves and those in Fig. 3-7 are (1) the standing-wave patterns are not recurrent with distance along the line; (2) the curves of magnitude no longer touch the axis at voltage or current minima, and they are rounded at those locations rather than forming sharp cusps; and (3) the plots of phase angles are no longer discontinuous at half-wavelength intervals and uniform in between; rather they change continuously at varying, but always finite, nonzero rates.

d. Short-circuited end: lossless line

With Z_R set equal to zero, the reflection coefficient becomes -1. Following the same development as for Eqs. 3-22 through 3-25, the following results may be written:

$$v(z,t) = 2V_{IM} \cos \omega t \sin \beta z \tag{3-30}$$

$$i(z,t) = 2\frac{V_{IM}}{Z_0} \sin \omega t \cos \beta z \tag{3-31}$$

$$V(z) = j\sqrt{2}V_{IM} \sin \beta z \tag{3-32}$$

$$I(z) = \sqrt{2}\frac{V_{IM}}{Z_0} \cos \beta z \tag{3-33}$$

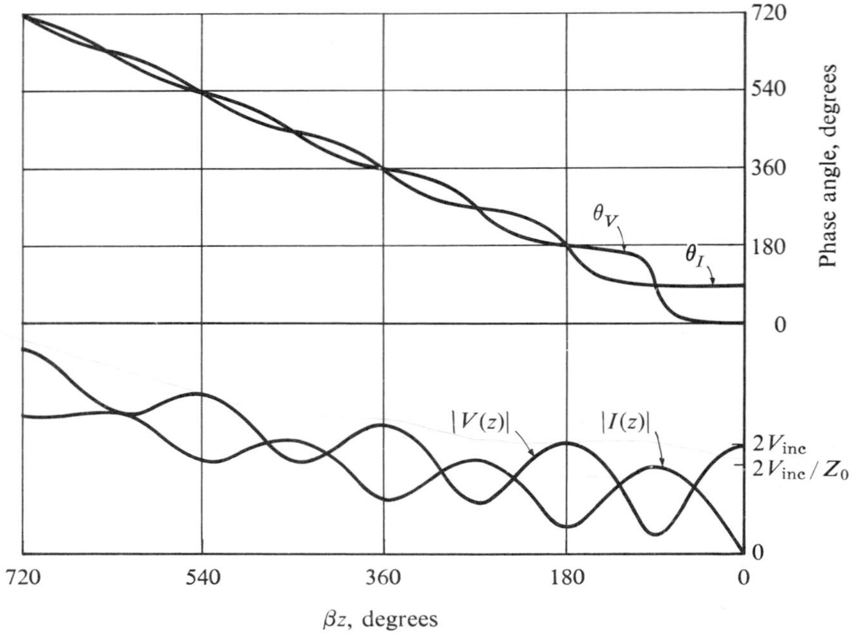

Figure 3-8 Magnitudes and relative phase angles of voltage and current on open-circuited distortionless transmission line: $\alpha/\beta = 0.1$ neper per radian

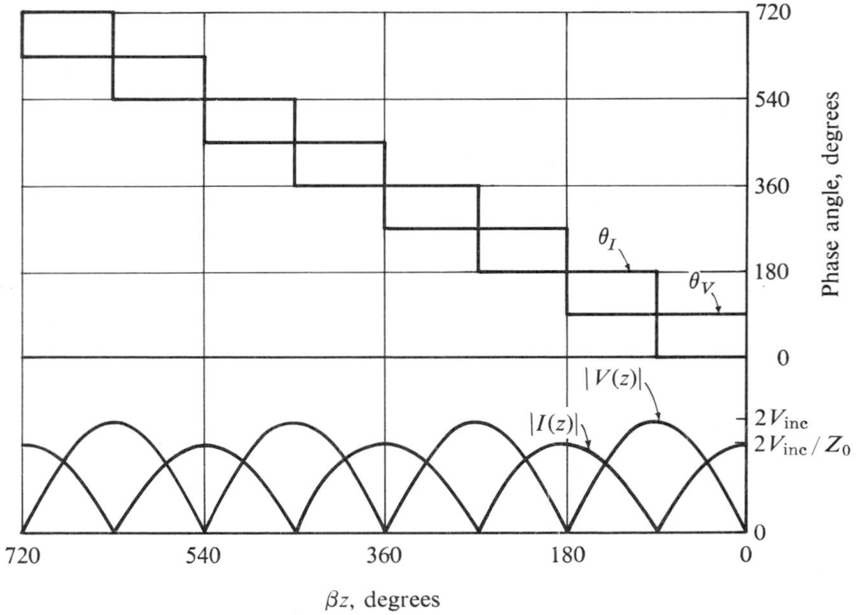

Figure 3-9 Magnitudes and relative phase angles of voltage and current on short-circuited lossless transmission line

Plots of magnitude and phase angle of voltage and current are given in Fig. 3-9. Comparison of these with Fig. 3-7 indicates that the patterns are identical if a shift of a quarter wavelength in βz is made.

e. Pure reactance as termination: lossless line

A lossless line will necessarily have a purely resistive characteristic impedance, and that combined with a purely reactive Z_R will invariably give a reflection coefficient whose magnitude is unity. The angle θ_K will depend on the relative magnitudes of Z_0 and Z_R, namely, R_0 and X_R:

$$\begin{aligned}\theta_K &= \tan^{-1}\left(\frac{X_R}{-R_0}\right) - \tan^{-1}\left(\frac{X_R}{R_0}\right)\\ &= \frac{\pi}{2} + \tan^{-1}\left(\frac{R_0}{X_R}\right) - \frac{\pi}{2} + \tan^{-1}\left(\frac{R_0}{X_R}\right)\\ &= 2\tan^{-1}\left(\frac{R_0}{X_R}\right) \qquad \textbf{(3-34)}\end{aligned}$$

In an example illustrated in Figs. 3-10 and 3-11, Z_R equals $0 + j1200$ ohms and Z_0 equals $600 + j0$ ohms. Thus the reflection coefficient is $1.0\epsilon^{j53.2°}$.

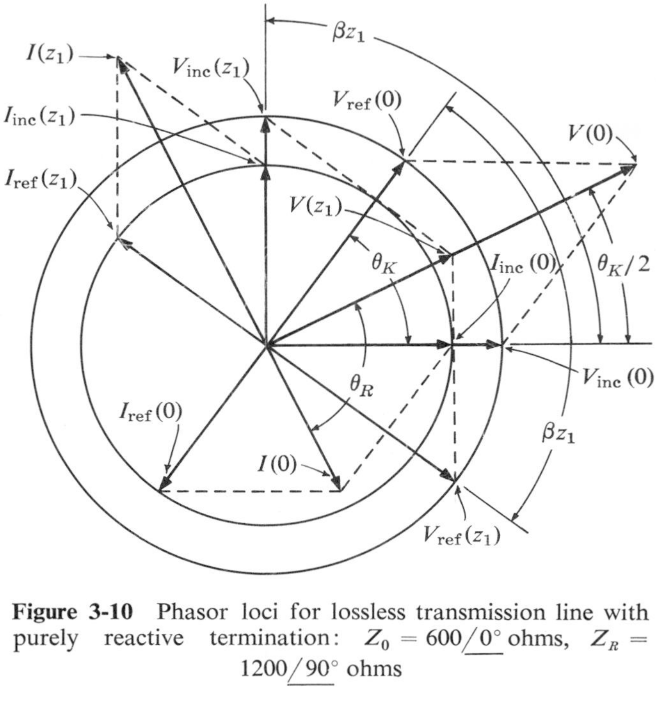

Figure 3-10 Phasor loci for lossless transmission line with purely reactive termination: $Z_0 = 600\underline{/0°}$ ohms, $Z_R = 1200\underline{/90°}$ ohms

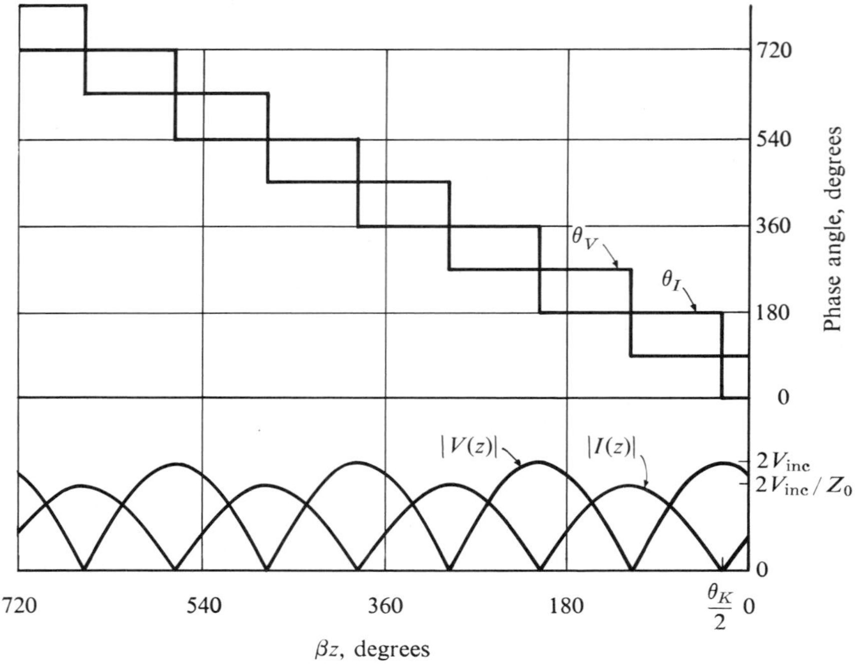

Figure 3-11 Magnitudes and relative phase angles of voltage and current on lossless transmission line with purely reactive termination: $Z_0 = 600\underline{/0^\circ}$ ohms, $Z_R = 1200\underline{/90^\circ}$ ohms

The general equations for voltage and current may be reduced as follows:

$$V(z) = \frac{V_{IM}}{\sqrt{2}}(\epsilon^{j\beta z} + \epsilon^{j\theta_K}\epsilon^{-j\beta z})$$

$$= \frac{V_{IM}}{\sqrt{2}}\epsilon^{j\theta_K/2}(\epsilon^{j(\beta z-\theta_K/2)} + \epsilon^{-j(\beta z-\theta_K/2)})$$

$$= \sqrt{2}V_{IM}\epsilon^{j\theta_K/2}\cos\left(\beta z - \frac{\theta_K}{2}\right) \qquad \textbf{(3-35)}$$

$$v(z,t) = 2V_{IM}\sin\left(\omega t + \frac{\theta_K}{2}\right)\cos\left(\beta z - \frac{\theta_K}{2}\right) \qquad \textbf{(3-36)}$$

$$I(z) = \sqrt{2}\frac{V_{IM}}{Z_0}j\epsilon^{j\theta_K/2}\sin\left(\beta z - \frac{\theta_K}{2}\right) \qquad \textbf{(3-37)}$$

$$i(z,t) = 2\frac{V_{IM}}{Z_0}\cos\left(\omega t + \frac{\theta_K}{2}\right)\sin\left(\beta z - \frac{\theta_K}{2}\right) \qquad \textbf{(3-38)}$$

Comparison of Fig. 3-11 with Fig. 3-7 indicates that the difference between the standing-wave pattern with a purely reactive termination and that with an open-circuit termination is a shift of $\theta_K/2$ in βz.

The open-circuit termination, the short-circuit termination, and the purely reactive termination have an important physical property in common—they are lossless. And as has been noted, when used with a lossless line they all yield reflection coefficients with magnitudes of unity. For conciseness of expression, the term "lossless termination" will be used hereafter in statements which are applicable interchangeably to open-circuit, short-circuit, and purely reactive terminations.

3-3. STANDING-WAVE RATIO

Standing waves result from the simultaneous presence of waves traveling in both directions on a line. The *standing-wave ratio* is a quantity which is easily found from measured voltage or current data, and it is functionally related to the magnitude of the reflection coefficient.

The ratio of the maximum resultant rms voltage to the minimum resultant rms voltage along a transmission line is called the *voltage-standing-wave ratio*, abbreviated VSWR. The corresponding ratio for currents is called the *current-standing-wave ratio*, ISWR. On an ideal lossless line, all rms voltage maxima are equal, and so are all rms voltage minima, rms current maxima, and rms current minima. Thus the ratio between any voltage maximum and any voltage minimum would yield the same numerical value, and the same is true of the ratio between any current maximum and any current minimum:

$$\text{VSWR} = \frac{|V(z)|_{\text{max}}}{|V(z)|_{\text{min}}} \tag{3-39}$$

$$\text{ISWR} = \frac{|I(z)|_{\text{max}}}{|I(z)|_{\text{min}}} \tag{3-40}$$

One may show by geometrical construction from Fig. 3-5 (or from the corresponding diagram for a general termination) that the following are true on a lossless line:

$$|V(z)|_{\text{max}} = \frac{V_{IM}}{\sqrt{2}}(1 + |K|) \tag{3-41}$$

$$|V(z)|_{\text{min}} = \frac{V_{IM}}{\sqrt{2}}(1 - |K|) \tag{3-42}$$

$$|I(z)|_{\text{max}} = \frac{V_{IM}}{Z_0\sqrt{2}}(1 + |K|) \tag{3-43}$$

$$|I(z)|_{\text{min}} = \frac{V_{IM}}{Z_0\sqrt{2}}(1 - |K|) \tag{3-44}$$

From the same construction one may see that the voltage maxima occur at the same values of βz (location on the line) as do the current minima, and vice versa.

If Eqs. 3-41 through 3-44 are substituted in Eqs. 3-39 and 3-40, one finds that the standing-wave ratio of a lossless line is the same for both voltage and current and that it is related to the magnitude of the reflection coefficient in the following manner:

$$\mathrm{SWR} = \frac{1 + |K|}{1 - |K|} \tag{3-45}$$

The lossless line with a lossless termination will have a reflection coefficient of magnitude unity; hence the standing-wave ratio will approach infinity. At the other extreme, a lossless line terminated with a resistor equal to the characteristic impedance will have a reflection coefficient of zero and a standing-wave ratio of unity; such a line is said to be "flat."

When losses are present, as indicated in Fig. 3-8, the minima located at successively greater distances from the terminated end become progressively greater. If the line is sufficiently long, a point will be found beyond which the slopes of the current and voltage magnitude plots are continuously upward, although with varying steepness, and no minima exist. Clearly the standing-wave ratio as a function lacks a unique value on a high-loss line, and the quantity must be interpreted with some discretion on any practical line.

3-4. SHUNT AND SERIES LUMPED-IMPEDANCE DISCONTINUITIES

Thus far only a simple type of discontinuity, that of a lumped-impedance termination, has been considered. More general situations include the following: (1) the tandem connection of two lines of differing characteristic impedances, (2) a lumped impedance connected from one conductor to the other midway along a line, (3) lumped impedances inserted in series with each conductor midway along a line, and (4) three or more lines converging at a junction. Discontinuities may be treated more directly in terms of impedances or admittances (as will be done in Chapter 4), rather than the voltage and current functions. For the sake of additional insight, two elementary examples will be examined here from the voltage-and-current point of view.*

a. Shunt discontinuity

Consider the line shown in Fig. 3-12, in which a lossless line is terminated with impedance Z_R, and in which a shunt resistor is connected between the

* Matrix methods may be used for calculation of the resultant effects of a discontinuity and two or more connecting sections of line. See Rabindra N. Ghose, *Microwave Circuit Theory and Analysis* (New York: McGraw-Hill Book Company, Inc., 1963).

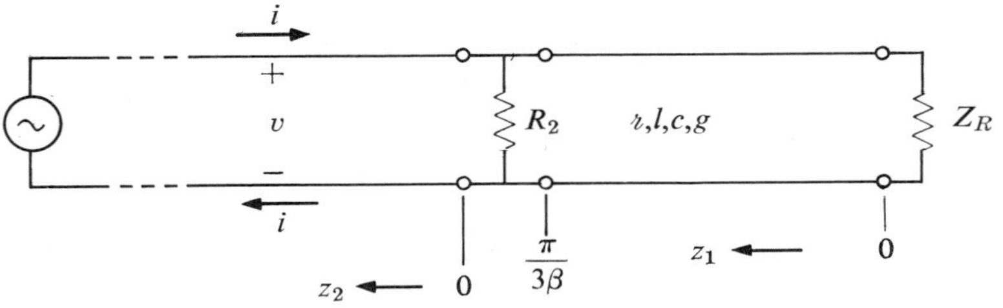

Figure 3-12 Terminated transmission line with shunt discontinuity

conductors at a distance of one-sixth wavelength from the termination. From Eqs. 3-18 and 3-19 the voltage and current on the Z_R side of resistor R_2 may be found in terms of V_{IM}. Voltage between conductors is the same on both sides of the shunt, but the line currents on the two sides of it differ by the current drawn by the shunt itself. Thus the plot of magnitude of resultant voltage will be continuous, but that of resultant current will be discontinuous at the shunt location. The shunt current is in phase with the resultant voltage at that location, and may be added to the current on the terminated side to yield the current on the supply side of the shunt.

To determine the voltage and current functions between R_2 and the input to the line, it is convenient to consider that portion of the line as terminated, at the location of R_2, by an impedance equal to the ratio of the voltage phasor to the current phasor on the input side of R_2. This may be combined with the characteristic impedance of the line to yield a new reflection coefficient which gives the ratio between the reflected and incident voltage phasors to the left of R_2. This situation is the subject of Problem 3-2.

b. Series discontinuity

In Fig. 3-13 the shunt resistor R_2 of the preceding problem has been replaced by two inductors, one in series with each conductor. (It will be assumed that the line is balanced; dividing the inductance in this manner will maintain that property.) The voltage and current functions on the

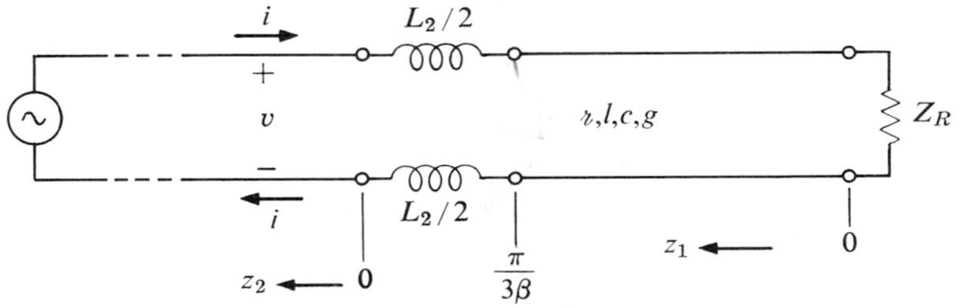

Figure 3-13 Terminated transmission line with series discontinuity

terminated side of the discontinuity are the same as before, but now the current is the same at both ends of the inserted inductors, whereas the voltage changes abruptly between the inductor ends. The voltage drop of the inductors leads the resultant current by 90 degrees, and may be added to the voltage on the terminated side. The technique of the preceding problem, that of computing an equivalent terminating impedance at the location of the lumped inductors, and thence a new reflection coefficient, may be followed here. Problem 3-3 illustrates this.

3-5. INSERTION LOSS

It may be anticipated that the terminations to actual telephone transmission lines will not be reflectionless. Reflected waves remove power from the signal and, if reflected again at the sending end, they also give rise to *echoes*. As part of the same process, they change the resultant voltages at the two ends of the line so that the logarithm of the ratio of those two voltages will not be equal to the attenuation of the line. As a measure of the overall effect of a given section of line on the output power of a particular system, the concept of *insertion loss* has been devised.

Insertion-loss determination involves a comparison between two

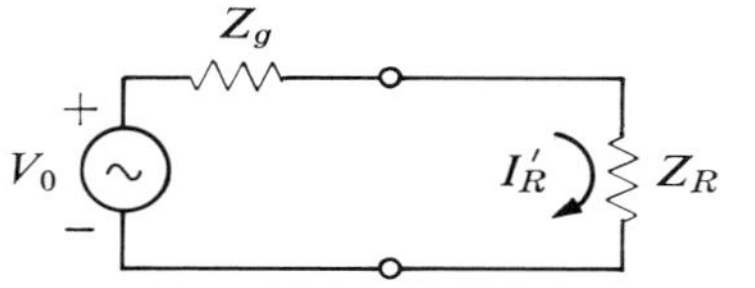

(*a*)

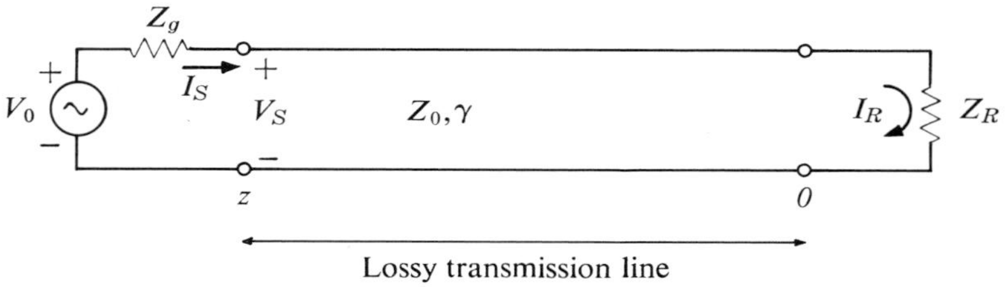

(*b*)

Figure 3-14 Connections for measurement of insertion loss of transmission line

measured values of current in the terminating impedance. The same supply voltage is used for both measurements. As shown in Fig. 3-14, one value, I'_R, is measured with the supply terminals connected directly to the load terminals, and the other value, I_R, is measured with the line section connected in tandem between the supply and load:

$$\text{Insertion loss} = \ln\left|\frac{I'_R}{I_R}\right| \quad \text{(nepers)} \qquad \text{or} \qquad 20\log_{10}\left|\frac{I'_R}{I_R}\right| \quad \text{(db)} \tag{3-46}$$

If the attenuation is known to be substantial, and the values of Z_g, Z_0, and Z_R are known, the insertion loss may be resolved mathematically into component losses which may be charged to the attenuation of the line and to the reflection-producing junctions. This is shown in the following analysis, beginning with Fig. 3-14(*a*):

$$V_0 = I'_R(Z_g + Z_R) \tag{3-47}$$

In Fig. 3-14(*b*) the following is applicable at the sending end:

$$V_0 = I_S Z_g + V_S \tag{3-48}$$

Sending-end voltage and current may be substituted from Eqs. 3-18 and 3-19:

$$V_0 = \frac{V_{IM}Z_g}{\sqrt{2}Z_0}(\epsilon^{\gamma z} - K\epsilon^{-\gamma z}) + \frac{V_{IM}}{\sqrt{2}}(\epsilon^{\gamma z} + K\epsilon^{-\gamma z}) \tag{3-49}$$

Receiving-end current may be stated in terms of V_{IM} from Eq. 3-19, and K in that expression eliminated by means of Eq. 3-17:

$$\begin{aligned} I_R &= \frac{V_{IM}}{\sqrt{2}Z_0}(1 - K) \\ &= \frac{\sqrt{2}V_{IM}}{Z_R + Z_0} \end{aligned} \tag{3-50}$$

Hence

$$V_{IM} = \frac{I_R(Z_R + Z_0)}{\sqrt{2}} \tag{3-51}$$

Equation 3-51 may be substituted in Eq. 3-49, and V_0 replaced by means of Eq. 3-47:

$$\begin{aligned} I'_R(Z_g + Z_R) &= \frac{I_R(Z_R + Z_0)[(Z_g + Z_0)\epsilon^{\gamma z} - K(Z_g - Z_0)\epsilon^{-\gamma z}]}{2Z_0} \\ &= \frac{I_R(Z_R + Z_0)(Z_g + Z_0)\epsilon^{\gamma z}}{2Z_0}\left[1 - \frac{K(Z_g - Z_0)\epsilon^{-2\gamma z}}{(Z_g + Z_0)}\right] \end{aligned} \tag{3-52}$$

The last term on the right may be discarded if the following is true:

$$\frac{|K|\,|Z_g - Z_0|\,\epsilon^{-2\alpha z}}{|Z_g + Z_0|} \ll 1 \tag{3-53}$$

Physically, this means that the echoes are considered to be negligible. The discarded term is sometimes called the *interaction factor*. Equation 3-52 may be rewritten as a current ratio with the approximation just noted:

$$\frac{I'_R}{I_R} = \frac{(Z_R + Z_0)(Z_g + Z_0)\epsilon^{\gamma z}}{2Z_0(Z_g + Z_R)} \tag{3-54}$$

As indicated in the definition in Eq. 3-46, insertion loss takes account only of the ratio of the magnitudes of the two currents, not their phase angles relative to the source:

$$\left|\frac{I'_R}{I_R}\right| = \frac{|Z_R + Z_0|\,|Z_0 + Z_g|\,\epsilon^{\alpha z}}{2\,|Z_0|\,|Z_g + Z_R|} \tag{3-55}$$

If numerator and denominator are both multiplied by $2\,|\sqrt{Z_g Z_R}|$, the terms apart from the exponential may be factored into three *reflection factors*, defined as follows:

$$k_{g0} = \frac{2\,|\sqrt{Z_g Z_0}|}{|Z_g + Z_0|} \tag{3-56}$$

$$k_{0R} = \frac{2\,|\sqrt{Z_0 Z_R}|}{|Z_0 + Z_R|} \tag{3-57}$$

$$k_{gR} = \frac{2\,|\sqrt{Z_g Z_R}|}{|Z_g + Z_R|} \tag{3-58}$$

hence

$$\left|\frac{I'_R}{I_R}\right| = \frac{k_{gR}\epsilon^{\alpha z}}{k_{g0}k_{0R}} \tag{3-59}$$

The logarithms of the inverses of the reflection factors are called *reflection losses*; insertion loss may be stated with the terms arranged on that basis.

$$\text{Insertion loss} = \ln\left(\frac{1}{k_{g0}}\right) + \ln\left(\frac{1}{k_{0R}}\right) - \ln\left(\frac{1}{k_{gR}}\right) + \alpha z \qquad \text{(nepers)} \tag{3-60}$$

The reflection factors are each equal to the geometric mean of two impedances involved divided by the algebraic mean. If the two impedances are equal, the reflection factor is unity and the reflection loss is zero. Should the two impedances both be purely resistive but unequal, the reflection factor will be less than unity, and the reflection loss will be positive. Two complex impedances, one inductive and the other capacitive, may yield a negative reflection loss.

In accordance with Eq. 3-60, insertion loss may be thought of as the attenuation plus the reflection losses due to impedance mismatch at each end of the line, less the reflection loss due to impedance mismatch when the supply and load are directly connected together.

3-6. VOLTAGE AND CURRENT PHASORS IN TERMS OF HYPERBOLIC FUNCTIONS

The expressions for $V(z)$ and $I(z)$ in Eqs. 3-18 and 3-19, and some of the equations derived from them, involve sums and differences of $\epsilon^{\gamma z}$ and $\epsilon^{-\gamma z}$. Substitution of hyperbolic functions of γz is possible and is sometimes advantageous, although the physical interpretation in terms of traveling-wave components is obscured thereby.

The hyperbolic sine, cosine, and tangent may be defined geometrically from a unit hyperbola, analogous to the definitions of the trigonometric functions from a unit circle, but for our purposes they are best regarded simply as algebraic combinations of exponentials with real arguments, just as trigonometric functions may be regarded as algebraic combinations of exponentials with imaginary arguments.

$$\sinh \alpha z = \frac{\epsilon^{\alpha z} - \epsilon^{-\alpha z}}{2} \tag{3-61}$$

$$\cosh \alpha z = \frac{\epsilon^{\alpha z} + \epsilon^{-\alpha z}}{2} \tag{3-62}$$

$$\tanh \alpha z = \frac{\sinh \alpha z}{\cosh \alpha z} \tag{3-63}$$

$$\sin \beta z = \frac{\epsilon^{j\beta z} - \epsilon^{-j\beta z}}{2j} \tag{3-64}$$

$$\cos \beta z = \frac{\epsilon^{j\beta z} + \epsilon^{-j\beta z}}{2} \tag{3-65}$$

$$\tan \beta z = \frac{\sin \beta z}{\cos \beta z} \tag{3-66}$$

The definitions given in Eqs. 3-61, 3-62, and 3-63 may be extended to include a complex argument:

$$\sinh \gamma z = \frac{\epsilon^{\gamma z} - \epsilon^{-\gamma z}}{2} \tag{3-67}$$

$$\cosh \gamma z = \frac{\epsilon^{\gamma z} + \epsilon^{-\gamma z}}{2} \tag{3-68}$$

$$\tanh \gamma z = \frac{\sinh \gamma z}{\cosh \gamma z} \tag{3-69}$$

If γz is purely imaginary, these reduce to the following:

$$\sinh j\beta z = j \sin \beta z \tag{3-70}$$

$$\cosh j\beta z = \cos \beta z \tag{3-71}$$

$$\tanh j\beta z = j \tan \beta z \tag{3-72}$$

Numerical values of the hyperbolic functions of a real argument may be assembled in compact single-entry tables, but for complex arguments a double-entry situation arises. This is because the real part and the imaginary part of a general complex argument may be chosen independently. Fortunately the hyperbolic functions of a complex argument may be resolved into combinations of hyperbolic functions of the real part of the argument and trigonometric functions of the imaginary part, as follows:

$$\begin{aligned}\sinh(\alpha z + j\beta z) &= \sinh \alpha z \cosh j\beta z + \cosh \alpha z \sinh j\beta z \\ &= \sinh \alpha z \cos \beta z + j \cosh \alpha z \sin \beta z \end{aligned} \tag{3-73}$$

$$\begin{aligned}\cosh(\alpha z + j\beta z) &= \cosh \alpha z \cosh j\beta z + \sinh \alpha z \sinh j\beta z \\ &= \cosh \alpha z \cos \beta z + j \sinh \alpha z \sin \beta z \end{aligned} \tag{3-74}$$

$$\begin{aligned}\tanh(\alpha z + j\beta z) &= \frac{\tanh \alpha z + \tanh j\beta z}{1 + \tanh \alpha z \tanh j\beta z} \\ &= \frac{\tanh \alpha z + j \tan \beta z}{1 + j \tanh \alpha z \tan \beta z} \end{aligned} \tag{3-75}$$

The following limiting values for hyperbolic functions with real arguments may be noted:

$$\sinh(0) = 0 \tag{3-76}$$

$$(\sinh u) \xrightarrow[u \to \infty]{} \frac{\epsilon^u}{2} \tag{3-77}$$

$$\cosh(0) = 1 \tag{3-78}$$

$$(\cosh u) \xrightarrow[u \to \infty]{} \frac{\epsilon^u}{2} \tag{3-79}$$

$$\tanh(0) = 0 \tag{3-80}$$

$$(\tanh u) \xrightarrow[u \to \infty]{} 1 \tag{3-81}$$

Some expressions, such as Eqs. 3-26 and 3-27 for voltage and current on an open-circuited lossy line, may be made more concise (and perhaps more "elegant") by substituting Eqs. 3-67 and 3-68:

$$V(z)_{oc} = \sqrt{2}\, V_{IM} \cosh \gamma z \tag{3-82}$$

$$I(z)_{oc} = \sqrt{2}\, \frac{V_{IM}}{Z_0} \sinh \gamma z \tag{3-83}$$

It should be recognized that an algebraic substitution, such as the replacing of a combination of exponential functions with an equivalent combination of hyperbolic functions, does not alter any physical laws or behavior.

Expressions for voltage and current along the line in terms of receiving-end voltage or current and hyperbolic functions of γz may also be derived.

From Eqs. 3-13, 3-16, and 3-17,

$$V_{\text{ter}} = \frac{V_{IM}}{\sqrt{2}}(1 + K)$$

$$= \frac{\sqrt{2}\, V_{IM} Z_R}{Z_R + Z_0} \qquad \textbf{(3-84)}$$

If this result is solved for V_{IM} and substituted in Eq. 3-18, and Eq. 3-17 is also substituted in Eq. 3-18, the following may be obtained:

$$V(z) = \frac{V_{\text{ter}}}{2Z_R}[(Z_R + Z_0)\epsilon^{\gamma z} + (Z_R - Z_0)\epsilon^{-\gamma z}]$$

Next, Eqs. 3-67 and 3-68 may be substituted:

$$V(z) = \frac{V_{\text{ter}}}{Z_R}(Z_R \cosh \gamma z + Z_0 \sinh \gamma z) \qquad \textbf{(3-85)}$$

Similarly,

$$I(z) = \frac{V_{\text{ter}}}{Z_R Z_0}(Z_0 \cosh \gamma z + Z_R \sinh \gamma z) \qquad \textbf{(3-86)}$$

If V_{ter}/Z_R is replaced by I_{ter}, the following are obtained:

$$V(z) = I_{\text{ter}}(Z_R \cosh \gamma z + Z_0 \sinh \gamma z) \qquad \textbf{(3-87)}$$

$$I(z) = \frac{I_{\text{ter}}}{Z_0}(Z_0 \cosh \gamma z + Z_R \sinh \gamma z) \qquad \textbf{(3-88)}$$

With Eqs. 3-70 and 3-71 one may show that, for a lossless line, Eqs. 3-85 and 3-86 simplify to the following:

$$V(z) = \frac{V_{\text{ter}}}{Z_R}(Z_R \cos \beta z + jZ_0 \sin \beta z) \qquad \textbf{(3-89)}$$

$$I(z) = \frac{V_{\text{ter}}}{Z_R Z_0}(Z_0 \cos \beta z + jZ_R \sin \beta z) \qquad \textbf{(3-90)}$$

3-7. CONCLUSIONS

The steady-state voltage and current functions existing on a transmission line with any terminating impedance may be expressed in terms of two oppositely moving traveling-wave component functions. The traveling-wave functions approaching and departing from the termination in question are known as the incident and reflected components, respectively. The ratio of the reflected-voltage phasor to the incident-voltage phasor, computed at the terminus, is known as the *reflection coefficient*. It is the following function of the load impedance Z_R and the characteristic impedance Z_0:

$$K = \frac{Z_R - Z_0}{Z_R + Z_0} \tag{3-17}$$

(In general Z_0, Z_R, and K are all complex quantities.)

At points away from the terminus, toward the source of the incident wave, the incident voltage and current phasors are increased in magnitude by the factor $\epsilon^{\alpha z}$ and lead the corresponding phasors at the termination by the angle βz. Reflected-wave phasors, on the other hand, are reduced in magnitude by the factor $\epsilon^{-\alpha z}$ and lag behind the corresponding phasors at the termination by the same angle βz.

In the event that the line is lossless and the termination too is lossless (open circuit, short circuit, or pure reactance), the reflection coefficient has a magnitude of unity. The rms values of resultant voltage and current vary with distance as sinusoidal half-wave loops, the voltage nulls occurring at the same locations as the current maxima, and vice versa. Within each half-wave span between nulls, the voltages at all points are in time phase with one another. Voltages at points with one null between them are in phase opposition. The same principle applies to the phase alignment among currents at various locations, but voltage and current are in time quadrature with each other at every location.

Losses in the line or in the load change the situation, in that the minima of rms voltage and current do not reach zero, and the phase angle of resultant voltage or current with respect to a given reference varies continuously, although in general not uniformly, with distance.

The ratio of maximum resultant rms voltage to minimum resultant rms voltage along a lossless line is equal to the corresponding ratio between resultant rms currents, and it is known as the *standing-wave ratio*, SWR. It is related to the magnitude of the reflection coefficient.

$$\text{SWR} = \frac{1 + |K|}{1 - |K|} \tag{3-45}$$

Insertion loss is a measure of the change in output power for a given system caused by insertion of a lossy line or network in tandem between the supply and the output impedance.

Hyperbolic functions of γz may be substituted for appropriate combinations of $\epsilon^{\gamma z}$ and $\epsilon^{-\gamma z}$. Numerical evaluation of either form tends to be tedious unless γz is either a purely real or purely imaginary quantity.

PROBLEMS

3-1. Compute the reflection coefficients for the following terminations to an "ideal" unloaded cable, one for which $\theta_0 = -45°$ and $\alpha = \beta$: (*a*) short circuit.

(*b*) resistive, $Z_R = |Z_0|$. (*c*) purely inductive, $Z_R = j|Z_0|$. Sketch loci similar to those in Fig. 3-3 and compute enough values to determine curves similar to those in Fig. 3-4 for the half wavelength of line nearest the termination.

3-2. In Fig. 3-12 let $Z_0 = 600\angle 0°$ ohms, $\alpha = 0$, $Z_R = 250\angle 0°$ ohms, and $R_2 = 400\angle 0°$ ohms. With $V_{\text{inc}}(0)$ as the reference phasor, compute V and I on the load and supply sides of R_2; sketch loci and curves similar to those in Figs. 3-5 and 3-6.

3-3. In Fig. 3-13 let $Z_0 = 600\angle 0°$ ohms, $\alpha = 0$, $Z_R = 250\angle 0°$ ohms, and $X_{L_2} = 100$ ohms. Compute results corresponding to those in Problem 3-2 and prepare appropriate sketches.

3-4. If a nondistortionless transmission line is to be terminated with a pure resistance, but reflections are to be kept to a minimum, what value of terminating resistance should be chosen? *Answer:* $R_R = |Z_0|$. (CAUTION: Do not confuse this problem with that of maximum power transfer.)

3-5. Find the insertion loss caused by the transmission line in Fig. 3-15.

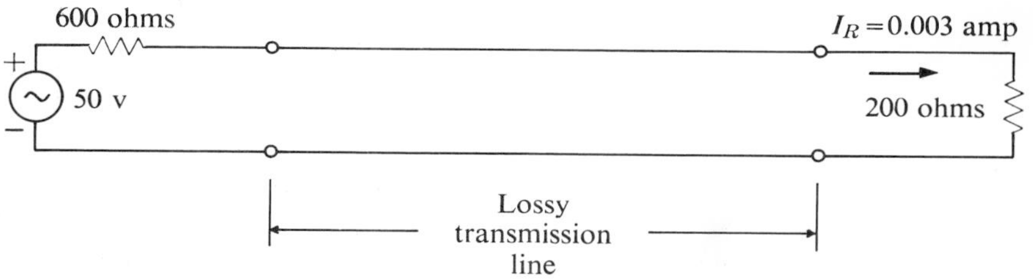

Figure 3-15 Circuit for Problem 3-5

3-6. Find the Taylor series expansions for sinh αz and cosh αz from those for $\epsilon^{\alpha z}$ and $\epsilon^{-\alpha z}$. Verify Eqs. 3-70 and 3-71 by means of those results and the Taylor series for the sine and cosine.

CHAPTER 4

Impedance, Admittance, and the Smith Chart

A most useful property of sinusoidal functions of the same frequency is that the relationship between any two such functions may be expressed in terms of a single complex quantity. That quantity has (1) a magnitude, which has dimensions appropriate to the physical interpretation of the two functions; and (2) a phase-displacement angle.

Impedance is one such quantity; it relates voltage and current in linear circuit analysis, and its units are ohms. Admittance is simply the reciprocal of impedance, and has units of mhos. Calculations related to network transformations, such as the paralleling of branches or the changing from a "T" into an equivalent delta, may be made more concisely in terms of impedances or admittances than in terms of branch currents and voltage drops. This simplification is welcome, but it should be recognized that complex impedance or admittance is, in a sense, one step farther removed from physical reality than voltage or current phasors.

In transmission-line calculations, the impedance concept provides an expedient means of handling most discontinuities. Direct analysis in terms of voltage and current functions, as outlined in Sec. 3-4, is usually more cumbersome.

4-1. INPUT IMPEDANCE: GENERAL

The complex ratio of the voltage phasor at any location on a transmission line to the current phasor at the same location is dimensionally an impedance. Physically, on a line with an energy source at only one end, that ratio is the impedance which would be observed if one opened both conductors at the given point and connected an impedance-measuring instrument (oscillator and bridge, for instance) to the pair of conductors leading to the terminated end. This impedance-dimensioned ratio may be readily envisioned as a continuous function of distance from the termination; it is commonly spoken of as the *input impedance* of the line at the given location:

$$Z(z) = \frac{V(z)}{I(z)} \tag{4-1}$$

Equations 3-18 and 3-19, or 3-85 and 3-86, may be substituted. (These are all based on the polarity-and-direction convention of Fig. 3-1.)

$$Z(z) = Z_0 \frac{\epsilon^{\gamma z} + K\epsilon^{-\gamma z}}{\epsilon^{\gamma z} - K\epsilon^{-\gamma z}} = Z_0 \frac{1 + K\epsilon^{-2\gamma z}}{1 - K\epsilon^{-2\gamma z}} \tag{4-2}$$

or

$$Z(z) = Z_0 \frac{Z_R \cosh \gamma z + Z_0 \sinh \gamma z}{Z_0 \cosh \gamma z + Z_R \sinh \gamma z} = Z_0 \frac{Z_R + Z_0 \tanh \gamma z}{Z_0 + Z_R \tanh \gamma z} \tag{4-3}$$

Equation 3-75 for the hyperbolic tangent of a complex argument is applicable to Eq. 4-3. Certain limiting cases have simpler solutions, and impedance variation on a lossless line is readily adaptable to a nomographic chart.

It should be noted in passing that the quotient of an instantaneous voltage divided by an instantaneous current has no obvious physical meaning (unless they are in time phase with each other); in particular one should realize that such a ratio is not a complex impedance. (As an illustration, divide Eq. 3-1 by Eq. 3-2, and note that the result cannot be equated to that found by dividing Eq. 3-5 by Eq. 3-6.)

4-2. LIMITING-CASE INPUT IMPEDANCES

Some of the limiting cases treated in Chapter 3 in terms of voltage and current functions may be reexamined here in terms of input impedance.

a. Terminating impedance equal to characteristic impedance

If Z_R is equal to Z_0, Eq. 4-3 will immediately reduce to

$$Z(z) = Z_0 \tag{4-4}$$

Thus any line which is terminated in its characteristic impedance will have that same value as its input impedance, regardless of how long the line is. This is a reflectionless termination, as noted in Sec. 3-2*a*.

b. Open-circuited end

If Z_R approaches infinity, Eq. 4-3 will reduce to

$$Z_{oc}(z) = Z_0 \coth \gamma z = \frac{Z_0}{\tanh \gamma z} \tag{4-5}$$

As an illustration of results, plots of $|Z_{oc}|$ and θ_Z are given in Fig. 4-1 for a lossy line, the same one for which voltage and current plots were given in Fig. 3-8. More tractable functions result when γ is either purely real or purely imaginary.

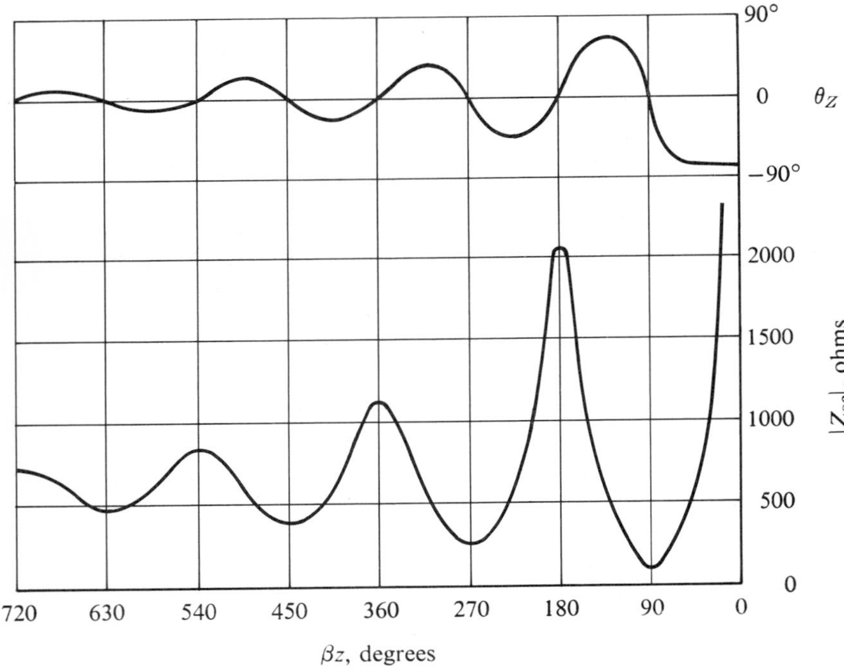

Figure 4-1 Open-circuit impedance of distortionless transmission line: α/β = 0.1 neper per radian, Z_0 = 600 ohms (see Fig. 3-8)

Direct-current excitation of a line with losses yields a purely real γ:

$$Z_{oc}(z) = \frac{Z_0}{\tanh \alpha z} \tag{4-6}$$

Substituting Eqs. 2-19 and 2-12, with ω set equal to zero, gives

$$Z_{oc}(z) = \sqrt{\frac{r}{g}} \frac{1}{\tanh z\sqrt{rg}} \tag{4-7}$$

Recalling the limiting values of the hyperbolic tangent given in Eqs. 3-80 and 3-81, it may be seen that the input impedance in this instance is infinite at z equal to zero, and approaches Z_0 as line length approaches infinity. It is a pure resistance, always greater than Z_0.

Should the line be lossless, but the frequency other than zero, γ is purely imaginary:

$$Z_{oc}(z) = -jZ_0 \cot \beta z \tag{4-8}$$

Substitution of Eqs. 2-19 and 2-12, with r and g set equal to zero, yields

$$Z_{oc}(z) = -j\sqrt{\frac{l}{c}} \cot z\omega\sqrt{lc} \tag{4-9}$$

The cotangent function is infinite at βz equal to zero, and becomes infinite at 180-degree intervals from there. This is in accordance with the results previously noted, in which voltage was finite but current zero at those locations. The cotangent is zero when its argument is 90 degrees, and at recurrent intervals of 180 degrees. Correspondingly the voltage is zero, but the current finite, at those locations.

The j factor in Eq. 4-9 indicates that for the lossless line with open-circuit termination, the input impedance is a pure reactance and that the voltage and current are in time quadrature with each other at all points on the line. The cotangent is alternately positive and negative in consecutive 90-degree intervals; hence the input impedance changes abruptly from a capacitive reactance to an inductive reactance and vice versa. This is in agreement with the results shown in Fig. 3-7.

Equation 4-8 could have been obtained by dividing Eq. 3-24 by Eq. 3-25, expressions for $V(z)$ and $I(z)$, respectively, for this line.

c. Short-circuited end

Setting Z_R equal to zero reduces Eq. 4-3 to

$$Z_{sc}(z) = Z_0 \tanh \gamma z \tag{4-10}$$

As in the open-circuited case, direct-current excitation gives an expression which is easier to evaluate:

$$Z_{sc}(z) = Z_0 \tanh \alpha z \tag{4-11}$$

$$Z_{sc}(z) = \sqrt{\frac{r}{g}} \tanh z\sqrt{rg} \tag{4-12}$$

Thus the d-c short-circuit impedance increases from zero to a limiting value of $\sqrt{r/g}$ as the line length is increased.

Should the line be lossless, but the frequency not equal to zero, Eq. 4-10 becomes

$$Z_{sc}(z) = jZ_0 \tan \beta z \tag{4-13}$$

$$Z_{sc}(z) = j\sqrt{\frac{l}{c}} \tan z\omega\sqrt{lc} \tag{4-14}$$

Observations comparable to those made concerning Eq. 4-9 may be made here; one should refer to Fig. 3-9.

d. Lossless line with purely reactive termination

The most direct way of getting a compact expression for input impedance to a lossless line terminated with a pure reactance is by dividing the expression

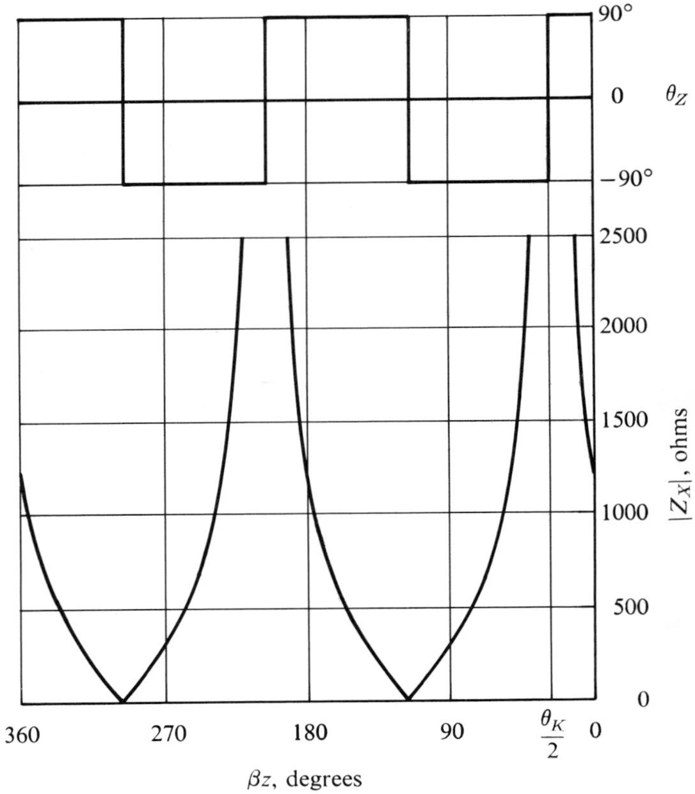

Figure 4-2 Input impedance on lossless line with purely reactive termination: $Z_0 = 600\underline{/0^\circ}$ ohms, $Z_R = 1200\underline{/90^\circ}$ ohms (see Figs. 3-10 and 3-11)

for $V(z)$, Eq. 3-35, by that for current, Eq. 3-37:

$$Z_X(z) = -jZ_0 \cot\left(\beta z - \frac{\theta_K}{2}\right) \tag{4-15}$$

$$\theta_K = 2 \tan^{-1}\left(\frac{R_0}{X_R}\right) \tag{3-34}$$

Here R_0 is the characteristic impedance, which is a pure resistance $\sqrt{l/c}$, and X_R is the terminating reactance.

Figures 3-10 and 3-11 dealt with a particular example of this type from the standpoint of voltage and current functions; the magnitude and angle of $Z_X(z)$ for the same line and termination are sketched in Fig. 4-2.

4-3. LINE PARAMETERS AS FUNCTIONS OF OPEN-CIRCUIT AND SHORT-CIRCUIT IMPEDANCES

The relationship between input impedance and the line parameters may be used in a reciprocal fashion as a means of determining the latter experimentally. Specifically, Eqs. 4-5 and 4-10 may be combined so as to yield the characteristic impedance and a function of the propagation function in terms of two readily measured impedances, $Z_{oc}(z)$ and $Z_{sc}(z)$:

$$Z_0 = \sqrt{Z_{oc}(z_1)Z_{sc}(z_1)} \tag{4-16}$$

$$\tanh \gamma z_1 = \sqrt{\frac{Z_{sc}(z_1)}{Z_{oc}(z_1)}} \tag{4-17}$$

The characteristic impedance is given directly by Eq. 4-16, but one has to find the inverse hyperbolic tangent of the right-hand side of Eq. 4-17, which in general is complex, to evaluate the propagation function.

a. Evaluation of propagation function from hyperbolic tangent: general case

The inverse hyperbolic tangent of a complex quantity is also complex; formulas for its real and imaginary parts may be derived as follows from Eqs. 3-67, 3-68, and 3-69.

$$\tanh \gamma z_1 = \frac{\epsilon^{\gamma z_1} - \epsilon^{-\gamma z_1}}{\epsilon^{\gamma z_1} + \epsilon^{-\gamma z_1}}$$

$$= \frac{1 - \epsilon^{-2\gamma z_1}}{1 + \epsilon^{-2\gamma z_1}} \tag{4-18}$$

Since $\gamma = \alpha + j\beta$,

$$\epsilon^{-2\gamma z_1} = \epsilon^{-2(\alpha+j\beta)z_1}$$

$$= \epsilon^{-2\alpha z_1}(\cos 2\beta z_1 - j \sin 2\beta z_1) \tag{4-19}$$

Let

$$\tanh \gamma z_1 = A + jB \tag{4-20}$$

Substitution of Eqs. 4-19 and 4-20 in Eq. 4-18 gives

$$A + jB = \frac{1 - \epsilon^{-2\alpha z_1} \cos 2\beta z_1 + j\epsilon^{-2\alpha z_1} \sin 2\beta z_1}{1 + \epsilon^{-2\alpha z_1} \cos 2\beta z_1 - j\epsilon^{-2\alpha z_1} \sin 2\beta z_1} \tag{4-21}$$

The right-hand side of Eq. 4-21 may be rationalized by multiplying numerator and denominator by the conjugate of the denominator. The resulting terms which involve $\sin^2$ and $\cos^2$ may be combined:

$$A + jB = \frac{1 - \epsilon^{-4\alpha z_1} + 2j\epsilon^{-2\alpha z_1} \sin 2\beta z_1}{1 + 2\epsilon^{-2\alpha z_1} \cos 2\beta z_1 + \epsilon^{-4\alpha z_1}} \tag{4-22}$$

The magnitude of $A + jB$ is also needed and may be found by multiplying Eq. 4-21 by its conjugate. Again terms involving $\sin^2$ and $\cos^2$ may be combined:

$$A^2 + B^2 = \frac{1 - 2\epsilon^{-2\alpha z_1} \cos 2\beta z_1 + \epsilon^{-4\alpha z_1}}{1 + 2\epsilon^{-2\alpha z_1} \cos 2\beta z_1 + \epsilon^{-4\alpha z_1}} \tag{4-23}$$

The denominators of the right-hand sides of Eqs. 4-22 and 4-23 are equal, and the real part of the numerator of Eq. 4-22 is free of β. By adding unity to both sides of Eq. 4-23 and placing the right-hand side over a common denominator, the numerator may be cleared of β:

$$A^2 + B^2 + 1 = \frac{2 + 2\epsilon^{-4\alpha z_1}}{1 + 2\epsilon^{-2\alpha z_1} \cos 2\beta z_1 + \epsilon^{-4\alpha z_1}} \tag{4-24}$$

Dividing the real part of Eq. 4-22 by Eq. 4-24 yields an expression for αz_1 in terms of A and B:

$$\frac{A}{A^2 + B^2 + 1} = \frac{1 - \epsilon^{-4\alpha z_1}}{2 + 2\epsilon^{-4\alpha z_1}}$$

Utilizing the relationship given in Eq. 4-18, the following is obtained:

$$\tanh 2\alpha z_1 = \frac{2A}{A^2 + B^2 + 1} \tag{4-25}$$

An expression for βz_1 may be obtained from Eq. 4-22 and the quantity $1 - A^2 - B^2$, which may be found from Eq. 4-23.

$$1 - A^2 - B^2 = \frac{4\epsilon^{-2\alpha z_1} \cos 2\beta z_1}{1 + 2\epsilon^{-2\alpha z_1} \cos 2\beta z_1 + \epsilon^{-4\alpha z_1}} \tag{4-26}$$

Dividing this into the imaginary part of Eq. 4-22 yields

$$\frac{B}{1 - A^2 - B^2} = \frac{2\epsilon^{-2\alpha z_1} \sin 2\beta z_1}{4\epsilon^{-2\alpha z_1} \cos 2\beta z_1} = \frac{\tan 2\beta z_1}{2}$$

Hence

$$\tan 2\beta z_1 = \frac{2B}{1 - A^2 - B^2} \tag{4-27}$$

The inverse hyperbolic tangent of a real argument has a unique value, but the inverse tangent function of a real argument has an infinite number of values, spaced 180 degrees apart:

$$\beta z_1 = \tfrac{1}{2} \tan^{-1}\left(\frac{2B}{1 - A^2 - B^2}\right) + \frac{n\pi}{2} \qquad \textbf{(4-28)}$$

An approximate value of the electrical length of the line, βz_1, accurate to the nearest quarter wavelength, must be known from other information in order to select the correct value of n in Eq. 4-28.

If the physical length of the line, z_1, is known, the results of Eqs. 4-25 and 4-28 may be reduced to α and β.

Illustrative problem: An open-wire telephone line 100 miles long has the following impedances when measured at 1000 cycles per second:

$$Z_{oc} = 1052\underline{/-36.4^\circ} \text{ ohms}$$

$$Z_{sc} = 403\underline{/19.8^\circ} \text{ ohms}$$

Find the characteristic impedance and the values of the attenuation function and the phase function.

From Eq. 4-16,

$$\begin{aligned} Z_0 &= \sqrt{(1052\underline{/-36.4^\circ})(403\underline{/19.8^\circ})} \\ &= \sqrt{42.4 \times 10^4\underline{/-16.6^\circ}} \\ &= 651\underline{/-8.3^\circ} \text{ ohms} \end{aligned}$$

From Eq. 4-17,

$$\begin{aligned} \tanh \gamma z_1 &= \sqrt{\frac{403\underline{/19.8^\circ}}{1052\underline{/-36.4^\circ}}} \\ &= \sqrt{0.383\underline{/56.2^\circ}} \\ &= 0.619\underline{/28.1^\circ} \\ &= 0.545 + j0.2915 \end{aligned}$$

From Eq. 4-25,

$$\begin{aligned} \tanh 2\alpha z_1 &= \frac{(2)(0.545)}{1 + 0.297 + 0.085} \\ &= 0.787 \\ 2\alpha z_1 &= 1.064 \\ \alpha z_1 &= 0.532 \text{ neper} \\ \alpha &= \frac{0.532}{100} \\ &= 5.32 \times 10^{-3} \text{ neper per mile} \end{aligned}$$

From Eq. 4-27,

$$\tan 2\beta z_1 = \frac{(2)(0.2915)}{1 - 0.297 - 0.085}$$
$$= 0.945$$

In accordance with Eq. 4-28,

$$\beta z_1 = \frac{43.4^\circ}{2} + (n)(90^\circ)$$

An approximate value of βz_1 is needed in order to fix n. Because of the open-wire type of construction, the phase velocity may be assumed to be approximately that of waves in free space:

$$v \approx 3 \times 10^8 \text{ m per sec}$$

$$\lambda = \frac{v}{f}$$
$$\approx \frac{3 \times 10^8}{1000} = 3 \times 10^5 \text{ m, or } 3 \times 10^5 \times 10^{-3} \times 0.6214 = 186 \text{ miles}$$

$$\beta = \frac{2\pi}{\lambda} \text{ radians per unit length, or } \frac{360}{\lambda} \text{ degrees per unit length}$$

$$\beta z_1 \approx \frac{(360)(100)}{186} = 193^\circ$$

This is a third-quadrant angle; hence $n = 2$:

$$\beta z_1 = 21.7 + 180$$
$$= 201.7^\circ$$

$$\beta = \frac{201.7}{100}$$
$$= 2.017^\circ \text{ per mile, or } 0.0352 \text{ radian per mile}$$

b. Direct evaluation of phase function for lossless line

The foregoing procedure may be greatly abbreviated if the line is lossless. Such a line, at other than zero frequency, will have purely reactive open-circuit and short-circuit impedances. One of these impedances is necessarily inductive and the other capacitive, as reference to Eqs. 4-9 and 4-14, or to Figs. 3-7 and 3-9, indicates. Thus tanh γz_1 is purely imaginary. Equation 3-72 may be substituted into Eq. 4-17, or Eq. 4-13 may be divided by Eq. 4-8 and the square root taken of both sides, yielding in either case,

$$\tan \beta z_1 = \pm\sqrt{\frac{|Z_{sc}(z_1)|}{|Z_{oc}(z_1)|}} \qquad \textbf{(4-29)}$$

As noted in connection with Eq. 4-27, the inverse tangent function is multivalued:

$$\beta z_1 = \tan^{-1}\left(\pm\sqrt{\frac{|Z_{sc}(z_1)|}{|Z_{oc}(z_1)|}}\right) + m\pi \qquad \textbf{(4-30)}$$

Here is suffices to know the approximate electrical length of the line to the nearest half wavelength to fix the value of m. If $Z_{sc}(z_1)$ is inductive, the exact electrical length will be an integral number of half wavelengths plus some fraction of a quarter wavelength, whereas if $Z_{sc}(z_1)$ is capacitive, the electrical length will be an integral number of half wavelengths minus some fraction of a quarter wavelength. Thus a positive sign is chosen for the radical in Eq. 4-30 in the former case, and a negative sign in the latter case.

c. Line resistance, inductance, capacitance, and conductance

The basic line parameters may be found from the characteristic impedance and the propagation function by the following relations derived from Eqs. 2-12 and 2-19:

$$r + j\omega l = (\alpha + j\beta)Z_0 \qquad \textbf{(4-31)}$$

$$g + j\omega c = \frac{\alpha + j\beta}{Z_0} \qquad \textbf{(4-32)}$$

The illustrative problem given in Sec. 4-3*a* may be extended to include evaluation of r, l, g, and c.

$$Z_0 = 651\underline{/-8.3^\circ} \text{ ohms}$$

$$\gamma = 5.32 \times 10^{-3} + j3.52 \times 10^{-2}$$

$$= 3.56 \times 10^{-2}\underline{/81.4^\circ} \text{ per mile}$$

From Eq. 4-31,

$$r + j\omega l = (3.56 \times 10^{-2}\underline{/81.4^\circ})(651\underline{/-8.3^\circ})$$

$$= 23.2\underline{/73.1^\circ}$$

$$= 6.75 + j22.2 \text{ ohm per mile}$$

$$r = 6.75 \text{ ohms per mile}$$

$$l = \frac{22.2}{(2\pi)(1000)} = 3.53 \times 10^{-3} \text{ henry per mile}$$

From Eq. 4-32,

$$g + j\omega c = \frac{3.56 \times 10^{-2}\underline{/81.4^\circ}}{651\underline{/-8.3^\circ}}$$

$$= 5.47 \times 10^{-5}\underline{/89.7^\circ}$$

$$= 2.9 \times 10^{-7} + j5.47 \times 10^{-5} \text{ mho per mile}$$

$$g = 2.9 \times 10^{-7} \text{ mho per mile}$$

$$c = \frac{5.47 \times 10^{-5}}{(2\pi)(1000)} = 8.7 \times 10^{-9} \text{ farad per mile}$$

4-4. LOSSLESS LINE: IMPEDANCE FUNCTION AND STANDING-WAVE RATIO

The lossless line is characterized by a repetition of the standing-wave patterns in voltage and current at half-wavelength intervals, regardless of what the terminating impedance may be. This was illustrated in Fig. 3-6 for a purely resistive termination. The principle of half-wavelength repetition also applies to the input impedance along such a line.

Standing-wave-pattern measurements provide a means, when the characteristic impedance is known, of finding the impedance of the termination. This experimental procedure is useful chiefly at radio and microwave frequencies.

a. Impedance variation along a lossless line

Equation 4-2 may be adapted to the lossless line by replacing γ with $j\beta$:

$$Z(z) = Z_0 \frac{1 + |K| \, \epsilon^{j(\theta_K - 2\beta z)}}{1 - |K| \, \epsilon^{j(\theta_K - 2\beta z)}} \tag{4-33}$$

Let

$$\phi = \theta_K - 2\beta z \tag{4-34}$$

Substitution of Eq. 4-34 into Eq. 4-33 yields

$$Z(z) = Z_0 \frac{1 + |K| \, \epsilon^{j\phi}}{1 - |K| \, \epsilon^{j\phi}} \tag{4-35}$$

To derive expressions for the resistive and reactive components of $Z(z)$, Eq. 4-35 should be separated into its real and imaginary parts. First $\epsilon^{j\phi}$ is replaced by $\cos\phi + j\sin\phi$:

$$Z(z) = Z_0 \frac{1 + |K| \cos\phi + j\,|K| \sin\phi}{1 - |K| \cos\phi - j\,|K| \sin\phi} \tag{4-36}$$

Equation 4-36 may be rationalized by multiplying numerator and denominator by the conjugate of the denominator. This result reduces to

$$Z(z) = Z_0 \frac{1 - |K|^2 + j2\,|K| \sin\phi}{1 - 2\,|K| \cos\phi + |K|^2} \tag{4-37}$$

Let

$$Z(z) = R(z) + jX(z) \tag{4-38}$$

It should be remembered that for a lossless line, the characteristic impedance is a pure resistance, equal to $\sqrt{l/c}$.

$$R(z) = Z_0 \frac{1 - |K|^2}{1 - 2\,|K| \cos\phi + |K|^2} \tag{4-39}$$

$$X(z) = Z_0 \frac{2\,|K| \sin\phi}{1 - 2\,|K| \cos\phi + |K|^2} \tag{4-40}$$

On the other hand, expressions for the polar components of $Z(z)$ may be desired.

Let

$$Z(z) = |Z(z)|\, \epsilon^{j\theta_Z(z)} \tag{4-41}$$

An equation for $\theta_Z(z)$ may be found from the numerator of Eq. 4-37:

$$\theta_Z(z) = \tan^{-1}\left(\frac{2\,|K|\,\sin\phi}{1 - |K|^2}\right) \tag{4-42}$$

A concise form for the magnitude of $Z(z)$ may be found by multiplying the numerator and denominator of Eq. 4-36 by their respective conjugates:

$$|Z(z)| = Z_0\sqrt{\frac{1 + 2\,|K|\cos\phi + |K|^2}{1 - 2\,|K|\cos\phi + |K|^2}} \tag{4-43}$$

From the definition of angle ϕ, Eq. 4-34, it is apparent that an increase in βz of π radians will reduce ϕ by 2π and leave the trigonometric functions of ϕ unchanged:

$$Z\left(z + \frac{\pi}{\beta}\right) = Z(z) \tag{4-44}$$

This confirms the property of repetition at half-wavelength intervals which was noted at the beginning of this section.

Plots of $R(z)$, $X(z)$, $\theta_Z(z)$, and $|Z(z)|$ are given in Fig. 4-3 for a lossless line with a purely resistive termination. Voltage and current functions for this line were shown in Fig. 3-6.

b. Standing-wave ratio and impedance maxima and minima

The maxima and minima of the magnitude of $Z(z)$ for a lossless line prove to be simple functions of the standing-wave ratio, which was introduced in Sec. 3-3. One may show by geometric construction that the maximum possible value of $1 + |K|\,\epsilon^{j\phi}$ as a function of ϕ is $1 + |K|$, and the minimum possible value is $1 - |K|$. These occur at $\epsilon^{j\phi} = 1$ and $\epsilon^{j\phi} = -1$, respectively, or $\phi = 2n\pi$ and $\phi = (2n + 1)\pi$, where n is any integer. At $\phi = 2n\pi$, $1 - |K|\,\epsilon^{j\phi}$ is a minimum $(1 - |K|)$, and at $\phi = (2n + 1)\pi$, it is a maximum $(1 + |K|)$. Hence, from Eq. 4-35,

$$\left.\begin{aligned} |Z(z)|_{\max} &= Z_0\frac{1 + |K|}{1 - |K|} \\ \theta_{Z\max} &= 0 \end{aligned}\right\} \qquad (\phi = 2n\pi) \tag{4-45}$$

$$\left.\begin{aligned} |Z(z)|_{\min} &= Z_0\frac{1 - |K|}{1 + |K|} \\ \theta_{Z\min} &= 0 \end{aligned}\right\} \qquad [\phi = (2n + 1)\pi] \tag{4-46}$$

(Alternatively, Eq. 4-43 for $|Z(z)|$ may be differentiated with respect to ϕ and the derivative set equal to zero in order to locate the extrema.)

Comparison of these results with the construction used to derive Eqs. 3-41 through 3-44 shows that a voltage maximum, current minimum, and impedance maximum occur at the same location on the line, and likewise

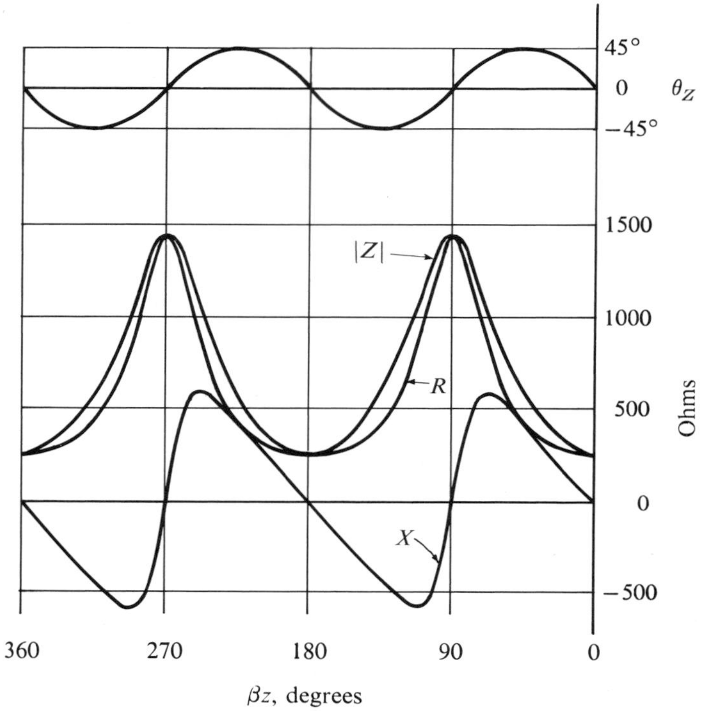

Figure 4-3 Input impedance on lossless line with resistive termination: $Z_0 = 600\angle 0°$ ohms, $Z_R = 250\angle 0°$ ohms (see Figs. 3-5 and 3-6)

that a voltage minimum, current maximum, and impedance minimum occur at the same location.

The expression for standing-wave ratio in terms of the magnitude of reflection coefficient, derived in Sec. 3-3, is appropriate as a simplifying substitution:

$$\text{SWR} = \frac{1 + |K|}{1 - |K|} \quad \textbf{(3-45)}$$

$$Z(z)_{\max} = (Z_0)(\text{SWR}) \quad \textbf{(4-47)}$$

$$Z(z)_{\min} = \frac{Z_0}{\text{SWR}} \quad \textbf{(4-48)}$$

As was indicated by Eqs. 4-45 and 4-46, $Z(z)_{max}$ and $Z(z)_{min}$ are both purely resistive and they are found alternately along the line at intervals of a quarter wavelength.

c. Quarter-wavelength section of line as transformer

The results of the preceding section suggest that a quarter-wavelength section of line might be used for impedance transformation. An example is

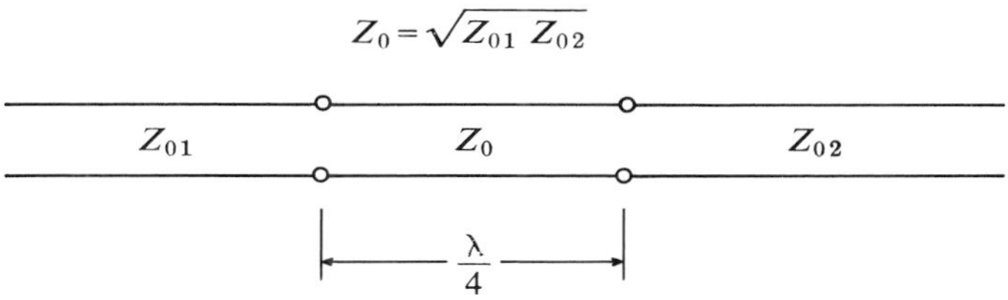

Figure 4-4 Two transmission lines tandem-linked by a quarter-wavelength impedance-matching section

shown in Fig. 4-4, in which two lines of differing characteristic impedances are linked in tandem. It will be assumed for the moment that $Z_{01} > Z_{02}$.

If Z_{01} corresponds to $Z(z)_{max}$ of the quarter-wavelength section, and Z_{02} to $Z(z)_{min}$, the value of Z_0 indicated in Fig. 4-4 may be found by multiplying Eq. 4-47 by Eq. 4-48:

$$\begin{aligned} Z_0 &= \sqrt{Z(z)_{max} Z(z)_{min}} \\ &= \sqrt{Z_{01} Z_{02}} \end{aligned}$$

The same result applies, of course, if $Z_{01} < Z_{02}$.

This arrangement is known as a quarter-wavelength transformer. Its input impedance is frequency-sensitive because the electrical length of a given physical section of line is proportional to the frequency; this effect is the subject of part of Problem 4-5.

d. Measurement of terminal impedances by means of standing-wave pattern

An experimentally measured standing-wave pattern of voltage, such as in Fig. 3-6 or 4-5, provides a means of finding the radio-frequency impedance of the termination. The standing-wave ratio may be computed from scaled maximum and minimum values, and Eq. 3-45 may be solved for $|K|$ in terms of SWR:

$$|K| = \frac{(\text{SWR}) - 1}{(\text{SWR}) + 1} \qquad \textbf{(4-49)}$$

The possible values for ϕ at voltage maxima and minima have been noted in Eqs. 4-45 and 4-46; hence if the characteristic impedance and the electrical distance βz from the termination to a voltage maximum or minimum were known, θ_K and the terminating impedance ($z = 0$) could be found from Eqs. 4-33 and 4-34.

As may be seen by inspection of Figs. 3-6 or 4-5, the resultant voltage changes more rapidly with displacement along the line in the vicinity of minima than in the vicinity of maxima; hence the locations of minima may be fixed more accurately from experimental data than can the locations of maxima. Accordingly a procedure for finding the terminating impedance will be detailed on the basis of using the locations of minima for distance calculations.

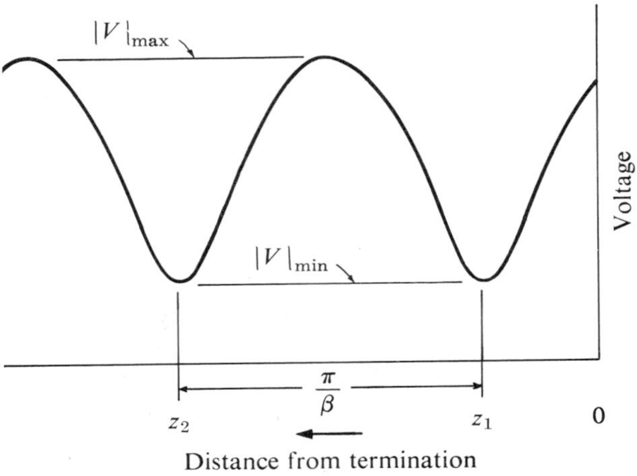

Figure 4-5 Voltage-standing-wave pattern for lossless line with general termination (SWR = 3.70)

The distance between two adjacent voltage minima, $z_2 - z_1$ as shown in Fig. 4-5, is half a wavelength; hence the electrical distance from the termination to the nearest voltage minimum is given by the following:

$$\beta z_1 = \frac{2\pi z_1}{2(z_2 - z_1)} \quad \text{(radians)}$$

$$= \frac{360 z_1}{2(z_2 - z_1)} \quad \text{(degrees)} \qquad \textbf{(4-50)}$$

At a voltage minimum, ϕ is an odd multiple of π, as noted in Eq. 4-46. Hence from Eq. 4-34,

$$\theta_K = 2\beta z_1 + \pi + 2n\pi \qquad \textbf{(4-51)}$$

Should one choose to take $|\theta_K|$ as less than, or possibly equal to, π, n in Eq. 4-51 will necessarily be -1. Then if βz_1 is less than $\pi/2$ radians, θ_K will be negative, whereas if βz_1 is between $\pi/2$ and π radians, θ_K will be positive. Since $|K|$, θ_K, and Z_0 are now known, Z_R may be found by setting z equal to zero in Eq. 4-33:

$$Z_R = Z_0 \frac{1 + |K| \epsilon^{j\theta_K}}{1 - |K| \epsilon^{j\theta_K}} \tag{4-52}$$

As an illustration of the foregoing, suppose that the standing-wave ratio on a lossless transmission line is 3.70, and that the distances z_1 and z_2 are 2.10 and 7.70 m, respectively. Assume that the characteristic impedance of the line is 600 ohms:

$$|K| = \frac{3.70 - 1}{3.70 + 1}$$

$$= 0.573$$

$$\beta z_1 = \frac{2.10\pi}{7.70 - 2.10}$$

$$= 1.18 \text{ radians}$$

$$\theta_K = (2)(1.18) - 3.14$$

$$= -0.78 \text{ radian, or } -44.7^\circ$$

$$Z_R = 600 \frac{1 + 0.573\underline{/-44.7^\circ}}{1 - 0.573\underline{/-44.7^\circ}}$$

$$= 1224\underline{/-50.2^\circ} \text{ ohms}$$

4-5. NOMOGRAPHIC CHART FOR IMPEDANCE CALCULATIONS

Graphical construction is a technique which in many instances may be used to circumvent lengthy calculations. Several charts have been devised to expedite the determination of the impedance along a transmission line.[1–10]

Perhaps the most generally useful chart for this purpose is that developed by P. H. Smith.[7,8] Basically this chart portrays the variation of the normalized impedance or admittance with the angle of a generalized reflection coefficient. It is directly applicable to analysis of a lossless line but, with some auxiliary calculations, problems involving a lossy line may be solved too.

a. Impedance and generalized reflection coefficient

The input impedance for the lossless line will be restated here:

$$Z(z) = Z_0 \frac{1 + |K| \epsilon^{j(\theta_K - 2\beta z)}}{1 - |K| \epsilon^{j(\theta_K - 2\beta z)}} \tag{4-33}$$

As z approaches zero, $Z(z)$ approaches the terminating impedance Z_R (Eq. 4-52). If the latter equation were solved for $|K| \epsilon^{j\theta_K}$, Eq. 3-17, which is repeated below, would result:

$$|K| \epsilon^{j\theta_K} = \frac{Z_R - Z_0}{Z_R + Z_0} \tag{3-17}$$

As in Sec. 4-4*a*, let

$$\phi = \theta_K - 2\beta z \tag{4-34}$$

Substitution of a particular distance z_1 into Eq. 4-33, followed by substitution of Eq. 4-34, yields

$$Z(z_1) = Z_0 \frac{1 + |K| \epsilon^{j\phi_1}}{1 - |K| \epsilon^{j\phi_1}} \tag{4-53}$$

Solving this equation for $|K| \epsilon^{j\phi_1}$ will yield

$$|K| \epsilon^{j\phi_1} = \frac{Z(z_1) - Z_0}{Z(z_1) + Z_0} \tag{4-54}$$

As suggested in Fig. 4-6, the impedance as viewed from any point z_2 on the line to the left of z_1 is the same whether the line extends to $z = 0$ and is

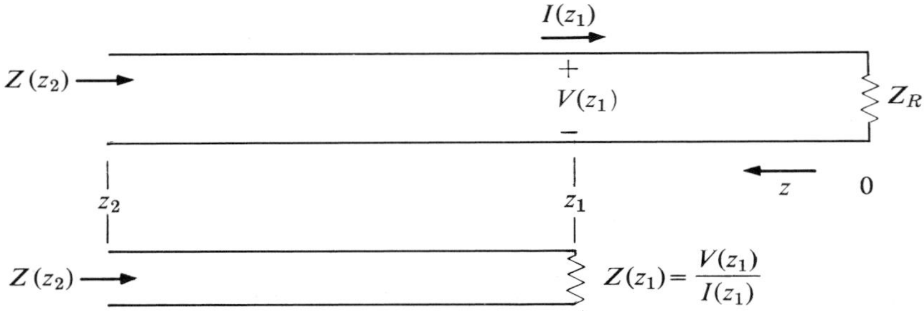

Figure 4-6 Transmission lines of equivalent performance when viewed at locations $z \geqslant z_1$

terminated with Z_R, or whether it is cut off at z_1 and terminated with a lumped impedance equal to $Z(z_1)$. The magnitudes of the reflection coefficients shown in Eqs. 3-17 and 4-54 for the respective terminations are the same, but their angles differ by $2\beta z_1$. It would seem that use of a polar form of chart, with $|K|$ as the radial distance coordinate and $2\beta z$ as an angular coordinate of direction or bearing, could capitalize on this convenient relationship. Loci of particular values of resistance and reactance could be plotted on the chart, and the locus of the complex impedance function $Z(z)$ for a lossless line with a specific termination would be a circle concentric with the origin. This is the basis of the Smith impedance chart.

b. Derivation of loci of transmission-line impedance chart

To derive the equations of loci of constant values of the resistive and reactive components of input impedance, Eq. 4-53 is separated into its real and imaginary parts, as was done with Eq. 4-35. The subscript 1 may be deleted; then the results found in Eqs. 4-39 and 4-40 are immediately applicable. The impedance components may be stated in normalized form by dividing the respective equations by Z_0. Let

$$\frac{Z(z)}{Z_0} = \mathscr{R} + j\mathscr{X} \tag{4-55}$$

or

$$\mathscr{R} = \frac{R(z)}{Z_0} \qquad \mathscr{X} = \frac{X(z)}{Z_0} \tag{4-56}$$

Here $\mathscr{R}$ and $\mathscr{X}$ are the normalized resistance and reactance, respectively; both are functions of ϕ and hence of z. Substituting Eq. 4-56 into Eqs. 4-39 and 4-40 yields

$$\mathscr{R} = \frac{1 - |K|^2}{1 - 2\,|K| \cos \phi + |K|^2} \tag{4-57}$$

$$\mathscr{X} = \frac{2\,|K| \sin \phi}{1 - 2\,|K| \cos \phi + |K|^2} \tag{4-58}$$

Loci of constant values of $\mathscr{R}$ and $\mathscr{X}$ as specified in Eqs. 4-57 and 4-58 prove to be circles, as shown below.

(1) $\mathscr{R}$-LOCI PARAMETERS. The radii and the locations of the centers of the $\mathscr{R}$ loci may be determined as follows. Let

$$u = |K| \cos \phi \tag{4-59}$$

$$v = |K| \sin \phi \tag{4-60}$$

$$|K|^2 = u^2 + v^2$$

The coordinates u, v, K, and ϕ are illustrated in Fig. 4-7.

Substitution of Eqs. 4-59 and 4-60 in Eq. 4-57, followed by multiplication of both sides by the denominator of the right-hand side, yields

$$\mathscr{R}(1 + u^2 + v^2 - 2u) = 1 - u^2 - v^2$$

$$(\mathscr{R} + 1)u^2 - 2u\mathscr{R} + (\mathscr{R} + 1)v^2 = 1 - \mathscr{R}$$

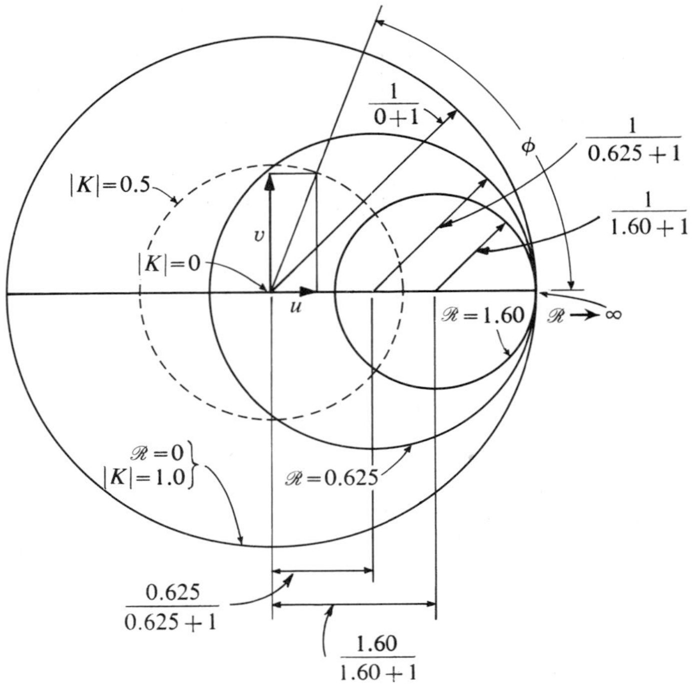

Figure 4-7 Loci of generalized reflection coefficient and normalized resistance on Smith impedance chart

To complete the square in u, the quantity $\mathscr{R}^2/(\mathscr{R}+1)$ is added to both sides, and the terms grouped as follows:

$$(\mathscr{R}+1)\left[u^2 - \frac{2u\mathscr{R}}{\mathscr{R}+1} + \frac{\mathscr{R}^2}{(\mathscr{R}+1)^2}\right] + (\mathscr{R}+1)v^2 = 1 - \mathscr{R} + \frac{\mathscr{R}^2}{\mathscr{R}+1}$$
$$= \frac{1}{\mathscr{R}+1}$$

This equation may be divided by $\mathscr{R}+1$, and the quadratic involving u factored:

$$\left(u - \frac{\mathscr{R}}{\mathscr{R}+1}\right)^2 + v^2 = \frac{1}{(\mathscr{R}+1)^2} \tag{4-61}$$

This is the equation for a circle. The radius of the locus circle for a particular value of normalized resistance $\mathscr{R}_1$ is $1/(\mathscr{R}_1+1)$. The displacement of its center in the v direction is zero, and hence the locus center is on the axis along which ϕ is zero. It is displaced from the origin in the u direction by the distance $\mathscr{R}_1/(\mathscr{R}_1+1)$.

Two other distances of interest are the *intercepts*, or distances from the chart center along the axis of ϕ equal to zero (or 180 degrees) to the intersections with the locus circle. The right-hand intercept of every $\mathscr{R}$-locus circle, found by adding the radius to the displacement of the locus center, proves to be unity. Thus all $\mathscr{R}$-locus circles are tangent to one another at the point $|K| = 1$; $\phi = 0$. The left-hand intercept, found by subtracting the radius from the displacement of center, is at $K_{\text{int}} = (\mathscr{R} - 1)/(\mathscr{R} + 1)$. The circle for $\mathscr{R}$ equal to unity passes through the center of the chart ($|K| = 0$). A significant reciprocity relationship is that the magnitude of the left-hand intercept for any $\mathscr{R}_1$ is equal to the corresponding intercept magnitude for its inverse, $1/\mathscr{R}_1$. Those intercepts are located in opposite directions from the chart center, however. For $\mathscr{R}$ equal to zero, the center of the locus circle coincides with the center of the chart, and the locus circle has unit radius. At the other extreme, the locus for $\mathscr{R}$ approaching infinity shrinks to a point at $|K| = 1$, $\phi = 0$.

(2) $\mathscr{X}$-LOCI PARAMETERS. The $\mathscr{X}$ loci may be examined in a corresponding manner. Equations 4-59 and 4-60 are substituted in Eq. 4-58, and the denominator multiplied out:

$$\mathscr{X}(1 + u^2 + v^2 - 2u) = 2v$$

$$\mathscr{X}(u^2 - 2u + 1) + \mathscr{X}\left(v^2 - \frac{2v}{\mathscr{X}}\right) = 0$$

The quantity $1/\mathscr{X}$ is added to both sides to complete the square in v:

$$\mathscr{X}(u^2 - 2u + 1) + \mathscr{X}\left(v^2 - \frac{2v}{\mathscr{X}} + \frac{1}{\mathscr{X}^2}\right) = \frac{1}{\mathscr{X}}$$

This is divided by $\mathscr{X}$ and the exact squares factored:

$$(u - 1)^2 + \left(v - \frac{1}{\mathscr{X}}\right)^2 = \frac{1}{\mathscr{X}^2} \qquad \textbf{(4-62)}$$

Equation 4-62 describes a circle. The $\mathscr{X}$ loci have radii of $1/\mathscr{X}$; their centers are displaced by unit distance to the right of the chart center, and each is displaced vertically by a distance equal to the radius of the particular circle. Thus all the $\mathscr{X}$ loci pass through the point $|K| = 1$, $\phi = 0$. For the case of $\mathscr{X}$ equal to zero, the displacement of the center and the radius both approach infinity; hence the locus becomes the axis of $\phi = 0$ (or 180 degrees) As $\mathscr{X}$ approaches infinity, the locus shrinks to a point at $|K| = 1$, $\phi = 0$. This is illustrated in Fig. 4-8.

The angle ϕ increases in the counterclockwise direction; from Eq. 4-34 it appears that movement along the transmission line from the terminated end toward the generator, which is the increasing direction of z (see Fig. 3-1), corresponds to a clockwise motion on the chart.

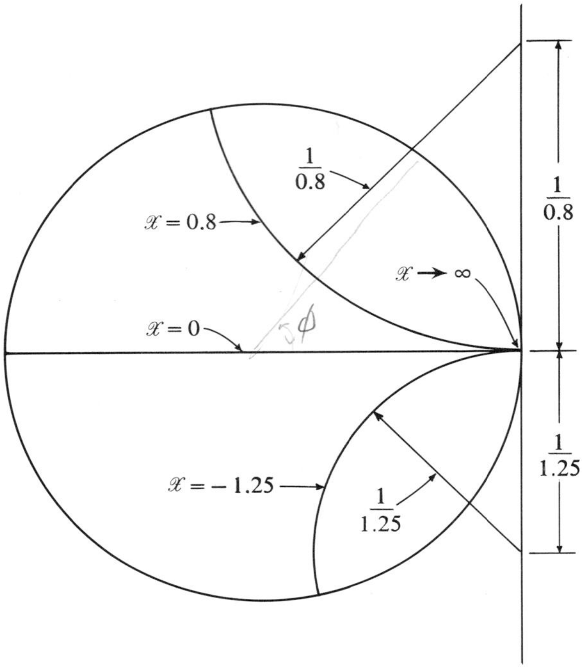

Figure 4-8 Loci of normalized reactance on Smith impedance chart

The $\mathscr{X}$ loci in the upper half of the chart are inductive, while those in the lower half are capacitive. This may be verified by reference to Eq. 4-13, the input impedance to a short-circuited lossless line. This impedance is a pure reactance, increasing through the inductive range from zero to infinity as βz increases from zero to $\pi/2$ radians. The zero-impedance locus point on the chart is at the extreme left, at $|K| = 1$, $\phi = 180°$. Clockwise movement by $2\beta z$ carries one along the upper half of the perimeter during the first quarter-wavelength change in βz.

c. Impedance-admittance reciprocity property of chart

Admittance is a more convenient function to work with than impedance when the problem involves shunt rather than series combinations of network elements. An impedance chart scaled for normalized values may, as shown below, be used as a normalized admittance chart through the following substitutions: (1) the $\mathscr{R}$ circles become loci of normalized conductance $\mathscr{G}$, (2) the $\mathscr{X}$ circles become loci of normalized susceptance $\mathscr{B}$, and (3) the upper half of the chart represents capacitive admittances rather than inductive impedances, and the lower half represents inductive admittances rather than capacitive impedances.

Admittance and impedance are reciprocal quantities, and the relation of this property to the chart may be demonstrated as follows. Dividing Eq. 4-53 by Z_0 yields

$$\frac{Z(z_1)}{Z_0} = \frac{1 + |K| \,\epsilon^{j\phi_1}}{1 - |K| \,\epsilon^{j\phi_1}} \tag{4-63}$$

Let

$$Y(z_1) = \frac{1}{Z(z_1)} \tag{4-64}$$

$$Y_0 = \frac{1}{Z_0} \tag{4-65}$$

Substituting Eqs. 4-64 and 4-65 into Eq. 4-63, and inverting the result, gives

$$\frac{Y(z_1)}{Y_0} = \frac{1 - |K| \,\epsilon^{j\phi_1}}{1 + |K| \,\epsilon^{j\phi_1}} \tag{4-66}$$

Let

$$\phi_1' = \phi_1 + \pi \tag{4-67}$$

$$\epsilon^{j\phi_1'} = -\epsilon^{j\phi_1} \tag{4-68}$$

Substitution of Eq. 4-68 into Eq. 4-66 gives the following expression, which parallels Eq. 4-63 for normalized impedance:

$$\frac{Y(z_1)}{Y_0} = \frac{1 + |K| \,\epsilon^{j\phi_1'}}{1 - |K| \,\epsilon^{j\phi_1'}} \tag{4-69}$$

The normalized admittance $Y(z_1)/Y_0$ may be stated in terms of normalized conductance $\mathscr{G}$ and normalized susceptance $\mathscr{B}$ as follows:

$$\frac{Y(z_1)}{Y_0} = \mathscr{G} + j\mathscr{B} \tag{4-70}$$

(It should be noted that capacitive susceptance is considered positive, and inductive susceptance negative, under the definition set forth in Eq. 4-70. Usage on this point is divided; to avoid confusion it is well, when stating a value for susceptance separately, to designate it as "inductive" or "capacitive" rather than relying on an algebraic sign to convey this information.)

The derivation carried out in Eqs. 4-37 through 4-40, and Eqs. 4-55 through 4-62, may be paralleled in terms of admittance, beginning with Eqs. 4-69 and 4-70. An item-for-item correspondence may thereby be established between the normalized impedance interpretation and the normalized admittance interpretation.

As indicated in Eq. 4-67, the angle ϕ_1' used in Eq. 4-69 differs by π radians from the angle ϕ_1 of the generalized reflection coefficient. Since the magnitude $|K|$ is the same in Eqs. 4-63 and 4-69, the locus points of the normalized impedance and the normalized admittance at any location z_1 are at the same radius and are separated by a semicircle; in other words, they lie

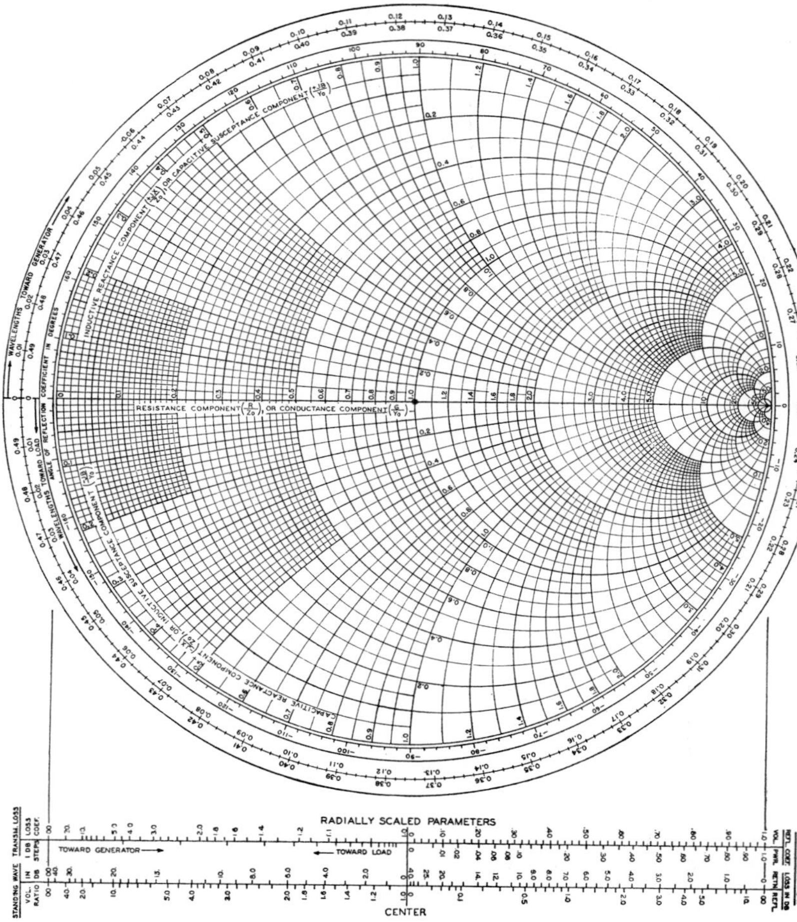

Figure 4-9 Commercial form of Smith impedance chart (copyright 1949 by Kay Electric Co., Pine Brook, N.J., reprinted by permission)

on a line passing through the center of the chart, at equal distances from the center.

A commercially published form of this chart has been reproduced in Fig. 4-9.* For convenience the circumference is scaled not only in degrees of ϕ but in decimal parts of a wavelength in βz.

d. Quarter-wavelength reciprocity on lossless line

An alternation between voltage maxima and minima at quarter-wavelength intervals on a lossless line, and an accompanying alternation between current minima and maxima, were illustrated in Fig. 3-6. The corresponding alternation of maxima and minima in impedance was brought out in Sec. 4-4*b*. In terms of the impedance or admittance chart, a displacement of a quarter wavelength yields a change in ϕ or ϕ' of π radians, or a semicircle. Let

$$\beta z_2 = \beta z_1 + \frac{\pi}{2} \tag{4-71}$$

Then, from Eq. 4-34,

$$\phi_2 = \phi_1 - \pi \tag{4-72}$$

From Eqs. 4-33 and 4-34,

$$\frac{Z(z_2)}{Z_0} = \frac{1 + |K|\,\epsilon^{j\phi_2}}{1 - |K|\,\epsilon^{j\phi_2}}$$

From Eq. 4-72,

$$\epsilon^{j\phi_2} = -\epsilon^{j\phi_1}$$

Hence

$$\frac{Z(z_2)}{Z_0} = \frac{1 - |K|\,\epsilon^{j\phi_1}}{1 + |K|\,\epsilon^{j\phi_1}} \tag{4-73}$$

This is the reciprocal of the normalized impedance at point z_1, Eq. 4-63. Hence

$$\frac{Z[z + (\pi/2\beta)]}{Z_0} = \frac{Z_0}{Z(z)} \tag{4-74}$$

As noted in Sec. 4-5*c*, the locus points for reciprocal complex quantities on the chart are on a line passing through the center of the chart, at equal distances from the center.

e. Impedance locus of transmission line with loss

When account is taken of line losses, the impedance locus changes from a circle whose radius has a constant magnitude $|K|$ to a spiral which converges toward the center of the chart with increasing z or diminishing ϕ. Investigation of this is the subject of Problem 4-8.

* "Expendable" paper charts are available from the General Radio Company, West Concord, Mass.; a slide-rule type of chart calculator made of plastic is manufactured by the Emeloid Company, Hillside, N.J., which also supplies paper charts.

4-6. SOME APPLICATIONS OF THE SMITH CHART

Procedures for use of a chart are perhaps made most meaningful if they are conveyed in the course of working some illustrative problems. Three such problems which will be examined here are (1) calculation of terminating impedance from standing-wave measurements, (2) input admittance to a line which has a resistive shunt between the input and the termination (see Fig. 3-12), and (3) single-stub matching on a radio-frequency line. Problems 4-9 through 4-12 amplify various aspects of these examples.

a. Terminating impedance found from standing-wave pattern

The illustrative problem at the close of Sec. 4-4*d*, which was worked by means of Eqs. 4-49 through 4-52, will be reworked here by means of the chart. As shown by Eq. 4-47, the normalized impedance at a voltage maximum is resistive and is equal to the standing-wave ratio. Thus the chart may be

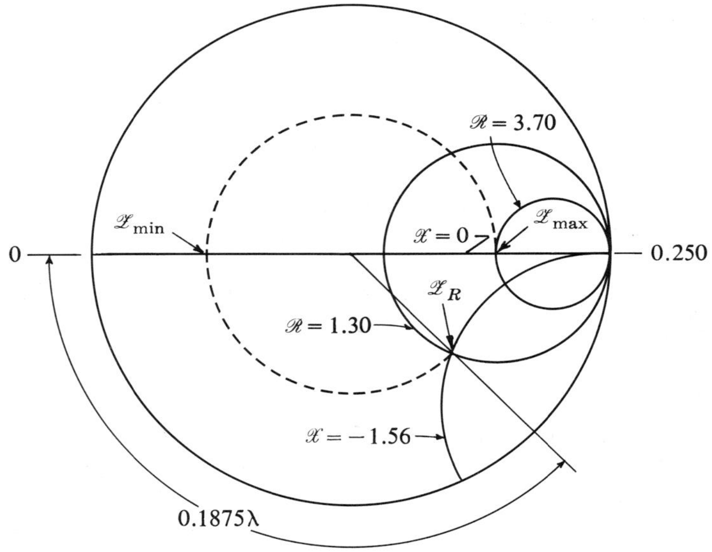

Figure 4-10 Graphical solution for terminating impedance from standing-wave pattern (SWR = 3.70)

entered at $\mathscr{R} = 3.70$, $\mathscr{X} = 0$, as shown in Fig. 4-10. At one quarter-wavelength displacement from this location is a voltage minimum, which would correspond to point z_1 on the line. (It may be noted that at the latter location $\mathscr{R} = 0.270$.) To locate the terminal-impedance locus point, one proceeds counterclockwise by an arc corresponding to $2.10/[(2)(7.70 - 2.10)]$, or

0.1875, wavelength. The normalized impedance of the termination may be scaled as $1.30 - j1.56$. The characteristic impedance was given as 600 ohms; hence the terminal impedance is $780 - j936$, or $1220\angle -50.4^\circ$, ohms. The latter result compares favorably with that found by numerical calculation in Sec. 4-4*d*.

b. Lossless line with shunt discontinuity

Problem 3-2, which is related to Fig. 3-12, was to be worked on the basis of voltage and current functions; it will be reworked here on an admittance basis with the Smith chart.

The two lumped impedances may be converted into normalized admittances as follows:

$$\mathscr{Y}_R = \frac{Z_0}{Z_R} = \frac{600}{250} = 2.40 + j0$$

$$\mathscr{Y}_{\text{sh}} = \frac{Z_0}{R_2} = \frac{600}{400} = 1.50 + j0$$

The chart is entered at $2.40 + j0$, as shown in Fig. 4-11. A radial line drawn through this point intersects the electrical distance scale at the periphery of the chart at the value of 0.250 wavelength. The distance between Z_R and R_2, $\pi/3\beta$, is equivalent to $\frac{1}{6}$, or 0.1667, wavelength, so one moves clockwise to a scale value of $0.250 + 0.1667$ or 0.4167, wavelength. A radial line drawn from the chart center to this peripheral point proves to intersect a circle drawn through the $\mathscr{Y}_R$ point at the admittance loci combination of $0.525 - j0.450$. This is the normalized admittance, $\mathscr{Y}_{SR}$, looking to the right from the right-hand side of R_2 in Fig. 3-12. To get the admittance as viewed from the left-hand side of R_2, $\mathscr{Y}_{SL}$, one adds the normalized admittance of R_2:

$$\mathscr{Y}_{SL} = 0.525 - j0.450 + 1.500 = 2.025 - j0.450$$

If input admittance viewed from some point on the line extending to the left

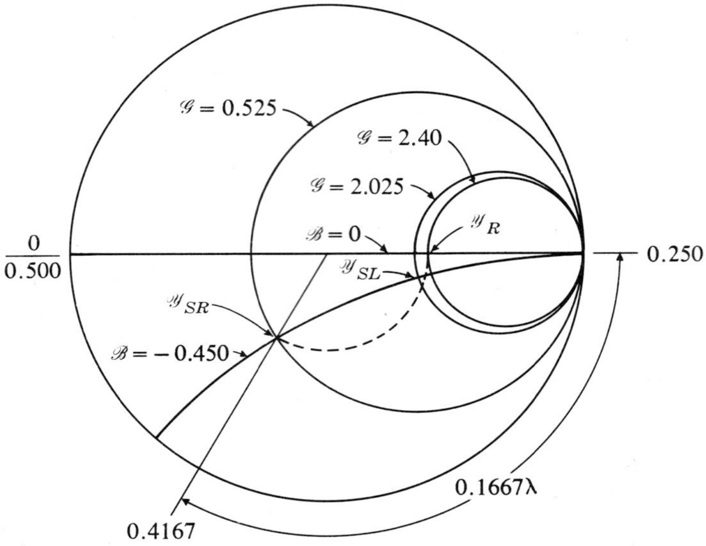

Figure 4-11 Graphical solution for input impedance to line with shunt resistor (see Fig. 3-12)

of R_2 is desired, the chart is entered at the point, $2.025 - j0.450$, as shown in Fig. 4-11, and a circular arc swung from there.

c. Single-stub admittance matching

A common application for radio-frequency transmission lines is as a feeder connection between a transmitter and an antenna. Such a line may extend many wavelengths, and ordinarily the input impedance to the antenna is not equal to the characteristic impedance of the line. Reduction or removal of the standing waves which may be expected is desirable because (1) more power can be transmitted without exceeding the corona onset voltage at any point on the line if no standing waves are present; (2) standing waves, if pronounced, increase losses noticeably; and (3) echoes in the signal caused by multiple reflections between mismatched terminals of the line may be objectionable in some applications. A technique which will eliminate standing waves in all but the immediate vicinity of the load, and which is feasible for wavelengths in the order of 5 m or less, is that of connecting a short-circuited stub in electrical parallel with (but spacially at right angles to) the given line. This is illustrated in Fig. 4-12. Determination of the correct location for the stub and its proper length provides an interesting example for utilization of the Smith chart.

A short-circuited stub will have as its input admittance a pure susceptance. If it is connected at a point on the line at which the input admittance

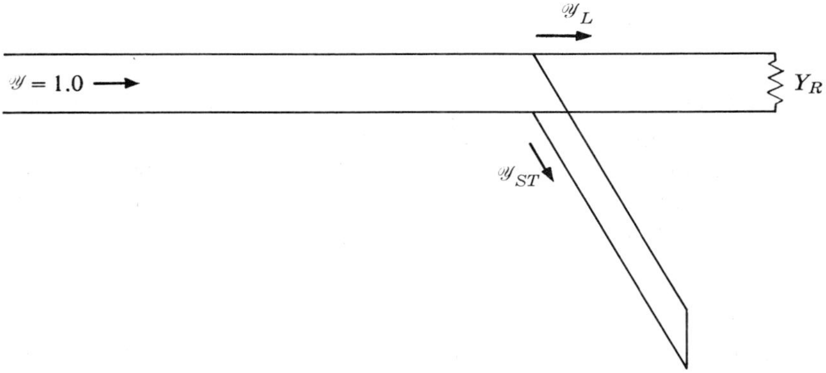

Figure 4-12 Transmission line with short-circuited stub connected in shunt

looking toward the load has a conductance component equal to the characteristic admittance of the line, and the susceptance component of that admittance is offset by that of the stub, the resultant admittance viewed from the generator side of the junction will be equal to characteristic admittance.

If the normalized admittance of the load is known, one enters the chart at that locus point, as indicated in Fig. 4-13. In the example shown, $\mathscr{Y}_R = 3.00 - j1.00$, and the corresponding reading on the peripheral scale for line

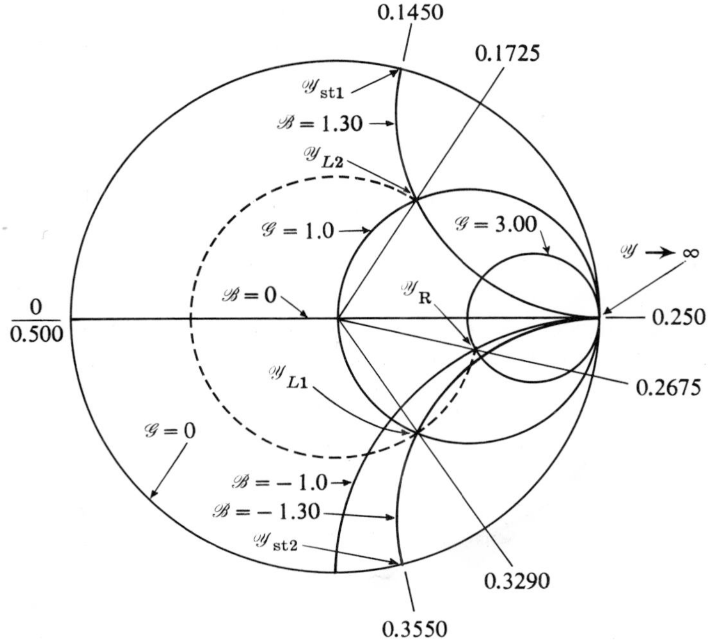

Figure 4-13 Single-stub matching of transmission-line admittance—solution by chart

location is 0.2675. A circular arc is swung clockwise to locate intersections with the $\mathcal{G} = 1.0$ circle. Two such intersections occur; one of the normalized admittances, $\mathcal{Y}_{L1}$, is $1.0 - j1.30$, and the other, $\mathcal{Y}_{L2}$, $1.00 + j1.30$. The corresponding line-location scale readings are 0.3290 and 0.1725. The first-stated admittance is inductive. Hence a capacitive stub would be needed if that location is chosen, whereas the reverse is true if the second location is used. The two cases will be examined separately.

(1) Capacitive-stub solution. In this instance the distance from the end of the line to the stub location is 0.3290 − 0.2675, or 0.0615, wavelength. The stub should present a normalized admittance, $\mathcal{Y}_{st1}$, of $0 + j1.30$; to find the correct length one enters the chart at the locus point of infinite admittance, which is at $|K| = 1$ and at 0.250 on the line-location scale. Proceeding clockwise to the point $0 + j1.30$, a distance of more than a quarter wavelength is traversed; the line-location scale reading is 0.1450. The stub length is 0.1450 + 0.500 − 0.250, or 0.3950, wavelength.

(2) Inductive-stub solution. Since the stub location is more than a quarter wavelength from the load, the distance is found as follows: 0.1725 + 0.5000 − 0.2675, or 0.4050, wavelength. The stub length is found by starting at the point of infinite admittance and proceeding clockwise to the locus point of $0 - j1.30$. The corresponding line-location scale reading is 0.3550, and the stub length is 0.3550 − 0.2500, or 0.1050, wavelength.

4-7. CONCLUSIONS

The complex ratio of the voltage phasor to the current phasor at any location on a transmission line is defined as the *input impedance* at that location. Many aspects arising out of reflections on a transmission line may be analyzed more expediently by means of input impedance or admittance than directly in terms of standing waves of voltage and current.

The open-circuit and short-circuit impedances of a line together furnish enough experimental data to determine the characteristic impedance. If, in addition, the electrical length of the line is known approximately and the physical length is known, the propagation constant and line parameters may be found.

On a lossless line the concept of generalized reflection coefficient is useful. The input impedance varies with electrical distance from the termination, but the effect is equivalent to a change in the reflection-coefficient angle from its value at the terminal. The Smith chart, which yields the resistance and reactance components of normalized input impedance, or conductance and susceptance components of normalized input admittance, utilizes this principle.

PROBLEMS

4-1. Find the limiting value approached by Eq. 4-7 as z approaches zero, given that $g \neq 0$.

4-2. Find the angle of $Z_{oc}(z)$, for z approaching zero, for a general, nondistortionless line. (HINT: $\tanh u \approx u$, if $u \ll 1$.) Compare the result with Fig. 4-1.

4-3. Find the distance from the end of an open-circuited "ideal" cable ($\theta_0 = -45°$, $\alpha = \beta$) at which $|Z(z)|$ is a minimum. Evaluate $Z(z)$ at this location.

4-4. Investigate the range of values of A in Eq. 4-22, particularly at those locations at which βz is a multiple of $\pi/2$.

4-5. Suppose that the right-hand section of line shown in Fig. 4-4 is terminated with its characteristic impedance, and that the left-hand side is energized at the design frequency. Let $Z_{01} = 3Z_{02}$. (*a*) Sketch $|I|$ and $|V|$ as functions of location along the composite line. (*b*) Find the input impedance, in terms of Z_{01}, to the "quarter-wavelength" section if the frequency is increased by 1 per cent, and compute the corresponding reflection coefficient.

4-6. Find the impedances of the transmission line sketched in Fig. 3-13 at (*a*) the right-hand side of the series reactors, (*b*) at the left-hand side of the series reactors, and (*c*) one-quarter of a wavelength to the left of the series reactors.

4-7. A lossless transmission line with $Z_0 = 150\underline{/0°}$ ohms is terminated with $Z_R = 120 + j180$ ohms. Where will the nearest voltage minimum be, and what will the standing-wave ratio be? If the rms voltage at the minimum point is 2 volts, what will the current be there?

4-8. Show that the Smith-chart locus of the impedance of a lossy line is a spiral of constant slope and that it intersects every $|K|$ circle at the angle whose tangent is α/β nepers per radian. (HINT: The slope is equal to a differential displacement in the radial direction, $d|K|$, divided by the corresponding circumferential distance, $|K|\, d\phi$.)

4-9. For the single-stub-matching example given in Sect. 4-6 *c*(2), draw a phasor diagram showing voltage and currents at the stub junction. Sketch the standing waves of voltage and current on the line with the stub attached, paying particular attention to continuity or discontinuity of each function at the stub junction.

4-10. A lossless transmission line, operating at 40 megacycles per second, has a characteristic impedance of 350 ohms, and the standing-wave ratio has been found from measurements to be 4.50. It is proposed to use a short-circuited stub to reduce the standing waves. Find the distance from a voltage minimum at which the stub should be located. How long should the stub be? (Find both inductive-stub and capacitive-stub solutions.) Work this by the Smith chart and also analytically.

4-11. A given radio-frequency line has the following properties: $Z_0 = 400\underline{/0°}$ ohms, $\gamma = 0 + j1.20$ radians per meter, $Z_R = 150\underline{/0°}$ ohms. It is proposed to eliminate standing waves (except in the vicinity of Z_R) by adding a purely resistive shunt. How far from the end should that shunt be placed and what should be its value in ohms? Sketch the standing-wave-magnitude patterns for voltage and current. Why would this "solution" be objectionable for practical application?

4-12. A lossless short-circuited stub with a characteristic impedance of 350 ohms is to have an input reactance of 450 ohms. The design frequency corresponds to a wavelength of 3.5 m. How long should the stub be if it is to be inductive? How long if capacitive? If stubs of those two lengths are operated at 5 per cent above the design frequency, what will their reactances be? Express the changes in reactances as percentages.

4-13. Figure 4-14 shows an impedance chart[1] similar to the Smith chart, but one in which the loci represent constant values of the polar coordinates of normalized impedance, $|\mathscr{Z}|$ and θ_z. Show (*a*) that the loci are circles, (*b*) that the u offsets of the $|\mathscr{Z}|$ circles are $(|\mathscr{Z}|^2 + 1)/(|\mathscr{Z}|^2 - 1)$, (*c*) that the radii of the

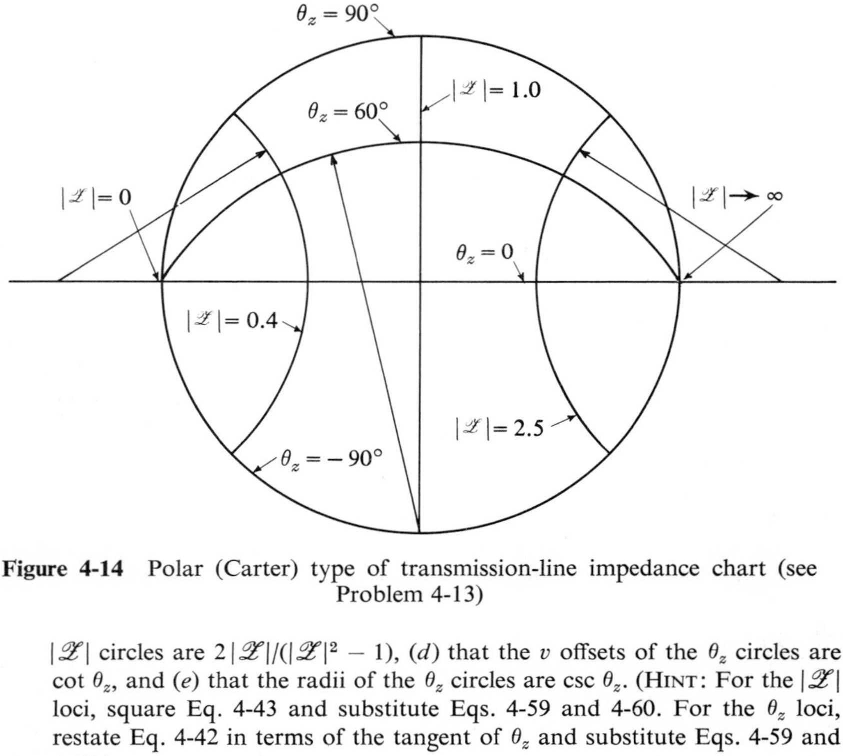

Figure 4-14 Polar (Carter) type of transmission-line impedance chart (see Problem 4-13)

$|\mathscr{Z}|$ circles are $2|\mathscr{Z}|/(|\mathscr{Z}|^2 - 1)$, (*d*) that the v offsets of the θ_z circles are $\cot \theta_z$, and (*e*) that the radii of the θ_z circles are $\csc \theta_z$. (HINT: For the $|\mathscr{Z}|$ loci, square Eq. 4-43 and substitute Eqs. 4-59 and 4-60. For the θ_z loci, restate Eq. 4-42 in terms of the tangent of θ_z and substitute Eqs. 4-59 and 4-60.)

REFERENCES

1. CARTER, P. S., "Charts for Transmission-Line Measurements and Computations," *RCA Rev.*, 3 (1939), 355–68.

2. CREAMER, WALTER J., *Communication Networks and Lines*, pp. 315–27. New York: Harper and Brothers, 1951.

3. EVERITT, W. L. and G. E. ANNER, *Communication Engineering* (3rd ed.), pp. 370–81. New York: McGraw-Hill Book Company, Inc., 1956.

4. KENNELLY, A. E., *Chart Atlas of Complex Hyperbolic and Circular Functions*. Cambridge, Mass.: Harvard University Press, 1914, 1921, 1924.

5. KIMBARK, EDWARD WILSON, *Electrical Transmission of Power and Signals*, pp. 185–98, 204, 205. New York: John Wiley & Sons, 1949.

6. Members of the Staff of the Radar School, Massachusetts Institute of Technology, *Principles of Radar* (3rd ed.), rev. by J. Francis Reintjes and Godfrey T. Coate, pp. 502–5. New York: McGraw-Hill Book Company, Inc., 1952.

7. SMITH, P. H., "An Improved Transmission Line Calculator," *Electronics*, 17, No. 1 (1944), 130–133, 318–325.

8. SMITH, P. H., "Transmission Line Calculator," *Electronics*, 12, No. 1 (1939), 29–31.

9. SOUTHWORTH, G. C., "More About Phil Smith and His Diagram," *Microwave J.*, 1, No. 2 (1958), 26–28.

10. WOODRUFF, L. F., *Principles of Electric Power Transmission* (2nd ed.). New York: John Wiley & Sons, 1938.

CHAPTER 5

Propagation and Multiple Reflections of Transient Surges

A study of transient traveling waves on transmission lines will complement the steady-state analysis of the preceding four chapters. The topic of transient waves was introduced in Sec. 1-4*c* as a corollary to the propagation properties of sinusoidal traveling waves on a lossless line and was mentioned again in Sec. 2-1*c*(3) in connection with the distortionless line. In both instances it was indicated that, because the phase velocity and the characteristic impedance were independent of frequency, (1) voltage waves of arbitrary shape would travel at a uniform speed of $1/\sqrt{lc}$ in either direction, and (2) such a voltage wave would be accompanied by a current wave of the same shape, with magnitude of $\sqrt{c/l}$ times that of the voltage.

Direct-substitution verification of this for a particular nonrecurrent surge was the subject of Problem 1-2. In that instance the function had continuous derivatives of all orders, but the wave equation is also satisfied by traveling-wave functions which have discontinuities. The step function and its first two derivatives, the impulse function and doublet function (as well as higher-order ones), have been used for several decades, but only recently have these functions been analyzed rigorously.[7]

In short, the following expressions are solutions to the equations for the lossless line, following the polarity convention of Fig. 1-1:

$$
\begin{aligned}
v(z,t) &= f_1(t - z\sqrt{lc} - t_1) + f_2(t + z\sqrt{lc} - t_2) \\
i(z,t) &= \sqrt{\frac{c}{l}}\, f_1(t - z\sqrt{lc} - t_1) - \sqrt{\frac{c}{l}}\, f_2(t + z\sqrt{lc} - t_2)
\end{aligned}
\qquad \textbf{(5-1)}
$$

Here f_1 and f_2 are any functions of the indicated arguments (for homogeneity, those functions must have the dimensions of voltage), and t_1 and t_2 are time delays which may be chosen to satisfy boundary conditions. Actually an infinite number of component waves traveling in each direction, with different time delays, may be present.

The analysis of reflections given in Sec. 3-1*a* was in terms of sinusoidal traveling waves. But the reflection coefficient found there is independent of frequency if both the characteristic impedance and the terminating impedance are purely resistive. Hence it is applicable to transient waves on a resistively terminated lossless line.

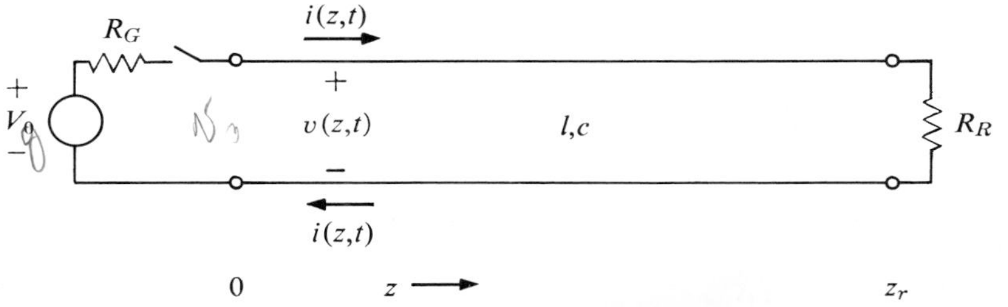

Figure 5-1 Lossless transmission line with resistive termination

In systems with a line of finite length, such as that shown in Fig. 5-1, any transient response consists in general of an infinite number of successively delayed waves. For the basic study of this, the Laplace transform[2] will be used, primarily because it is sufficiently general to accommodate readily more complicated situations, such as (1) inductive and capacitive terminations, and (2) lossy lines which are not distortionless.

If the line is lossless or distortionless, the inverse transforms are simple in form and the wave forms which they represent may be easily sketched. Once the basic pattern of reflection coefficients and delay times is understood, the solutions for many boundary-condition situations can be written at sight.

For the usual physical line, r/l is many times g/c. If account is taken of losses, the transforms of voltage and current involve fractional powers of quantities containing the complex variable s. The corresponding inverse transforms include relatively unfamiliar functions, and graphical interpretation may be feasible only with the aid of some auxiliary calculations.

5-1. TRANSFORMS OF VOLTAGE AND CURRENT ON LOSSLESS LINE

The wave equation for the lossless line will be repeated here:

$$\frac{\partial^2 v(z,t)}{\partial z^2} = lc\,\frac{\partial^2 v(z,t)}{\partial t^2} \qquad \textbf{(1-12)}$$

Let $V(z,s)$ be the Laplace transform of $v(z,t)$ with respect to t, in accordance with the standard definition:

$$V(z,s) = \int_0^\infty v(z,t)\epsilon^{-st}\,dt = \mathscr{L}[v(z,t)] \tag{5-2}$$

Capital letters, with functional dependence on s stated explicitly, will be used to designate the Laplace transforms of functions of time. The operation of taking the Laplace transform of a given function of time will be indicated by a capital script $\mathscr{L}$ followed by square brackets.

The transform of the time derivative of a function for which the transform has been defined as $V(z,s)$ is as follows:

$$\mathscr{L}\left[\frac{\partial v(z,t)}{\partial t}\right] = sV(z,s) - v(z,0) \tag{5-3}$$

The *initial-value* term $v(z,0)$ describes the voltage distribution along the line (as a function of z) existing at the instant of zero reference time.

The transform of the second derivative with respect to time, which is needed to find the transform of the wave equation, is

$$\mathscr{L}\left[\frac{\partial^2 v(z,t)}{\partial t^2}\right] = s^2V(z,s) - sv(z,0) - v'(z,0) \tag{5-4}$$

Here $v'(z,0)$ is the initial distribution of the rate of change of voltage with respect to time. Reference to Eq. 1-8 indicates that this function could be other than zero only if current were flowing in the line at the instant $t = 0$, and then only if the current were not the same at all points on the line.

The transform integral, Eq. 5-2, is unaffected by differentiations with respect to variables other than t; hence the second derivative with respect to z, which is needed to transform the wave equation, 1-12, has the following transform:

$$\mathscr{L}\left[\frac{\partial^2 v(z,t)}{\partial z^2}\right] = \frac{d^2V(z,s)}{dz^2} \tag{5-5}$$

Replacing the transforms of the terms in Eq. 1-12 with Eqs. 5-4 and 5-5 yields the following result:

$$\frac{d^2V(z,s)}{dz^2} = lc[s^2V(z,s) - sv(z,0) - v'(z,0)] \tag{5-6}$$

The relationship between the voltage and current transforms may be found by means of the transform of either Eqs. 1-7 or 1-8. (Equation 1-12 was found by eliminating current from that pair of equations.) Let $I(z,s)$ be the Laplace transform of $i(z,t)$ with respect to t:

$$\frac{dV(z,s)}{dz} = -l[sI(z,s) - i(z,0)] \tag{5-7}$$

$$\frac{dI(z,s)}{dz} = -c[sV(z,s) - v(z,0)] \tag{5-8}$$

For an initial illustration, consider the lossless line shown in Fig. 5-1, with a d-c source, a resistive termination, and neither initial voltage nor initial current on the line. Equation 5-6 reduces to the following:

$$\frac{d^2V(z,s)}{dz^2} = lcs^2V(z,s) \tag{5-9}$$

This is an ordinary differential equation of the second order in z, and may be solved conveniently by the following substitution. Let

$$V(z,s) = V_A(s)\epsilon^{mz} \tag{5-10}$$

Here $V_A(s)$ and m are undetermined functions which are postulated to be independent of z. Differentiation of Eq. 5-10 with respect to z and substitution in Eq. 5-9 yields

$$m^2V_A(s)\epsilon^{mz} = lcs^2V_A(s)\epsilon^{mz} \tag{5-11}$$

Cancelling like terms from both sides and solving for m yields this result:

$$m = \pm s\sqrt{lc} \tag{5-12}$$

Since there are two roots to the characteristic equation, there will be two components in the solution for $V(z,s)$, each of which may be multiplied by an arbitrary function of s:

$$V(z,s) = V_A(s)\epsilon^{-sz\sqrt{lc}} + V_B(s)\epsilon^{sz\sqrt{lc}} \tag{5-13}$$

Substituting this result into Eq. 5-7 and solving for $I(z,s)$ yields the following:

$$I(z,s) = \sqrt{\frac{c}{l}}\,V_A(s)\epsilon^{-sz\sqrt{lc}} - \sqrt{\frac{c}{l}}\,V_B(s)\epsilon^{sz\sqrt{lc}} \tag{5-14}$$

Thus for the lossless line the two components of the voltage and current transforms are related by the same value of impedance $\sqrt{l/c}$ as was found in the steady-state a-c analysis in Eq. 1-20. Since Z_0 for a lossless line was found to be independent of frequency, this result is reasonable.

5-2. BOUNDARY CONDITIONS: RESISTIVE TERMINATIONS

The transforms given in Eqs. 5-13 and 5-14 are applicable to any lossless line with no initial charge or current. The arbitrary functions $V_A(s)$ and $V_B(s)$ must be specified before the inverse transforms can be obtained, and those functions are determined by the boundary conditions, namely, the nature of the energy sources and the impedances at the two ends of the line. The simplest results arise when the impedances at the sending and receiving ends are purely resistive. For this situation (see Fig. 5-1) the following transform equation is applicable at the sending end:

$$V(0,s) = \mathscr{L}[v_g(t)] - R_GI(0,s) \tag{5-15}$$

Closing the switch will apply the constant voltage V_0 suddenly to the resistor R_G and the transmission line in series with it. This statement may be expressed mathematically with the aid of the *unit function* $U(t)$. The unit function has, by definition, a value of zero whenever its argument is negative and a value of plus unity (dimensionless) whenever its argument is positive. The unit function is discontinuous when its argument is equal to zero. Hence this driving function is described as follows:

$$v_g(t) = V_0 U(t) \tag{5-16}$$

The corresponding Laplace transform is

$$\mathscr{L}[v_g(t)] = \frac{V_0}{s} \tag{5-17}$$

At the distant termination, where z is equal to z_r, the following relationship applies:

$$V(z_r,s) = R_R I(z_r,s) \tag{5-18}$$

Substitution of Eqs. 5-13 and 5-14 into Eqs. 5-15 and 5-18, with the z's in the former equations set equal to zero or to z_r, plus substitution of Eq. 5-17 in Eq. 5-15, yields the following two equations:

$$V_A(s) + V_B(s) = \frac{V_0}{s} - R_G\sqrt{\frac{c}{l}}\,V_A(s) + R_G\sqrt{\frac{c}{l}}\,V_B(s) \tag{5-19}$$

$$V_A(s)\epsilon^{-sz_r\sqrt{lc}} + V_B(s)\epsilon^{sz_r\sqrt{lc}} = R_R\sqrt{\frac{c}{l}}\,V_A(s)\epsilon^{-sz_r\sqrt{lc}} - R_R\sqrt{\frac{c}{l}}\,V_B(s)\epsilon^{sz_r\sqrt{lc}} \tag{5-20}$$

Equation 5-20 may be solved for $V_B(s)$:

$$V_B(s) = V_A(s)\epsilon^{-2sz_r\sqrt{lc}}\,\frac{R_R - \sqrt{l/c}}{R_R + \sqrt{l/c}} \tag{5-21}$$

A reflection coefficient ρ_R may be defined in a manner corresponding to Eq. 3-17 for the a-c steady-state case (the symbol K represented a complex number; here ρ will represent either a real number or a function of s):

$$\rho_R = \frac{R_R - \sqrt{l/c}}{R_R + \sqrt{l/c}} \tag{5-22}$$

This will reduce Eq. 5-21 to the following:

$$V_B(s) = V_A(s)\epsilon^{-2sz_r\sqrt{lc}}\rho_R \tag{5-23}$$

In like manner, Eq. 5-19 may be solved for $V_A(s)$:

$$V_A(s) = \frac{V_0}{s(R_G\sqrt{c/l} + 1)} + V_B(s)\,\frac{R_G - \sqrt{l/c}}{R_G + \sqrt{l/c}} \tag{5-24}$$

A second reflection coefficient, ρ_G, may be defined as follows:

$$\rho_G = \frac{R_G - \sqrt{l/c}}{R_G + \sqrt{l/c}} \tag{5-25}$$

This will reduce Eq. 5-24 to the following:

$$V_A(s) = \frac{V_0}{s(R_G\sqrt{c/l} + 1)} + V_B(s)\rho_G \tag{5-26}$$

Simultaneous solution of Eqs. 5-23 and 5-26 will yield the transforms $V_A(s)$ and $V_B(s)$, which may be substituted into Eqs. 5-13 and 5-14, which are the transforms of voltage and current. Inverse transforms of the resulting equations will be $v(z,t)$ and $i(z,t)$. Some specific cases will now be examined.

a. Line terminated with characteristic impedance

A simple solution results if the terminating resistance R_R is equal to the characteristic impedance $\sqrt{l/c}$, for then the reflection coefficient ρ_R vanishes and $V_B(s)$ is equal to zero in accordance with Eq. 5-23. Equation 5-26 reduces to the following:

$$V_A(s) = \frac{V_0}{s(R_G\sqrt{c/l} + 1)} \tag{5-27}$$

Substitution of these results into Eqs. 5-13 and 5-14 yields the following:

$$V(z,s) = \frac{V_0}{s(R_G\sqrt{c/l} + 1)}\epsilon^{-sz\sqrt{lc}} \tag{5-28}$$

$$I(z,s) = \frac{V_0}{s(R_G + \sqrt{l/c})}\epsilon^{-sz\sqrt{lc}} \tag{5-29}$$

In accordance with the shifting theorem, the inverse transforms of these equations are

$$v(z,t) = \frac{V_0}{R_G\sqrt{c/l} + 1}U(t - z\sqrt{lc}) \tag{5-30}$$

$$i(z,t) = \frac{V_0}{R_G + \sqrt{l/c}}U(t - z\sqrt{lc}) \tag{5-31}$$

The unit function with the argument $t - z\sqrt{lc}$ is particularly significant, since it indicates that at each location z on the line, the voltage and current are both zero up to the instant that t equals the product of the particular value of z and the factor $\sqrt{lc}$, but that after that instant the value of voltage or current indicated by the multiplying constant (or function) is present at that point on the line and remains there indefinitely afterward.

The phase velocity for a lossless line was defined as follows in Chapter 1:

$$v = \frac{1}{\sqrt{lc}} \tag{1-21}$$

Thus a wave front of voltage and current progresses along the line from the sending end ($z = 0$) to the terminated end ($z = z_r$) at the velocity of propagation v. The proportion between voltage and current in the traveling wave is exactly the same as that required by the terminating resistor; hence no reflection occurs and the transient is completed in $z_r\sqrt{lc}$ seconds. Plots of voltage and current at two points along the line are shown in Fig. 5-2.

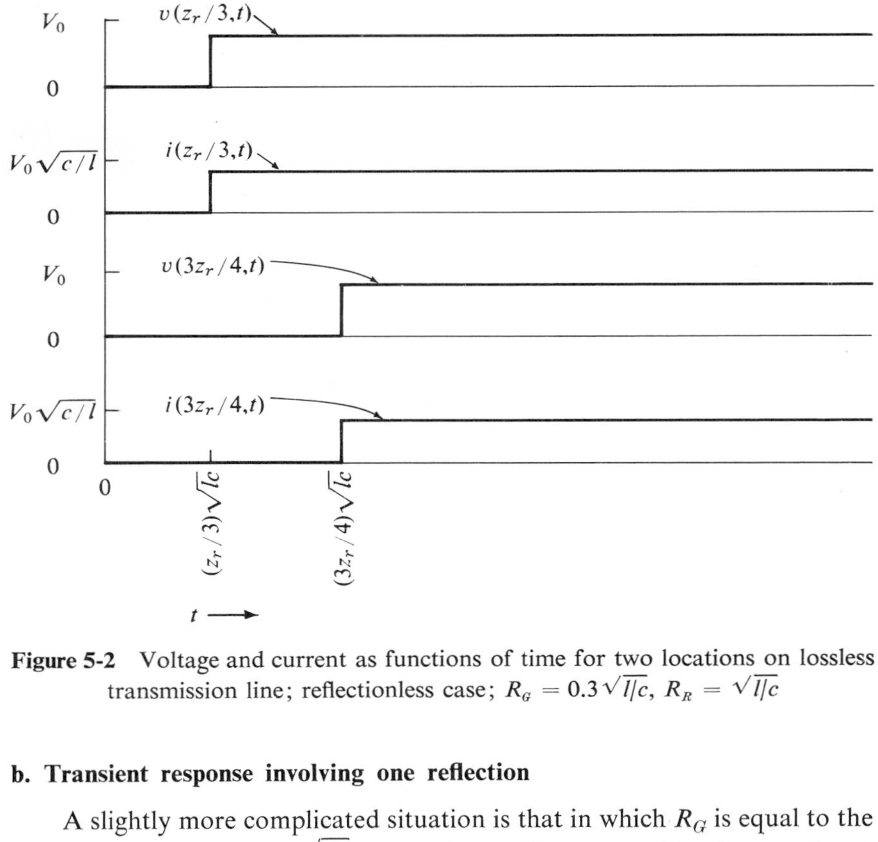

Figure 5-2 Voltage and current as functions of time for two locations on lossless transmission line; reflectionless case; $R_G = 0.3\sqrt{l/c}$, $R_R = \sqrt{l/c}$

b. Transient response involving one reflection

A slightly more complicated situation is that in which R_G is equal to the characteristic impedance ($\sqrt{l/c}$) but R_R is not. Then ρ_G vanishes in accordance with Eq. 5-25, and Eq. 5-26 reduces to the following:

$$V_A(s) = \frac{V_0}{2s} \tag{5-32}$$

Substitution of this result and Eq. 5-23 in Eqs. 5-13 and 5-14 yields the following for the transforms of voltage and current:

$$V(z,s) = \frac{V_0}{2s}\left[\epsilon^{-sz\sqrt{lc}} + \rho_R \epsilon^{-s(2z_r - z)\sqrt{lc}}\right] \qquad \textbf{(5-33)}$$

$$I(z,s) = \frac{V_0}{2s}\sqrt{\frac{c}{l}}\left[\epsilon^{-sz\sqrt{lc}} - \rho_R \epsilon^{-s(2z_r - z)\sqrt{lc}}\right] \qquad \textbf{(5-34)}$$

The inverse transforms are

$$v(z,t) = \frac{V_0}{2}\left[U(t - z\sqrt{lc}) + \rho_R U(t - 2z_r\sqrt{lc} + z\sqrt{lc})\right] \qquad \textbf{(5-35)}$$

$$i(z,t) = \frac{V_0}{2}\sqrt{\frac{c}{l}}\left[U(t - z\sqrt{lc}) - \rho_R U(t - 2z_r\sqrt{lc} + z\sqrt{lc})\right] \qquad \textbf{(5-36)}$$

Interpretation of the unit-function multipliers indicates that initially a voltage wave front of magnitude $V_0/2$, accompanied by a current wave front of magnitude $(V_0/2)\sqrt{c/l}$, moves at velocity v from the sending end to the distant end. Immediately after the arrival of those waves at the termination ($t = z_r\sqrt{lc}$), a voltage wave front and current wave front begin to move from the terminated end back toward the generator end, again with velocity v but with magnitudes proportional to the reflection coefficient ρ_R. Plots of voltage and current as functions of time for two distinct locations on the line are given in Fig. 5-3.

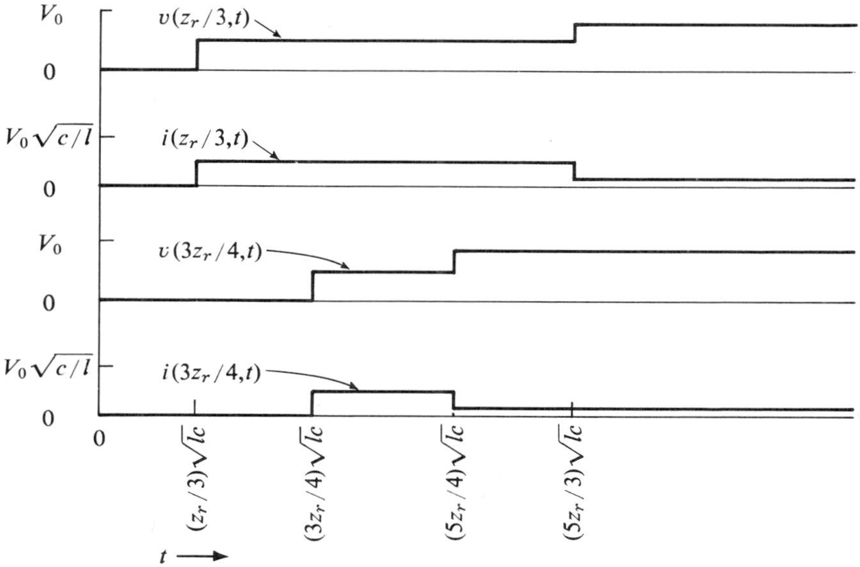

Figure 5-3 Voltage and current as functions of time on lossless transmission line; single-reflection case: $R_G = \sqrt{l/c}$, $R_R = 5\sqrt{l/c}$

The transient ends with the arrival of the reflected waves at the generator end ($t = 2z_r\sqrt{lc}$), by which time the voltage at all points on the line has become $V_0R_R/(R_G + R_R)$, and the current at all points is $V_0/(R_G + R_R)$.

c. Transient response with infinite succession of reflections

A more general situation is that in which neither R_R nor R_G equals the characteristic impedance. Then an infinite succession of reflected waves results. Equation 5-23 for $V_B(s)$ may be substituted into Eq. 5-26, and the resulting expression solved for $V_A(s)$:

$$V_A(s) = \frac{V_0}{s(R_G\sqrt{c/l} + 1)(1 - \rho_G\rho_R\epsilon^{-2sz_r\sqrt{lc}})} \tag{5-37}$$

This result may be substituted into Eq. 5-23 to yield an expression for $V_B(s)$, and both results substituted into Eqs. 5-13 and 5-14 for $V(z,s)$ and $I(z,s)$:

$$V(z,s) = \frac{V_0}{s(R_G\sqrt{c/l} + 1)} \cdot \frac{\epsilon^{-sz\sqrt{lc}} + \epsilon^{sz\sqrt{lc}}\rho_R\epsilon^{-2sz_r\sqrt{lc}}}{1 - \rho_G\rho_R\epsilon^{-2sz_r\sqrt{lc}}} \tag{5-38}$$

$$I(z,s) = \frac{V_0}{s(R_G + \sqrt{l/c})} \cdot \frac{\epsilon^{-sz\sqrt{lc}} - \epsilon^{sz\sqrt{lc}}\rho_R\epsilon^{-2sz_r\sqrt{lc}}}{1 - \rho_G\rho_R\epsilon^{-2sz_r\sqrt{lc}}} \tag{5-39}$$

Before attempting to take the inverse transforms, it is convenient to make the following substitution:

$$\frac{1}{1 - \rho_G\rho_R\epsilon^{-2sz_r\sqrt{lc}}} = 1 + \rho_G\rho_R\epsilon^{-2sz_r\sqrt{lc}} + \rho_G^2\rho_R^2\epsilon^{-4sz_r\sqrt{lc}} + \rho_G^3\rho_R^3\epsilon^{-6sz_r\sqrt{lc}} + \cdots \tag{5-40}$$

After substitution of Eq. 5-40, the terms in Eqs. 5-38 and 5-39 may be grouped as follows:

$$V(z,s) = \frac{V_0}{s(R_G\sqrt{c/l} + 1)}[\epsilon^{-sz\sqrt{lc}} + \rho_R\epsilon^{-s(2z_r-z)\sqrt{lc}} + \rho_G\rho_R\epsilon^{-s(2z_r+z)\sqrt{lc}} + \rho_G\rho_R^2\epsilon^{-s(4z_r-z)\sqrt{lc}} + \rho_G^2\rho_R^2\epsilon^{-s(4z_r+z)\sqrt{lc}} + \rho_G^2\rho_R^3\epsilon^{-s(6z_r-z)\sqrt{lc}} + \cdots] \tag{5-41}$$

$$I(z,s) = \frac{V_0}{s(R_G + \sqrt{l/c})}[\epsilon^{-sz\sqrt{lc}} - \rho_R\epsilon^{-s(2z_r-z)\sqrt{lc}} + \rho_G\rho_R\epsilon^{-s(2z_r+z)\sqrt{lc}} - \rho_G\rho_R^2\epsilon^{-s(4z_r-z)\sqrt{lc}} + \cdots] \tag{5-42}$$

The inverse transforms are

$$v(z,t) = \frac{V_0}{R_G\sqrt{c/l}+1}[U(t - z\sqrt{lc}) + \rho_R U(t - 2z_r\sqrt{lc} + z\sqrt{lc}) + \rho_G\rho_R U(t - 2z_r\sqrt{lc} - z\sqrt{lc}) + \rho_G\rho_R^2 U(t - 4z_r\sqrt{lc} + z\sqrt{lc}) + \cdots] \quad (5\text{-}43)$$

$$i(z,t) = \frac{V_0}{R_G+\sqrt{l/c}}[U(t - z\sqrt{lc}) - \rho_R U(t - 2z_r\sqrt{lc} + z\sqrt{lc}) + \rho_G\rho_R U(t - 2z_r\sqrt{lc} - z\sqrt{lc}) - \rho_G\rho_R^2 U(t - 4z_r\sqrt{lc} + z\sqrt{lc}) + \cdots] \quad (5\text{-}44)$$

Thus the response consists of an infinite series of voltage and current "layers" which are added successively as the wave front sweeps from generator to terminated end and back. Unless both reflection coefficients have unity magnitudes, the magnitudes of the added layers will progressively

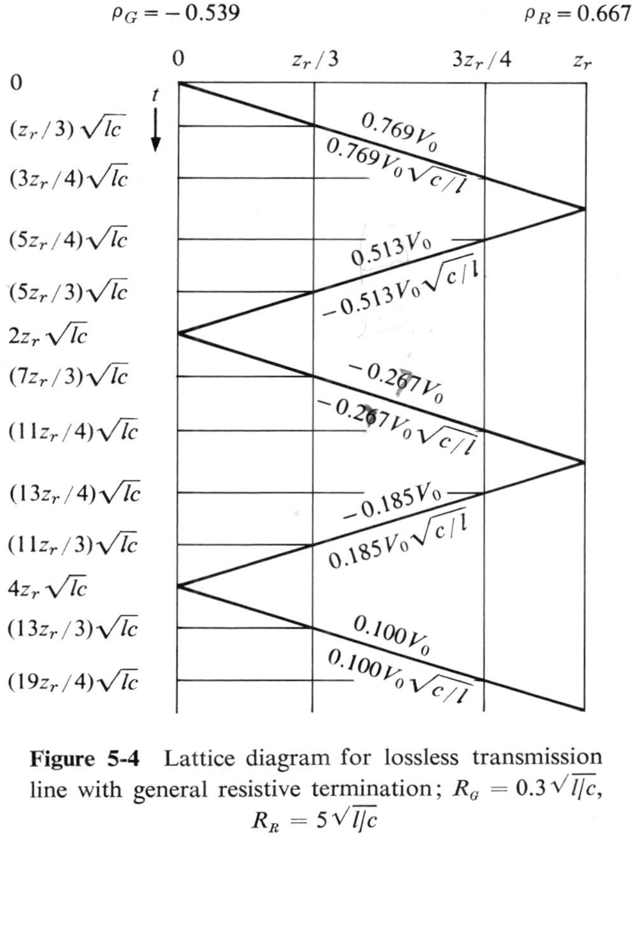

Figure 5-4 Lattice diagram for lossless transmission line with general resistive termination; $R_G = 0.3\sqrt{l/c}$, $R_R = 5\sqrt{l/c}$

diminish, and the following steady-state conditions will be approached:

$$v(z,\infty) \to \frac{V_0 R_R}{R_G + R_R} \tag{5-45}$$

$$i(z,\infty) \to \frac{V_0}{R_G + R_R} \tag{5-46}$$

The lattice diagram devised by Bewley[1,3] provides a convenient graphical means of keeping track of multiple reflections. Its application to this relatively simple problem is shown in Fig. 5-4. The time-distance locus of a wave traveling in the increasing z direction is a line sloping downward to the right, whereas the locus of one traveling in the decreasing z direction is a line sloping downward to the left. The ordinate and abscissa scales and the slopes of the traveling-wave loci are related such that $\Delta t = |\Delta z|/v$. The transform or other description of each voltage wave may be written above the corresponding locus and the description of the accompanying current wave below it. Each reflection introduces the multiplier ρ_R or ρ_G in the voltage function and $-\rho_R$ or $-\rho_G$ in the current function.

Voltage and current responses at any particular location may be determined by drawing a vertical line through the z value desired and noting the

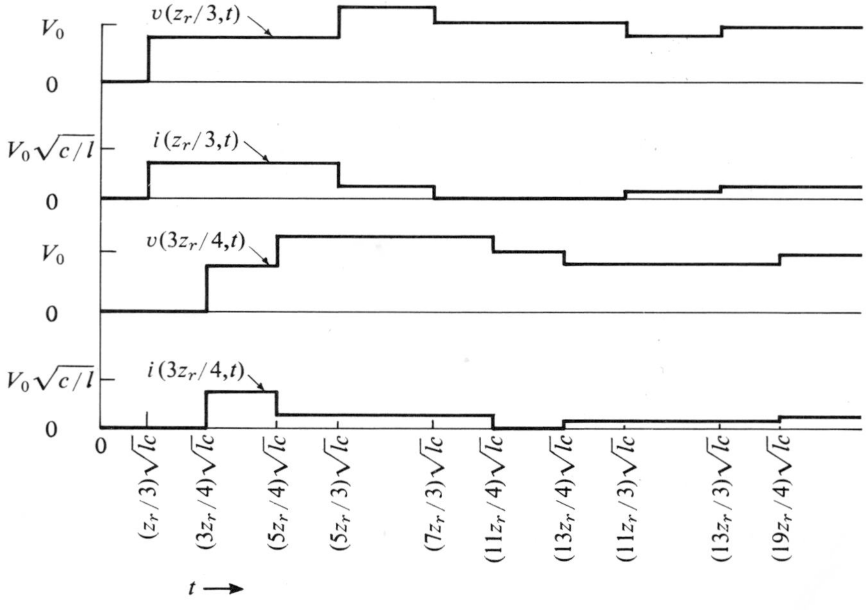

Figure 5-5 Voltage and current as functions of time on lossless transmission line; case with infinite sequence of reflections: $R_G = 0.3\sqrt{l/c}$, $R_R = 5\sqrt{l/c}$

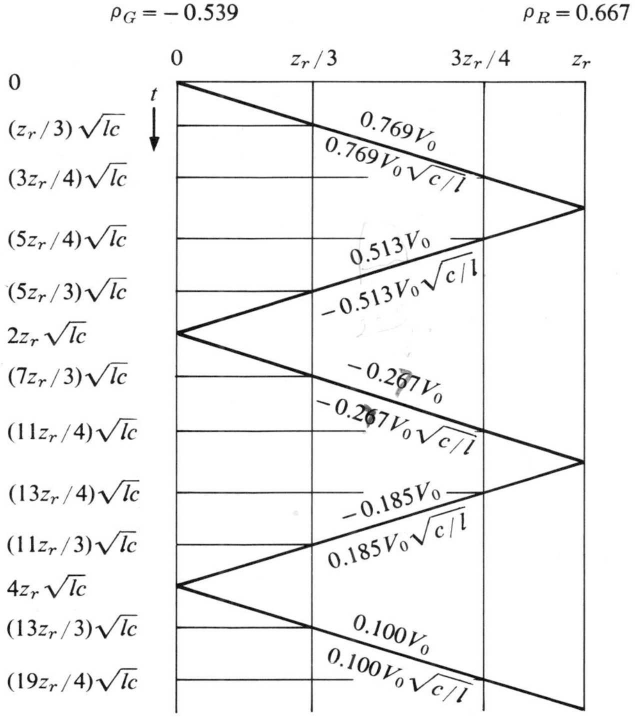

successive values of time corresponding to intersections of the sloping loci with the given vertical line. At the arrival time of the front of each reflected wave, that wave is added to what has been accumulated from preceding waves. This is illustrated in Fig. 5-5.

A d-c source was used here for simplicity, but it may be noted that had any other driving function been used, each component response at a given location on the line would have had the same shape as the driving function. This is because the sole effect of the lossless line is to introduce a time delay inversely proportional to the velocity of propagation, and the effect of resistive non-Z_0 terminations is to produce reflected voltages and currents which are instantaneously in direct proportion to the incident voltages and currents.

d. Discharge of an initially charged line

As an illustration of nonzero initial conditions, the initially charged isolated line shown in Fig. 5-6, which is to be discharged through resistor R

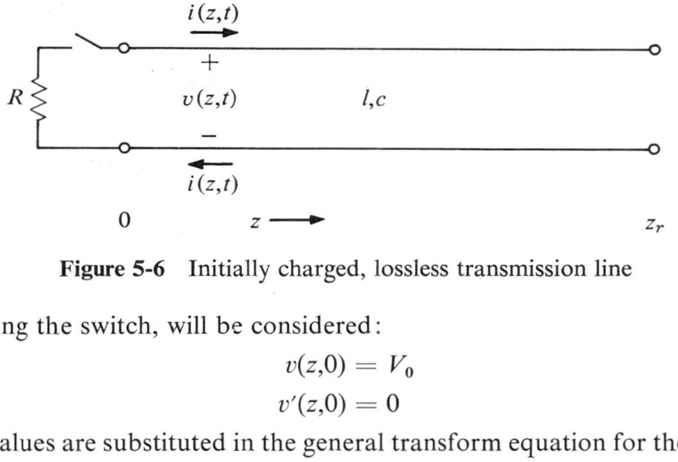

Figure 5-6 Initially charged, lossless transmission line

by closing the switch, will be considered:

$$v(z,0) = V_0 \tag{5-47}$$

$$v'(z,0) = 0 \tag{5-48}$$

These values are substituted in the general transform equation for the lossless line, Eq. 5-6:

$$\frac{d^2V(z,s)}{dx^2} = lc[s^2V(z,s) - sV_0] \tag{5-49}$$

Whereas Eq. 5-9 was homogeneous in z, Eq. 5-49 is not. The assumed exponential solution given in Eqs. 5-10 and 5-12 is satisfactory for the complementary function, but a particular integral is also needed. It may be seen by inspection that the particular solution V_0/s will satisfy Eq. 5-49 identically if substituted for $V(z,s)$. Hence the complete solution, paralleling Eq. 5-13, may be written

$$V(z,s) = V_A(s)\epsilon^{-sz\sqrt{lc}} + V_B(s)\epsilon^{sz\sqrt{lc}} + \frac{V_0}{s} \tag{5-50}$$

Substituting this result into Eq. 5-7 for current $[i(z,0) = 0]$ yields

$$I(z,s) = V_A(s)\sqrt{\frac{c}{l}}\,\epsilon^{-sz\sqrt{lc}} - V_B(s)\sqrt{\frac{c}{l}}\,\epsilon^{sz\sqrt{lc}} \tag{5-51}$$

Since the line is to be kept open-circuited at z_r, the following boundary condition is applicable:

$$I(z_r,s) = 0 \tag{5-52}$$

Substitution of this boundary condition into Eq. 5-51 gives the following result:

$$V_B(s) = V_A(s)\epsilon^{-2sz_r\sqrt{lc}} \tag{5-53}$$

The following relationship applies at $z = 0$, keeping in mind the assumed positive directions of voltage and current:

$$V(0,s) = -RI(0,s) \tag{5-54}$$

Substitution of Eqs. 5-50 and 5-51, with z set equal to zero, in Eq. 5-54 yields the following:

$$V_A(s) + V_B(s) + \frac{V_0}{s} = -R\sqrt{\frac{c}{l}}\,V_A(s) + R\sqrt{\frac{c}{l}}\,V_B(s) \tag{5-55}$$

This may be solved for $V_A(s)$:

$$V_A(s) = -\frac{V_0}{s(R\sqrt{c/l} + 1)} + V_B(s)\frac{R\sqrt{c/l} - 1}{R\sqrt{c/l} + 1} \tag{5-56}$$

A reflection coefficient ρ_0 may be defined as follows:

$$\rho_0 = \frac{R\sqrt{c/l} - 1}{R\sqrt{c/l} + 1} \tag{5-57}$$

This will be substituted into Eq. 5-56:

$$V_A(s) = -\frac{V_0}{s(R\sqrt{c/l} + 1)} + \rho_0 V_B(s) \tag{5-58}$$

Substitution of Eq. 5-53 for $V_B(s)$ yields an equation in $V_A(s)$ which reduces to the following:

$$V_A(s) = \frac{-V_0}{s(R\sqrt{c/l} + 1)(1 - \rho_0\epsilon^{-2sz_r\sqrt{lc}})} \tag{5-59}$$

The procedure of substituting Eq. 5-59 in Eqs. 5-53, 5-50, and 5-51 and finding the inverse transforms parallels that of the preceding illustration and is left as Problem 5-3.

5-3. BOUNDARY CONDITIONS WITH GENERAL TERMINATIONS

When the sending-end impedance or the terminating impedance includes an inductor or capacitor, the corresponding reflection coefficient becomes a function of s. This complicates the process of finding the inverse transform and will cause each reflected wave leaving such an end to differ from the corresponding incoming wave.

A single example will be introduced here, one in which the line is terminated with a lumped inductor L_R at z_r. The series resistance at the generator end will be assumed equal to the characteristic impedance (see Fig. 5-7).

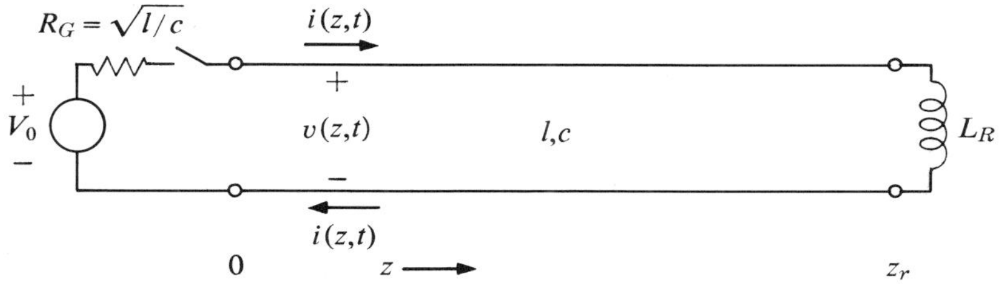

Figure 5-7 Lossless transmission line with purely inductive termination and reflectionless source

It will be assumed that the line is initially uncharged and that the initial current is zero both in the inductor and on the line:

$$V(z_r,s) = sL_R I(z_r,s) \tag{5-60}$$

Comparison with Eqs. 5-18 and 5-20 through 5-21 indicates that the reflection coefficient will now be a function of s, defined as follows:

$$\rho_R(s) = \frac{L_R s - \sqrt{l/c}}{L_R s + \sqrt{l/c}} \tag{5-61}$$

Again, as in Sec. 5-2*b* for the one-reflection transient on a line with resistive termination, ρ_G is zero and, because $R_G\sqrt{c/l} = 1$, $V_A(s)$ as given in Eq. 5-26 reduces to the same value as in that section:

$$V_A(s) = \frac{V_0}{2s} \tag{5-32}$$

The resulting voltage transform closely parallels Eq. 5-33, except that the dependence of the reflection coefficient on s must be taken into account when performing the inverse transformation:

$$\begin{aligned} V(z,s) &= \frac{V_0}{2s}\left[\epsilon^{-sz\sqrt{lc}} + \rho_R(s)\epsilon^{-s(2z_r-z)\sqrt{lc}}\right] \\ &= \frac{V_0}{2s}\epsilon^{-sz\sqrt{lc}} + \frac{V_0(L_R s - \sqrt{l/c})}{2s(L_R s + \sqrt{l/c})}\epsilon^{-s(2z_r-z)\sqrt{lc}} \end{aligned} \tag{5-62}$$

By means of a partial fraction expansion, the latter part of the transform may be broken into simpler components:

$$V(z,s) = \frac{V_0}{2s}\epsilon^{-sz\sqrt{lc}} - \frac{V_0}{2s}\epsilon^{-s(2z_r-z)\sqrt{lc}} + \frac{V_0}{s + (\sqrt{l/c}/L_R)}\epsilon^{-s(2z_r-r)\sqrt{lc}} \tag{5-63}$$

The inverse transformation yields this result:

$$v(z,t) = \frac{V_0}{2} U(t - z\sqrt{lc}) - \frac{V_0}{2} [1 - 2\epsilon^{-(\sqrt{l/c}/L_R)(t-2z_r\sqrt{lc}+z\sqrt{lc})}] \times U(t - 2z_r\sqrt{lc} + z\sqrt{lc}) \quad \text{(5-64)}$$

The current function may be shown to be

$$i(z,t) = \frac{V_0}{2}\sqrt{\frac{c}{l}}\, U(t - z\sqrt{lc}) + \frac{V_0}{2}\sqrt{\frac{c}{l}}\, [1 - 2\epsilon^{-(\sqrt{l/c}/L_R)(t-2z_r\sqrt{lc}+z\sqrt{lc})}] \times U(t - 2z_r\sqrt{lc} + z\sqrt{lc}) \quad \text{(5-65)}$$

Plots of voltage and current as observed from two locations on the line

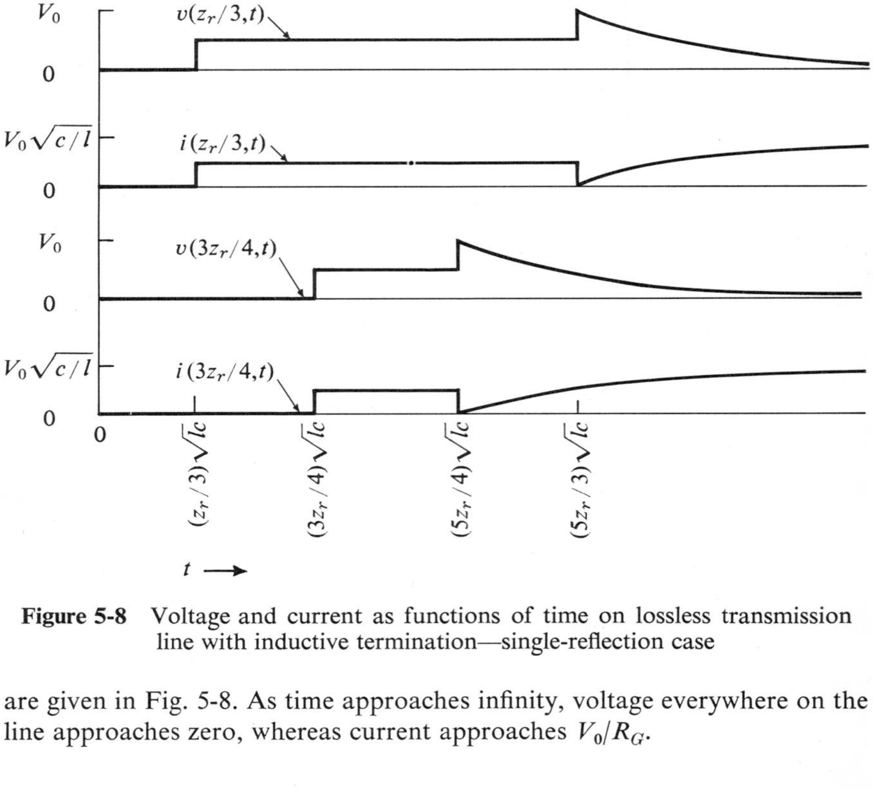

Figure 5-8 Voltage and current as functions of time on lossless transmission line with inductive termination—single-reflection case

are given in Fig. 5-8. As time approaches infinity, voltage everywhere on the line approaches zero, whereas current approaches V_0/R_G.

5-4. REFLECTIONS ON LOSSLESS LINE WITH DISCONTINUITIES OR BRANCHES

The preceding examples have all involved a single section of transmission line, with various lumped impedances at its ends. Greater complexity arises when two or more sections of line, perhaps with differing characteristic impedances, are joined in tandem through lumped-impedance networks, or when several lines converge at a single junction.

a. Tandem connection of two lines

Figure 5-9 illustrates a line-and-discontinuity situation. Here waves may travel in both directions on both sections of the line but at different voltage-to-current ratios. From the viewpoint of a wave approaching the discontinuity from the left, the outgoing line presents a resistance of $\sqrt{l_2/c_2}$ in

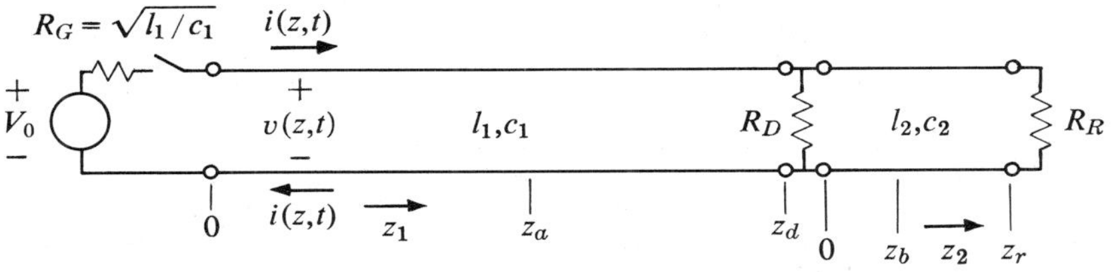

Figure 5-9 Composite lossless transmission line

parallel with R_D, and a reflection coefficient ρ_{1D2} may be computed on that basis. Thus

$$Z_{01} = \sqrt{\frac{l_1}{c_1}} \tag{5-66}$$

$$Z_{02} = \sqrt{\frac{l_2}{c_2}} \tag{5-67}$$

Let
$$Z_{T1} = \frac{R_D Z_{02}}{R_D + Z_{02}} \tag{5-68}$$

Then
$$\rho_{1D2} = \frac{Z_{T1} - Z_{01}}{Z_{T1} + Z_{01}} \tag{5-69}$$

A wave approaching from the right, on the other hand, would encounter at the discontinuity the characteristic impedance $\sqrt{l_1/c_1}$ in parallel with R_D, and hence would have a different reflection coefficient ρ_{2D1}, unless the two characteristic impedances were equal. In both instances the transmitted voltage wave continuing onto the outgoing line in the original direction would be equal, at the discontinuity, to the algebraic sum of the incident and reflected waves related to it. The transmitted current wave, however, would be less than the algebraic sum of the incident and reflected current waves by the amount shunted by the resistor R_D.

For simplicity, the sending-end resistor R_G has been made equal to the

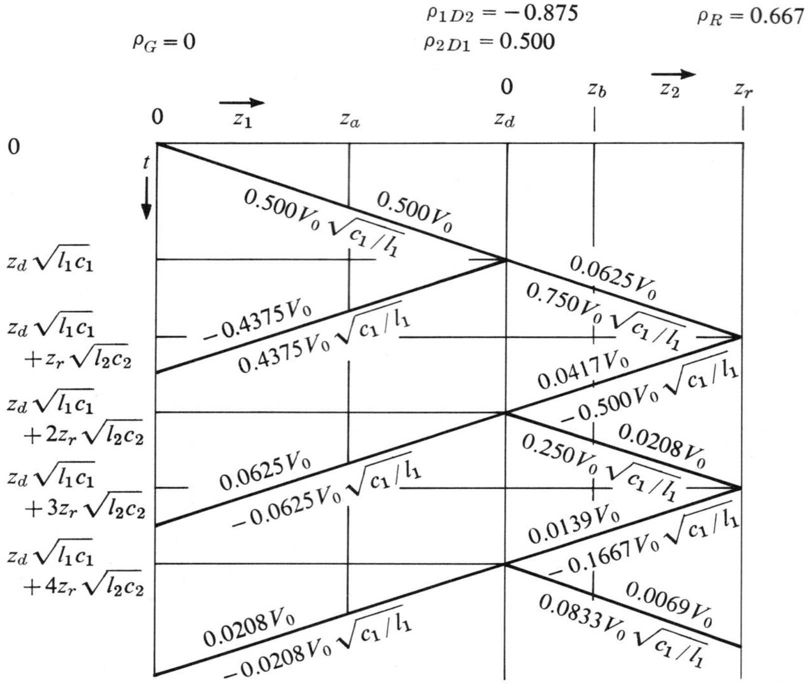

Figure 5-10 Lattice diagram for composite transmission line: $\sqrt{l_1/c_1} = 12\sqrt{l_2/c_2}$, $R_G = \sqrt{l_1/c_1}$, $R_D = 4\sqrt{l_2/c_2}$, $R_R = 5\sqrt{l_2/c_2}$, $1/\sqrt{l_1c_1} = 2/\sqrt{l_2c_2}$

characteristic impedance of the left section of line, thereby suppressing reflections from the generator end of the system. An infinite number of reflections will take place between the discontinuity point and the termination at the right-hand end of the system, and each wave of this set which strikes the discontinuity will send a transmitted wave leftward toward the generator.

The lattice diagram is a more practical means of representing these successive components than a series of mathematical terms; such a diagram is given in Fig. 5-10, and plots of voltage and current as functions of time are given in Fig. 5-11 for two locations on the line, one in each section.

b. Multiple-line junction

Branching of a line, as illustrated in Fig. 5-12, increases the complexity, in that two transmitted waves plus a reflected wave may be expected whenever a wave on any of the three line sections reaches the junction. If the characteristic impedances differ, the reflection coefficients applicable to the three

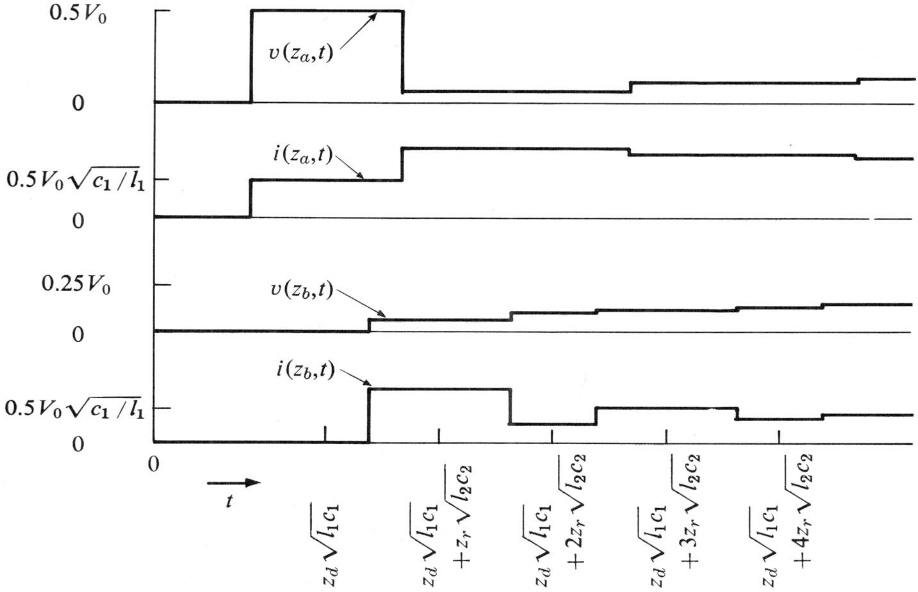

Figure 5-11 Voltage and current as functions of time on composite lossless transmission line (see Fig. 5-10)

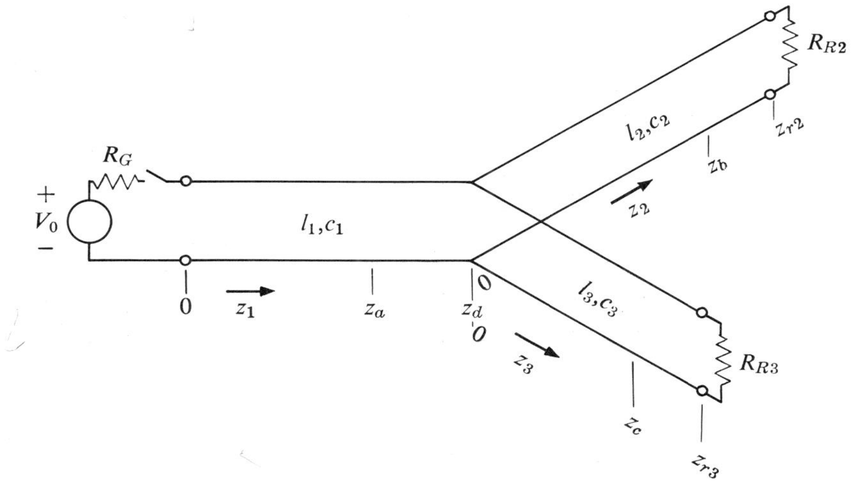

Figure 5-12 Branched transmission line (see Problem 5-7)

lines will differ. They would be computed in the following manner:

$$Z_{T1} = \frac{Z_{02}Z_{03}}{Z_{02} + Z_{03}}$$

$$Z_{T2} = \frac{Z_{01}Z_{03}}{Z_{01} + Z_{03}} \qquad \text{etc.} \tag{5-70}$$

$$\rho_1 = \frac{Z_{T1} - Z_{01}}{Z_{T1} + Z_{01}} \qquad \text{etc.} \tag{5-71}$$

A relatively simple example is given in Problem 5-7.

5-5. LINE WITH RESISTANCE

The derivation of transform equations given in Sec. 5-1 may be readily extended to the four-parameter line. One should recognize the variability of the resistance of physical conductors during a transient because of skin effect.[3,5,6,9,10] No attempt will be made here to incorporate this effect into the transform equations; the reader will merely be reminded that the mathematical results are, at best, approximations.

Because of the difficulty in executing appropriate inverse transforms, the scope of this treatment will be drastically limited as far as solution of physical problems is concerned. Three principal cases will be examined: (1) the distortionless line, (2) the line with zero shunt conductance, and (3) the unloaded cable, using an approximate analysis in which inductance is ignored.

a. Transform equations for general line

The wave equation of the general line was as follows:

$$\frac{\partial^2 v(z,t)}{\partial z^2} = \imath g v(z,t) + (\imath c + lg)\frac{\partial v(z,t)}{\partial t} + lc\frac{\partial^2 v(z,t)}{\partial t^2} \tag{2-5}$$

The Laplace transform of Eq. 2-5 is

$$\frac{d^2V(z,s)}{dz^2} = [\imath g + (\imath c + lg)s + lcs^2]V(z,s) - (\imath c + lg)v(z,0) - lcsv(z,0) - lcv'(z,0) \tag{5-72}$$

If initial charge and initial current are both assumed to be zero, the following homogeneous differential equation in z remains

$$\frac{d^2V(z,s)}{dz^2} = [\imath g + (\imath c + lg)s + lcs^2]V(z,s) \tag{5-73}$$

Substitution of the exponential solution postulated in Eq. 5-10 $[V_A(s)\epsilon^{mz}]$

yields

$$m = \pm\sqrt{(r + ls)(g + cs)} \tag{5-74}$$

The solution for the voltage transform, paralleling Eq. 5-13 for the lossless line, is

$$V(z,s) = V_A(s)\epsilon^{-z\sqrt{(r+ls)(g+cs)}} + V_B(s)\epsilon^{z\sqrt{(r+ls)(g+cs)}} \tag{5-75}$$

The current may be found from the voltage by means of the transform of the following equation:

$$\frac{\partial i(z,t)}{\partial z} = -gv(z,t) - c\,\frac{\partial v(z,t)}{\partial t} \tag{2-4}$$

The transform of Eq. 2-4 is

$$\frac{dI(z,s)}{dz} = -(g + cs)V(z,s) - cv(z,0) \tag{5-76}$$

The last term is eliminated by the assumption of zero initial charge. Substitution of Eq. 5-75 in Eq. 5-76, followed by integration with respect to z, gives this expression for the transform of current:

$$I(z,s) = \sqrt{\frac{g + cs}{r + ls}}\,V_A(s)\epsilon^{-z\sqrt{(r+ls)(g+cs)}} - \sqrt{\frac{g + cs}{r + ls}}\,V_B(s)\epsilon^{z\sqrt{(r+ls)(g+cs)}} \tag{5-77}$$

Here it may be observed that the complex characteristic impedance of the steady-state a-c case, $\sqrt{(r + j\omega l)/(g + j\omega c)}$, Eq. 2-19, has an analogy in the form of an *operational characteristic impedance*, $\sqrt{(r + ls)/(g + cs)}$, one which is an irrational function of s. Likewise the complex propagation function, $\sqrt{(r + j\omega l)(g + j\omega c)}$, Eq. 2-12, has an analogy in an *operational propagation function* $\sqrt{(r + ls)(g + cs)}$. Irrational functions of s give rise to inverse transforms which are more complicated than those encountered in the lossless-line examples previously examined.

b. Distortionless line

The transform equations are drastically simplified if the line parameters are proportioned in accordance with the following equation, the criterion for the distortionless line:

$$\frac{r}{l} = \frac{g}{c} \tag{2-16}$$

Elimination of g from Eqs. 5-75 and 5-77 by substitution of Eq. 2-16 gives the following:

$$V(z,s) = V_A(s)\epsilon^{-z(r\sqrt{c/l}+s\sqrt{lc})} + V_B(s)\epsilon^{z(r\sqrt{c/l}+s\sqrt{lc})} \tag{5-78}$$

$$I(z,s) = \sqrt{\frac{c}{l}}\,V_A(s)\epsilon^{-z(r\sqrt{c/l}+s\sqrt{lc})} - \sqrt{\frac{c}{l}}\,V_B(s)\epsilon^{z(r\sqrt{c/l}+s\sqrt{lc})} \tag{5-79}$$

These should be compared with the corresponding results for the lossless line, Eqs. 5-13 and 5-14. The two sets differ in that Eqs. 5-78 and 5-79 include as multiplying factors the exponential functions of $-z\imath\sqrt{c/l}$ and $z\imath\sqrt{c/l}$. Since these factors do not depend on s, they are constants insofar as the inverse-transform procedure is concerned. Problem 5-8 calls for some complete solutions.

c. Line with finite resistance but zero shunt conductance

Problems involving transient response of a nondistortionless transmission line often have results which are so complicated that they disclose little information of a general character. If one limits the scope of analysis to the semi-infinite line ($0 \leqslant z < \infty$) of zero shunt conductance and seeks only the current which results when a d-c source is switched directly to the line, a reasonably compact result is obtained.

(1) Derivation of current function. The restriction of semi-infinite length rather than finite length eliminates reflected waves; hence the function $V_B(s)$ in Eqs. 5-75 and 5-77 must be zero. Conductance g is set equal to zero, after which those equations may be rewritten as follows:

$$V(z,s) = V_A(s)\epsilon^{-z\sqrt{lc}\sqrt{s(s+\imath/l)}} \tag{5-80}$$

$$I(z,s) = \sqrt{\frac{c}{l}}\sqrt{\frac{s}{(s+\imath/l)}}\,V_A(s)\epsilon^{-z\sqrt{lc}\sqrt{s(s+\imath/l)}} \tag{5-81}$$

The boundary condition of a constant voltage V_0 switched directly onto the line at z equal to zero gives the following:

$$V(0,s) = \frac{V_0}{s} \tag{5-82}$$

Hence, by setting z equal to zero in Eq. 5-80,

$$V_A(s) = \frac{V_0}{s} \tag{5-83}$$

This is substituted for $V_A(s)$ in Eqs. 5-80 and 5-81:

$$V(z,s) = \frac{V_0}{s}\,\epsilon^{-z\sqrt{lc}\sqrt{s(s+\imath/l)}} \tag{5-84}$$

$$I(z,s) = V_0\sqrt{\frac{c}{l}}\,\frac{1}{\sqrt{s(s+\imath/l)}}\,\epsilon^{-z\sqrt{lc}\sqrt{s(s+\imath/l)}} \tag{5-85}$$

The inverse transform of $I(z,s)$ is derivable by contour integration[9]:

$$i(z,t) = V_0\sqrt{\frac{c}{l}}\,\epsilon^{-(\imath/2l)t}I_0\left[\frac{\imath}{2l}\sqrt{t^2 - z^2lc}\right]U(t - z\sqrt{lc}) \tag{5-86}$$

Here the symbol I_0 represents the modified Bessel function of the first kind, zero order.[4] It is defined for a general argument p by the following series expansion:

$$I_0(p) = 1 + \left(\frac{p}{2}\right)^2 + \left(\frac{p}{2}\right)^4 \frac{1}{2^2} + \left(\frac{p}{2}\right)^6 \frac{1}{(3!)^2} + \cdots \tag{5-87}$$

(This function is compared with other Bessel functions in Sec. B-1*b* and in Fig. B-1.)

(2) PROPERTIES OF WAVE FRONT OF CURRENT. The unit function in Eq. 5-86 states that no current flows at a given location z until $z\sqrt{lc}$ seconds after the switch is closed. Since Eq. 5-87 shows that $I_0(0)$ is equal to unity, it appears that the current rises abruptly to the following value when the wave front passes:

$$\begin{aligned} i(z,z\sqrt{lc}) &= V_0\sqrt{\frac{c}{l}}\,\epsilon^{-(r/2l)z\sqrt{lc}} \\ &= V_0\sqrt{\frac{c}{l}}\,\epsilon^{-z(r/2)\sqrt{c/l}} \end{aligned} \tag{5-88}$$

The series-expansion technique may be used advantageously to determine the manner of change of the current at a given z during a short interval of time after the passage of the wave front. Small-quantity terms (Δt) through the third order will be carried. Let

$$t = z\sqrt{lc} + \Delta t \tag{5-89}$$

Substitution of Eq. 5-89 in Eq. 5-86, and expansion of the terms in the radical of the argument of the Bessel function, yields the following:

$$\begin{aligned} i(z,t) &= V_0\sqrt{\frac{c}{l}}\,\epsilon^{-z(r/2)\sqrt{c/l}}\epsilon^{-(r/2l)\Delta t}\, I_0\left[\frac{r}{2l}\sqrt{2\,\Delta t z\sqrt{lc} + (\Delta t)^2}\right]U(\Delta t) \\ &= V_0\sqrt{\frac{c}{l}}\,\epsilon^{-z(r/2)\sqrt{c/l}}\epsilon^{-(r/2l)\Delta t}\, I_0\left[\sqrt{\frac{r^2\,\Delta t z}{2l}\sqrt{\frac{c}{l}} + \left(\frac{r\,\Delta t}{2l}\right)^2}\right]U(\Delta t) \end{aligned} \tag{5-90}$$

This function may be expressed more concisely in terms of the following dimensionless variables:

$$u = \frac{r\,\Delta t}{2l} \tag{5-91}$$

$$v = zr\sqrt{\frac{c}{l}} \tag{5-92}$$

Substitution of Eqs. 5-91 and 5-92 reduces Eq. 5-90 to the following:

$$i(z,t) = V_0\sqrt{\frac{c}{l}}\,\epsilon^{-(v/2)}\epsilon^{-u}I_0[\sqrt{uv + u^2}]U(\Delta t) \tag{5-93}$$

The exponential of $-u$ and the Bessel function will be replaced with power series (see Eq. 5-87):

$$\epsilon^{-u} \approx 1 - u + \frac{u^2}{2} - \frac{u^3}{6} \tag{5-94}$$

$$I_0[\sqrt{uv + u^2}] \approx 1 + \frac{uv + u^2}{4} + \frac{(uv + u^2)^2}{64} + \frac{(uv + u^2)^3}{2304} \tag{5-95}$$

These two series are multiplied together; by retaining all product terms in u up to and including the third power, the result will be valid to the third order in Δt (higher-order terms in u are discarded in accordance with the reasoning set forth in Sec. 2-3a):

$$\begin{aligned} \epsilon^{-u} I_0[\sqrt{uv + u^2}] &\approx 1 - u + \frac{uv}{4} + \frac{u^2}{2} + \frac{u^2}{4} - \frac{u^2 v}{4} + \frac{u^2 v^2}{64} - \frac{u^3}{6} \\ &\quad + \frac{u^3 v}{8} - \frac{u^3}{4} - \frac{u^3 v^2}{64} + \frac{u^3 v}{32} + \frac{u^3 v^3}{2304} \\ &\approx 1 - u\left(1 - \frac{v}{4}\right) + u^2\left(\frac{3}{4} - \frac{v}{4} + \frac{v^2}{64}\right) \\ &\quad - u^3\left(\frac{5}{12} - \frac{5v}{32} + \frac{v^2}{64} - \frac{v^3}{2304}\right) \end{aligned} \tag{5-96}$$

Substituting Eq. 5-96 in Eq. 5-93 and then replacing the u's and v's with Eqs. 5-91 and 5-92 gives this series expansion for current; it is valid at values of Δt and z at which u and the product uv are both small compared to unity.

$$\begin{aligned} i(z,t) \approx V_0\sqrt{\frac{c}{l}}\,\epsilon^{-z(r/2)\sqrt{c/l}}\Bigg\{1 &- \frac{r\,\Delta t}{2l}\left(1 - \frac{zr}{4}\sqrt{\frac{c}{l}}\right) \\ &+ \left(\frac{r\,\Delta t}{2l}\right)^2\left[\frac{3}{4} - \frac{zr}{4}\sqrt{\frac{c}{l}} + \frac{1}{64}\left(zr\sqrt{\frac{c}{l}}\right)^2\right] \\ &- \left(\frac{r\,\Delta t}{2l}\right)^3\left[\frac{5}{12} - \frac{5}{32}zr\sqrt{\frac{c}{l}} + \frac{1}{64}\left(zr\sqrt{\frac{c}{l}}\right)^2 - \frac{1}{2304}\left(zr\sqrt{\frac{c}{l}}\right)^3\right]\Bigg\}U(\Delta t) \end{aligned} \tag{5-97}$$

Utilizing Eq. 5-88, let

$$i(z,t) \approx i(z,z\sqrt{lc})[1 + a_1\,\Delta t + a_2(\Delta t)^2 + a_3(\Delta t)^3]U(\Delta t) \tag{5-98}$$

Comparison of Eqs. 5-97 and 5-98 discloses the following values for the coefficients a_1, a_2, and a_3:

$$a_1 = -\frac{r}{2l}\left(1 - \frac{zr}{4}\sqrt{\frac{c}{l}}\right) \tag{5-99}$$

$$a_2 = \left(\frac{r}{2l}\right)^2\left[\frac{3}{4} - \frac{zr}{4}\sqrt{\frac{c}{l}} + \frac{1}{64}\left(zr\sqrt{\frac{c}{l}}\right)^2\right] \tag{5-100}$$

$$a_3 = -\left(\frac{r}{2l}\right)^3\left[\frac{5}{12} - \frac{5}{32}zr\sqrt{\frac{c}{l}} + \frac{1}{64}\left(zr\sqrt{\frac{c}{l}}\right)^2 - \frac{1}{2304}\left(zr\sqrt{\frac{c}{l}}\right)^3\right] \tag{5-101}$$

The coefficient a_1 is proportional to the rate of change of current immediately after the wave front has passed point z, and it should be noted that its algebraic sign depends on z. Let

$$z_1 = \frac{4}{r}\sqrt{\frac{l}{c}} \tag{5-102}$$

It appears that if z is less than z_1, a_1 is negative, but if z is greater than z_1, a_1 is positive. Substitution of Eq. 5-102 for z in Eq. 5-100 will also cause a_2 to vanish; Eq. 5-97 reduces to the following at $z = z_1$:

$$i(z_1,t) \approx V_0\sqrt{\frac{c}{l}}\,\epsilon^{-2}\left[1 - \frac{1}{72}\left(\frac{r\,\Delta t}{2l}\right)^3\right]U(\Delta t) \tag{5-103}$$

The coefficient a_2 will also vanish at the following value of z:

$$z_2 = \frac{12}{r}\sqrt{\frac{l}{c}} \tag{5-104}$$

$$i(z_2,t) \approx V_0\sqrt{\frac{c}{l}}\,\epsilon^{-6}\left[1 + 2\frac{r\,\Delta t}{2l} - \frac{1}{24}\left(\frac{r\,\Delta t}{2l}\right)^3\right]U(\Delta t) \tag{5-105}$$

Numerical substitution in Eq. 5-100 indicates that a_2 is positive for $z < z_1$, negative for $z_1 < z < z_2$, and positive for $z_2 < z$.

Some observations may be made on the distorting or changing of the current function with distance along the line. Were the line lossless, the current function would be

$$i(z,t) = V_0\sqrt{\frac{c}{l}}\,U(t - z\sqrt{lc}) \tag{5-106}$$

A distortionless line would have almost as simple a current function:

$$i(z,t) = V_0\sqrt{\frac{c}{l}}\,\epsilon^{-zr\sqrt{c/l}}\,U(t - z\sqrt{lc}) \tag{5-107}$$

Inasmuch as half the losses in a distortionless line take place in the series resistance and half in the shunt conductance, Eq. 5-107 and the first terms of Eq. 5-97, for which the shunt conductance is zero, compare favorably.

Noting the results obtained in Eqs. 5-98 through 5-105 on the coefficients of the series expansion, it appears that for values of z less than z_1 the current begins to drop immediately after the wave front passes. At location z_1 the current remains constant momentarily after passage of the wave front, and then begins to decrease by an amount which is proportional to $(\Delta t)^3$. At locations between z_1 and z_2, the current increases immediately after the passage of the wave front, but at a diminishing slope which, as is shown in the next section, eventually becomes negative. Thus a maximum is formed which is distinct from the wave front. Beyond z_2 the current initially increases with an increasing slope; higher-order terms in Δt eventually reduce the slope to

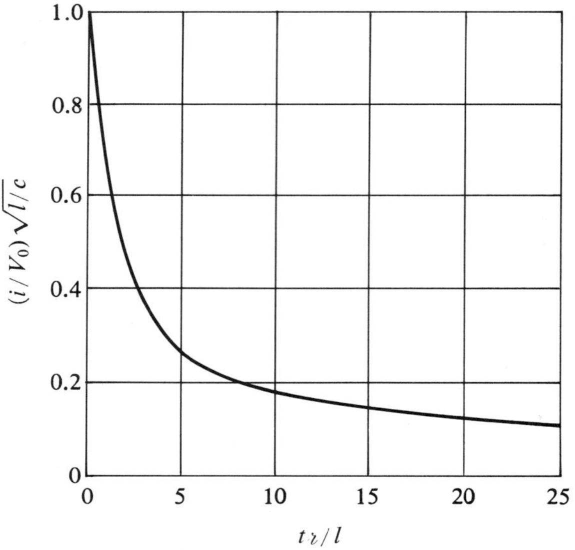

Figure 5-13 Current at input to semi-infinite line with distributed resistance, inductance, and capacitance; d-c voltage of magnitude V_0 switched directly to uncharged line

zero and then make it negative. The foregoing is illustrated in Figs. 5-13, 5-14, and 5-15.

(3) ASYMPTOTE FOR CURRENT AT LARGE VALUES OF TIME. The behavior of the current at large values of t may be examined by means of the leading term of the asymptotic approximation* for $I_0(p)$:

$$I_0(p) \approx \frac{\epsilon^p}{\sqrt{2\pi p}} \qquad (p \to \infty) \tag{5-108}$$

The following series approximation of the Bessel-function argument proves useful:

$$\sqrt{t^2 - z^2lc} = t\sqrt{1 - \frac{z^2lc}{t^2}}$$

$$\approx t\left(1 - \frac{z^2lc}{2t^2}\right) \qquad (t \gg z\sqrt{lc}) \tag{5-109}$$

The approximation in Eq. 5-109 is substituted into Eq. 5-86, and the Bessel

* Asymptotic approximations approach the given function more and more closely as the value of the *argument* is increased; a good introductory discussion is given in von Karman and Biot,[8] pages 51–4.

function is approximated by Eq. 5-108:

$$i(z,t) \approx \frac{V_0\sqrt{\dfrac{c}{l}}\,\epsilon^{-(rcz^2/4t)}}{\sqrt{(\pi r/l)[t-(z^2lc/2t)]}}$$

$$\approx V_0\sqrt{\frac{c}{\pi r t}}\,\epsilon^{-(rcz^2/4t)} \qquad (t \gg z\sqrt{lc};\, t \gg 2l/r) \qquad \textbf{(5-110)}$$

If, in addition, $t \gg rcz^2$,

$$i(z,t) \approx V_0\sqrt{\frac{c}{\pi r t}} \qquad \textbf{(5-111)}$$

Thus the current will approach zero for increasingly large values of time, but it will do so very slowly. It should be appreciated that decrease as the inverse square root of time is very different from an exponential decrease with

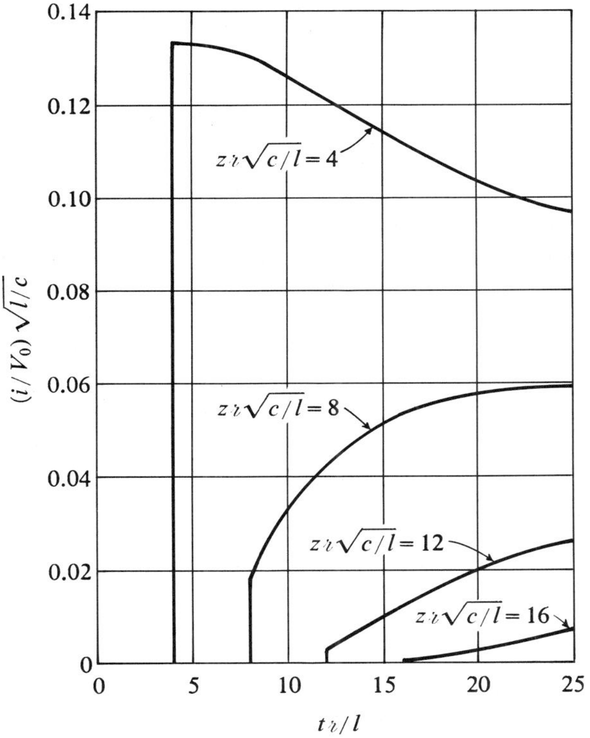

Figure 5-14 Currents at four locations along semi-infinite line with distributed resistance, inductance, and capacitance; d-c voltage of magnitude V_0 switched directly to uncharged line

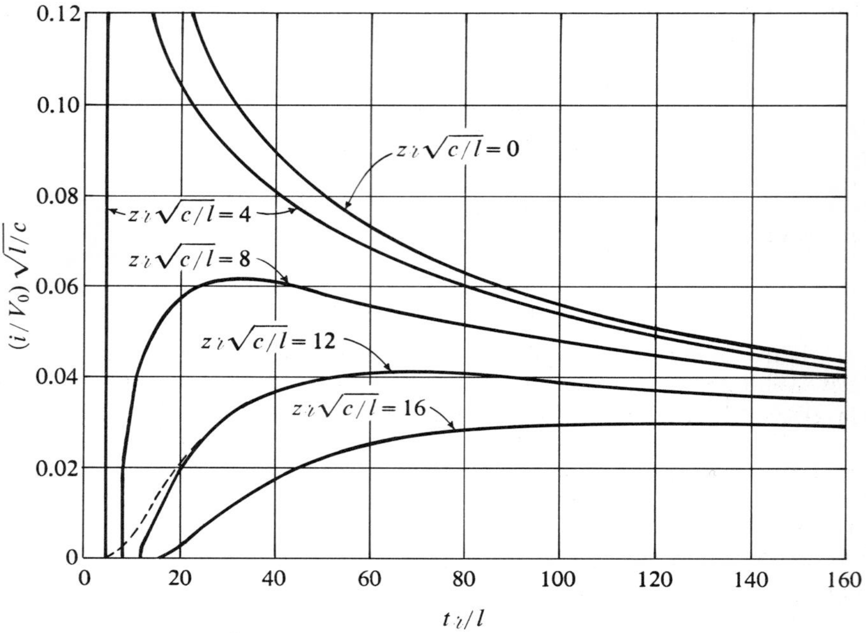

Figure 5-15 Currents on line with distributed resistance, inductance, and capacitance; as in Figs. 5-13 and 5-14 but with compressed time scale (dashed line is approximate solution, Eq. 5-110)

time. The proportionate effect of a unit increase in the argument of a negative exponential is the same whether the initial value of the argument is small or large:

$$\frac{\epsilon^{-2}}{\epsilon^{-1}} = 0.368$$

$$\frac{\epsilon^{-1001}}{\epsilon^{-1000}} = 0.368$$

A corresponding comparison for the inverse-square-root function yields the following:

$$\frac{(1/\sqrt{2})}{(1/\sqrt{1})} = 0.707$$

$$\frac{(1/\sqrt{1001})}{(1/\sqrt{1000})} = 0.9995$$

To achieve the same proportionate reduction when starting with an argument of 1000, as was achieved by changing the argument from 1 to 2, the new argument would have to be 2000.

This mode of behavior is illustrated in Fig. 5-15; the approximation of Eq. 5-110 is shown by a dashed line for the location of $z\imath\sqrt{c/l} = 12$. Good agreement with the exact solution is indicated except near the wave front.

d. Zero-inductance approximation for unloaded cable

A simplification which is mathematically convenient is that of setting both the inductance and the conductance equal to zero.* This procedure has the effect of ignoring the important physical property of a maximum velocity of energy propagation. The theoretical properties of such a line, the "ideal" unloaded cable, were examined in Chapter 2 for steady-state a-c conditions. Equations 2-41, 2-47, and 2-48 gave the characteristic impedance, propagation function, and velocity of propagation as derived under this approximation. As was pointed out in Chapter 2, those formulas typically are not valid at frequencies above the audio range. Inasmuch as a transient signal is composed of the continuous frequency band from zero to infinity (excepting possibly certain discrete frequencies), a response computed under those assumptions may be expected to differ, at least in some particulars, from physical reality. Nevertheless this is, if interpreted with discretion, a useful limiting-case situation and an approximation to the line discussed in Sec. 5-5*c*. This approximation is valid for those values of t which are much greater than $z\sqrt{lc}$ for the z under consideration and also much greater than $2l/\imath$.

Substitution of the constraints $l = 0$ and $g = 0$ into Eqs. 5-75 and 5-76 gives the following:

$$V(z,s) = V_A(s)\epsilon^{-z\sqrt{\imath cs}} + V_B(s)\epsilon^{z\sqrt{\imath cs}} \quad \textbf{(5-112)}$$

$$I(z,s) = V_A(s)\sqrt{\frac{cs}{\imath}}\,\epsilon^{-z\sqrt{\imath cs}} - V_B(s)\sqrt{\frac{cs}{\imath}}\,\epsilon^{z\sqrt{\imath cs}} \quad \textbf{(5-113)}$$

Here, as in the preceding case, the analysis will be limited to finding the current function on a semi-infinite line to which a d-c source is switched directly. Again, no reflections will occur and the propagation will be only in the positive z direction; hence $V_B(s)$ is equal to zero:

$$V_A(s) = \frac{V_0}{s} \quad \textbf{(5-83)}$$

$$I(z,s) = V_0\sqrt{\frac{c}{\imath s}}\,\epsilon^{-z\sqrt{\imath cs}} \quad \textbf{(5-114)}$$

The inverse transform of this function is derivable by contour integration[9]:

$$i(z,t) = V_0\sqrt{\frac{c}{\pi\imath t}}\,\epsilon^{-(\imath cz^2/4t)}U(t) \quad \textbf{(5-115)}$$

* If g and l in the equation of telegraphy, 2-5, are set equal to zero, the result is an equation known in classical physics as the *diffusion equation.* The same form of equation arises in the analysis of one-dimensional transient heat flow.[2]

It may be observed that this result is the same as Eq. 5-110, an approximation for the line with finite inductance but no conductance, valid for t much greater than both $z\sqrt{lc}$ and $2l/r$.

This function is plotted in Fig. 5-16; it may be examined for the location of its maximum and points of inflection far more readily than Eq. 5-86, the solution in which account is taken of inductance. Thus if the reader works Problem 5-11 he will find that the function of Eq. 5-115 has a maximum at t

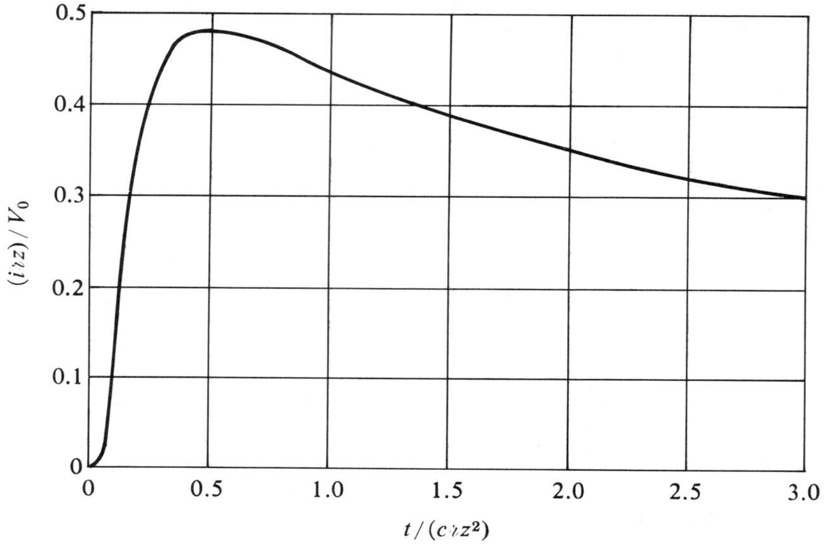

Figure 5-16 Current at location z along "ideal" unloaded cable (line with zero distributed inductance and zero shunt conductance); d-c voltage of magnitude V_0 switched directly to uncharged line

equal to $0.5rcz^2$ and points of inflection at $0.5(1 \pm \sqrt{\frac{2}{3}})rcz^2$. He will also find that the function is zero for $t = 0$, assuming that z is not zero, and that the function is extremely "flat" at that instant, in that all finite-ordered derivatives are zero then.

The function is, however, nonzero for all nonzero values of t. It curves upward abruptly as t is increased from zero, then rises rapidly toward its maximum, after which it slowly decreases. Thus the behavior of the function for small values of t ($t/rcz^2 \ll 1$) differs markedly from the solution found in Eq. 5-86 for the line with nonzero inductance. In the latter solution the current is absolutely zero until a finite time $z\sqrt{lc}$ has elapsed, at which time the current jumps instantaneously to the value $V_0\sqrt{c/l}\epsilon^{-z(r/2)\sqrt{c/l}}$.

The scales of Fig. 5-16 may be readily changed to those of Fig. 5-15 if one wishes to consider the function as an approximate solution (Eq. 5-108) for the physical unloaded cable, one which necessarily has nonzero distributed inductance. The numerical value of $zr\sqrt{c/l}$ is computed for the particular z of interest; this expression is then solved for z (with r, c, and l in literal form) and substituted into $t/(crz^2)$ and irz/V_0. Thus for $zr\sqrt{c/l} = 12$, the abscissa scale measure becomes $tr/144l$, and the ordinate scale, $(12i/V_0)\sqrt{l/c}$. In other words, 1.0 on the abscissa scale of Fig. 5-16 corresponds, for that particular z, to 144 on the scale in Fig. 5-15, and 1.0 on the ordinate scale of Fig. 5-16 corresponds to $\frac{1}{12}$ or 0.0833 on the ordinate scale of Fig. 5-15.

Substitution of the value of time cited earlier ($0.5rcz^2$) for current maximum into Eq. 5-115 gives

$$i_{\max}(z) = V_0 \frac{\epsilon^{-0.5}}{rz\sqrt{\pi/2}} = \frac{0.483V_0}{rz} \tag{5-116}$$

Thus it may be seen that the current maximum reached at any location on the line varies inversely with distance from the source. The time required for current to build up to the maximum at any location varies as the square of the distance z; hence the maximum travels with an ever-decreasing velocity.

If a telegraph signal is treated as a superposition of functions of this type initiated at successively delayed times, the signal will be distinct at locations of z closer than say $\sqrt{T/(rc)}$, wherein T is the duration of a dot or the interval between consecutive dots or dashes. At locations several times as far from the source, the front and crest portions of the functions resulting from the beginning and end of a signal pulse, and those from consecutive pulses, will overlap to such an extent that (1) the amplitude of current variation is greatly reduced, and (2) the wave shape bears scant resemblance to the input.

5-6. CONCLUSIONS

Nonsinusoidal signals impressed on a lossless line give rise to voltage and current waves or surges which travel at a constant velocity of propagation equal to $1/\sqrt{lc}$. If examined at different distances from the source, the observed wave shapes differ only by fixed time delays. The shifting theorem of the Laplace transform readily accommodates the time-delay-with-distance property of the traveling wave. The concept of reflection coefficient, if generalized into an operational function of s, systematizes the study of terminations involving an inductor or capacitor instead of a resistor, or any network combination of parameters of these three types.

Transient response on a distortionless line differs basically from that on a lossless line only by reason of attenuation at the rate of $r\sqrt{c/l}$ nepers per unit of distance traversed by the voltage or current function.

The transforms of voltage and current for the general (nondistortionless) line involve irrational functions of s. The corresponding inverse transforms are commonly so complicated that one can sense little as to details of wave shape by mere inspection of the mathematical result. Rather it is necessary to resort to such dissecting approaches as plots for particular values of parameters, series expansions to bring out the behavior at small values of the argument, and asymptotic expressions to show the dominant trend at large values.

A semi-infinite line with resistance, inductance, and capacitance, to which a d-c voltage is switched directly, will have a current function with the following properties:

(1) Current is zero at every location until a wave front, traveling at the finite velocity of $1/\sqrt{lc}$ has passed the given location.

(2) The height of the wave front decreases exponentially with the distance traveled.

(3) At points more remote than $zr\sqrt{c/l} = 4$, the current rises after the passing of the wave front, reaching a maximum at some later time.

(4) At points for which $zr\sqrt{c/l} \geqslant 16$ the current function, when plotted, is almost indistinguishable from that which is computed if inductance is ignored.

(5) Among points as remote as suggested in (4), the current maximum decreases as the inverse first power of distance, and throughout that range it is very much greater than the corresponding wave front. Thus for practical purposes the latter is scarcely discernable on a plotted curve. Similarly, the wave front is not likely to produce a response in the receiving instrument of a physical line or cable which is significant in comparison to the response produced by the current maximum.

(6) Among locations suggested in (4), the time delay from the closing of the switch until current maximum is proportional to the square of the distance.

(7) When t is large ($t \gg crz^2$ and $t \gg 2l/r$), the current at every location decreases in proportion to the inverse square root of time.

More comprehensive treatments of transient traveling waves may be found in the references in this chapter and in many other works. Because of the mathematical bulkiness of solutions relating to nondistortionless lines, the reader may well sense a point of diminishing returns along a path of progressive increases in generality of boundary conditions, etc. It is to be hoped that such a point was not passed within this chapter!

PROBLEMS

5-1. Sketch wave shapes corresponding to those in Fig. 5-3 for the case in which $R_G = \sqrt{l/c}$ and $R_R = 0.2\sqrt{l/c}$.

5-2. Sketch wave shapes corresponding to those in Fig. 5-5 for the case in which $R_G = 4.0\sqrt{l/c}$ and $R_R = 0.2\sqrt{l/c}$.

5-3. Given the initially charged line shown in Fig. 5-6 and discussed in Sec. 5-2*d*, write the transforms $V(z, s)$ and $I(z, s)$ and obtain the inverse transforms. Sketch the voltage and current as functions of time at two locations on the line for the following cases: (*a*) $R = \sqrt{l/c}$, (*b*) $R = 4\sqrt{l/c}$, and (*c*) $R = 0.25\sqrt{l/c}$.

5-4. In Fig. 5-7 let the terminal impedance be replaced by L_R and R_R in series. Write expressions for $V(z, s)$, $I(z, s)$, $v(z, t)$, and $i(z, t)$ and sketch wave shapes for the following cases: (*a*) $R_R = \sqrt{l/c}$, and (*b*) $R_R = 0.5\sqrt{l/c}$.

5-5. In Fig. 5-7 let $R_G = 0.25\sqrt{l/c}$. Obtain, as functions of time, the first four traveling-wave components of voltage and current, and sketch.

5-6. In Fig. 5-9 let the shunt resistor R_D be replaced by two resistors $R_S/2$, one connecting the upper conductors of lines 1 and 2 and the other joining the two lower conductors. Write expressions for the reflection coefficients ρ_{1S2} and ρ_{2S1}, and discuss the relationships among the incident and transmitted waves of voltage and current.

5-7. Assume the following relationships among the parameters in Fig. 5-12: $l_1 = l_2 = l_3$, $c_1 = c_2 = c_3$, $R_G = \sqrt{l_1/c_1}$, $R_{R2} = \sqrt{l_2/c_2}$, and $R_{R3} = 10\sqrt{l_3/c_3}$. Assume that the lines are initially uncharged, and that the source V_0 is a battery. If the switch closes at t equals zero, find $v(t)$ and $i(t)$ at locations z_a, z_b, and z_c for values of time prior to the third reflection from R_{R3}. Sketch these functions.

5-8. Assume that the lines shown in Figs. 5-1 and 5-7 are distortionless, with $\alpha z_r = 1.40$. Find $v(z, t)$ and $i(z, t)$ for the boundary conditions specified in the examples worked in Sec. 5-2*b* and 5-3, respectively, and sketch wave shapes corresponding to Figs. 5-3 and 5-8.

5-9. Compute the distance z_1, Eq. 5-102, for (*a*) the open-wire line described in Fig. 2-2, and (*b*) the cable described in Fig. 2-3. Assume that the shunt conductance g is zero in both cases.

5-10. Suppose that a dot in telegraphic transmission has a duration of $\frac{1}{24}$ second. To what numerical value of increment on the abscissa scales of Fig. 5-13, 5-14, and 5-15 does this time interval correspond for the two lines considered in the preceding problem?

5-11. Locate the maximum and the points of inflection with respect to time of the function $i(z, t)$ given in Eq. 5-115.

REFERENCES

1. Bewley, L. V., *Traveling Waves on Transmission Systems* (*2nd ed.*). New York: John Wiley & Sons, Inc., 1951.

2. Cheng, D. K., *Analysis of Linear Systems*. Reading, Mass.: Addison-Wesley Publishing Company, Inc., 1959.

3. *Electrical Transmission and Distribution Reference Book*. East Pittsburgh, Pa.: Westinghouse Electric Corporation, 1950.

4. McLachlan, N. W., *Bessel Functions for Engineers*, 2nd ed. London: Oxford University Press, 1961.

5. Nahman, N. S., "A Discussion on the Transient Analysis of Coaxial Cables Considering High-Frequency Losses," *IRE Trans. Circuit Theory*, CT-9, No. 2 (1962), 144–52.

6. Pélissier, R., "Propagation of Transient and Periodic Waves along Transmission Lines" (in French), *Rev. Gen. Elec.*, 59 (1950), 379–99, 437–54, 502–12.

7. Van der Pol, Balthasar and H. Bremmer, *Operational Calculus Based on the Two-Sided Laplace Integral* (2nd ed.), chap. V. London: Cambridge University Press, 1955.

8. von Kármán, Theodore and M. A. Biot, *Mathematical Methods in Engineering*. New York: McGraw-Hill Book Company, Inc., 1940.

9. Weber, Ernst, *Linear Transient Analysis, Vol. II*. New York: John Wiley & Sons, Inc., 1956.

10. Wigington, R. L. and N. S. Nahman, "Transient Analysis of Coaxial Cable Considering Skin Effect," *Proc. IRE*, 45, No. 2 (1957), 166–74.

CHAPTER 6

Lumped-Parameter Networks Related to Transmission Lines

This treatment of lumped-parameter networks, following as it does a discussion of distributed-parameter transmission lines, will be a specialized study directed toward a particular class known as *two-terminal-pair* networks. Such networks have properties closely analogous to the characteristic impedance and propagation function of a transmission line, and tandem assemblies of identical sections of a certain type may simulate a transmission line over a limited range of frequencies. Such a network is sometimes used as a delay line, or it may be used as an "artificial line" for laboratory study of standing waves, etc.

Other two-terminal-pair networks may be used in conjunction with distributed-parameter lines for such functions as (1) frequency-discriminating or filtering, (2) attenuating, (3) impedance matching, and (4) equalizing, or the offsetting of attenuation distortion or phase distortion (see footnote to Sec. 2-3*c*).

Networks of this type may be classified as symmetrical or unsymmetrical; the properties of the former class more closely resemble those of a transmission line and hence will be discussed first.

6-1. SYMMETRICAL NETWORKS: GENERAL PROPERTIES

The basic symmetrical two-terminal-pair section may have either a "T" or pi form, as shown in Fig. 6-1. This analysis will not be concerned with

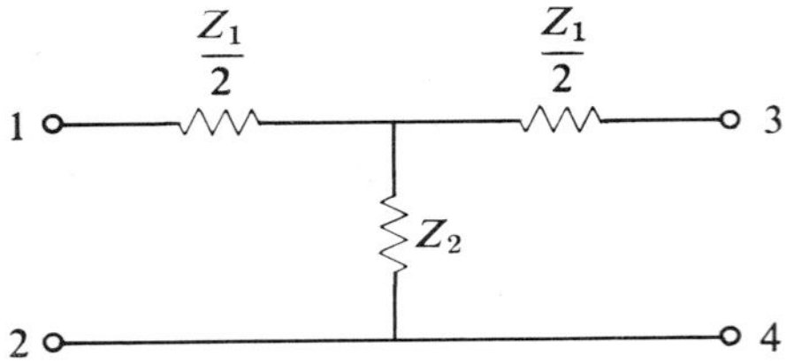

(*a*) T section

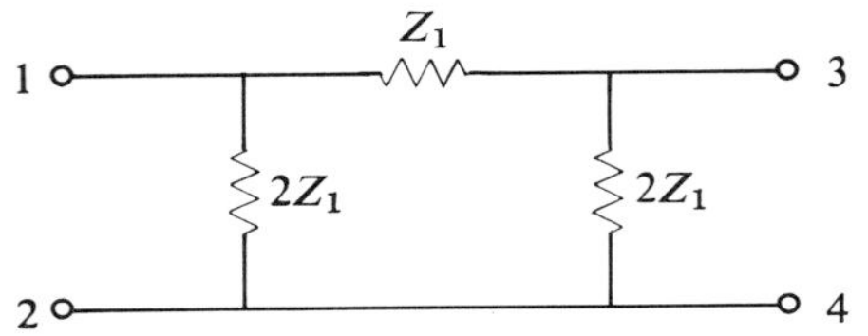

(*b*) Pi section

Figure 6-1 Symmetrical two-terminal-pair networks

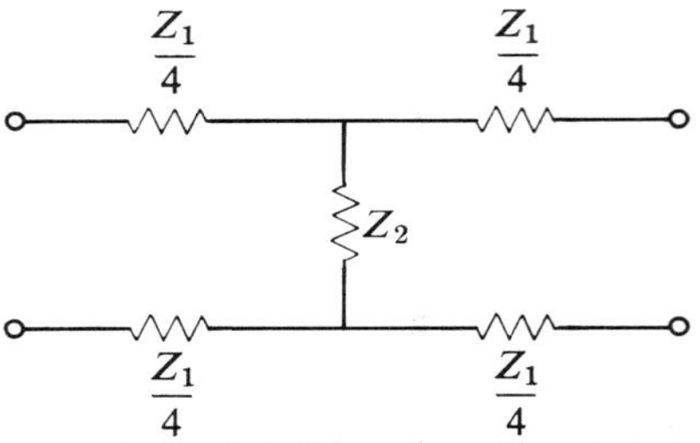

(*a*) T section

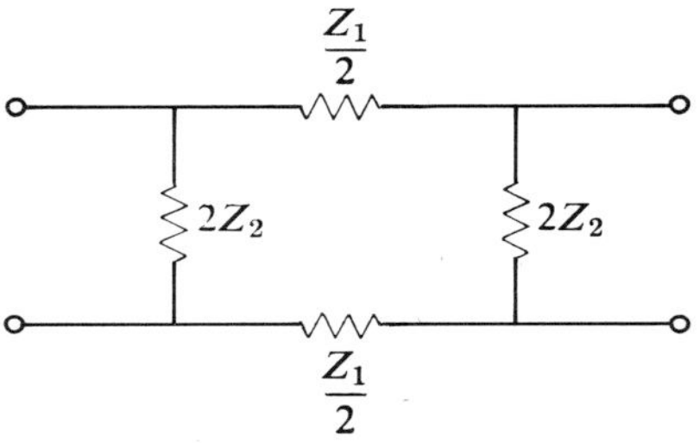

(*b*) Pi section

Figure 6-2 Balanced symmetrical two-terminal-pair networks

feedback systems, and it is contemplated that a network or transmission line will be connected to terminals 1 and 2, and another network or line to terminals 3 and 4, but that no external connections will be made from terminals 1 or 2 or points to the left of them, to terminals 3 or 4 or points to the right of them. The customary notation is, as indicated, Z_1 for the total series impedance per section and Z_2 for the resultant shunt impedance per section. The section may be drawn in balanced form, as shown in Fig. 6-2, with the series impedance divided equally between the top and bottom conductors. Impedances Z_1 and Z_2 may each be composed of a single resistor, inductor, or capacitor, or any combination of elements of any two types, or of all three types.

If several symmetrical sections are connected in tandem so as to form a ladder network, as suggested in Fig. 6-3, a degree of uniformity is introduced.

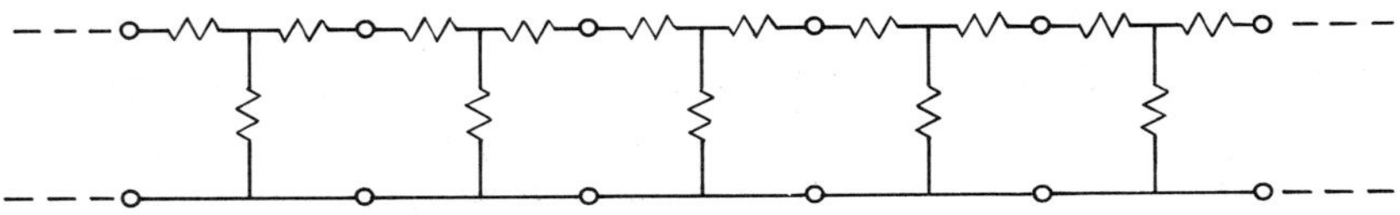

Figure 6-3 Ladder network of symmetrical T sections

To an observer concerned with voltage-current relationships at the junction points of the pairs, it resembles a succession of incremental sections along a distributed-parameter line. From this analogy two derived parameters may be formulated, the iterative impedance and the iterative transfer function.

a. Iterative impedance

It was found in the study of the transmission line that if the line is terminated in an impedance known as the characteristic impedance, Eq. 2-19, the input impedance has that same value, independent of the line length. By analogy, a ladder network might consist of an integral number of symmetrical

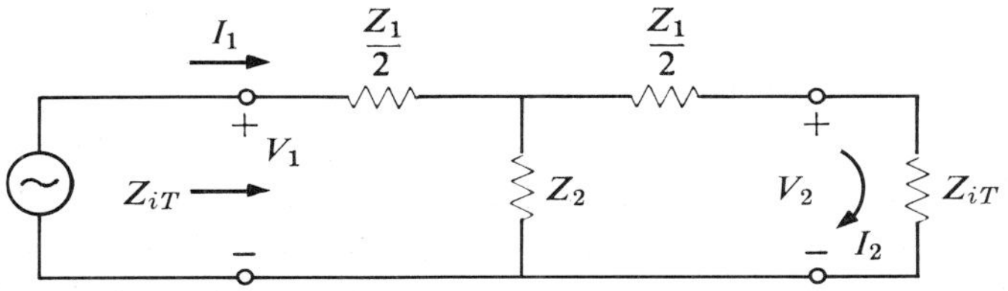

Figure 6-4 Symmetrical T section with iterative-impedance termination

sections, and an impedance should exist which, if used to terminate the network, would yield the same value for the input impedance. That impedance will be called the *iterative impedance.* If one section is terminated in its iterative impedance, a second, identical section connected to the input terminals of the first section would also be terminated in iterative impedance, and hence would have the same value as its input impedance.

Hence, in accordance with Fig. 6-4, for a T section,

$$Z_{iT} = \frac{Z_1}{2} + \frac{Z_2(Z_1/2 + Z_{iT})}{Z_2 + (Z_1/2) + Z_{iT}} \qquad \textbf{(6-1)}$$

This may be solved for Z_{iT} to yield

$$Z_{iT} = \sqrt{Z_1 Z_2 + \frac{Z_1^2}{4}} \qquad \textbf{(6-2)}$$

$$Z_{iT} = \sqrt{Z_1 Z_2}\sqrt{1 + \frac{Z_1}{4Z_2}} \qquad \textbf{(6-3)}$$

For a pi section the admittance point of view is more expedient:

$$Y_{i\pi} = \frac{Y_2}{2} + \frac{Y_1(Y_2/2 + Y_{i\pi})}{Y_1 + (Y_2/2) + Y_{i\pi}}$$

This leads to

$$Y_{i\pi} = \sqrt{Y_1 Y_2 + \frac{Y_2^2}{4}} \tag{6-4}$$

This may be restated in terms of impedances:

$$Z_{i\pi} = \frac{1}{\sqrt{\dfrac{1}{Z_1 Z_2} + \dfrac{1}{4Z_2^2}}}$$

$$= \frac{\sqrt{Z_1 Z_2}}{\sqrt{1 + (Z_1/4Z_2)}} \tag{6-5}$$

b. Iterative transfer function

The propagation function of a transmission line is a complex quantity of which the real part is the attenuation function, and the imaginary part, the phase function, of a traveling wave. A single traveling wave can exist on a line of finite length Δz if the line is terminated with its characteristic impedance; then the sending-end and receiving-end voltage and current phasors would be related to the propagation function as follows:

$$\epsilon^{\gamma\,\Delta z} = \frac{V_S}{V_R}$$

$$= \frac{I_S}{I_R} \tag{6-6}$$

By analogy, the *iterative transfer function* Γ of a single symmetrical section of a ladder network will be defined as follows, where it is understood that the section is terminated with its iterative impedance:

$$\epsilon^{\Gamma} = \frac{V_1}{V_2}$$

$$= \frac{I_1}{I_2} \tag{6-7}$$

$$\Gamma = \ln\left(\frac{V_1}{V_2}\right)$$

$$= \ln\left(\frac{I_1}{I_2}\right) \tag{6-8}$$

The ratio of the current phasors in the T section may be found by examination of Fig. 6-4:

$$I_1 = I_2 \frac{Z_{iT} + (Z_1/2)}{Z_2} + I_2$$

$$\frac{I_1}{I_2} = 1 + \frac{Z_{iT}}{Z_2} + \frac{Z_1}{2Z_2}$$

$$= 1 + \sqrt{\frac{Z_1}{Z_2}}\sqrt{1 + \frac{Z_1}{4Z_2}} + \frac{Z_1}{2Z_2} \qquad \textbf{(6-9)}$$

The same result may be found for the pi section by using voltage phasors and admittances. Substitution of Eq. 6-9 in Eq. 6-8 gives the following:

$$\Gamma = \ln\left(1 + \frac{Z_1}{2Z_2} + \sqrt{\frac{Z_1}{Z_2}}\sqrt{1 + \frac{Z_1}{4Z_2}}\right) \qquad \textbf{(6-10)*}$$

Problem 6-1 deals with an interesting property of this function.

The following forms may be derived from Eq. 6-10 with the aid of identities:

$$\Gamma = \cosh^{-1}\left(1 + \frac{Z_1}{2Z_2}\right) \qquad \textbf{(6-11)}$$

$$\Gamma = 2\sinh^{-1}\left(\frac{1}{2}\sqrt{\frac{Z_1}{Z_2}}\right) \qquad \textbf{(6-12)}$$

Equations 6-11 and 6-12 are useful if Z_1 and Z_2 are both purely resistive, or both purely reactive; otherwise Eq. 6-10 is generally the easiest to evaluate for Γ.

c. Z_i and Γ in terms of open-circuit and short-circuit impedances

Another expression for Γ, also derivable by identities, is the following:

$$\Gamma = \tanh^{-1}\left(\frac{\sqrt{Z_1^2 + 4Z_1Z_2}}{Z_1 + 2Z_2}\right) \qquad \textbf{(6-13)}$$

If one writes expressions for the open-circuit and short-circuit impedances (Z_{oc} and Z_{sc}) of a single section of a symmetrical T network, the following identities may be easily obtained (see Problem 6-6):

$$Z_i = \sqrt{Z_{oc}Z_{sc}} \qquad \textbf{(6-14)}$$

$$\tanh\Gamma = \sqrt{\frac{Z_{sc}}{Z_{oc}}} \qquad \textbf{(6-15)}$$

These should be compared with Eqs. 4-16 and 4-17, the corresponding results for a finite length of a distributed-parameter line. The procedure derived in Sec. 4-3 for calculating the inverse hyperbolic tangent of a complex argument is, of course, immediately applicable here.

* The reader is reminded that the natural logarithm of a complex argument is also complex, and has as its real part the natural logarithm of the magnitude of the argument, and as its imaginary part, the angle of the argument, stated in radians: $\ln(|A| \underline{/\theta_A}) = \ln|A| + j\theta_A$.

6-2. SIMULATED LINE AND CONSTANT-k LOW-PASS FILTER

A lossless transmission line has only series inductance and shunt capacitance, and a two-terminal-pair network intended to simulate a short section of such a line would logically have a purely inductive Z_1 and capacitive Z_2. By proper choice of values, including the length of line to be simulated by one section, the correspondence between the properties of the line and the network may be made very good over the band of frequencies between zero and some specified value, yet at higher frequencies the network properties will differ markedly from those of the line. Effectively the network would be a *low-pass filter*, a member of a class known as constant-k filters. The fundamental properties of the low-pass filter of this type will be developed to highlight the differences between a lumped-parameter delay line and a distributed-parameter transmission line.

a. Definition and equivalent values: derived parameters

The designator "constant k" applies to any symmetrical two-terminal-pair network for which Z_1 and Z_2 are purely reactive and obey the following constraint with respect to frequency:

$$Z_1 Z_2 = k^2 \tag{6-16}$$

Here k is a real number.

For the low-pass filter the following are applicable:

$$Z_1 = j\omega L_1 \tag{6-17}$$

$$Z_2 = \frac{1}{j\omega C_2} \tag{6-18}$$

In terms of a simulated line section of length Δz_{sec}, and distributed inductance and capacitance per unit length of l and c, the parameters L_1 and C_2 would be as follows:

$$L_1 = \Delta z_{\text{sec}} l \tag{6-19}$$

$$C_2 = \Delta z_{\text{sec}} c \tag{6-20}$$

Equations 6-17 and 6-18 may be substituted into Eqs. 6-3, 6-5, and 6-10:

$$Z_{\text{iT}} = \sqrt{\frac{L_1}{C_2}}\sqrt{1 - \frac{\omega^2 L_1 C_2}{4}} \tag{6-21}$$

$$Z_{\text{i}\pi} = \sqrt{\frac{L_1}{C_2}}\frac{1}{\sqrt{1 - \dfrac{\omega^2 L_1 C_2}{4}}} \tag{6-22}$$

$$\Gamma = \ln\left(1 - \frac{\omega^2 L_1 C_2}{2} + \omega\sqrt{-L_1 C_2}\sqrt{1 - \frac{\omega^2 L_1 C_2}{4}}\right) \tag{6-23}$$

b. Cutoff frequency

The expressions just listed have two differing sets of properties depending on whether the discriminant $1 - (\omega^2 L_1 C_2/4)$ is positive or negative, in that (1) the iterative impedances are resistive in the former case but reactive in the latter, and (2) the argument of the logarithm in Eq. 6-23 is complex in the former case but purely real in the latter. Thus two distinct modes of behavior may be expected, depending on the frequency. The frequency at which the discriminant vanishes, in other words, the boundary between these two modes, is known as the *cutoff frequency*, ω_c:

$$\omega_c = \frac{2}{\sqrt{L_1 C_2}} \tag{6-24}$$

This may be put in terms of a simulated line section by substituting Eqs. 6-19 and 6-20:

$$\omega_c = \frac{2}{\Delta z_{\text{sec}}\sqrt{lc}} \tag{6-25}$$

Thus a simulated line with a stated equivalent length may be designed with a cutoff frequency as high as desired, short of the microwave range. (There the physical components of the network have appreciable electrical length.) One has merely to use a sufficiently large number of network sections in tandem, with each section representing a correspondingly short length of line.

It is convenient to substitute Eq. 6-24 for the L_1C_2 products in Eqs. 6-21 through 6-23. Then

$$Z_{\text{iT}} = \sqrt{\frac{L_1}{C_2}}\sqrt{1 - \left(\frac{\omega}{\omega_c}\right)^2} \tag{6-26}$$

$$Z_{\text{i}\pi} = \sqrt{\frac{L_1}{C_2}}\frac{1}{\sqrt{1 - \left(\frac{\omega}{\omega_c}\right)^2}} \tag{6-27}$$

$$\Gamma = \ln\left[1 - 2\left(\frac{\omega}{\omega_c}\right)^2 + 2j\frac{\omega}{\omega_c}\sqrt{1 - \left(\frac{\omega}{\omega_c}\right)^2}\right] \tag{6-28}$$

$$\Gamma = \ln\left[1 - 2\left(\frac{\omega}{\omega_c}\right)^2 + 2\frac{\omega}{\omega_c}\sqrt{\left(\frac{\omega}{\omega_c}\right)^2 - 1}\right] \tag{6-29}$$

The same substitutions may be made in Eqs. 6-11 and 6-12:

$$\Gamma = \cosh^{-1}\left[1 - 2\left(\frac{\omega}{\omega_c}\right)^2\right] \tag{6-30}$$

$$\Gamma = 2\sinh^{-1}\left(\pm j\frac{\omega}{\omega_c}\right) \tag{6-31}$$

Frequencies below the cutoff frequency are said to be in the *pass band*, whereas those above it are in the *stop band*. The appropriateness of this terminology is borne out in the discussion of iterative impedance and iterative transfer function as functions of frequency.

c. Iterative impedance as a function of frequency

The iterative impedances for the T and pi sections are plotted versus frequency in Fig. 6-5. For $\omega \ll \omega_c$, the radicals in Eqs. 6-26 and 6-27 may be

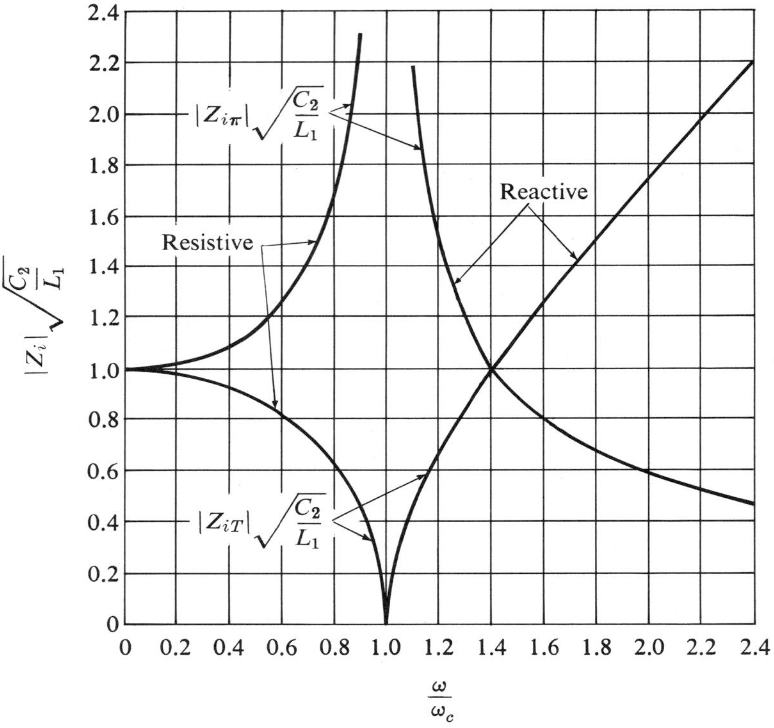

Figure 6-5 Iterative impedances of constant-k low-pass filter

approximated by the first two terms in their series expansions:

$$Z_{iT} \approx \sqrt{\frac{L_1}{C_2}}\left[1 - \frac{1}{2}\left(\frac{\omega}{\omega_c}\right)^2\right] \tag{6-32}$$

$$Z_{i\pi} \approx \sqrt{\frac{L_1}{C_2}}\left[1 + \frac{1}{2}\left(\frac{\omega}{\omega_c}\right)^2\right] \tag{6-33}$$

Thus $Z_i = \sqrt{L_1/C_2}$ is the low-frequency asymptote for both functions, and the initial modes of deviation from that asymptote (for increasing frequency) are as the square of frequency.

Of particular interest is the fact that the iterative impedances are resistive at frequencies below cutoff, but reactive at higher frequencies. (The change is abrupt for a lossless network; if resistance is present, a smooth transition takes place in which the angle of Z_i changes continuously, although not uniformly.)

Below cutoff frequency a set of sections in tandem, if terminated in iterative impedance, will transmit power from the supply to the terminating resistor. This behavior corresponds to that of a lossless transmission line terminated in its characteristic impedance. Average power enters the sending end in both cases, but no power is dissipated in the network or line, because both are composed of pure reactances.

Above cutoff frequency, a system consisting of a set of sections in tandem with an iterative-impedance termination is purely reactive throughout. No average power will be absorbed in the terminating reactance, hence none can be transmitted by the network. Rather the energy movement in the system will be oscillatory, and volt-amperes, wherever measured, will be reactive.

One may anticipate that practical applications of the two-terminal-pair network would involve terminations of either (1) fixed resistances, or (2) relatively simple networks, which would not vary with frequency in a manner approaching Eqs. 6-26 or 6-27. The question may be raised regarding the worth of analyses based on the assumption of an iterative-impedance termination. The answer is that of the simplicity with which a good approximation may be obtained for multiunit filters. Exact analyses would involve multiloop or multinode procedures; in the iterative-impedance approach, the phase shift and attenuation of each section are calculated independently of the other sections, and the corresponding quantities for each section are added together. Except for frequencies in the immediate vicinity of cutoff, the error is comfortingly small.

d. Properties of iterative transfer function

The attenuation and phase functions may be designated separately. Let

$$\Gamma = \bar{\alpha} + j\bar{\beta} \tag{6-34}$$

The iterative transfer function has differing properties in the pass and stop bands.

(1) PASS BAND. If $(\omega/\omega_c) < 1$, one may show in Eq. 6-28, by squaring the real and imaginary parts, that the argument of the logarithm has a magnitude of unity. Hence

$$\bar{\alpha} = 0 \tag{6-35}$$

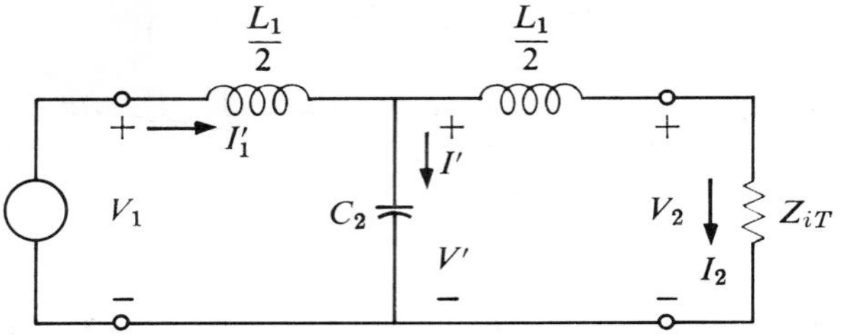

(*a*) Circuit diagram

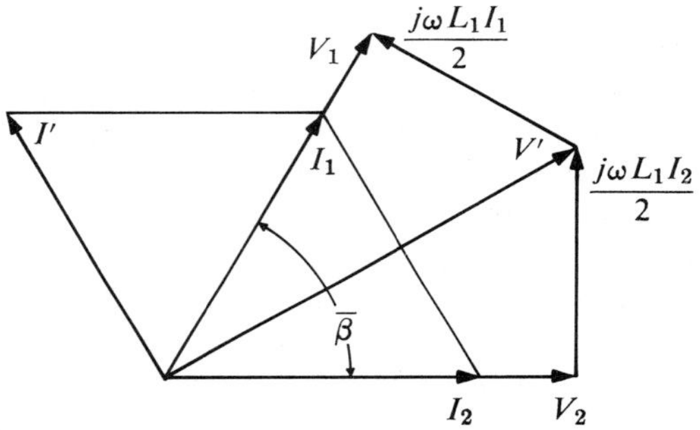

(*b*) Phasor diagram for pass band

Figure 6-6 Constant-*k* low-pass filter, T section

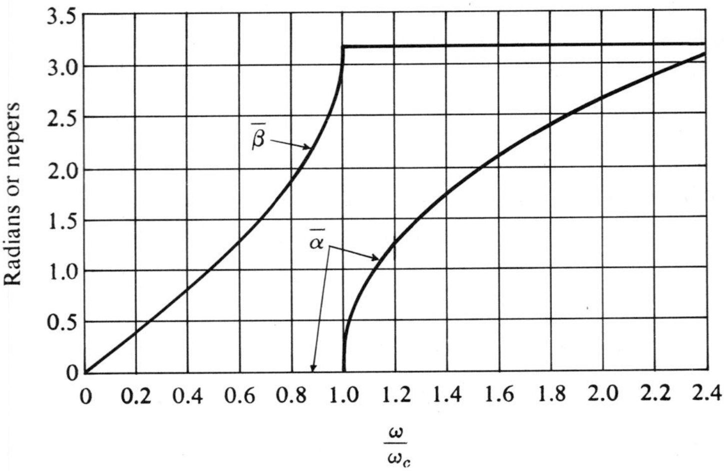

Figure 6-7 Attenuation and phase functions of constant-*k* low-pass filter section

The phase function may be stated as the inverse tangent of the ratio of the imaginary part to the real part of the logarithmic argument, but a more compact expression may be developed from Eq. 6-31. The hyperbolic sine of $\Gamma/2$ may be expanded into hyperbolic functions of $\bar{\alpha}/2$ and trigonometric functions of $\bar{\beta}/2$:

$$\sinh\frac{\Gamma}{2} = \sinh\frac{\bar{\alpha}}{2}\cosh\frac{j\bar{\beta}}{2} + \cosh\frac{\bar{\alpha}}{2}\sinh\frac{j\bar{\beta}}{2}$$

$$= \sinh\frac{\bar{\alpha}}{2}\cos\frac{\bar{\beta}}{2} + j\cosh\frac{\bar{\alpha}}{2}\sin\frac{\bar{\beta}}{2} \tag{6-36}$$

Substitution of Eq. 6-36 in Eq. 6-31 gives

$$\sinh\frac{\bar{\alpha}}{2}\cos\frac{\bar{\beta}}{2} + j\cosh\frac{\bar{\alpha}}{2}\sin\frac{\bar{\beta}}{2} = \pm j\frac{\omega}{\omega_c} \tag{6-37}$$

The real and imaginary parts may be equated separately:

$$\sinh\frac{\bar{\alpha}}{2}\cos\frac{\bar{\beta}}{2} = 0 \tag{6-38}$$

$$\cosh\frac{\bar{\alpha}}{2}\sin\frac{\bar{\beta}}{2} = \pm\frac{\omega}{\omega_c} \tag{6-39}$$

Since $\bar{\alpha}$ has already been found to be zero, Eq. 6-38 is satisfied and Eq. 6-39 reduces to the following:

$$\sin\frac{\bar{\beta}}{2} = \pm\frac{\omega}{\omega_c} \tag{6-40}$$

Construction of a phasor diagram such as Fig. 6-6 shows that the positive sign should be used in Eq. 6-40; that is, the output voltage and current lag the input quantities (the reverse is true in a high-pass filter):

$$\bar{\beta} = 2\sin^{-1}\left(\frac{\omega}{\omega_c}\right) \tag{6-41}$$

The phase function is shown in Fig. 6-7 as a function of frequency. For $\omega \ll \omega_c$, a series approximation to Eq. 6-41 is informative:

$$\sin^{-1} x \approx x + \frac{x^3}{6} + \cdots \qquad (x^2 < 1)$$

$$\bar{\beta} \approx 2\frac{\omega}{\omega_c} + \frac{1}{3}\left(\frac{\omega}{\omega_c}\right)^3 + \cdots \tag{6-42}$$

The first term represents a straight line and is the low-frequency asymptote of Fig. 6-7.

A related function, of interest as an indicator of the phase distortion produced by a section of the network, is the *delay time*. Ideally it should be independent of frequency. Let

$$v_{\text{in}} = V_0 \sin \omega t \tag{6-43}$$

$$\begin{aligned} v_{\text{out}} &= V_0 \sin(\omega t - \bar{\beta}) \\ &= V_0 \sin \omega \left(t - \frac{\bar{\beta}}{\omega} \right) \end{aligned} \tag{6-44}$$

The function v_{out} will be delayed with respect to v_{in} by the time interval $\bar{\beta}/\omega$. Thus if $\bar{\beta}$ were directly proportional to ω, the delay time would be the same for all frequencies, and a composite wave consisting of components of several frequencies would undergo no phase distortion in passing through the network. This condition is satisfied approximately in the lower part of the pass band to the extent indicated by Eq. 6-42.

(2) STOP BAND. For $(\omega/\omega_c) > 1$, Eq. 6-29 is the appropriate form rather than Eq. 6-28. In this instance the argument of the logarithm will be a negative real number. Depending on whether a negative sign or a positive sign is given to the square-root quantity, the magnitude of the logarithmic argument will be greater or less than unity. (See Problem 6-1 regarding the mathematical relationship between the two results and Problem 6-4 regarding physical interpretation.) The first-named choice, that of a negative sign for the radical, will yield an argument magnitude greater than unity and hence a positive $\bar{\alpha}$. As indicated by the outcome of Problem 6-5, this result is meaningful in filter applications, whereas a negative $\bar{\alpha}$ is not.

The angle of the logarithmic argument is π radians:

$$\bar{\beta} = \pi \tag{6-45}$$

This will satisfy Eq. 6-38 and will reduce Eq. 6-39 to the following:

$$\cosh \frac{\bar{\alpha}}{2} = \frac{\omega}{\omega_c} \tag{6-46}$$

$$\bar{\alpha} = 2 \cosh^{-1} \left(\frac{\omega}{\omega_c} \right) \tag{6-47}$$

The attenuation function is also shown in Fig. 6-7 as a function of frequency. Since the iterative impedance in the stop band is purely reactive, "attenuation" consists of a reduction in volt-amperes reactive between input and output, rather than an absorption of power.

The behavior of the constant-k low-pass filter in the stop band has no resemblance to that of a distributed-parameter transmission line.

Some of the foregoing concepts of symmetrical networks are reviewed in Problems 6-7 and 6-8.

6-3. UNSYMMETRICAL NETWORKS: IMPEDANCE MATCHING

An unsymmetrical two-terminal-pair T network is shown in Fig. 6-8. It may be viewed as a generalization of the symmetrical network, and the concepts of iterative impedance and iterative transfer function may be modified so as to describe properties which are associated with the use of such a network in a transmission system.

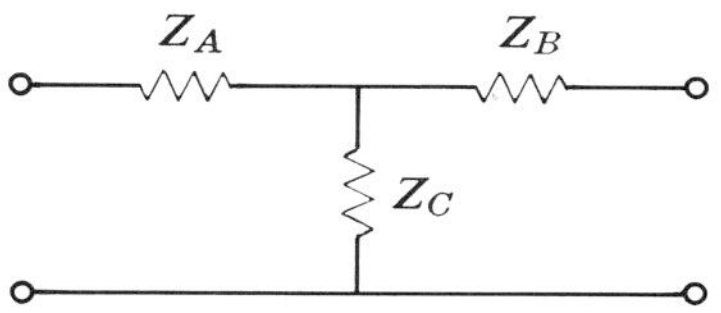

Figure 6-8 Unsymmetrical two-terminal-pair network, T section

An application which illustrates the elementary theory is an unsymmetrical T network tandem-linking two lines of differing characteristic impedances, as shown in Fig. 6-9; ideally no reflections should occur in either direction.

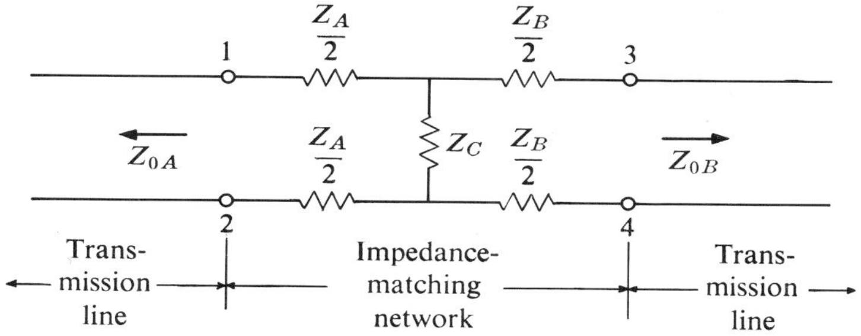

Figure 6-9 Balanced unsymmetrical T network connected to transmission lines

a. Image impedances

To avoid reflections, the input impedance at terminals 1-2 should be equal to Z_{0A}, whereas that at terminals 3-4 should be equal to Z_{0B}. These input impedances are given the name *image impedances* and may be described in lumped-parameter form as shown in Fig. 6-10. The following equations may be written for the input impedances to the two networks:

$$Z_{iA} = Z_A + \frac{Z_C(Z_B + Z_{iB})}{Z_C + Z_B + Z_{iB}} \tag{6-48}$$

$$Z_{iB} = Z_B + \frac{Z_C(Z_A + Z_{iA})}{Z_C + Z_A + Z_{iA}} \tag{6-49}$$

Simultaneous solution of these equations[3] yields the following:

$$Z_{iA} = \sqrt{\frac{Z_A + Z_C}{Z_B + Z_C}(Z_A Z_B + Z_B Z_C + Z_A Z_C)} \tag{6-50}$$

$$Z_{iB} = \sqrt{\frac{Z_B + Z_C}{Z_A + Z_C}(Z_A Z_B + Z_B Z_C + Z_A Z_C)} \tag{6-51}$$

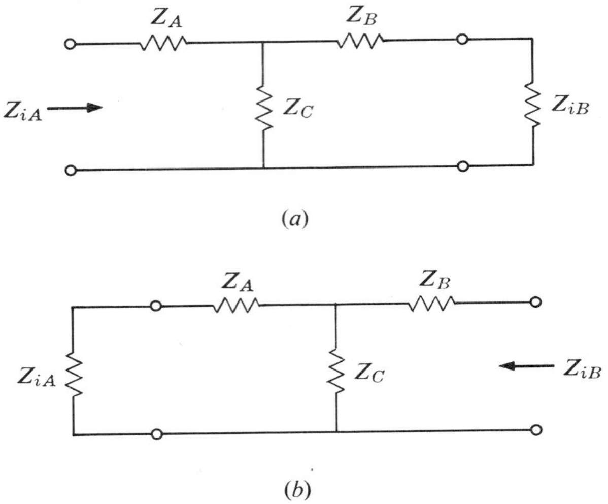

Figure 6-10 Unsymmetrical two-terminal-pair network terminated in image impedances

These will reduce to Eq. 6-3, the iterative impedance of a symmetrical section, if $Z_A = Z_B = (Z_1/2)$ and $Z_C = Z_2$.

b. Image transfer function

The concept of transfer function as the natural logarithm of the complex ratio between input and output voltage or current phasors, which was used for the symmetrical section, is inadequate here. This is because the voltage and current ratios are different if Z_{iA} and Z_{iB} are not equal. A reasonable basis for assessing "input-to-output performance" under these circumstances is the ratio of power input to power output. Parenthetically, the decibel unit is founded on this.*

$$\text{Loss in db} = 10 \log_{10}\left(\frac{P_{\text{in}}}{P_{\text{out}}}\right) \tag{6-52}$$

* If the image impedances are purely resistive, R_{iA} and R_{iB}, the loss in an unsymmetrical two-terminal-pair network terminated in image impedance R_{iB} will be

$$\begin{aligned}\text{Loss in } db &= 10 \log_{10}\left(\frac{I_{\text{in}}^2 R_{iA}}{I_{\text{out}}^2 R_{iB}}\right)\\ &= 20 \log_{10}\left(\frac{I_{\text{in}}}{I_{\text{out}}}\sqrt{\frac{R_{iA}}{R_{iB}}}\right)\\ &= 20 \log_{10}\left(\frac{V_{\text{in}}}{V_{\text{out}}}\sqrt{\frac{R_{iB}}{R_{iA}}}\right)\end{aligned} \tag{6-53}$$

These equations are valid in terms of general image impedances Z_{iA} and Z_{iB} (rather than R_{iA} and R_{iB}), provided their angles are equal.

If the image impedances are equal, Eq. 6-53 reduces to the form of Eq. 2-14. The latter

To describe magnitude change and phase shift in a manner comparable to that used for the symmetrical section, yet mathematically consistent for differing image impedances (which might be complex), the image transfer function Γ_i is introduced. It is formally defined as follows:

$$\Gamma_i = \ln\sqrt{\frac{V_{\text{in}}I_{\text{in}}}{V_{\text{out}}I_{\text{out}}}} \tag{6-54}$$

It is assumed that the network is terminated in its image impedance.

The "physical reality" which may be ascribed to the image transfer function varies with the nature of the image impedances. If Z_{iA} and Z_{iB} are both resistive, the real part of Γ_i represents a reduction in power between input and output, and the imaginary part is the phase shift between the input and output voltage phasors and, likewise, between input and output current phasors. Should the image impedances be pure reactances, the real part of Γ_i represents a reduction in vars between input and output, and the imaginary part again represents phase shift. In the general case of complex image impedances with different angles, the real part of Γ_i represents simply a reduction in volt-amperes, and the imaginary part is the average of the phase shift between the input and output voltages and that between the input and output currents.

The derivation of expressions for Γ_i in terms of the branch impedances follows the general approach used for Eq. 6-10, although the procedure is longer.[3] Results are as follows:

$$\Gamma_i = \ln\left(\frac{\sqrt{(Z_A + Z_C)(Z_B + Z_C)} + \sqrt{Z_A Z_B + Z_B Z_C + Z_A Z_C}}{Z_C}\right) \tag{6-55}$$

$$\Gamma_i = \cosh^{-1}\left(\frac{\sqrt{(Z_A + Z_C)(Z_B + Z_C)}}{Z_C}\right) \tag{6-56}$$

$$\Gamma_i = \sinh^{-1}\left(\frac{\sqrt{Z_A Z_B + Z_B Z_C + Z_A Z_C}}{Z_C}\right) \tag{6-57}$$

$$\Gamma_i = \tanh^{-1}\sqrt{\frac{Z_A Z_B + Z_B Z_C + Z_A Z_C}{(Z_A + Z_C)(Z_B + Z_C)}} \tag{6-58}$$

One may verify by interchanging Z_A and Z_B in each of the foregoing expressions that the image transfer function is the same in both directions through the network.

---

defined the attenuation, in decibels, of a finite section of an infinitely long, lossy line; along such a line the input impedance is everywhere equal to the characteristic impedance, and hence the impedance level is the same at all locations. The same is true of a line of finite length which is terminated in its characteristic impedance.

c. Branch impedances for specified performance

In the design of networks one would probably be given the image impedances and perhaps the transfer function and wish to know the three branch impedances. The following expressions, derivable from Eqs. 6-50, 6-51, 6-57 and 6-58, are applicable:

$$Z_C = \frac{\sqrt{Z_{iA}Z_{iB}}}{\sinh \Gamma_i} \tag{6-59}$$

$$Z_A = \frac{Z_{iA}}{\tanh \Gamma_i} - Z_C \tag{6-60}$$

$$Z_B = \frac{Z_{iB}}{\tanh \Gamma_i} - Z_C \tag{6-61}$$

One network of this type which is considered in the problems at the end of this chapter is a *pad*, or purely resistive network. A pad may be utilized primarily to introduce a desired amount of attenuation, or it may be intended as an impedance-matching device with an unavoidable loss. With three resistors to be chosen, three degrees of freedom exist and the two image impedances (resistive) and the attenuation may be specified. Some combinations may call for a negative resistor; these are not realizable.

The limiting case in which one of the series resistors is zero is also the pad of minimum attenuation for a given pair of image impedances. Let Z_B vanish, and replace Γ_i with $\bar{\alpha}_{\text{min}}$. Equation 6-61 reduces to

$$Z_C = \frac{Z_{iB}}{\tanh \bar{\alpha}_{\text{min}}} \tag{6-62}$$

Impedance Z_C may be eliminated between Eqs. 6-59 and 6-62, and the resulting equation solved for $\bar{\alpha}_{\text{min}}$.

$$\cosh \bar{\alpha}_{\text{min}} = \sqrt{\frac{Z_{iA}}{Z_{iB}}} \tag{6-63}$$

Reactive impedance-matching networks (L networks) with purely resistive image impedances may be derived on the same basis, again setting $Z_B = 0$ and replacing Γ_i by $j\bar{\beta}$:

$$\cos \bar{\beta} = \sqrt{\frac{Z_{iA}}{Z_{iB}}} \qquad (Z_B = 0) \tag{6-64}$$

Equations 6-59 and 6-60 then reduce to

$$Z_C = \frac{\sqrt{Z_{iA}Z_{iB}}}{j \sin \bar{\beta}} \tag{6-65}$$

$$Z_A = \frac{Z_{iA}}{j \tan \bar{\beta}} - Z_C \tag{6-66}$$

If one disregards skin effect, the behavior of a pad is independent of frequency, whereas the impedance-matching property of a purely reactive network is highly sensitive to changes in frequency.

Problems 6-9 through 6-12 deal with applications of unsymmetrical-network concepts.

6-4. LOADING COILS ON TELEPHONE LINES

Loading, or the increasing of the inductance of telephone lines to increase the characteristic impedance and reduce attenuation, was discussed in Sec. 2-4. When loading is obtained by connecting ferromagnetic coils in tandem with sections of the line, the overall line is not a simple, distributed-parameter system. By spacing the coils uniformly and making them identical,

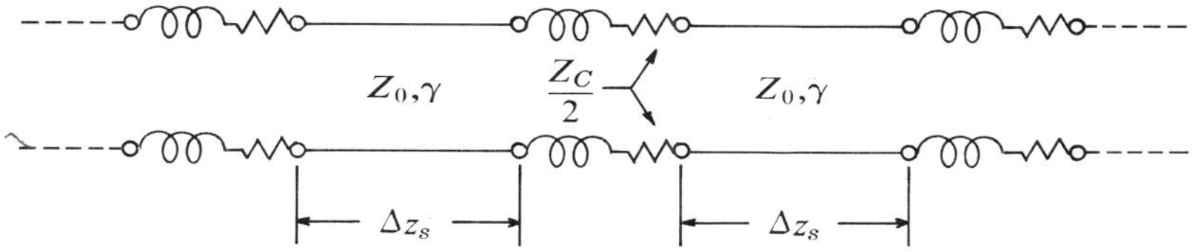

Figure 6-11 Lump-loaded, balanced transmission line

a repetitive network structure is obtained as indicated in Fig. 6-11. Such a line may be divided mathematically on a mid-coil or a midline-section basis, and corresponding iterative impedances derived.[1,2] The iterative transfer function Γ' of a section of lump-loaded line is as follows:[2]

$$\Gamma' = 2 \tanh^{-1} \sqrt{\frac{2Z_0 \tanh(\gamma\, \Delta z_s/2) + Z_C}{2Z_0 \coth(\gamma\, \Delta z_s/2) + Z_C}} \qquad \textbf{(6-67)}$$

Other forms may be derived with the aid of identities.

The functional relationship between Γ' and frequency is complicated, but the low-pass-filter property of the system may be demonstrated if one assumes a lossless line and lossless loading coils and assumes further that the spacing is such that $\beta\, \Delta z_s$ is much less than unity:

$$\tanh \frac{\gamma\, \Delta z_s}{2} = j \tan \frac{\beta\, \Delta z_s}{2}$$

$$\approx \frac{j\beta\, \Delta z_s}{2}$$

$$\approx \frac{j\omega\sqrt{lc}\, \Delta z_s}{2}$$

$$\coth \frac{\gamma\, \Delta z_s}{2} \approx \frac{2}{j\omega\sqrt{lc}\, \Delta z_s}$$

$$Z_0 = \sqrt{\frac{l}{c}}$$

$$Z_C = j\omega L_C$$

Substitution of the foregoing expressions in Eq. 6-67 reduces it to

$$\Gamma' \approx \tanh^{-1} \sqrt{\frac{j\omega l\,\Delta z_s + j\omega L_C}{\dfrac{4}{j\omega c\,\Delta z_s} + j\omega L_C}} \tag{6-68}$$

The radical will be negative, and hence Γ' imaginary, if the first term in the denominator is greater than the second; otherwise the radical will be positive and Γ' real. Thus the cutoff frequency ω_c is

$$\omega_c = \frac{2}{\sqrt{c\,\Delta z_s L_C}} \tag{6-69}$$

For economical spacings of coils, the cutoff frequency proves to be too low for carrier-frequency communication; hence the application of lumped loading has been progressively restricted in recent years to local-service lines and to those long-distance circuits which have very light traffic.

6-5. CONCLUSIONS

The behavior of two-terminal-pair networks may be described in a manner resembling that for a distributed-parameter transmission line. The iterative impedance and iterative transfer function are derived parameters for a symmetrical network analogous to the characteristic impedance and the propagation function.

A tandem assembly of symmetrical two-terminal-pair sections in which the series elements are inductive and the shunt elements capacitive has current and voltage relationships at the junctions between sections which correspond closely to those on a transmission line, provided the frequency is sufficiently low. Such a network is also a low-pass filter (specifically, a constant-k filter if its elements are purely reactive) and is characterized by a cutoff frequency. Below this cutoff frequency a purely reactive filter section has a resistive iterative impedance, zero attenuation, and a phase function which increases with frequency. Above cutoff frequency such a filter section has a reactive iterative impedance, a phase shift of π radians, and an attenuation which increases with frequency.

Unsymmetrical two-terminal-pair networks may be used in conjunction with transmission lines, and the derived parameters of image impedance and image transfer function are useful for that purpose.

A lump-loaded telephone line has filter properties similar to those of a constant-k low-pass filter. This limits the frequency range within which transmission is satisfactory.

PROBLEMS

6-1. In Eq. 6-10, let Γ_1 be the result found by taking the negative root of one of the radicals and Γ_2 the result found by taking the positive roots of both radicals. Show that Γ_1 is the negative of Γ_2 if the argument of the logarithm is a real quantity. Show that the same principle applies to Eq. 6-29 with respect to the choice of sign for the radical.

6-2. Prove that Eqs. 6-11 and 6-12 are equivalent to Eq. 6-10.

6-3. Sketch a phasor diagram similar to Fig. 6-6(*b*) for a pi-section constant-*k* low-pass filter in the pass band. Accompany it with an adequately labeled circuit diagram.

6-4. Compute Z_{iT} and $\bar{\alpha}$ for a constant-*k* low-pass filter at $\omega = 2\omega_c$. Let $\sqrt{L_1/C_2}$ equal 600 ohms. Assume an output voltage of 1 volt, compute branch currents and voltage drops, and construct a phasor diagram for each of these cases: (*a*) Z_{iT} is assumed to be inductive, and (*b*) Z_{iT} is assumed to be capacitive. Comment on the respective interpretations of $\bar{\alpha}$.

6-5. Let the filter discussed in Problem 6-4 be terminated in a 600-ohm resistor. Assuming an output voltage of 1 volt, compute the input voltage and current and the input impedance by exact network theory and draw a phasor diagram. Compute Γ from these results, using Eq. 6-54. Compare these results with those found in Problem 6-4.

6-6. Write expressions for the open-circuit and short-circuit impedances of a *T*-form symmetrical two-terminal-pair network [Fig. 6-1(*a*)]. From these, find expressions for $\sqrt{Z_{oc}Z_{sc}}$ and $\sqrt{Z_{sc}/Z_{oc}}$, as called for in Eqs. 6-14 and 6-15. Investigate the corresponding relationships for the unsymmetrical *T* section.

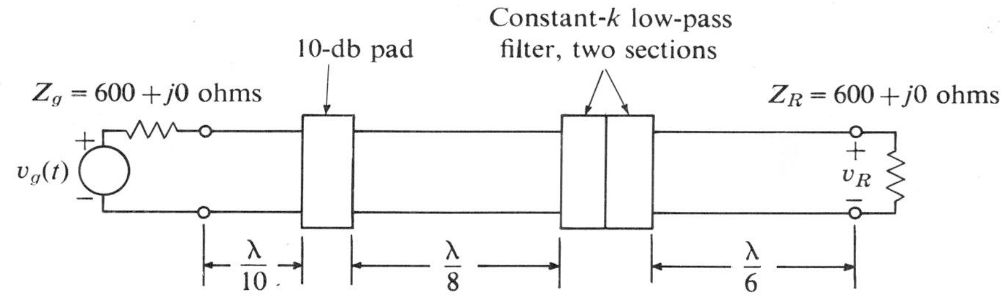

Figure 6-12 Circuit for Problem 6-7

6-7. Refer to Fig. 6-12. All three transmission lines have characteristic impedances of 600 ohms (resistive) and are lossless. The filter has a cutoff frequency of 4000 cps. Reflectionless matches exist at junctions between the lines and the pad and between the lines and the filter. The output voltage v_R is 1.5 sin (5000*t*) volts. Write an expression for $v_g(t)$.

6-8. A 10-mile section of telephone line is to be simulated with a symmetrical *T* network: $r = 6.74$ ohms per mile of line, $l = 3.53 \times 10^{-3}$ henry per mile,

$c = 8.71 \times 10^{-9}$ farad per mile, and $g = 0.29 \times 10^{-6}$ mho per mile. Compute the cutoff frequency of the network, assuming that r and g are both zero. Compute Z_0 and $\gamma\, \Delta z_{sec}$ of the distributed-parameter line, and Z_{iT} and Γ for the network, taking account of r and g, for (*a*) $\omega = 0.1\omega_c$, and (*b*) $\omega = 0.4\omega_c$. Compare corresponding results.

6-9. Compute the branch resistances for a pad with image impedances (resistive) of 600 and 450 ohms and an attenuation of 15 db.

6-10. A minimum-loss pad is to have image impedances (resistive) of 600 and 450 ohms. Find the attenuation it will cause, and compute the branch resistances.

6-11. A purely reactive L network is to have image impedances (resistive) of 600 and 450 ohms. Find the phase shift which it causes and the branch reactances, and sketch a phasor diagram. Two solutions are possible.

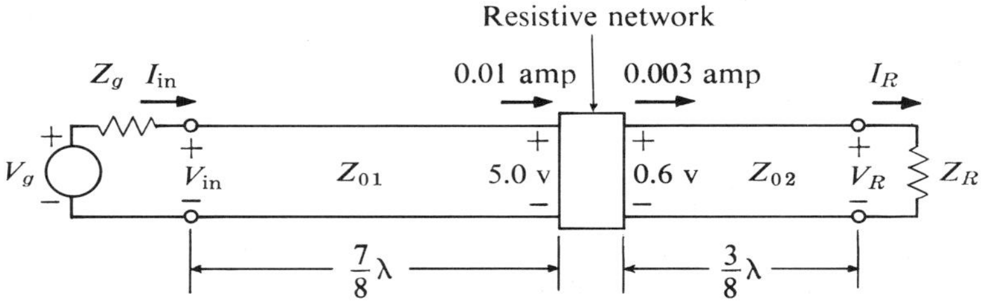

Figure 6-13 Circuit for Problem 6-12

6-12. Refer to Fig. 6-13. Both transmission lines are lossless, and reflectionless matches exist at all junctions. (*a*) Find the attenuation of the network. (*b*) Find Z_{01}, Z_{02}, Z_R, and Z_g. (*c*) Find I_R, V_R, I_{in}, V_{in}, and V_g (rms magnitudes).

REFERENCES

1. CREAMER, WALTER J., *Communication Networks and Lines*, pp. 247–51. New York: Harper & Brothers, 1951.
2. JOHNSON, K. S., *Transmission Circuits for Telephone Communication*, pp. 153–57. New York: D. Van Nostrand Company, Inc., 1925.
3. KIMBARK, EDWARD WILSON, *Electrical Transmission of Power and Signals*, pp. 231–35. New York: John Wiley & Sons, Inc., 1949.

CHAPTER 7

The Electromagnetic Fields and Maxwell's Equations

For the study of macroscopic electromagnetic effects apart from the circuit quantities of current and voltage, the following set of vector fields is postulated: (1) magnetic-flux density (***B***, webers per square meter); (2) magnetic-field intensity (***H***, amperes per meter); (3) electric-flux density (***D***, coulombs per square meter); and (4) electric-field intensity (***E***, volts per meter).

These fields are interrelated by means of Maxwell's equations, and they are also related to observable quantities, notably to electric charge, to the movement of such charges, and to mechanical forces between charged or charge-carrying bodies. The classical electromagnetic-field concept is inapplicable to quantized, atomic-scale effects, yet it has been retained over the years because it enables an accurate prediction of known macroscopic phenomena arising in what one might call "electrically activated" systems.

To obtain explicit solutions for the fields in particular geometrical situations, such as the space between two infinitely long concentric cylinders (coaxial cable) or within an infinitely long rectangular tube (rectangular wave guide), coordinate systems are introduced. The rectangular, circular-cylindrical, and spherical systems will be used in this text.

7-1. VECTOR ANALYSIS: ALGEBRAIC OPERATIONS AND VECTOR-FIELD INTEGRALS

To express concisely the relationships among vector-type physical quantities, vector algebra and field theory were devised during the nineteenth century. Mathematical operations were defined by various investigators, notably Hamilton, Grassmann, and Gibbs.[7] In the course of time a sifting process took place. Those operations which described relevant physical phenomena most advantageously received general acceptance and were retained, whereas others, more artificial, were discarded.

Vector-type operations are definable on an *invariantive* basis, namely, one under which the definitions are not dependent upon a particularly chosen coordinate system. (The word "invariantive" may seem awesome because it is used in discussions of relativity; here its significance is merely an acknowledgment of the obvious principle that physical phenomena take place without regard to the scheme of coordinates or system of units which observers may use to describe those phenomena.) Coordinate systems are introduced into specific problems as conveniences, and vector operations may be restated in terms of the components of the various vectors in the coordinate system selected. To encourage the invariantive point of view, discussion of coordinate systems will be postponed until Sec. 7-4, after Maxwell's equations have been introduced and surveyed descriptively.

Vectors will be designated by boldface italic letters. A boldface italic capital letter, such as $\boldsymbol{A}$, will indicate a general vector which might represent any physical space-directed quantity and could be a function of one or more variables; then the boldface italic lower-case letter $\boldsymbol{a}$, with any subscript, will indicate a *unit vector*, one which has unit magnitude (dimensionless) and simply defines direction. A unit vector may be multiplied by a dimensioned scalar constant or function to represent a physical quantity. The *magnitude* of a vector may be designated as $|\boldsymbol{A}|$, for example.

a. Vector algebra[4,7]

Vector-algebra operations of immediate interest are (1) the equating of one vector to another; (2) addition and subtraction of vectors; (3) scalar, or dot, multiplication of two vectors; and (4) vector, or cross, multiplication of two vectors. It is assumed that the reader has previously studied vector algebra; hence the main concepts will be quickly reviewed rather than derived in detail.

(1) EQUALITY AMONG VECTORS. Two vectors are said to be equal to each other if their directions are parallel and their magnitudes equal. The latter property can be true in physical applications only if the two quantities represented have the same dimensions. When the vectors are resolved into components along coordinate directions, the criterion of equality requires that equality exist between corresponding components.

(2) ADDITION AND SUBTRACTION OF VECTORS. The addition of vectors may be visualized geometrically as follows: (1) represent each vector with a

line segment parallel to the vector, making the length proportional to the magnitude of the vector; (2) designate the ends of each as "base" and "tip" such that the direction from base to tip is the direction of the vector represented; (3) translate one line segment in space (moving it such that it remains parallel to its original position) until the tip of one touches the base of the

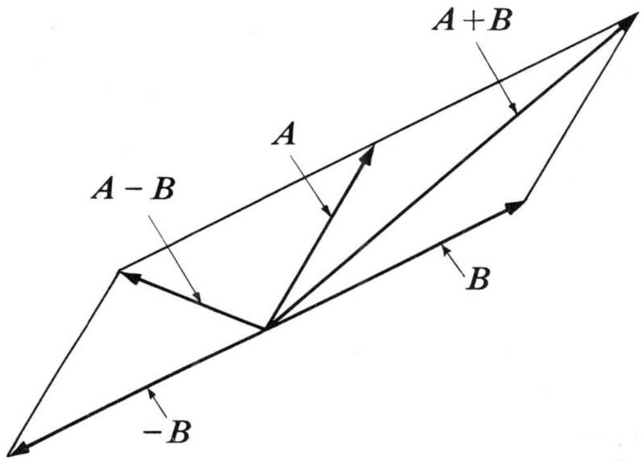

(*a*) Vector addition and subtraction

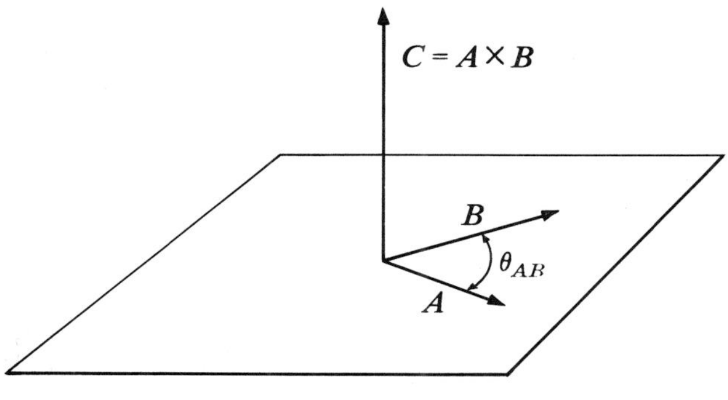

(*b*) Vector product of two vectors

Figure 7-1 Operations in vector algebra

other; then (4) a line segment drawn from the base of the former to the tip of the latter represents the vector sum or resultant. This is shown graphically in Fig. 7-1(*a*). If one vector is to be subtracted from another, the first vector is reversed in direction and then added to the second. The operation of addition is physically meaningful only among quantities which have the same dimensions.

(3) MULTIPLICATION OF VECTORS. Two operations of multiplication of vectors are defined in vector analysis. These are chosen with a view toward aiding the concise description of those physical phenomena in which some quantity is, among other things, proportional to the magnitudes of two vectors. In most instances such a derived physical quantity falls in one of two classes; it is either (1) a scalar, in which case it is proportional also to the cosine of the angle between the two vectors, or (2) a vector which is perpendicular to the plane of the other two vectors, and then it is proportional in magnitude to the sine of the angle between those two vectors. "Scalar multiplication" and "vector multiplication" are therefore defined so as to take advantage of the common characteristics of such functions.

(*a*) *Scalar multiplication.* The scalar product of two vectors may be indicated as follows:

$$W = \boldsymbol{F} \cdot \boldsymbol{L} \tag{7-1}$$

It is evaluated by multiplying together the magnitudes of vectors $\boldsymbol{F}$ and $\boldsymbol{L}$ and the cosine of the angle between them. The result W is a scalar, devoid of any space-directed properties, but it has an algebraic sign which depends on the cosine of the angle between the vectors; thus it is positive if that angle is less than a right angle and negative if the angle is greater. If the angle between the two vectors is a right angle, the scalar product vanishes. The principal applications of the scalar product in electromagnetic theory are in the evaluating of line integrals and surface integrals, concepts which will be discussed in Sec. 7-1*b*.

(*b*) *Vector multiplication.* The vector product of two vectors may be indicated as follows:

$$\boldsymbol{A} \times \boldsymbol{B} = \boldsymbol{C} \tag{7-2}$$

The magnitude of $\boldsymbol{C}$ is equal to the product of the magnitudes of $\boldsymbol{A}$ and $\boldsymbol{B}$ and the sine of the angle between them, measuring the angle such that it is less than π radians. In terms of Fig. 7-1(*b*),

$$|\boldsymbol{C}| = |\boldsymbol{A}|\,|\boldsymbol{B}| \sin \theta_{AB} \tag{7-3}$$

The magnitude, and hence the vector product, vanishes if vectors $\boldsymbol{A}$ and $\boldsymbol{B}$ are collinear.

The direction of $\boldsymbol{C}$ is perpendicular to the plane of vectors $\boldsymbol{A}$ and $\boldsymbol{B}$, and ambiguity is avoided by including in the definition a right-hand rule. The product vector is assigned the direction in which a right-handed screw would advance when rotated in the direction from the first-named vector ($\boldsymbol{A}$) to the second-named vector ($\boldsymbol{B}$), going through the smaller angle.

Interchanging $\boldsymbol{A}$ and $\boldsymbol{B}$ in the foregoing discussion leads to the following conclusion:

$$\boldsymbol{A} \times \boldsymbol{B} = -\boldsymbol{B} \times \boldsymbol{A} \tag{7-4}$$

The conciseness and economy of expression to be gained through the concept of the vector product should be apparent if one compares Eq. 7-2 with the explanation in prose which follows it.

b. Fields and field integrals

A *field* is a function which has a value at every point in space or within some designated region. If the function has both a direction and a magnitude, it is called a *vector field*; if it has magnitude only, it is called a *scalar field*. Examples of vector fields are the gravitational force field, the velocity pattern of the water in a river, and the four electromagnetic fields, $\boldsymbol{B}$, $\boldsymbol{H}$, $\boldsymbol{D}$, and $\boldsymbol{E}$. Some familiar scalar fields are the temperature distribution within some given volume and the density of air in the atmosphere.

The mathematical operation of integration is useful in the analysis of physical problems; it is defined basically for a scalar function of a single variable. The integration concept may be applied to field functions with the aid of some supplementary definitions and restrictions. In practice three specific operations prove especially useful; they are known as (1) the *volume integral* (of a scalar field), (2) the *line integral* (of a vector field), and (3) the *surface integral* (of a vector field).

The volume integral is evaluated simply by integrating the given scalar function with respect to the coordinate directions throughout some specified volume. For example, the volume integral of the air-density function mentioned above will yield the mass of air in a given volume.

The two vector-field integrals have more involved definitions which will be detailed below. All three integrals are used in the derivation of relations among the electromagnetic-field functions. Subsequently equations involving those integrals may be replaced by differential equations known as *Maxwell's equations*. Those equations use two specially defined differential functions, the *divergence* and the *curl*. These are derivable from the field integrals, as will be shown at a later stage of this development (Sec. 7-3).

(1) LINE INTEGRAL. An example which will introduce the line integral is the calculation of the work done in moving along some prescribed path from location L_A to L_B in a force field $\boldsymbol{F}$, which depends solely on position in that field:

$$W_{AB} = -\int_{L_A}^{L_B} \boldsymbol{F} \cdot d\boldsymbol{L} \tag{7-5}$$

Figure 7-2 shows the force vectors and differential-displacement vectors at several points along such a path.

The operation called for is (1) taking the scalar product of each differential segment of path and the vector field at the corresponding location, and (2) summing, by means of ordinary integration, those differential scalar products. This computational procedure may be practiced on an easier

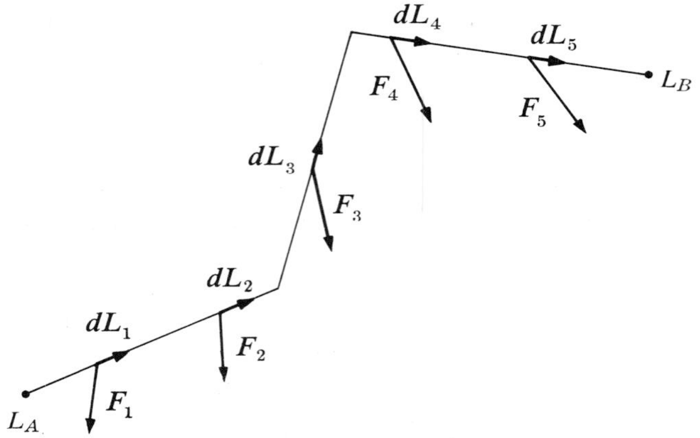

Figure 7-2 Vector relationships for line integral

example, the first part of Problem 7-1, in which the specified path segments are parallel to the given coordinate axes and the integrals may be evaluated in closed form. More complicated paths might test one's skill in elementary calculus or make numerical integration expedient. The same concept may be applied to vector fields whose dimensions are other than those of mechanical force; line integrals of the $\boldsymbol{E}$ and the $\boldsymbol{H}$ fields are used in electromagnetic theory.

An important class of vector fields has the property that the line integral between any two end points is independent of the particular path traversed. Such a field is said to be *conservative*. (The gravitational field and the static $\boldsymbol{E}$ field are members of this class, but time-varying $\boldsymbol{E}$, $\boldsymbol{H}$, $\boldsymbol{D}$, and $\boldsymbol{B}$ fields are not.)

A special type of line integral is that for which the path of integration is a closed curve, and this will be indicated with a small circle superposed on the integral sign. If the field is conservative, the line integral around any closed path is zero. In terms of the static $\boldsymbol{E}$ field, this result is stated as follows:

$$\oint \boldsymbol{E} \cdot \boldsymbol{dL} = 0 \qquad (\boldsymbol{E} \text{ not a function of time}) \tag{7-6}$$

(2) Surface integral. An example which will introduce the surface integral is the relationship between the current density within a conducting mass and the current i entering or leaving part of it through a specified cross section. This is illustrated in Fig. 7-3. The current density constitutes a vector field $\boldsymbol{J}$, the magnitude and direction of which may differ from one location to another. A given cross section may be divided into differential-area surfaces, each represented by a vector $\boldsymbol{dS}$ which is normal to its orientation plane and is assigned a magnitude equal to the differential area. The current through each differential area is equal to the current density at the point

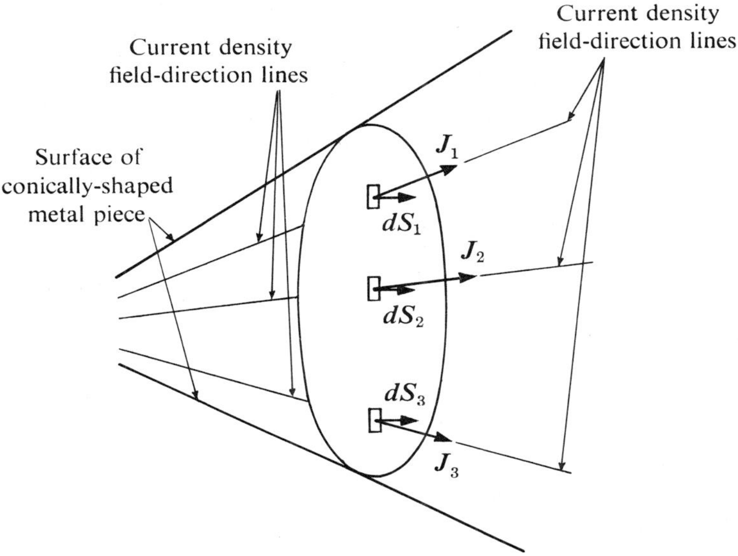

Figure 7-3 Geometry for evaluation of surface integral (surface bounded by closed curve)

multiplied by the differential area and by the cosine of the angle between $\boldsymbol{J}$ and $\boldsymbol{dS}$. The scalar product expedites the statement of this relationship:

$$di = \boldsymbol{J} \cdot \boldsymbol{dS}$$

The sum of the differential currents for all the differential areas in the cross section is the resultant current:

$$i = \iint \boldsymbol{J} \cdot \boldsymbol{dS} \tag{7-7}$$

This is the surface integral, a scalar quantity. In this instance the limits are understood to be fixed by the closed curve formed by the intersection of the given cross-sectional surface with the walls of the conducting mass. Bases for choosing limits depend on the particular physical problem.

The same mathematical operation is applied to the $\boldsymbol{B}$ and $\boldsymbol{D}$ fields in electromagnetic theory, and the resulting scalar quantities are known as *magnetic flux* (ϕ, webers) and *electric flux* (ψ, coulombs), respectively.

If the angle between the current-density (or flux-density) vector and the vector representing area is less than a right angle, the differential current or flux is positive, whereas if that angle is greater than a right angle, the differential current or flux is negative. One must decide at the outset which direction through the surface is to be considered positive.

Integrals over *enclosing* surfaces are used in the derivation of Maxwell's equations. An enclosed-surface integral will be designated by a small ellipse or oval linking the two integral signs $\left(\oiint\right)$. Conventionally the direction outward from an enclosing surface is considered positive. It may be noted that flux which enters an enclosing surface offsets that which leaves it, and, if the two amounts are equal, the surface integral is zero.

7-2. AN OVERVIEW OF CLASSICAL ELECTROMAGNETICS[1,6]

It is helpful to review some of the basic concepts of the electromagnetic fields, with emphasis on those aspects which bear directly on wave propagation.

The following question may well occur to the reader: "Why ought one complicate the voltage-and-current concept of transmission lines by hypothesizing a set of vector fields?"

The immediate value of field theory in transmission-line analysis is that it enables one to relate the circuit parameters of distributed inductance and distributed capacitance to the cross-sectional geometry of the line. But field theory has a larger role; the concepts of voltage and current, as they are routinely used in circuit analysis and as they were used in the preceding chapters, pertain to one particular mode of electromagnetic-energy movement. This is not the only possible mode, nor even the only important one. In communication engineering, wave guides and wave-guide modes of propagation are widely used, and modes of this type are best described in terms of vector fields.

The following elementary phenomena indicate the *space pervasiveness* of electromagnetic effects:

(1) The presence of current in two circuits in proximity to each other is accompanied by mechanical forces on each conductor, forces which change if either current is changed.

(2) A changing of the current in either of two such circuits is accompanied by an induced voltage in the other.

(3) Capacitors consisting of metallic spheres or other conducting bodies suspended in vacuum or in an insulating medium may be charged and later discharged. During these processes wire-borne current flows onto one sphere and off the other.

(4) The presence of electric charges on two bodies is accompanied by a mechanical force on each, forces which change if either charge is changed.

Mechanical-force effects, items 1 and 4, have been mentioned primarily because they help in assigning directions to the fields. Item 2 states an application of Faraday's law, and item 3 describes a situation in which the displacement current, postulated by Maxwell, complements a discontinuous conduction current to yield, as a resultant, a composite current which is continuous.

a. Directional properties of the electric and magnetic fields

The direction to be assigned to a vector field is an important part of the definition of the function and is chosen in the light of the physical situation to which it relates. It is rather obvious for the electric field, but less so for the magnetic field.

Curves may be faired in a vector field such that they are continuously tangent to the local direction of the field; such lines are called *field-direction lines*, and for many physical fields, have easily identifiable properties.

(1) ELECTRIC FIELD. The direction of a static electric field at a given location is defined as that of the force which would be exerted on a small, positively charged test sphere. The direction lines of a static electric field extend from charges of one polarity to charges of the opposite polarity.

(2) MAGNETIC FIELD. A small, circular test coil may be visualized for investigation of the vector-related aspects of the magnetic-field effects noted in items 1 and 2. If current is flowing in the test coil while the coil is in an external field, the differential forces acting on the various parts of the coil will yield, in general, a resultant translational force and a torque. A coil orientation can be found, at each location, for which the torque vanishes.

Let the generator supplying current to the test coil be replaced by a ballistic galvanometer,[2] and the external field suddenly strengthened or weakened. In accordance with Faraday's law, a current surge will pass through the galvanometer. The galvanometer response, as a function of the orientation of the test coil at the given location, will be greatest when the orientation is the same as that for torque equilibrium in the preceding test. The normal to the plane of the test coil when it is thus oriented is designated as the alignment of the field.

Direction lines of the static magnetic field (if one excludes the phenomenon of permanent magnetism) form closed loops around current-carrying conductors or parts of such conductors. Conventionally the positive direction of the magnetic field is defined as clockwise around a current which is flowing away from the observer.

b. Quantitative properties

For quantitative study of vector fields, the line integral and surface integral, which were introduced in Sec. 7-1*b*, are useful in that they may be identified with circuit-type quantities.

(1) STATIC FIELDS IN A HOMOGENEOUS MEDIUM. For the present, let the electric-field magnitude at a given location be defined as proportional to the magnitude of the force which would be exerted on a small, positively charged

test sphere, divided by the magnitude of the test charge. Let the magnitude of the magnetic field at a given location produced by a particular coil be thought of as proportional to the Faraday effect galvanometer deflection caused by a unit change in the coil current, when the plane of the test coil is normal to the field-direction lines.

The following results are obtained if the medium surrounding the charged bodies or the coil is homogeneous:

(1) The surface integral of the magnetic field over an enclosing surface is zero.

(2) The surface integral of the electric field over an enclosing surface is proportional to the charge enclosed.

(3) The line integral of the magnetic field around a closed path is proportional to the current encircled.

(4) The line integral of the electric field around a closed path is zero, and the line integral between any two points is independent of the path of integration chosen.

Results (2) and (3) are the bases for the definition of the magnitudes of the ***D*** and ***H*** fields; in the *mks* (meter-kilogram-second) system of units those proportionalities are equalities:

$$\oiint \mathbf{D} \cdot d\mathbf{S} = \sum q \tag{7-8}$$

Here ***D*** has the units coulombs per square meter, area is measured in square meters, and q has the units coulombs.

$$\oint \mathbf{H} \cdot d\mathbf{L} = i \tag{7-9}$$

Here ***H*** has the units amperes per meter, incremental length of path is in meters, and i is in amperes.

(2) PROPERTIES OF PHYSICAL MEDIA AND THEIR EFFECTS. Various physical media have differing properties with respect to electric and magnetic fields; these may be expressed in terms of three parameters, the permittivity ϵ (farads per meter), the conductivity σ (mhos per meter), and the permeability μ (henrys per meter). These are scalar constants for the media to be considered in this analysis.*

An increase in permittivity in the region of an electric field, leaving the geometry and the charge distribution unchanged, will not affect the ***D*** field

* It is necessary in some physical media that one or more of these quantities be *tensors*, that is to say, that a given proportionality described in Maxwell's equations is not the same in all directions at a given point. Such a material is said to be *anisotropic* with respect to that property. *Ferrites*[5] constitute a class of anisotropic materials which are important in microwave techniques, but their analysis is beyond the scope of the present text. Anisotropy is also a cardinal aspect of such phenomena as magnetostriction and the piezoelectric behavior of crystals.

but will decrease the force exerted on the test charge by the ratio of the permittivities. Specifically, let the $\boldsymbol{E}$ field be defined as follows:

$$\boldsymbol{E}\epsilon = \boldsymbol{D} \tag{7-10}$$

The units of $\boldsymbol{E}$ are volts per meter; those of ϵ and $\boldsymbol{D}$ have been noted previously.

The force on the test charge is directly proportional to the $\boldsymbol{E}$ field, regardless of ϵ.

In composite media the line integral of $\boldsymbol{E}$ proves to be independent of path, whereas that is not true in general of $\boldsymbol{D}$. The line integral of $\boldsymbol{E}$ in a static field is defined as the *voltage:*

$$\begin{aligned} V_{ab} &= -\int_b^a \boldsymbol{E} \cdot \boldsymbol{dL} \\ &= \int_a^b \boldsymbol{E} \cdot \boldsymbol{dL} \end{aligned} \tag{7-11}$$

Likewise the forces arising from magnetic fields are altered by the presence of ferromagnetic materials, and it is expedient to define the $\boldsymbol{B}$ field as follows:

$$\boldsymbol{B} = \mu \boldsymbol{H} \tag{7-12}$$

Here $\boldsymbol{B}$ has the units webers per square meter, and those of μ and $\boldsymbol{H}$ have been noted previously.

In composite media the enclosed surface integral of $\boldsymbol{B}$ always vanishes, whereas that is not true in general for $\boldsymbol{H}$:

$$\oiint \boldsymbol{B} \cdot \boldsymbol{dS} = 0 \tag{7-13}$$

(3) CURRENT: CONDUCTION AND DISPLACEMENT. Conduction current consists of the movement of charge. When attention is directed to its distribution within a conducting mass, it is properly regarded as a vector field $\boldsymbol{J}$, with units of amperes per square meter. It is related to the static electric field in a conducting medium as follows:

$$\boldsymbol{J} = \sigma \boldsymbol{E} \tag{7-14}$$

As noted in the discussion of surface integrals in Sec. 7-1*b*, $\boldsymbol{J}$ and i are related in the following manner:

$$\iint \boldsymbol{J} \cdot \boldsymbol{dS} = i \tag{7-7}$$

In terms of the charging of a capacitor, the positive charge accumulated on one conducting surface by reason of current flowing onto that plate is

$$q = \int i \, dt \tag{7-15}$$

The integral of $\boldsymbol{D}$ over a surface which surrounds that plate, except for the cross section of the wire which brings in the conduction current, would increase at the same rate as q increases

$$\iint \frac{\partial \boldsymbol{D}}{\partial t} \cdot d\boldsymbol{S} = i$$

The time rate of change of $\boldsymbol{D}$ thus has the nature of a current density, and proves to have corresponding properties in terms of magnetic-field effects. It is the displacement-current density, and will be designated $\boldsymbol{J}_D$:

$$\boldsymbol{J}_D = \frac{\partial \boldsymbol{D}}{\partial t} \tag{7-16}$$

Its units, like those of $\boldsymbol{J}$, are amperes per square meter. Under the dynamic conditions of time-varying fields, Eq. 7-9 must be generalized to the following:

$$\oint \boldsymbol{H} \cdot d\boldsymbol{L} = \iint \left(\frac{\partial \boldsymbol{D}}{\partial t} + \boldsymbol{J}\right) \cdot d\boldsymbol{S}$$
$$= \iint \left(\epsilon \frac{\partial \boldsymbol{E}}{\partial t} + \sigma \boldsymbol{E}\right) \cdot d\boldsymbol{S} \tag{7-17}$$

(4) ELECTROMAGNETIC INDUCTION. The changing of current in a coil changes the magnetic field associated with it, and the latter is regarded as the mechanism whereby voltage is induced in a nearby circuit. The voltage induced in a single-turn coil is equal to the time rate of change in magnetic flux passing through the coil, or, in terms of line and surface integrals,

$$\oint \boldsymbol{E} \cdot d\boldsymbol{L} = -\iint \frac{\partial \boldsymbol{B}}{\partial t} \cdot d\boldsymbol{S} \tag{7-18}$$

This is Faraday's law of electromagnetic induction.

Lenz's law serves as a memory aid with respect to the negative sign in this equation; it states that the voltage induced by a change in magnetic field is so directed as to tend to produce a current which will create a component magnetic field in opposition to the impressed change.

c. Absolute and relative permittivity and permeability[2,3]

The absolute permittivity and permeability of physical media are related to the respective values for free space, ϵ_0 and μ_0 as follows:

$$\epsilon = \kappa_\epsilon \epsilon_0 \tag{7-19}$$

$$\mu = \kappa_\mu \mu_0 \tag{7-20}$$

Here κ_ϵ and κ_μ, which are dimensionless, are the relative permittivity and relative permeability, respectively.

The permeability of free space μ_0 is defined in the *mks* system as

$$\mu_0 = 4\pi \times 10^{-7} \text{ henry per meter} \tag{7-21}$$

As is shown in Sec. 8-1*d*, the velocity of propagation of a plane electromagnetic wave in space is related to the permeability and permittivity in the following manner:

$$\nu = \frac{1}{\sqrt{\mu_0 \epsilon_0}} \tag{7-22}$$

This velocity has been determined experimentally as 2.998×10^8 meters per second. The permittivity of space ϵ_0 is evaluated from Eq. 7-22:

$$\begin{aligned} \epsilon_0 &= \frac{1}{(4\pi \times 10^{-7})(2.998 \times 10^8)^2} \\ &= 8.854 \times 10^{-12} \text{ farad per meter} \\ &\approx \frac{10^{-9}}{36\pi} \text{ farad per meter} \end{aligned} \tag{7-23}$$

7-3. VECTOR ANALYSIS: REDUCTION OF FIELD EQUATIONS TO DIFFERENTIAL FORM

Equations 7-8, 7-13, 7-17, and 7-18, which involve line integrals and surface integrals, may be designated as Maxwell's equations in the integral form. Their application to many problems may be expedited by restating them as differential equations. Two differential functions of a vector field are introduced for this purpose, the divergence and the curl. Two other differential functions, the gradient of a scalar field and the laplacian will, for unity and completeness, be introduced here too, although they will be used only in connection with the traveling-wave solutions to Maxwell's equations in Chapters 10 and 11.

a. Conservation of electric flux

$$\oiint \boldsymbol{D} \cdot d\boldsymbol{S} = \sum q \tag{7-8}$$

Electric flux is postulated to emanate from positive charges and to terminate on negative charges. The algebraic sum of such charges within the designated surface of integration in Eq. 7-8 was indicated by $\sum q$. The net outwardly directed flux, $\oiint \boldsymbol{D} \cdot d\boldsymbol{S}$, is equal to the algebraic sum of the enclosed charge. For macroscopic applications, charge may be viewed in a mathematical sense which differs from the physical form.

(1) Electric charge and mathematical functions. Experimentally, electric charge has been found to be concentrated in electrons and protons,

"particles" of submicroscopic, yet nonzero, size. If one accepts the restriction that classical electromagnetic theory will be used only to describe macroscopic phenomena, actual charge distributions may be replaced by forms which are easier to work with mathematically.

The following are idealized charge distributions: (1) a finite charge q concentrated in a geometric point, (2) a finite amount of charge per unit length ρ_L concentrated in a geometric line, (3) a finite charge per unit area ρ_S concentrated in a geometric surface, and (4) a continuous distribution of charge density ρ throughout a volume. Charge density under (4) constitutes a scalar field.

In the traditional language of vector analysis, built primarily on hydrodynamics, the positive charges are *sources* of electric flux, the negative charges, *sinks*. In some dynamic situations, such as waves which have been radiated from an antenna, or certain modes of propagation in wave guides, electric-field-direction lines form closed loops, and there are no sources or sinks. Air and space will be assumed to be charge-free in the field analyses considered in this text, but charges on conducting surfaces will have important roles in satisfying boundary conditions.

The continuous-distribution concept will be used in the following section to develop the divergence function. If all the charge within a given enclosing surface is in the continuously distributed form, the following substitution may be made.

$$\sum q = \iiint \rho \, dv \tag{7-24}$$

The right-hand side is a volume integral, as described in Sec. 7-1*b*. Equation 7-24 is substituted in Eq. 7-8:

$$\oiint \boldsymbol{D} \cdot d\boldsymbol{S} = \iiint \rho \, dv \tag{7-25}$$

(2) THE DIVERGENCE FUNCTION. Consider a small enclosing surface in the $\boldsymbol{D}$ field, in a region of finite charge density. If the volume enclosed is small enough, the charge density will be essentially uniform throughout that volume, and the volume integral becomes simply the product of the local charge density and the volume, which may be indicated by Δv. Volume may then be divided into the surface integral to yield an expression for average charge density in terms of the surface integral. Let the enclosing surface be shrunk around some discrete point. The given ratio then approaches, as a limit, the charge density at that point. This mathematical result is defined as the *divergence* of $\boldsymbol{D}$, and is written div $\boldsymbol{D}$ or $\nabla \cdot \boldsymbol{D}$. It is a scalar function of location in the $\boldsymbol{D}$ field:

$$\nabla \cdot \boldsymbol{D} = \left[\frac{\oiint \boldsymbol{D} \cdot d\boldsymbol{S}}{\Delta v} \right]_{\lim \Delta v \to 0} \tag{7-26}$$

It may be noted that the inverted delta symbol introduced above is customarily called "del" when it is designated separately. The symbol "∇" behaves *formally* in mathematics as a vector. The paragraph preceding Eq. 7-26 gives the *definition* of divergence, and accordingly it is preferable that the expression "$\nabla \cdot \boldsymbol{D}$" be read "divergence of D" rather than "del dot D". The same principle applies to other derivative functions with symbols which incorporate del.

(3) DIFFERENTIAL EQUATION OF CONTINUITY. A general theorem in vector analysis known as the *divergence theorem* states the following[4,7]:

$$\oiint \boldsymbol{D} \cdot d\boldsymbol{S} = \iiint (\nabla \cdot \boldsymbol{D})\, dv \tag{7-27}$$

It is understood that the volume indicated on the right-hand side is that enclosed by the surface indicated on the left-hand side. (As mentioned in Sec. 7-1*b*(2), $d\boldsymbol{S}$ is directed outward.) Equation 7-27 may be substituted into Eq. 7-25; the volumes over which the integrals are taken are identical and may include all space or any part thereof. Hence

$$\nabla \cdot \boldsymbol{D} = \rho \tag{7-28}$$

In regions devoid of charge, the divergence of $\boldsymbol{D}$ vanishes.

b. Conservation of magnetic flux

A corresponding constraint upon the magnetic field was noted in Sec. 7-2*b*(2):

$$\oiint \boldsymbol{B} \cdot d\boldsymbol{S} = 0 \tag{7-13}$$

This is a mathematical statement of the physical observation that sources and sinks of magnetic flux are unknown. The surface integral of $\boldsymbol{B}$ in Eq. 7-13 may be replaced by the volume integral of its divergence. Because the equation is valid for any surface, including an infinitesimally small one surrounding any given point in space, the divergence of $\boldsymbol{B}$ must be identically zero:

$$\nabla \cdot \boldsymbol{B} = 0 \tag{7-29}$$

c. Ampere's law

The following relationship concerning the magnetic field which accompanies current, whether of the conduction or displacement type, was stated in Sec. 7-2*b*(3):

$$\oint \boldsymbol{H} \cdot d\boldsymbol{L} = \iint \left(\epsilon \frac{\partial \boldsymbol{E}}{\partial t} + \sigma \boldsymbol{E} \right) \cdot d\boldsymbol{S} \tag{7-17}$$

The surface of integration may be any finite surface which is bounded by the closed curve used as a path for the line integral of $\boldsymbol{H}$.

(1) THE CURL FUNCTION. If an exceedingly small planar loop within the current-carrying region is visualized as the bounding edge of the surface and as the path of line integration, the current density will be essentially uniform across that surface, and the surface integral may be replaced by the product of the area (which will be denoted by ΔS) and the component of current density normal to the plane of the loop. Next the loop may be revolved until that product is a maximum, in other words, so that the plane of the loop is normal to the local current-density vector field. If the line integral around the loop is divided by the area bounded by the loop and the limit taken by shrinking the loop onto a point, the result is the current density at that point, and the mathematical operation is defined as the *curl* of $\boldsymbol{H}$. This is written as curl $\boldsymbol{H}$ or $\nabla \times \boldsymbol{H}$. It is a vector field which is a function of location in the $\boldsymbol{H}$ field; its orientation at every point is normal to the corresponding differential surface, and it is directed such that the path taken for the line integral is clockwise when one looks along the curl vector from base to tip:

$$\nabla \times \boldsymbol{H} = \left[\frac{\oint \boldsymbol{H} \cdot d\boldsymbol{L}}{\Delta S}\right] \boldsymbol{a}_{\max}\ _{\lim \Delta S \to 0} \qquad \textbf{(7-30)}$$

Here $\boldsymbol{a}_{\max}$ is a unit vector which is so directed as to maximize the coefficient by which it is multiplied.

(2) GENERALIZED DIFFERENTIAL FORM OF AMPERE'S LAW. The following is a general theorem in vector analysis, known as *Stokes' theorem*[4,7]:

$$\oint \boldsymbol{H} \cdot d\boldsymbol{L} = \iint (\nabla \times \boldsymbol{H}) \cdot d\boldsymbol{S} \qquad \textbf{(7-31)}$$

It is understood that the surface indicated on the right-hand side is bounded by the closed curve indicated on the left-hand side. Equation 7-31 may be substituted in Eq. 7-17:

$$\iint (\nabla \times \boldsymbol{H}) \cdot d\boldsymbol{S} = \iint \left(\epsilon \frac{\partial \boldsymbol{E}}{dt} + \sigma \boldsymbol{E}\right) \cdot d\boldsymbol{S}$$

The integrations are over the same area, which may extend over any part of space:

$$\nabla \times \boldsymbol{H} = \epsilon \frac{\partial \boldsymbol{E}}{\partial t} + \sigma \boldsymbol{E} \qquad \textbf{(7-32)}$$

d. Faraday's law

The principle of electromagnetic induction was given as follows in Sec. 7-2*b*(4):

$$\oint \boldsymbol{E} \cdot d\boldsymbol{L} = -\iint \frac{\partial \boldsymbol{B}}{\partial t} \cdot d\boldsymbol{S} \qquad \textbf{(7-18)}$$

Stokes' theorem, Eq. 7-31, may, if written in terms of $\boldsymbol{E}$, be substituted for the left-hand side, giving the following:

$$\iint (\nabla \times \boldsymbol{E}) \cdot d\boldsymbol{S} = -\iint \frac{\partial \boldsymbol{B}}{\partial t} \cdot d\boldsymbol{S}$$

As with Ampere's law, the surface of integration is the same on both sides of the equality sign and may be any surface in space:

$$\nabla \times \boldsymbol{E} = -\frac{\partial \boldsymbol{B}}{\partial t} \tag{7-33}$$

Substitution of Eq. 7-12 yields

$$\nabla \times \boldsymbol{E} = -\mu \frac{\partial \boldsymbol{H}}{\partial t} \tag{7-34}$$

e. Additional differential functions

Equations 7-28, 7-29, 7-32, and 7-34, together with auxiliary equations 7-10 and 7-12, constitute Maxwell's equations. In the course of separating variables in order to solve those differential equations, two additional differential field functions are useful, the gradient of a scalar field and the laplacian.

(1) GRADIENT OF A SCALAR FIELD. The gradient is a vector function which is encountered principally in connection with static fields, but it is also part of a vector identity, Eq. 10-49, which is used in deriving the wave equation.

If a scalar point function depends on position in space, its value will, in general, change with small displacements from a given location. This result may be formulated as a useful differential function by defining a vector field, the gradient, as follows: (1) the direction of the gradient at each point is the direction in which the rate of change of the scalar function with respect to displacement is greatest, and (2) the magnitude of the gradient at each point is the rate of change of the scalar function for a differential displacement in the direction just noted. The symbol for the gradient of the scalar field V is grad V or ∇V.

(2) LAPLACIAN FUNCTION. Since the gradient of a scalar field is itself a vector field, the divergence operation may be performed on the gradient. The result, which is a scalar field, is a special type of second-order derivative (with respect to displacement) of the original scalar field and is given the name *laplacian*. The symbol for the laplacian is ∇^2:

$$\nabla^2 V = \nabla \cdot (\nabla V) \tag{7-35}$$

This function arises frequently in mathematical physics in connection with scalar-field functions. For the laplacian of a vector field, see Eq. 10-49 and the accompanying discussion.

7-4. COORDINATE SYSTEMS

The rectangular (or cartesian), circular-cylindrical, and spherical coordinate systems will be used in this work. In particular, the forms of the divergence, curl, gradient, and laplacian function, in terms of the components of a vector field in those systems, will be needed. A text emphasizing the mathematical aspect of vector analysis would devote attention to the derivation of these functions in different coordinate systems and to the transformation of them from one system to another.[4,7] Here the results will be given directly.

a. Rectangular coordinates

The rectangular coordinate system is based on three mutually perpendicular coordinate axes, each axis straight and of infinite extent. The set of axes may be initially oriented, however, to suit the user. The directions of the coordinate axes may be designated with three unit vectors (having direction and unit magnitude, but no dimensions) $\boldsymbol{a}_x$, $\boldsymbol{a}_y$, and $\boldsymbol{a}_z$. These are arranged in a right-handed order, which is most easily visualized by holding one's right hand with thumb and forefinger extended and the middle finger bent inwardly, such that they are mutually perpendicular. If the thumb is pointed in the $\boldsymbol{a}_x$ direction and the forefinger in the $\boldsymbol{a}_y$ direction, the middle finger will indicate the $\boldsymbol{a}_z$ direction.

Differential length and differential volume have the following forms in rectangular coordinates:

$$\boldsymbol{dL} = dx\,\boldsymbol{a}_x + dy\,\boldsymbol{a}_y + dz\,\boldsymbol{a}_z \qquad \textbf{(7-36)}$$

$$dv = dx\,dy\,dz \qquad \textbf{(7-37)}$$

The specific forms of the scalar product and the vector product in terms of rectangular-coordinate components may be set forth. The various products among the three unit vectors will be noted first. In the first three of the following equations, m and n may represent x, y, or z, but it is understood that m and n may not represent the same direction:

$$\begin{aligned} \boldsymbol{a}_m \cdot \boldsymbol{a}_m &= 1 \\ \boldsymbol{a}_m \cdot \boldsymbol{a}_n &= 0 \\ \boldsymbol{a}_m \times \boldsymbol{a}_m &= 0 \end{aligned} \qquad \textbf{(7-38)}$$

$$\begin{aligned} \boldsymbol{a}_x \times \boldsymbol{a}_y &= \boldsymbol{a}_z = -\boldsymbol{a}_y \times \boldsymbol{a}_x \\ \boldsymbol{a}_y \times \boldsymbol{a}_z &= \boldsymbol{a}_x = -\boldsymbol{a}_z \times \boldsymbol{a}_y \\ \boldsymbol{a}_z \times \boldsymbol{a}_x &= \boldsymbol{a}_y = -\boldsymbol{a}_x \times \boldsymbol{a}_z \end{aligned} \qquad \textbf{(7-39)}$$

The scalar and vector products of two general vectors $\boldsymbol{K}$ and $\boldsymbol{L}$ are

$$\boldsymbol{K} \cdot \boldsymbol{L} = K_x L_x + K_y L_y + K_z L_z \tag{7-40}$$

$$\boldsymbol{K} \times \boldsymbol{L} = (K_y L_z - K_z L_y)\boldsymbol{a}_x + (K_z L_x - K_x L_z)\boldsymbol{a}_y + (K_x L_y - K_y L_x)\boldsymbol{a}_z \tag{7-41}$$

The vector product may also be stated in determinantal form as a memory aid:

$$\boldsymbol{K} \times \boldsymbol{L} = \begin{vmatrix} \boldsymbol{a}_x & \boldsymbol{a}_y & \boldsymbol{a}_z \\ K_x & K_y & K_z \\ L_x & L_y & L_z \end{vmatrix} \tag{7-42}$$

Let a vector field $\boldsymbol{A}$ be defined as follows:

$$\boldsymbol{A} = A_x \boldsymbol{a}_x + A_y \boldsymbol{a}_y + A_z \boldsymbol{a}_z \tag{7-43}$$

The divergence and curl of $\boldsymbol{A}$, stated in rectangular coordinates, are

$$\nabla \cdot \boldsymbol{A} = \frac{\partial A_x}{\partial x} + \frac{\partial A_y}{\partial y} + \frac{\partial A_z}{\partial z} \tag{7-44}$$

$$\nabla \times \boldsymbol{A} = \left(\frac{\partial A_z}{\partial y} - \frac{\partial A_y}{\partial z}\right)\boldsymbol{a}_x + \left(\frac{\partial A_x}{\partial z} - \frac{\partial A_z}{\partial x}\right)\boldsymbol{a}_y + \left(\frac{\partial A_y}{\partial x} - \frac{\partial A_x}{\partial y}\right)\boldsymbol{a}_z \tag{7-45}$$

The curl may also be stated in determinantal form:

$$\nabla \times \boldsymbol{A} = \begin{vmatrix} \boldsymbol{a}_x & \boldsymbol{a}_y & \boldsymbol{a}_z \\ \dfrac{\partial}{\partial x} & \dfrac{\partial}{\partial y} & \dfrac{\partial}{\partial z} \\ A_x & A_y & A_z \end{vmatrix} \tag{7-46}$$

The gradient and laplacian of a scalar function V, in rectangular coordinates, are

$$\nabla V = \frac{\partial V}{\partial x}\boldsymbol{a}_x + \frac{\partial V}{\partial y}\boldsymbol{a}_y + \frac{\partial V}{\partial z}\boldsymbol{a}_z \tag{7-47}$$

$$\nabla^2 V = \frac{\partial^2 V}{\partial x^2} + \frac{\partial^2 V}{\partial y^2} + \frac{\partial^2 V}{\partial z^2} \tag{7-48}$$

b. Cylindrical coordinates

A set of circular-cylindrical coordinates is built around a longitudinal axis, whose orientation may be chosen at will and along which the unit vector $\boldsymbol{a}_z$ may be pointed in either direction. The radial unit vector $\boldsymbol{a}_r$ is perpendicular to the axis and points outward. The azimuthal unit vector $\boldsymbol{a}_\phi$ is perpendicular to both $\boldsymbol{a}_r$ and $\boldsymbol{a}_z$ at each given location in space. The three unit vectors form a right-handed set, so that the appropriate direction for $\boldsymbol{a}_\phi$ may be found by holding the right hand with the middle finger bent inwardly, pointing the thumb in the $\boldsymbol{a}_r$ direction and the middle finger in the $\boldsymbol{a}_z$ direction, whereupon the forefinger will indicate the $\boldsymbol{a}_\phi$ direction.

Differential length and differential volume have the following forms:

$$d\boldsymbol{L} = dr\,\boldsymbol{a}_r + r\,d\phi\,\boldsymbol{a}_\phi + dz\,\boldsymbol{a}_z \tag{7-49}$$

$$dv = r\,d\phi\,dr\,dz \tag{7-50}$$

It should be noted that whereas $\boldsymbol{a}_r$ and $\boldsymbol{a}_\phi$ have the same dimensions (both are dimensionless), dr and $d\phi$ do not (dr has the dimensions of length; $d\phi$ is dimensionless).

The three equations in set 7-38 for scalar and vector products among unit vectors are applicable to cylindrical coordinates if m and n represent r, ϕ, or z. The other vector products among the unit vectors are

$$\begin{aligned} \boldsymbol{a}_r \times \boldsymbol{a}_\phi &= \boldsymbol{a}_z = -\boldsymbol{a}_\phi \times \boldsymbol{a}_r \\ \boldsymbol{a}_\phi \times \boldsymbol{a}_z &= \boldsymbol{a}_r = -\boldsymbol{a}_z \times \boldsymbol{a}_\phi \\ \boldsymbol{a}_z \times \boldsymbol{a}_r &= \boldsymbol{a}_\phi = -\boldsymbol{a}_r \times \boldsymbol{a}_z \end{aligned} \tag{7-51}$$

The scalar and vector products of two general vectors $\boldsymbol{K}$ and $\boldsymbol{L}$ are

$$\boldsymbol{K} \cdot \boldsymbol{L} = K_r L_r + K_\phi L_\phi + K_z L_z \tag{7-52}$$

$$\boldsymbol{K} \times \boldsymbol{L} = (K_\phi L_z - K_z L_\phi)\boldsymbol{a}_r + (K_z L_r - K_r L_z)\boldsymbol{a}_\phi + (K_r L_\phi - K_\phi L_r)\boldsymbol{a}_z \tag{7-53}$$

Let a vector field $\boldsymbol{A}$ be defined as follows:

$$\boldsymbol{A} = A_r \boldsymbol{a}_r + A_\phi \boldsymbol{a}_\phi + A_z \boldsymbol{a}_z \tag{7-54}$$

The divergence and curl of $\boldsymbol{A}$, stated in cylindrical coordinates, are

$$\nabla \cdot \boldsymbol{A} = \frac{1}{r}\frac{\partial(rA_r)}{\partial r} + \frac{1}{r}\frac{\partial A_\phi}{\partial \phi} + \frac{\partial A_z}{\partial z} \tag{7-55}$$

$$\nabla \times \boldsymbol{A} = \left(\frac{1}{r}\frac{\partial A_z}{\partial \phi} - \frac{\partial A_\phi}{\partial z}\right)\boldsymbol{a}_r + \left(\frac{\partial A_r}{\partial z} - \frac{\partial A_z}{\partial r}\right)\boldsymbol{a}_\phi + \left(\frac{1}{r}\frac{\partial(rA_\phi)}{\partial r} - \frac{1}{r}\frac{\partial A_r}{\partial \phi}\right)\boldsymbol{a}_z \tag{7-56}$$

The gradient and laplacian of a scalar function V are

$$\nabla V = \frac{\partial V}{\partial r}\boldsymbol{a}_r + \frac{1}{r}\frac{\partial V}{\partial \phi}\boldsymbol{a}_\phi + \frac{\partial V}{\partial z}\boldsymbol{a}_z \tag{7-57}$$

$$\nabla^2 V = \frac{1}{r}\frac{\partial(r\,\partial V/\partial r)}{\partial r} + \frac{1}{r^2}\frac{\partial^2 V}{\partial \phi^2} + \frac{\partial^2 V}{\partial z^2} \tag{7-58}$$

c. Spherical coordinates

The spherical-coordinate system is built around an arbitrarily selected origin and polar axis. Radial distance and direction in the spherical sense are different from the corresponding concepts in the cylindrical coordinate system and will be distinguished by the symbol $\mathring{r}$. The unit radial vector $\boldsymbol{a}_{\mathring{r}}$ is directed outward from the origin; the unit vector $\boldsymbol{a}_\theta$ is directed along circles whose centers are at the origin and whose planes contain the polar axis; and the unit vector $\boldsymbol{a}_\phi$ is directed along circles whose centers are on the polar axis and whose planes are perpendicular to that axis. The angle θ measures colatitude; one direction along the polar axis from the origin is designated as $\theta = 0$, and the opposite direction is $\theta = \pi$. The angle ϕ measures longitude; any plane which contains the polar axis may be chosen as $\phi = 0$. A right-handed set is formed by the unit vectors when taken in the order $\boldsymbol{a}_{\mathring{r}}$, $\boldsymbol{a}_\theta$, $\boldsymbol{a}_\phi$.

Differential length and differential volume have the following forms:

$$\boldsymbol{dL} = d\mathring{r}\,\boldsymbol{a}_{\mathring{r}} + \mathring{r}\,d\theta\,\boldsymbol{a}_\theta + \mathring{r}\sin\theta\,d\phi\,\boldsymbol{a}_\phi \tag{7-59}$$

$$dv = \mathring{r}^2 \sin\theta\,d\mathring{r}\,d\theta\,d\phi \tag{7-60}$$

As with cylindrical coordinates, the three equations in set 7-38 for scalar and vector products among unit vectors are applicable to spherical coordinates if m and n represent $\mathring{r}$, θ, or ϕ. The other vector products among the unit vectors are

$$\begin{aligned}\boldsymbol{a}_{\mathring{r}} \times \boldsymbol{a}_\theta &= \boldsymbol{a}_\phi = -\boldsymbol{a}_\theta \times \boldsymbol{a}_{\mathring{r}}\\ \boldsymbol{a}_\theta \times \boldsymbol{a}_\phi &= \boldsymbol{a}_{\mathring{r}} = -\boldsymbol{a}_\phi \times \boldsymbol{a}_\theta\\ \boldsymbol{a}_\phi \times \boldsymbol{a}_{\mathring{r}} &= \boldsymbol{a}_\theta = -\boldsymbol{a}_{\mathring{r}} \times \boldsymbol{a}_\phi\end{aligned} \tag{7-61}$$

The scalar and vector products of two general vectors $\boldsymbol{K}$ and $\boldsymbol{L}$ are

$$\boldsymbol{K}\cdot\boldsymbol{L} = K_{\mathring{r}}L_{\mathring{r}} + K_\theta L_\theta + K_\phi L_\phi \tag{7-62}$$

$$\boldsymbol{K}\times\boldsymbol{L} = (K_\theta L_\phi - K_\phi L_\theta)\boldsymbol{a}_{\mathring{r}} + (K_\phi L_{\mathring{r}} - K_{\mathring{r}} L_\phi)\boldsymbol{a}_\theta + (K_{\mathring{r}} L_\theta - K_\theta L_{\mathring{r}})\boldsymbol{a}_\phi \tag{7-63}$$

Let a vector field $\boldsymbol{A}$ be defined as follows:

$$\boldsymbol{A} = A_{\mathring{r}}\boldsymbol{a}_{\mathring{r}} + A_\theta\boldsymbol{a}_\theta + A_\phi\boldsymbol{a}_\phi \tag{7-64}$$

The divergence and curl of $\boldsymbol{A}$, stated in spherical coordinates, are

$$\nabla\cdot\boldsymbol{A} = \frac{1}{\mathring{r}^2}\frac{\partial(\mathring{r}^2 A_{\mathring{r}})}{\partial\mathring{r}} + \frac{1}{\mathring{r}\sin\theta}\frac{\partial(\sin\theta\,A_\theta)}{\partial\theta} + \frac{1}{\mathring{r}\sin\theta}\frac{\partial A_\phi}{\partial\phi} \tag{7-65}$$

$$\begin{aligned}\nabla\times\boldsymbol{A} = {} & \frac{1}{\mathring{r}\sin\theta}\left[\frac{\partial(\sin\theta\,A_\phi)}{\partial\theta} - \frac{\partial A_\theta}{\partial\phi}\right]\boldsymbol{a}_{\mathring{r}} + \left[\frac{1}{\mathring{r}\sin\theta}\frac{\partial A_{\mathring{r}}}{\partial\phi} - \frac{1}{\mathring{r}}\frac{\partial(\mathring{r}A_\phi)}{\partial\mathring{r}}\right]\boldsymbol{a}_\theta\\ & + \frac{1}{\mathring{r}}\left[\frac{\partial(\mathring{r}A_\theta)}{\partial\mathring{r}} - \frac{\partial A_{\mathring{r}}}{\partial\theta}\right]\boldsymbol{a}_\phi\end{aligned} \tag{7-66}$$

The gradient and laplacian of a scalar function V are

$$\nabla V = \frac{\partial V}{\partial \mathring{r}} \boldsymbol{a}_{\mathring{r}} + \frac{1}{\mathring{r}} \frac{\partial V}{\partial \theta} \boldsymbol{a}_\theta + \frac{1}{\mathring{r} \sin \theta} \frac{\partial V}{\partial \phi} \boldsymbol{a}_\phi \tag{7-67}$$

$$\nabla^2 V = \frac{1}{\mathring{r}^2} \frac{\partial}{\partial \mathring{r}} \left(\mathring{r}^2 \frac{\partial V}{\partial \mathring{r}} \right) + \frac{1}{\mathring{r}^2 \sin \theta} \frac{\partial}{\partial \theta} \left(\sin \theta \frac{\partial V}{\partial \theta} \right) + \frac{1}{\mathring{r}^2 \sin^2 \theta} \frac{\partial^2 V}{\partial \phi^2} \tag{7-68}$$

7-5. CONCLUSIONS

Macroscopic electromagnetic-wave phenomena may be described by means of (1) four vector fields, $\boldsymbol{B}$, $\boldsymbol{H}$, $\boldsymbol{D}$, and $\boldsymbol{E}$; (2) the parameters of permittivity ϵ, permeability μ, and conductivity σ (constant scalars for the media of interest in this text); and (3) electric-charge volume density ρ (a scalar field). Two of the vector fields are related to the other two by direct proportion:

$$\boldsymbol{D} = \epsilon \boldsymbol{E} \tag{7-10}$$

$$\boldsymbol{B} = \mu \boldsymbol{H} \tag{7-12}$$

Maxwell's differential equations constrain and interrelate the fields, independently of any specific coordinate system, by means of two rate-of-change-with-distance functions of a vector field, the divergence and the curl. These equations are

$$\nabla \cdot \boldsymbol{D} = \rho \tag{7-28}$$

$$\nabla \cdot \boldsymbol{B} = 0 \tag{7-29}$$

$$\nabla \times \boldsymbol{H} = \sigma \boldsymbol{E} + \epsilon \frac{\partial \boldsymbol{E}}{\partial t} \tag{7-32}$$

$$\nabla \times \boldsymbol{E} = -\mu \frac{\partial \boldsymbol{H}}{\partial t} \tag{7-34}$$

Two auxiliary vector fields which are convenient in some applications are the conduction-current density $\boldsymbol{J}$ and the displacement-current density $\boldsymbol{J}_D$:

$$\boldsymbol{J} = \sigma \boldsymbol{E} \tag{7-14}$$

$$\boldsymbol{J}_D = \frac{\partial \boldsymbol{D}}{\partial t} \tag{7-16}$$

Actual electrical-charge distributions are approximated by finite, continuous volume-charge-density distributions, or by point charges, line charges, or surface charges.

Coordinate systems are introduced as aids in the mathematical description of the particular fields which exist when specific boundary surfaces are present. The various operations of vector algebra and vector calculus may be stated in terms of components of the appropriate vectors in any of several coordinate systems.

PROBLEMS

7-1. Given the force field

$$\boldsymbol{F} = -F_0\left(\frac{x}{b} + \frac{y}{f}\right)\boldsymbol{a}_x - F_0\left(\frac{y}{c} + \frac{x}{f}\right)\boldsymbol{a}_y$$

find the work done in moving from point (0, c) to point (2b, 2c) by evaluating the line integral of $\boldsymbol{F}$ along the following paths: (*a*) from (0, c) parallel to the Y axis to (0, 2c), and then parallel to the X axis to (2b, 2c); and (*b*), from (0, c) parallel to the X axis to (2b, c), and then parallel to the Y axis to (2b, 2c). Find curl $\boldsymbol{F}$ and comment on its relation to the line-integral results.

7-2. Direct current is flowing in a non-homogeneous circular conductor of radius r_a. $\boldsymbol{E} = E_0\boldsymbol{a}_z$. The conductivity is a function of radius: $\sigma = \sigma_0[1 + (r^2/8r_a^2)]$. Write an expression for the conduction-current density, and evaluate a surface integral to find the current in the conductor.

7-3. A coaxial line has a solid inner conductor of radius r_a and an outer conductor with inner and outer radii r_b and r_c. Direct current I is flowing in the $\boldsymbol{a}_z$ direction in the inner conductor and in the $-\boldsymbol{a}_z$ direction in the outer. Evaluate the net currents enclosed by circles of radii r_1, r_2, and r_3, where $r_1 < r_a$, $r_a < r_2 < r_b$, and $r_b < r_3 < r_c$. Find the magnetic field in the respective regions, using Ampere's law. Take the curl of the function found for $\boldsymbol{H}$ in each region and verify that it is equal to the corresponding current density.

REFERENCES

1. DIBNER, BERN, *Ten Founding Fathers of the Electrical Science.* Norwalk, Conn.: Burndy Library, 1954.
2. HARRIS, FOREST K., *Electrical Measurements.* New York: John Wiley & Sons, Inc., 1952.
3. KINNARD, ISAAC F., *Applied Electrical Measurements.* New York: John Wiley & Sons, Inc., 1956.
4. SPIEGEL, MURRAY R., *Theory and Problems of Vector Analysis.* New York: Schaum Publishing Co., 1959.
5. WALDRON, R. A., *Ferrites, An Introduction for Microwave Engineers.* London: D. Van Nostrand Company, Ltd., 1961.
6. WHITTAKER, EDMUND, *A History of the Theories of Aether and Electricity—The Classical Theories.* New York: Philosophical Library, Inc., 1951.
7. WILLS, A. P., *Vector Analysis, with an Introduction to Tensor Analysis.* New York: Prentice-Hall, Inc., 1931. Also Dover Publications, Inc., 1958.

CHAPTER 8

Propagation and Reflection of Plane Electromagnetic Waves

The simplest illustration of electromagnetic-wave propagation is the hypothetical one of sinusoidal plane waves of infinite extent in a homogeneous, charge-free medium. A considerable portion of the wave front of radiation from an antenna closely approaches this hypothetical configuration at long distances from the source, and the solution is applicable in localized regions in other problems.

An elementary situation involving a nonhomogeneous region for the waves is that of two uniform media of semi-infinite extent, with a planar boundary between them. A traveling-wave set of plane fields incident on such a boundary surface will give rise to a transmitted field set, of different magnitudes, and a reflected field set.

An important limiting case of reflection is that in which one medium is a metal of infinite conductivity.

8-1. TRAVELING-WAVE FIELDS IN INFINITE MEDIUM

Rectangular coordinates are appropriate. The $\boldsymbol{E}$ field is assumed to be (1) everywhere parallel to the X axis, (2) a function of time and of displacement in the $\boldsymbol{a}_z$ direction, but (3) not a function of displacement in the $\boldsymbol{a}_x$ or $\boldsymbol{a}_y$ directions.

$$\boldsymbol{E} = E_x(z,t)\boldsymbol{a}_x \tag{8-1}$$

It may be seen by inspection that this function satisfies the requirement of zero divergence of the $\boldsymbol{D}$ field (Eqs. 7-28 and 7-10, with zero charge-density postulated) because E_x, the only nonzero component of $\boldsymbol{E}$, is not a function of x (Eq. 7-44 for the divergence function).

a. Derivation of wave equation: duality with transmission line

By substituting the assumed $\boldsymbol{E}$ into Maxwell's curl equations successively, $\boldsymbol{H}$ may be eliminated from the set and a scalar differential equation in E_x obtained. The curl of Eq. 8-1 is found by means of Eq. 7-45:

$$\nabla \times \boldsymbol{E} = \frac{\partial E_x(z,t)}{\partial z}\,\boldsymbol{a}_y \tag{8-2}$$

Substitution of this into Maxwell's equation in curl $\boldsymbol{E}$, Eq. 7-34, gives

$$-\frac{\partial \boldsymbol{H}}{\partial t} = \frac{1}{\mu}\frac{\partial E_x(z,t)}{\partial z}\,\boldsymbol{a}_y \tag{8-3}$$

Thus the accompanying $\boldsymbol{H}$ field has only one component, $H_y(z,t)$. In other words, the $\boldsymbol{E}$ and $\boldsymbol{H}$ fields are in space quadrature with each other.

The curl of Eq. 8-3 is

$$\nabla \times \left(\frac{\partial \boldsymbol{H}}{\partial t}\right) = \frac{1}{\mu}\frac{\partial^2 E_x(z,t)}{\partial z^2}\,\boldsymbol{a}_x$$

Continuity of the functions and their derivatives will be assumed; hence the order of differentiation of $\boldsymbol{H}$ may be interchanged.

$$\frac{\partial}{\partial t}(\nabla \times \boldsymbol{H}) = \frac{1}{\mu}\frac{\partial^2 E_x(z,t)}{\partial t^2}\,\boldsymbol{a}_x \tag{8-4}$$

The time derivative of Maxwell's equation in curl $\boldsymbol{H}$, Eq. 7-32, may be substituted for the left-hand side of Eq. 8-4 to eliminate the $\boldsymbol{H}$ function. The following partial differential equation in E_x results:

$$\frac{\partial^2 E_x(z,t)}{\partial z^2} = \epsilon\mu\,\frac{\partial^2 E_x(z,t)}{\partial t^2} + \sigma\mu\,\frac{\partial E_x(z,t)}{\partial t} \tag{8-5}$$

If one starts with an assumed function $H_y(z,t)$, $\boldsymbol{E}$ may be eliminated from the set and the same equation as 8-5 obtained in terms of $H_y(z,t)$ instead of $E_x(z,t)$.

Comparison of Eq. 8-5 with Eq. 2-5 for the general transmission line discloses a term-for-term correspondence between the two as listed below, except that r in Eq. 2-5 has no counterpart in Eq. 8-5:

$$\begin{aligned} v(z,t) &\sim E_x(z,t) \\ g &\sim \sigma \\ l &\sim \mu \\ c &\sim \epsilon \end{aligned} \tag{8-6}$$

Here the symbol $\sim$ indicates "analogous to."

The mathematical parallelism just indicated between (1) the relationships among the dependent variables, the independent variables, and the parameters of one physical problem, and (2) the corresponding relationships in the other physical problem, is known as *dualism*. This property exists despite different physical interpretations and different dimensions for the members of a given pair of analogous or dual quantities from the two systems.* One pair of dual quantities indicated in set 8-6 consists of (1) the voltage in volts between two transmission-line conductors, and (2) the electric-field intensity in volts per meter of an electromagnetic disturbance of (mathematically) infinite transverse extent. The parallelism extends to the solutions of the differential equations.

b. Sinusoidal-traveling-wave general solution

The same technique of assuming sinusoidal-traveling-wave solutions and resolving into complex exponential form that was followed in Chapter 2 may be used here. Only the key equations will be given. Let

$$\boldsymbol{E}_1(z,t) = E_{x1M}\epsilon^{-\alpha z}\sin(\omega t - \beta z)\boldsymbol{a}_x \tag{8-7}$$

$$\boldsymbol{E}_1(z,t) = \text{Im}[E_{x1M}\epsilon^{-(\alpha+j\beta)z}\epsilon^{j\omega t}]\boldsymbol{a}_x \tag{8-8}$$

$$\boldsymbol{E}_2(z,t) = E_{x2M}\epsilon^{\alpha z}\sin(\omega t + \beta z)\boldsymbol{a}_x \tag{8-9}$$

$$\boldsymbol{E}_2(z,t) = \text{Im}[E_{x2M}\epsilon^{(\alpha+j\beta)z}\epsilon^{j\omega t}]\boldsymbol{a}_x \tag{8-10}$$

Substitution of either Eq. 8-8 or 8-10 into Eq. 8-5 yields the following relationship between the propagation function and the parameters μ, ϵ, σ, and ω:

$$\alpha + j\beta = \sqrt{j\omega\mu(\sigma + j\omega\epsilon)} \tag{8-11}$$

The corresponding magnetic-field-intensity functions $\boldsymbol{H}_1(z,t)$ and $\boldsymbol{H}_2(z,t)$ may be found by differentiating Eqs. 8-8 and 8-10 with respect to z,

* Applications of dualism to wave propagation and diffusion phenomena in electromagnetic, mechanical and thermal systems are given by R. K. Moore in *Traveling Wave Engineering* (New York: McGraw-Hill Book Company, Inc., 1960) and *Wave and Diffusion Analogies* (McGraw-Hill, 1964).

substituting in Eq. 8-3, and integrating with respect to time:

$$\frac{\partial E_{x1}(z,t)}{\partial z} = \text{Im}[-(\alpha + j\beta)E_{x1M}\epsilon^{-(\alpha+j\beta)z}\epsilon^{j\omega t}] \tag{8-12}$$

$$\boldsymbol{H}_1(z,t) = \text{Im}\left[\frac{(\alpha + j\beta)}{j\omega\mu} E_{x1M}\epsilon^{-(\alpha+j\beta)z}\epsilon^{j\omega t}\right]\boldsymbol{a}_y \tag{8-13}$$

Likewise

$$\boldsymbol{H}_2(z,t) = \text{Im}\left[\frac{-(\alpha + j\beta)}{j\omega\mu} E_{x2M}\epsilon^{(\alpha+j\beta)z}\epsilon^{j\omega t}\right]\boldsymbol{a}_y \tag{8-14}$$

From Eq. 8-11,

$$\frac{(\alpha + j\beta)}{j\omega\mu} = \sqrt{\frac{(\sigma + j\omega\epsilon)}{j\omega\mu}} \tag{8-15}$$

The reciprocal of this quantity has the units of ohms, and is given the name *intrinsic impedance* (η). It is analogous to the characteristic impedance of a transmission line. For a conducting medium, η will be complex:

$$|\eta| \angle\theta_\eta = \sqrt{\frac{j\omega\mu}{\sigma + j\omega\epsilon}} \tag{8-16}$$

Equations 8-13 and 8-14 may be rewritten as follows:

$$\boldsymbol{H}_1(z,t) = \text{Im}\left[\frac{E_{x1M}}{|\eta|}\epsilon^{-(\alpha+j\beta)z}\epsilon^{j(\omega t-\theta_\eta)}\right]\boldsymbol{a}_y \tag{8-17}$$

$$\boldsymbol{H}_1(z,t) = \frac{E_{x1M}}{|\eta|}\epsilon^{-\alpha z}\sin(\omega t - \theta_\eta - \beta z)\boldsymbol{a}_y \tag{8-18}$$

$$\boldsymbol{H}_2(z,t) = \text{Im}\left[\frac{-E_{x2M}}{|\eta|}\epsilon^{(\alpha+j\beta)z}\epsilon^{j(\omega t-\theta_\eta)}\right]\boldsymbol{a}_y \tag{8-19}$$

$$\boldsymbol{H}_2(z,t) = \frac{-E_{x2M}}{|\eta|}\epsilon^{\alpha z}\sin(\omega t - \theta_\eta + \beta z)\boldsymbol{a}_y \tag{8-20}$$

These results should be compared with the corresponding expressions for current on a general transmission line, Eqs. 2-20 and 2-21.

c. TEM-mode designation: polarization

For both traveling-wave solutions which were examined here, the $\boldsymbol{E}$ and $\boldsymbol{H}$ fields are everywhere perpendicular to the direction of motion, $\boldsymbol{a}_z$ or $-\boldsymbol{a}_z$. A wave set which has these properties is said to be in the *transverse-electromagnetic* (*TEM*) *mode*. This designation will prove applicable in Chapter 9, where the fields of specific transmission lines are analyzed.

The functions $\boldsymbol{E}_1$ and $\boldsymbol{E}_2$ in Eqs. 8-7 and 8-9 are special solutions within the class of sinusoidal waves which could propagate in the assigned directions in that each electric field is everywhere parallel to a single reference direction, $\boldsymbol{a}_x$. As such they are known as *linearly polarized* waves. Consider the following special solutions, either (or both) of which could exist simultaneously with $\boldsymbol{E}_1$:

$$\boldsymbol{E}_3(z,t) = E_{y3M}\epsilon^{-\alpha z}\sin(\omega t - \beta z)\boldsymbol{a}_y \tag{8-21}$$

$$\boldsymbol{E}_4(z,t) = E_{y4M}\epsilon^{-\alpha z}\cos(\omega t - \beta z)\boldsymbol{a}_y \tag{8-22}$$

Addition of Eqs. 8-7 and 8-21 yields

$$\boldsymbol{E}_1(z,t) + \boldsymbol{E}_3(z,t) = \epsilon^{-\alpha z}\sin(\omega t - \beta z)(E_{x1M}\boldsymbol{a}_x + E_{y3M}\boldsymbol{a}_y) \tag{8-23}$$

This too is a linearly polarized wave, even though the direction of polarization is not parallel to one of the coordinate axes. On the other hand, addition of $\boldsymbol{E}_1$ and $\boldsymbol{E}_4$ yields an effect known as *elliptical polarization*:

$$\boldsymbol{E}_1(z,t) + \boldsymbol{E}_4(z,t) = \epsilon^{-\alpha z}[E_{x1M}\sin(\omega t - \beta z)\boldsymbol{a}_x + E_{y4M}\cos(\omega t - \beta z)\boldsymbol{a}_y] \tag{8-24}$$

At any given value of z the resultant field never goes to zero but varies in magnitude between the extremes of $E_{x1M}\epsilon^{-\alpha z}$ and $E_{y4M}\epsilon^{-\alpha z}$. The direction of the resultant field changes continuously in the xy plane. A special case is that in which the magnitudes E_{x1M} and E_{y4M} are equal; then the resultant is constant in magnitude and rotates uniformly. This is called *circular polarization*. Some antennas are designed to produce circularly polarized fields, and elliptical polarization may be inadvertently produced in practical communication systems.

d. Approximations and limiting forms of propagation parameters

Whether a given conductivity is "high" or "low" in wave-propagation problems may be a relative matter with respect to frequency; specifically it may be considered "high" if σ is much greater than $\omega\epsilon$, or "low" if $\omega\epsilon$ is much greater than σ. Both situations may be examined with power-series approximations.

(1) Medium of low conductivity. If conductivity is low, Eqs. 8-11 and 8-16 may be rearranged and expanded in series as follows:

$$\begin{aligned}\alpha + j\beta &= j\omega\sqrt{\mu\epsilon}\sqrt{1 - \frac{j\sigma}{\omega\epsilon}} \\ &\approx j\omega\sqrt{\mu\epsilon}\left(1 - \frac{j\sigma}{2\omega\epsilon}\right) \\ &\approx \frac{\sigma}{2}\sqrt{\frac{\mu}{\epsilon}} + j\omega\sqrt{\mu\epsilon}\end{aligned} \tag{8-25}$$

$$\begin{aligned}\eta &= \sqrt{\frac{\mu}{\epsilon}}\frac{1}{\sqrt{1+\dfrac{\sigma}{j\omega\epsilon}}}\\ &\approx \sqrt{\frac{\mu}{\epsilon}}\left(1+\frac{j\sigma}{2\omega\epsilon}\right)\\ &\approx \sqrt{\frac{\mu}{\epsilon}}\,\epsilon^{j\tan^{-1}(\sigma/2\omega\epsilon)}\\ &\approx \sqrt{\frac{\mu}{\epsilon}}\,\epsilon^{j(\sigma/2\omega\epsilon)}\end{aligned}\tag{8-26}$$

In the limiting case of zero conductivity, these reduce to

$$\begin{aligned}\alpha &= 0\\ \beta &= \omega\sqrt{\mu\epsilon}\\ \eta &= \sqrt{\frac{\mu}{\epsilon}}\\ \theta_\eta &= 0\end{aligned}\tag{8-27}$$

The following relationship between phase function and phase velocity was noted in the discussion of transmission lines:

$$v = \frac{\omega}{\beta}\tag{2-15}$$

Substitution of Eq. 8-27 gives the following for the phase velocity of electromagnetic waves in a nonconducting medium:

$$v = \frac{1}{\sqrt{\mu\epsilon}}\tag{8-28}$$

From Eqs. 8-27 and 8-28 the following observations may be made concerning the propagation of $\boldsymbol{E}$ and $\boldsymbol{H}$ waves through a nonconducting medium: (1) both fields travel without attenuation, (2) all frequency components of both fields travel with the same velocity, (3) for each frequency component the $\boldsymbol{E}$ and $\boldsymbol{H}$ fields are in time phase, and (4) the proportion between the magnitudes of the $\boldsymbol{E}$ and $\boldsymbol{H}$ fields is the same for all frequencies.

A corollary of these findings is that a recurrent, nonsinusoidal wave will be propagated in a nonconducting medium with no distortion, since it may be resolved into a Fourier series of sinusoidal waves and these all propagate in the same manner. A corresponding conclusion is applicable to nonrecurrent pulses.

(2) MEDIUM OF HIGH CONDUCTIVITY. For this case, Eqs. 8-11 and 8-16 may be rearranged and expanded in series as follows:

$$\begin{aligned}\alpha + j\beta &= \sqrt{j\omega\mu\sigma}\sqrt{1 + \frac{j\omega\epsilon}{\sigma}} \\ &\approx \sqrt{j\omega\mu\sigma}\left(1 + \frac{j\omega\epsilon}{2\sigma}\right) \\ &\approx \sqrt{\frac{\omega\mu\sigma}{2}}\left(1 - \frac{\omega\epsilon}{2\sigma}\right) + j\sqrt{\frac{\omega\mu\sigma}{2}}\left(1 + \frac{\omega\epsilon}{2\sigma}\right)\end{aligned} \tag{8-29}$$

$$\begin{aligned}|\eta|\underline{/\theta_\eta} &= \sqrt{\frac{j\omega\mu}{\sigma}}\frac{1}{\sqrt{1 + \dfrac{j\omega\epsilon}{\sigma}}} \\ &\approx \sqrt{\frac{j\omega\mu}{\sigma}}\left(1 - \frac{j\omega\epsilon}{2\sigma}\right) \\ &\approx \sqrt{\frac{\omega\mu}{\sigma}}\,\epsilon^{j(\pi/4 - \omega\epsilon/2\sigma)}\end{aligned} \tag{8-30}$$

$$v \rightarrow \sqrt{\frac{2\omega}{\mu\sigma}} \qquad (\text{as } \omega\epsilon/\sigma \rightarrow 0) \tag{8-31}$$

It should be recognized that these approximations are not valid for frequencies approaching infinity.

Conclusions to be noted from Eqs. 8-29, 8-30, and 8-31 for media for which $\omega\epsilon/\sigma \rightarrow 0$ are: (1) attenuation, phase velocity, and magnitude of intrinsic impedance vary markedly with frequency; (2) attenuation in nepers per meter is equal to phase function in radians per meter; and (3) for each separate frequency component, the $\boldsymbol{H}$ field lags the $\boldsymbol{E}$ field in time phase by 45 degrees.

e. Poynting's vector

It was noted in the derivation of the wave-equation solutions for the plane wave that $\boldsymbol{E}$ and $\boldsymbol{H}$ are in space quadrature with respect to each other and with respect to the direction of propagation. This suggests that the vector product of those two fields might be used to indicate the direction in which the waves are traveling. Furthermore, the product of $|\boldsymbol{E}|$, volts per meter, and $|\boldsymbol{H}|$, amperes per meter, has the units of watts per square meter, those of power density on a surface.

The following vector-field identity makes possible a linking of the vector product just suggested with the rate of change of stored energy and the rate of conversion of electromagnetic energy into heat:

$$\nabla \cdot (\boldsymbol{E} \times \boldsymbol{H}) = \boldsymbol{H} \cdot (\nabla \times \boldsymbol{E}) - \boldsymbol{E} \cdot (\nabla \times \boldsymbol{H}) \tag{8-32}$$

Maxwell's curl equations, 7-32 and 7-34, may be substituted into the right-hand side:

$$\nabla \cdot (\boldsymbol{E} \times \boldsymbol{H}) = -\mu \boldsymbol{H} \cdot \frac{\partial \boldsymbol{H}}{\partial t} - \boldsymbol{E} \cdot \left(\epsilon \frac{\partial \boldsymbol{E}}{\partial t} + \sigma \boldsymbol{E}\right) \tag{8-33}$$

$$\mu \boldsymbol{H} \cdot \frac{\partial \boldsymbol{H}}{\partial t} = \frac{\partial}{\partial t}\left(\frac{\mu\, |\boldsymbol{H}|^2}{2}\right) \tag{8-34}$$

$$\epsilon \boldsymbol{E} \cdot \frac{\partial \boldsymbol{E}}{\partial t} = \frac{\partial}{\partial t}\left(\frac{\epsilon\, |\boldsymbol{E}|^2}{2}\right) \tag{8-35}$$

$$\sigma \boldsymbol{E} \cdot \boldsymbol{E} = \sigma\, |\boldsymbol{E}|^2 \tag{8-36}$$

Let

$$w_\epsilon = \frac{\epsilon\, |\boldsymbol{E}|^2}{2} \tag{8-37}$$

$$w_\mu = \frac{\mu\, |\boldsymbol{H}|^2}{2} \tag{8-38}$$

The functions w_ϵ and w_μ are scalar fields with the dimensions of energy per unit volume.

The energy stored in the electric field of a capacitor is equal to the volume integral of w_ϵ over all the space occupied by the field, and the energy stored in the magnetic field of a circuit is equal to the volume integral of w_μ over all the space occupied by that field.[3] Problems 8-2 and 8-3 call for verification of these principles in some specific cases.

If one allocates the field energies on a distributed basis throughout the regions where the fields are nonzero, w_ϵ and w_μ may appropriately be called the *electric-field-energy density* and the *magnetic-field-energy density*, respectively. Substitution into Eq. 8-33 yields

$$\nabla \cdot (\boldsymbol{E} \times \boldsymbol{H}) = -\frac{\partial w_\epsilon}{\partial t} - \frac{\partial w_\mu}{\partial t} - \sigma\, |\boldsymbol{E}|^2 \tag{8-39}$$

Each term in this equation has the units of power per unit volume. The last term represents the rate of conversion of electromagnetic energy into heat.

Equation 8-39 may be integrated over the volume enclosed by some given surface:

$$\iiint \nabla \cdot (\boldsymbol{E} \times \boldsymbol{H})\, dv = -\iiint \left(\frac{\partial w_\epsilon}{\partial t} + \frac{\partial w_\mu}{\partial t} + \sigma\, |\boldsymbol{E}|^2\right) dv \tag{8-40}$$

The divergence theorem, Eq. 7-27, may be substituted for the left-hand side:

$$-\oiint (\boldsymbol{E} \times \boldsymbol{H}) \cdot \boldsymbol{dS} = +\iiint \left(\frac{\partial w_\epsilon}{\partial t} + \frac{\partial w_\mu}{\partial t} + \sigma\, |\boldsymbol{E}|^2\right) dv \tag{8-41}$$

Thus the negative of the surface integral of $\boldsymbol{E} \times \boldsymbol{H}$ (with $\boldsymbol{dS}$ directed outwardly) is equal to the time rate of increase of energy within the enclosed volume.

Poynting's vector $\boldsymbol{P}$ is defined as

$$\boldsymbol{P} = \boldsymbol{E} \times \boldsymbol{H} \tag{8-42}$$

The vector $\boldsymbol{P}$ is commonly interpreted as representing the energy-flow density at a point, and this is in many instances a reasonable and helpful point of view. This interpretation is not always valid. An oft-cited example is that of a simultaneous static magnetic field and static electric field. Together they could have a nonzero Poynting-vector field even though there is no sustained movement of energy; however, the surface integral of that function over any enclosing surface vanishes. As a matter of fact any field which had zero divergence could be added to $\boldsymbol{P}$ and the enclosed-surface integral would not be changed.

For the traveling-wave set described by Eqs. 8-7 and 8-18, Poynting's vector is as follows:

$$\begin{aligned}\boldsymbol{P} &= \frac{E_{x1M}^2}{|\eta|}\,\epsilon^{-2\alpha z}\sin(\omega t - \beta z)\sin(\omega t - \theta_\eta - \beta z)\boldsymbol{a}_z \\ &= \frac{E_{x1M}^2}{2\,|\eta|}\,\epsilon^{-2\alpha z}[\cos\theta_\eta - \cos(2\omega t - \theta_\eta - 2\beta z)]\boldsymbol{a}_z\end{aligned}$$

This may be time-averaged over an integral number of cycles to yield $\boldsymbol{P}_{av}$:

$$\boldsymbol{P}_{av} = \frac{E_{x1M}^2}{2\,|\eta|}\,\epsilon^{-2\alpha z}\cos\theta_\eta\,\boldsymbol{a}_z \tag{8-43}$$

The surface integral of $\boldsymbol{P}_{av}$ *entering* a closed surface yields the time-averaged power loss within.

Elsewhere in this text Poynting's vector will be used for the calculation of (1) losses in conducting surfaces, and (2) the radiation resistance of an antenna. Integration over an enclosing surface is either used explicitly as in Eq. 13-47, or may be visualized.

8-2. REFLECTION AND REFRACTION AT NORMAL INCIDENCE

If electromagnetic waves are propagating in a region containing two or more media with different intrinsic impedances, reflected waves will arise to satisfy requirements of continuity of the fields at the boundary surfaces. If the waves are plane and uniform, and the direction of propagation is normal to the plane of the boundary surface, the result proves to be analogous to the reflections on a terminated transmission line.

a. Component traveling-wave sets

A diagram of coordinate directions and related information is given in Fig. 8-1. It will be assumed that the boundary surface $z = 0$ is of infinite extent and that media 1 and 2 extend from zero to infinity in the $-\boldsymbol{a}_z$ and $+\boldsymbol{a}_z$ directions, respectively. It will be assumed further that an electromagnetic traveling-wave field called the incident wave set, $\boldsymbol{E}_I(z,t)$ and $\boldsymbol{H}_I(z,t)$,

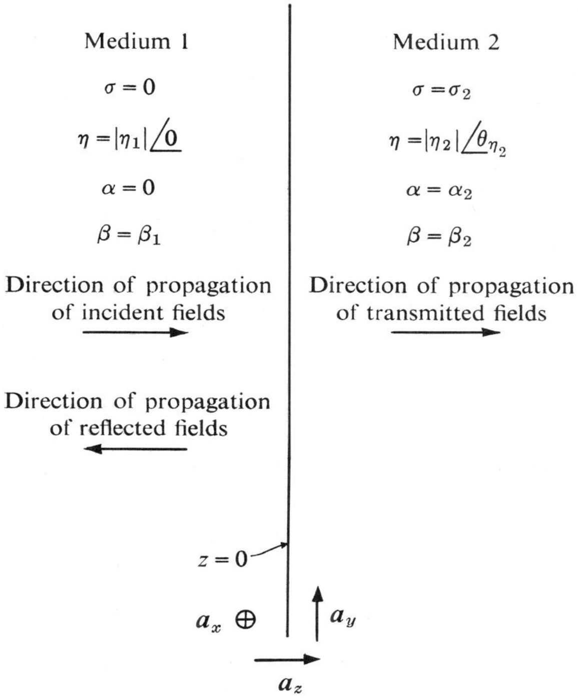

Figure 8-1 Coordinate-and-direction plan for analysis of reflection at normal incidence

is moving through medium 1 to the boundary surface. Medium 1 will be assumed lossless, and appropriate expressions may be obtained from Eqs. 8-7 and 8-18 by setting α and θ_η equal to zero.

$$\boldsymbol{E}_I(z,t) = E_{xIM} \sin(\omega t - \beta_1 z)\boldsymbol{a}_x \tag{8-44}$$

$$\boldsymbol{H}_I(z,t) = \frac{E_{xIM}}{\eta_1} \sin(\omega t - \beta_1 z)\boldsymbol{a}_y \tag{8-45}$$

The principal relationships may be illustrated readily if medium 2 is assumed to have losses as indicated in Fig. 8-1. Equations for the transmitted radiation proceeding from the reflecting surface through medium 2 would be as follows:

$$\boldsymbol{E}_T(z,t) = E_{xTM}\epsilon^{-\alpha_2 z}\sin(\omega t + \theta_T - \beta_2 z)\boldsymbol{a}_x \tag{8-46}$$

$$\boldsymbol{H}_T(z,t) = \frac{E_{xTM}}{|\eta_2|}\,\epsilon^{-\alpha_2 z}\sin(\omega t + \theta_T - \theta_{\eta_2} - \beta_2 z)\boldsymbol{a}_y \tag{8-47}$$

Here θ_T is a phase-shift angle.

The reflected waves travel in medium 1, and hence are unattenuated, but they move in the $-\boldsymbol{a}_z$ direction. The phase-shift angle associated with the reflection process will be taken as θ_K, the same as in Sec. 3-1 for the terminated transmission line.

$$\boldsymbol{E}_R(z,t) = E_{xRM}\sin(\omega t + \theta_K + \beta_1 z)\boldsymbol{a}_x \tag{8-48}$$

$$\boldsymbol{H}_R(z,t) = -\frac{E_{xRM}}{\eta_1}\sin(\omega t + \theta_K + \beta_1 z)\boldsymbol{a}_y \tag{8-49}$$

b. Boundary conditions and reflection coefficient

Since the resultant $\boldsymbol{E}$ in each medium consists of a single component which varies only in the z direction, and the same is true of $\boldsymbol{H}$, rather simple expressions for the curls of those functions will result from substitution in the general rectangular-coordinate equation, 7-45:

$$\nabla \times \boldsymbol{E} = \frac{\partial E_x(z,t)}{\partial z}\,\boldsymbol{a}_y$$

$$\nabla \times \boldsymbol{H} = -\frac{\partial H_y(z,t)}{\partial z}\,\boldsymbol{a}_x$$

Thus if $\boldsymbol{E}$ or $\boldsymbol{H}$ were discontinuous at the boundary surface, curl $\boldsymbol{E}$ or curl $\boldsymbol{H}$, respectively, would be infinite there. Maxwell's equations involving the curl operator are

$$\nabla \times \boldsymbol{E} = -\mu\frac{\partial \boldsymbol{H}}{\partial t} \tag{7-34}$$

$$\nabla \times \boldsymbol{H} = \epsilon\frac{\partial \boldsymbol{E}}{\partial t} + \sigma\boldsymbol{E} \tag{7-32}$$

Finite rates of time variation of $\boldsymbol{H}$ and $\boldsymbol{E}$ have been assumed, in that all the fields are sinusoidal functions of ωt. Hence Eq. 7-34 could not be satisfied if E_x were discontinuous at the boundary, and Eq. 7-32 could not be satisfied if H_y were discontinuous, unless σ were infinite. The latter possibility will be examined later as a limiting case, but if it is excluded for the present, one concludes that H_y must be continuous at the boundary surface.

Equations may be written paralleling Eqs. 3-11 and 3-12 for the transmission line:

$$E_{xT}(0,t) = E_{xI}(0,t) + E_{xR}(0,t) \tag{8-50}$$

$$H_{yT}(0,t) = H_{yI}(0,t) + H_{yR}(0,t) \tag{8-51}$$

As was done in Chapter 3, it is convenient to replace the instantaneous forms of the sinusoidal time functions given by Eqs. 8-44 through 8-49 with phasors. Thus

$$\boldsymbol{E}_I(z,t) = \text{Im}[\sqrt{2}\, E_{x\text{inc}}(z)\epsilon^{j\omega t}]\boldsymbol{a}_x \text{ etc.} \tag{8-52}$$

where

$$E_{x\text{inc}}(z) = \frac{E_{xIM}}{\sqrt{2}}\,\epsilon^{-j\beta_1 z} \text{ etc.} \tag{8-53}$$

Substitution of the phasor quantities into Eqs. 8-50 and 8-51, followed by deletion of the Im operator (since the relationships must be valid for all values of time) and cancellation of $\epsilon^{j\omega t}$ from each term yields

$$E_{x\text{tr}}(0) = E_{x\text{inc}}(0) + E_{x\text{ref}}(0) \tag{8-54}$$

$$\frac{E_{x\text{tr}}(0)}{\eta_2} = \frac{E_{x\text{inc}}(0)}{\eta_1} - \frac{E_{x\text{ref}}(0)}{\eta_1} \tag{8-55}$$

$E_{x\text{tr}}(0)$ may be eliminated from this set and the resulting equation solved for the reflected phasor in terms of the incident phasor and the intrinsic impedances:

$$E_{x\text{ref}}(0) = E_{x\text{inc}}(0)\,\frac{\eta_2 - \eta_1}{\eta_2 + \eta_1} \tag{8-56}$$

A reflection coefficient may be defined in the same manner as for the terminated transmission line: (Equation 3-17.)

$$|K|\,\epsilon^{j\theta_K} = \frac{E_{x\text{ref}}(0)}{E_{x\text{inc}}(0)} = \frac{E_{xRM}}{E_{xIM}}\,\epsilon^{j\theta_K} \tag{8-57}$$

Then, from Eq. 8-56

$$K = \frac{\eta_2 - \eta_1}{\eta_2 + \eta_1} \tag{8-58}$$

The relationship between the incident and reflected magnetic fields may be found as follows:

$$H_{y\text{inc}}(z) = \frac{E_{x\text{inc}}(z)}{\eta_1} \tag{8-59}$$

$$H_{y\text{ref}}(z) = -\frac{E_{x\text{ref}}(z)}{\eta_1} \tag{8-60}$$

If z is set equal to zero in Eqs. 8-59 and 8-60 and the E_x's eliminated by means of Eq. 8-57, the following results:

$$H_{y\text{ref}}(0) = -KH_{y\text{inc}}(0) \tag{8-61}$$

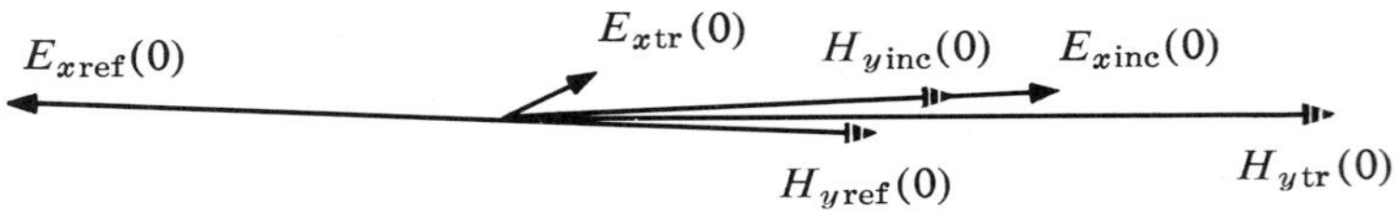

Figure 8-2 Phasor diagram for traveling-wave component fields at reflecting surface for normal incidence, air to sea water (drawn to scale from results of Problem 8-5)

The time-phase pattern among the component $\boldsymbol{E}$ and $\boldsymbol{H}$ fields at the boundary surface may be displayed to advantage by means of a phasor diagram. An example is given in Fig. 8-2, based on the numerical results to Problem 8-5, in which radio-frequency fields are normally incident upon a poorly conducting medium, sea water. The parameters for that problem were chosen so that the conduction-current density and displacement-current density would be of the same order of magnitude.

c. Reflection process as a function of conductivity

The effect of varying σ, while keeping the other parameters (μ, ϵ, and ω) constant, should be noted.

For the limiting case of σ equal to zero, so that medium 2 is nonconducting, the following simplifications result: (1) the intrinsic impedance η_2 is purely resistive, (2) no attenuation takes place in medium 2, (3) the reflection coefficient is a purely real number, and (4) the phasors corresponding to those shown in Fig. 8-2 are collinear.

If σ is increased toward infinity, a situation representative of most metals ($\sigma \gg \omega\epsilon$), the following relationships are approached:

$$\eta_2 = \sqrt{\frac{\omega\mu}{\sigma}}\,\epsilon^{j\pi/4} \tag{8-62}$$

$$|\eta_2| \ll \eta_1 \tag{8-63}$$

The numerator and denominator of Eq. 8-58 may be divided by η_1, and the resulting denominator replaced by the first two terms of the Taylor series, as was done in Chapter 2:

$$K = \frac{(\eta_2/\eta_1) - 1}{(\eta_2/\eta_1) + 1} \tag{8-64}$$

$$K \approx \left(\frac{\eta_2}{\eta_1} - 1\right)\left(1 - \frac{\eta_2}{\eta_1}\right)$$

$$\approx -1 + \frac{2\eta_1}{\eta_2} \tag{8-65}$$

From this it may be concluded that the reflected component of $\boldsymbol{E}$ will be essentially equal to the incident component and very nearly in phase opposition with it. The transmitted component of $\boldsymbol{E}$ will be small, but an approximation can be readily obtained:

$$\begin{aligned} E_{xTM}\epsilon^{j\theta_T} &= E_{xIM}(1 + K) \\ &= E_{xIM}\frac{2\eta_2}{\eta_1 + \eta_2} \\ &\approx E_{xIM}\frac{2\eta_2}{\eta_1} \end{aligned} \tag{8-66}$$

As is shown numerically in Problem 8-6, the electric field transmitted into copper by normally incident waves in air is exceedingly small compared to the incident electric field, but it is definitely nonzero. Whatever the precise magnitude of the ratio, the transmitted electric field at the surface of the metal leads the incident electric field by 45 degrees in time phase.

In accordance with Eq. 8-61 the reflected magnetic field in this instance will be essentially equal to the incident magnetic field in magnitude and very nearly in time phase with it. Thus the transmitted magnetic field, at the surface of the metal, will have approximately twice the magnitude of the incident magnetic field and be almost in time phase with it. The transmitted magnetic field is, of course, related to the transmitted electric field by the intrinsic impedance of medium 2.

The attenuation constant in copper is 15 nepers per millimeter at 1 megacycle per second [see Eq. 8-29; also compare with the numerical result of Problem 8-1(*b*)]; hence the transmitted fields at radio frequencies are largely confined to a shallow layer immediately below the reflecting surface.

d. Conduction-current density in metals

The current-density function in a metallic reflecting medium should be examined in order to place some commonly used concepts—*surface-current density*, *surface resistance*, and *skin depth*—in good perspective.

Displacement-current density is negligible in comparison with the conduction-current density and hence will be ignored. The latter function is

$$\boldsymbol{J}_T(z,t) = \sigma_2 \boldsymbol{E}_T(z,t)$$

Equation 8-46 for $\boldsymbol{E}_T$ may be put into complex exponential form and Eq. 8-66 substituted.

$$\boldsymbol{J}_T(z,t) = \mathrm{Im}\left[\sigma_2 \frac{2\eta_2}{\eta_1} E_{xIM}\epsilon^{-(\alpha_2 + j\beta_2)z}\epsilon^{j\omega t}\right]\boldsymbol{a}_x \tag{8-67}$$

First-order approximations from Eqs. 8-29 and 8-30 may be substituted for α_2 and η_2.

$$\boldsymbol{J}_T(z,t) = \mathrm{Im}\left[\frac{2\sqrt{\omega\mu_2\sigma_2}}{\eta_1} E_{xIM}\epsilon^{-\sqrt{\omega\mu_2\sigma_2/2}\,z}\epsilon^{j(\omega t + (\pi/4) - \beta_2 z)}\right]\boldsymbol{a}_x \tag{8-68}$$

(1) SURFACE-CURRENT DENSITY. From Eq. 8-68 it appears that an increase in σ_2 will increase the magnitude of conduction-current density at the surface of the metal, but, by increasing the attenuation function, it will also rapidly diminish the magnitude at any given depth in proportion to that at the surface. The limiting condition which is approached is that of a sheet of current of infinite volume density but infinitesimally thin. To obtain a more useful measure of the current field at this limit, consider the integral of conduction-current density with respect to depth:

$$\begin{aligned}\int_0^\infty \boldsymbol{J}_T(z,t)\,dz &= \mathrm{Im}\left[\int_0^\infty \sigma_2 \frac{2\eta_2}{\eta_1} E_{xIM}\epsilon^{-(\alpha_2+j\beta_2)z}\epsilon^{j\omega t}\,dz\right]\boldsymbol{a}_x \\ &= \mathrm{Im}\left[-\sigma_2 \frac{2\eta_2}{\eta_1}\frac{E_{xIM}}{\alpha_2+j\beta_2}\epsilon^{-(\alpha_2+j\beta_2)z}\epsilon^{j\omega t}\right]_0^\infty \boldsymbol{a}_x \\ &= \mathrm{Im}\left[\sigma_2 \frac{2\eta_2}{\eta_1}\frac{E_{xIM}}{\alpha_2+j\beta_2}\epsilon^{j\omega t}\right]\boldsymbol{a}_x \end{aligned} \tag{8-69}$$

Substitution of Eqs. 8-29 and 8-30, with $\omega\epsilon/\sigma \to 0$, reduces this to

$$\begin{aligned}\int_0^\infty \boldsymbol{J}_T(z,t)\,dz &= \mathrm{Im}\left[\frac{2E_{xIM}}{\eta_1}\epsilon^{j\omega t}\right]\boldsymbol{a}_x \\ &= |2\boldsymbol{H}_I(0,t)|\,\boldsymbol{a}_x \\ &= |\boldsymbol{H}_I(0,t) + \boldsymbol{H}_R(0,t)|\,\boldsymbol{a}_x \end{aligned} \tag{8-70}$$

Thus the resultant found by integrating the conduction-current density with respect to depth has a magnitude which is equal at every instant to the magnitude of the resultant magnetic field just above the surface. It is assigned the name of *surface-current density*, $\boldsymbol{J}_S(t)$:

$$\boldsymbol{J}_S(t) = \int_0^\infty \boldsymbol{J}_T(z,t)\,dz \tag{8-71}$$

Surface-current density has the units amperes per meter, and it flows at right angles with respect to the impinging magnetic field. The directions are consistent with the familiar right-hand rule for the magnetic field accompanying a current:

$$\boldsymbol{J}_S(t) \times \boldsymbol{a}_n = \boldsymbol{H}(0,t) \tag{8-72}$$

Here $\boldsymbol{a}_n$ is a unit vector directed outward from the conducting surface.

(2) SURFACE RESISTANCE. The changing of electromagnetic energy into heat when a set of electromagnetic fields is normally incident upon a metallic slab may be expressed in terms of the magnitude of the surface-current density and an equivalent resistance known as the surface resistance. This

relationship may be derived from the energy conversion rate of the fields in the metal, stated on a volume-density basis.

The instantaneous rate of changing energy into the heat form in the conducting region is

$$p_{\text{att}}(z,t) = \frac{|\boldsymbol{J}_T(z,t)|^2}{\sigma_2} \qquad \text{(watts per cubic meter)} \tag{8-73}$$

Equation 8-68 for $\boldsymbol{J}_T$ will be restated explicitly as a sinusoidal function

$$(H_{yIM} = E_{xIM}/\eta_1):$$

$$\boldsymbol{J}_T(z,t) = 2\sqrt{\omega\mu_2\sigma_2}\, H_{yIM}\epsilon^{-\alpha_2 z} \sin\left(\omega t + \frac{\pi}{4} - \beta_2 z\right)\boldsymbol{a}_x \tag{8-74}$$

$$\begin{aligned} p_{\text{att}}(z,t) &= 4\omega\mu_2 H_{yIM}^2 \epsilon^{-2\alpha_2 z} \sin^2\left(\omega t + \frac{\pi}{4} - \beta_2 z\right) \\ &= 2\omega\mu_2 H_{yIM}^2 \epsilon^{-2\alpha_2 z}\left[1 - \sin 2\left(\omega t + \frac{\pi}{4} - \beta_2 z\right)\right] \end{aligned} \tag{8-75}$$

When time-averaged over an integral number of cycles this reduces to

$$P_{\text{att}}(z) = 2\omega\mu_2 H_{yIM}^2 \epsilon^{-2\alpha_2 z} \tag{8-76}$$

The power input to the conducting slab may be found on the basis of watts per square meter of surface by integrating $P_{\text{att}}(z)$ with respect to z:

$$\begin{aligned} P_{\text{loss}} &= -\frac{2\omega\mu_2}{2\alpha_2} H_{yIM}^2 \epsilon^{-2\alpha_2 z}\Big]_0^\infty \\ &= \sqrt{\frac{2\omega\mu_2}{\sigma_2}}\, H_{yIM}^2 \end{aligned} \tag{8-77}$$

As σ_2 approaches infinity, the limit of this expression is zero, a result which seems reasonable. An alternate approach to computing P_{loss} is to evaluate Poynting's vector (see Problem 8-7).

The surface-current-density magnitude is, from Eqs. 8-59, 8-70, and 8-71:

$$\boldsymbol{J}_S = 2H_{yIM} \sin \omega t\, \boldsymbol{a}_x$$

Let J_{xSM} be the maximum value of the magnitude of $\boldsymbol{J}_S$:

$$J_{xSM} = 2H_{yIM}$$

Equation 8-77 may be restated as follows:

$$\begin{aligned} P_{\text{loss}} &= \sqrt{\frac{2\omega\mu_2}{\sigma_2}}\left(\frac{J_{xSM}}{2}\right)^2 \\ &= \sqrt{\frac{\omega\mu_2}{2\sigma_2}}\left(\frac{J_{xSM}}{\sqrt{2}}\right)^2 \end{aligned} \tag{8-78}$$

The quantity $J_{xSM}/\sqrt{2}$ is the root-mean-square or effective value of the surface-current density, and $\sqrt{\omega\mu_2/2\sigma_2}$ is dimensionally a resistance. It is given the name *surface resistance*, R_S:

$$R_S = \sqrt{\frac{\omega\mu_2}{2\sigma_2}} \tag{8-79}$$

If η_2 as defined in Eq. 8-62 is put into rectangular form,

$$\eta_2 = \sqrt{\frac{\omega\mu_2}{2\sigma_2}} + j\sqrt{\frac{\omega\mu_2}{2\sigma_2}} \tag{8-80}$$

The real part of Eq. 8-80 corresponds to the surface resistance as defined in Eq. 8-79.

(3) SKIN DEPTH. Equation 8-79 may be rearranged as follows:

$$R_S = \frac{1}{\sigma_2}\sqrt{\frac{\omega\mu_2\sigma_2}{2}} \tag{8-81}$$

It may be recalled that the d-c resistance (R_{dc}) of a slab of metal of length s, width w, thickness δ, and conductivity σ is the following:

$$R_{dc} = \frac{s}{\delta w \sigma}$$

If the length is equal to the width, so that the slab is a square of thickness δ, with resistance measured from one edge to the opposite one, the resistance is independent of the size of the square. It may be designated R_{dcsq}:

$$R_{dcsq} = \frac{1}{\delta\sigma} \tag{8-82}$$

Comparison between Eqs. 8-81 and 8-82 suggests that surface-resistance loss may be thought of as that produced in a slab of conductivity σ_2 and thickness $\sqrt{2/(\omega\mu_2\sigma_2)}$, with the surface-current density $J_{xSM}/\sqrt{2}$ distributed uniformly (and in time phase) over the edgewise cross section. The condition of equality between R_S and R_{dcsq} is

$$\delta = \sqrt{\frac{2}{\omega\mu_2\sigma_2}} \tag{8-83}$$

The name *skin depth* is given to δ as just defined. This may be compared with the first-order approximation in Eq. 8-29 for the attenuation function, from which the following may be seen by inspection:

$$\delta = \frac{1}{\alpha} \tag{8-84}$$

The quantity δ is sometimes referred to as the "depth of penetration."

This expression is misleading (and so is "skin depth") in that the electric and magnetic fields at a depth of δ have magnitudes of $1/\epsilon$ times the magnitudes which they have at the surface, and hence "penetrate" well beyond that depth; even at 4δ the field strengths are almost 2 per cent of what they are at the surface.

8-3. REFLECTION AT OBLIQUE INCIDENCE

Reflection phenomena for oblique angles of incidence is an important subject, even though the mathematical analysis is cumbersome. Radio waves generally strike the earth at orientations other than that of normal incidence, and one may note that the fields in a hollow wave guide are contained within the guide essentially by oblique reflections at the wall surfaces. The treatment here will be limited to a summary of results, with emphasis on those relating to highly conducting reflecting surfaces.

a. Geometry of oblique-reflection problem

The principal geometrical relationships in oblique reflection are shown in Fig. 8-3. Traveling-wave-type incident and reflected fields will be postulated. A transverse-plane traveling-wave-type transmitted field as shown is applicable if the second medium is nonconducting[2,3]; a more complicated situation ensues if it is of finite conductivity,[3] and a surface-current sheet with no transmitted fields is the result if the medium is of infinite conductivity.

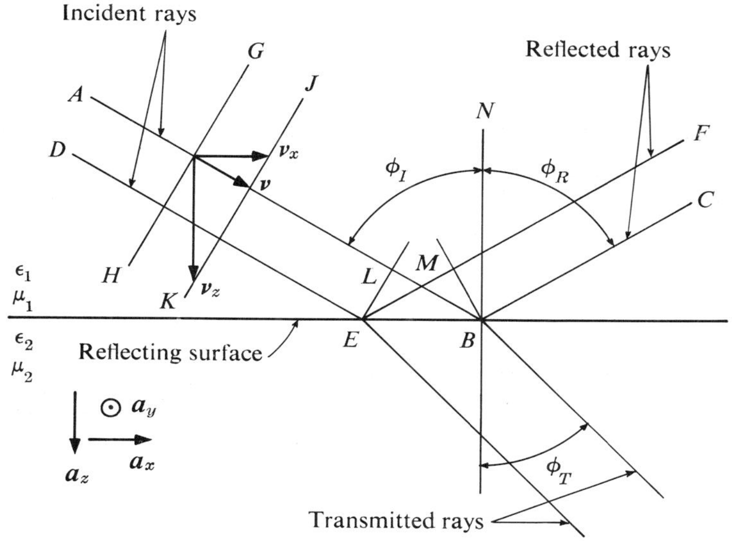

Figure 8-3 Geometry of reflection at oblique incidence

The *plane of incidence* is perpendicular to the reflecting surface and parallel to the direction of propagation, or the *rays*, of the incident waves. Lines *AB* and *DE*, which are parallel to each other, are incident rays, and *BC* and *EF*, also parallel to each other, are reflected rays. Lines *GH*, *JK*, and *LE* represent *equiphase surfaces* of the incident waves; *MB* is an equiphase surface of the reflected waves.

The direction of approach of the incident waves is defined within the plane of incidence by means of the *angle of incidence* ϕ_I, which is measured from a line normal to the reflecting surface to the incident ray. (In some writing it is measured from the plane of reflection; this point should be checked to avoid misunderstandings when consulting other works.)

The necessary relationship between the angles of incidence and reflection may be determined by reference to Fig. 8-3. The equiphase planes of the incident and reflected waves are perpendicular to their respective ray directions, and both sets travel at the same velocity. Hence line segments *LB* and *EM* must be equal and triangles *ELB* and *EBM* must be congruent; therefore, since *BC* is parallel to *EF*,

$$\phi_I = \phi_R \tag{8-85}$$

Thus the angle of reflection is equal to the angle of incidence.

Since the direction of propagation of the incident wave set is in the plane of $\boldsymbol{a}_x$ and $\boldsymbol{a}_z$ but not parallel to either of these unit vectors, phase constants β_x and β_z must be derived if the traveling-wave functions are to have x and z for arguments. The phase velocities in those two coordinate directions may be found in terms of the velocity normal to the wave front v and the angle of incidence. From Fig. 8-3 it may be seen that for the wave front *GH* to advance to *JK*, the phase velocities must be as follows:

$$v_x = \frac{v}{\sin \phi_I} \tag{8-86}$$

$$v_z = \frac{v}{\cos \phi_I} \tag{8-87}$$

The basic relation between phase velocity and phase function is

$$\beta = \frac{\omega}{v} \tag{2-15}$$

Hence the phase functions for the $\boldsymbol{a}_x$ and $\boldsymbol{a}_z$ directions are

$$\beta_x = \beta \sin \phi_I \tag{8-88}$$

$$\beta_z = \beta \cos \phi_I \tag{8-89}$$

b. Boundary conditions

Constraints of continuity are enjoined upon the electromagnetic fields by Maxwell's equations. The necessity for continuity of the tangential component of $\boldsymbol{E}$ and $\boldsymbol{H}$ was brought out in the earlier discussion of normal incidence (Sec. 8-2*b*). The same reasoning is applicable to the tangential components with oblique incidence, but mathematical statement of the constraint is more involved. For normal incidence the coordinate system could, without loss of generality, be rotated about the z axis to make the x axis parallel to the $\boldsymbol{E}$ field, and the y axis then would necessarily parallel the $\boldsymbol{H}$ field. For oblique incidence, as illustrated in Fig. 8-3, the x axis is parallel to the plane of incidence, and one must anticipate that each field may contain tangential components in both the x and y directions. Hence the equations corresponding to Eqs. 8-50 and 8-51, applicable at $z = 0$, are

$$\begin{aligned} E_{xI} + E_{xR} &= E_{xT} \\ E_{yI} + E_{yR} &= E_{yT} \\ H_{xI} + H_{xR} &= H_{xT} \\ H_{yI} + H_{yR} &= H_{yT} \end{aligned} \tag{8-90}$$

Should the reflecting surface be a perfect conductor, the transmitted $\boldsymbol{E}$ field would vanish and a current sheet would replace the transmitted $\boldsymbol{H}$ field:

$$\begin{aligned} E_{xI} + E_{xR} &= 0 \\ E_{yI} + E_{yR} &= 0 \\ H_{xI} + H_{xR} &= -J_{yS} \\ H_{yI} + H_{yR} &= J_{xS} \end{aligned} \tag{8-91}$$

Furthermore, a normal component of either $\boldsymbol{E}$ or $\boldsymbol{H}$, or possibly both, will be present. A normal component would be z-directed, and continuity at the boundary would depend on the derivative with respect to z. The divergence operator utilizes that derivative of the normal component, as indicated in Eq. 7-44. Maxwell's equations for the continuity of the $\boldsymbol{B}$ and $\boldsymbol{D}$ fields, Eqs. 7-29 and 7-28, reduce to the following:

$$\nabla \cdot \boldsymbol{B} = \frac{\partial B_z}{\partial z} = \mu \frac{\partial H_z}{\partial z} = 0 \tag{8-92}$$

$$\nabla \cdot \boldsymbol{D} = \frac{\partial D_z}{\partial z} = \epsilon \frac{\partial E_z}{\partial z} = \rho \tag{8-93}$$

The first of these equations requires continuity of B_z at the boundary:

$$\mu_1 H_{zI} + \mu_1 H_{zR} = \mu_2 H_{zT} \tag{8-94}$$

Volume-charge density was assumed to be zero in mediums 1 and 2, but ρ was shown to indicate formally the possible existence of a surface charge on the reflecting surface. That would correspond to an infinite volume-charge density in the surface and would permit a discontinuity in D_z.

If the surface is nonconducting, continuity of D_z is required:

$$\epsilon_1 E_{zI} + \epsilon_1 E_{zR} = \epsilon_2 E_{zT} \tag{8-95}$$

Should the reflecting surface be a perfect conductor, B_z will not penetrate it, so B_{zT} will be zero. On the other hand, a surface-charge density $-\rho_S$ may be present to terminate the impinging D_z:

$$\mu_1 H_{zI} + \mu_1 H_{zR} = 0$$
$$H_{zI} + H_{zR} = 0 \qquad \text{(8-96)}$$
$$\epsilon_1 E_{zI} + \epsilon_1 E_{zR} = -\rho_S \qquad \text{(8-97)}$$

c. Wave-set modes

The reflection coefficients of electromagnetic wave sets striking a surface at oblique incidence prove to be dependent on the polarization, or orientation, of the field-direction lines with respect to the surface; specifically, two modes of behavior exist, one for wave sets in which the electric field is parallel to the reflecting surface and another for wave sets in which the magnetic field is parallel to it. A plane electromagnetic wave set which is oriented so that neither its electric nor its magnetic field is parallel to the given surface may be resolved into two component wave sets, one of each type.

The terminology for designing the two wave-set modes has been complicated by separate developments of the subject by physicists working in optics and electrical engineers working with radio. Their viewpoints differed, with the result that physicists spoke of "perpendicular" polarization when referring to a wave set in which the ***E*** field is perpendicular to the plane of *incidence* and "parallel" polarization if the ***E*** field were parallel to the plane of incidence, whereas radio engineers spoke of "horizontal" polarization for the former case and "vertical" polarization for the latter. The frame of reference for "horizontal" and "vertical" is that of the level surface of the earth as the reflecting surface, with the incident fields coming from a dipole antenna which is either horizontal or vertical. The expressions "perpendicular" and "parallel" are less ambiguous and hence will be used in the remainder of this discussion.

d. Reflection coefficients and transmitted components

As was indicated earlier, the solutions for cases other than that of a surface of infinite conductivity are complicated, so general comments will be made and references cited.

(1) REFLECTING MEDIUM OF ZERO CONDUCTIVITY. It will be assumed that $\mu_1 = \mu_2$ and that $\epsilon_1 < \epsilon_2$. The solution is straightforward, although lengthy.[2] The reflection coefficients for the two wave sets are as follows:

$$|K_\perp|\angle\theta_{K\perp} = \frac{\cos\phi_I - \sqrt{(\epsilon_2/\epsilon_1) - \sin^2\phi_I}}{\cos\phi_I + \sqrt{(\epsilon_2/\epsilon_1) - \sin^2\phi_I}} \qquad \text{(perpendicular polarization)} \qquad \text{(8-98)}$$

$$\theta_{K\perp} = \pi \qquad (\text{for } 0 \leqslant \phi_I < \pi/2)$$

$$|K_\parallel|\angle\theta_{K\parallel} = \frac{(\epsilon_2/\epsilon_1)\cos\phi_I - \sqrt{(\epsilon_2/\epsilon_1) - \sin^2\phi_I}}{(\epsilon_2/\epsilon_1)\cos\phi_I + \sqrt{(\epsilon_2/\epsilon_1) - \sin^2\phi_I}} \qquad \text{(parallel polarization)} \qquad \text{(8-99)}$$

The latter reflection coefficient vanishes at a critical angle of incidence, known as *Brewster's angle*, ϕ_{IB}.

$$\phi_{IB} = \tan^{-1}\sqrt{\frac{\epsilon_2}{\epsilon_1}} \tag{8-100}$$

$$\theta_{K\|} = 0 \qquad (\text{for } 0 \leqslant \phi_I < \phi_{IB})$$

$$\theta_{K\|} = \pi \qquad (\text{for } \phi_{IB} < \phi_I < \pi/2)$$

The magnitudes of the two reflection coefficients are shown as functions of ϕ_I in Fig. 8-4 for $\epsilon_2/\epsilon_1 = 4$.

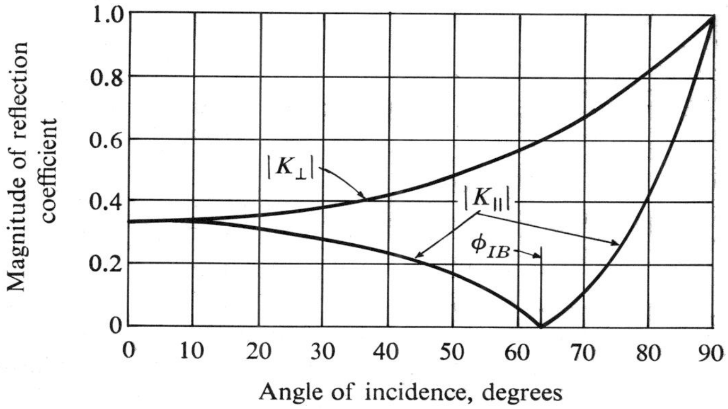

Figure 8-4 Reflection coefficients for waves obliquely incident upon nonconducting material; $\epsilon_2/\epsilon_1 = 4.0$

The transmitted, or refracted, wave set moves along rays inclined at angle ϕ_T, which is, according to Snell's law (see Problem 8-8),

$$\frac{\sin \phi_T}{\sin \phi_I} = \sqrt{\frac{\epsilon_1}{\epsilon_2}} \tag{8-101}$$

(2) REFLECTING MEDIUM OF FINITE, NONZERO CONDUCTIVITY. This situation is of importance in signal-propagation studies for radiobroadcasting. The reflection coefficients, which are complex, may be found by replacing ϵ_2 in Eqs. 8-98 and 8-99 with $\epsilon_2 + (\sigma_2/j\omega)$.[2,3] Charts of computed values are given in Refs. 1, 2, and 4. Some qualitative observations concerning the differences between these results and those for the nonconducting reflecting medium are the following: (1) the reflection-coefficient magnitude for parallel polarization dips to a minimum at an angle analogous to Brewster's angle (pseudo-Brewster angle, in some writing) but does not go to zero, (2) the phase angles for the reflection coefficients of both modes vary continuously with the angle of incidence, and (3) the transmitted wave set is not strictly TEM, and the angle of refraction differs from that given in Eq. 8-101.

Results obtained from rigorous analyses of this general case justify the simplified solutions for the infinite-conductivity case, which will be discussed in the next section.

(3) Reflecting medium of infinite conductivity. The magnitudes of both reflection coefficients are unity for a surface of infinite conductivity, but the phase-shift angle is π radians for perpendicular polarization and zero for parallel polarization. Complete descriptions of the fields will be written out.

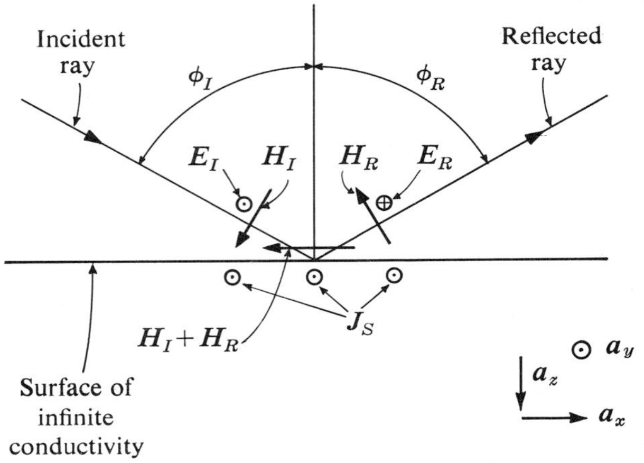

Figure 8-5 Perpendicularly polarized waves obliquely incident on ideal conductor

(a) *Perpendicular polarization.* A perpendicularly polarized incident wave set can be described as follows, in accordance with Fig. 8-5:

$$\boldsymbol{E}_I = E_M \sin(\omega t - \beta_x x - \beta_z z)\boldsymbol{a}_y \tag{8-102}$$

$$\boldsymbol{H}_I = \frac{E_M}{\eta_0}(-\cos\phi_I\,\boldsymbol{a}_x + \sin\phi_I\,\boldsymbol{a}_z)\sin(\omega t - \beta_x x - \beta_z z) \tag{8-103}$$

In accordance with the requirement of no tangential $\boldsymbol{E}$ field at the surface $z = 0$, the reflected $\boldsymbol{E}$ field would be

$$\boldsymbol{E}_R = -E_M \sin(\omega t - \beta_x x + \beta_z z)\boldsymbol{a}_y \tag{8-104}$$

For the wave set to propagate away from the surface, the accompanying $\boldsymbol{H}$ field would be

$$\boldsymbol{H}_R = \frac{E_M}{\eta_0}(-\cos\phi_I\,\boldsymbol{a}_x - \sin\phi_I\,\boldsymbol{a}_z)\sin(\omega t - \beta_x x + \beta_z z) \tag{8-105}$$

The surface-current density needed to maintain the difference between the

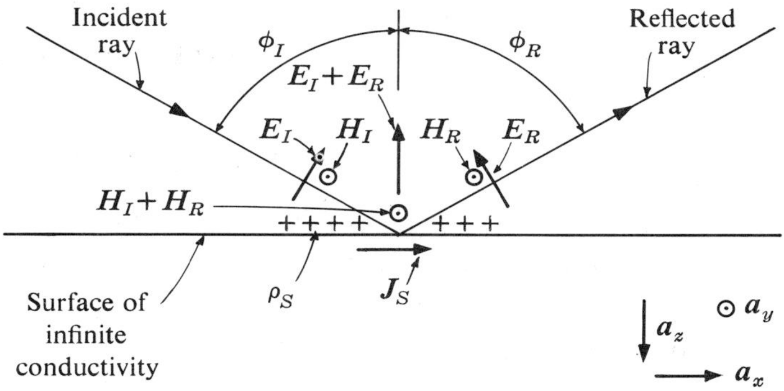

Figure 8-6 Parallel-polarized waves obliquely incident on ideal conductor

sum of $\boldsymbol{H}_I$ and $\boldsymbol{H}_R$ above the reflecting surface, and no magnetic field below it, is

$$\boldsymbol{J}_S = \frac{2E_M}{\eta_0} \cos \phi_I \sin(\omega t - \beta_x x)\boldsymbol{a}_y \qquad \textbf{(8-106)}$$

(b) *Parallel polarization.* A parallel-polarized incident wave set could be described as follows, in accordance with Fig. 8-6:

$$\boldsymbol{E}_I = E_M(\cos \phi_I \, \boldsymbol{a}_x - \sin \phi_I \, \boldsymbol{a}_z) \sin(\omega t - \beta_x x - \beta_z z) \qquad \textbf{(8-107)}$$

$$\boldsymbol{H}_I = \frac{E_M}{\eta_0} \sin(\omega t - \beta_x x - \beta_z z)\boldsymbol{a}_y \qquad \textbf{(8-108)}$$

The reflected waves would be as follows:

$$\boldsymbol{E}_R = E_M(-\cos \phi_I \, \boldsymbol{a}_x - \sin \phi_I \, \boldsymbol{a}_z) \sin(\omega t - \beta_x x + \beta_z z) \qquad \textbf{(8-109)}$$

$$\boldsymbol{H}_R = \frac{E_M}{\eta_0} \sin(\omega t - \beta_x x + \beta_z z)\boldsymbol{a}_y \qquad \textbf{(8-110)}$$

The surface-current density is

$$\boldsymbol{J}_S = \frac{2E_M}{\eta_0} \sin(\omega t - \beta_x x)\boldsymbol{a}_x \qquad \textbf{(8-111)}$$

To terminate the $\boldsymbol{D}$ flux impinging on the surface, the following surface-charge density is necessary:

$$\rho_S = 2E_M\epsilon_0 \sin \phi_I \sin(\omega t - \beta_x x) \qquad \textbf{(8-112)}$$

Some further aspects of reflection phenomena are developed in Problem 8-9.

8-4. QUASI-TEM FIELDS TRAVELING PARALLEL TO HIGHLY CONDUCTING SURFACES

Metallic conductor pairs or sets are used abundantly to guide traveling electromagnetic fields. Nominally the TEM mode of transmission prevails, but this is strictly true only if the conductor surfaces are of infinite conductivity. In practice $\boldsymbol{E}$ will have a small but nonzero longitudinal component.[2]

a. Fields between parallel planes

To investigate approximately the manner in which the TEM mode is altered by finite-conductivity surfaces, consider the two parallel, highly

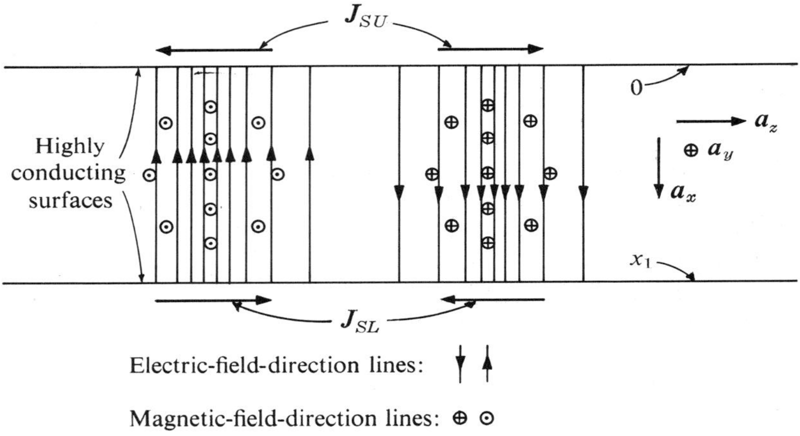

Figure 8-7 Parallel-plane conductors, TEM mode

conducting planes sketched in Fig. 8-7. A set of TEM fields will be postulated as a first approximation. Let

$$\boldsymbol{E} \approx E_M \sin(\omega t - \beta z)\boldsymbol{a}_x \tag{8-113}$$

$$\boldsymbol{H} \approx \frac{E_M}{\eta_0} \sin(\omega t - \beta z)\boldsymbol{a}_y \tag{8-114}$$

The boundary condition related to an $\boldsymbol{H}$ field tangential to a highly conducting surface requires the presence of surface-current densities as follows:

$$\begin{aligned} \boldsymbol{J}_{SU} &= H_y \boldsymbol{a}_z \qquad \text{(upper surface)} \\ \boldsymbol{J}_{SL} &= -H_y \boldsymbol{a}_z \qquad \text{(lower surface)} \end{aligned} \tag{8-115}$$

In the limiting case of surfaces of infinite conductivity, expressions 8-113 and 8-114 would be equalities rather than approximations, and those equations plus 8-115 would suffice to describe the fields. A high but finite conductivity for the surface would require the presence of a longitudinal component of electric field E_z. Exact analyses indicate that E_{tan} and $|\boldsymbol{J}_S|$ are related, to a very good approximation, by the intrinsic impedance of the metal, even though that relationship was the result found for a normally incident wave set:

$$\eta_M = \sqrt{\frac{j\omega\mu}{\sigma}}$$

$$= \sqrt{\frac{\omega\mu}{\sigma}}\,\underline{/45^\circ} \tag{8-62}$$

$$E_z(0) \approx \frac{E_M}{\eta_0}\sqrt{\frac{\omega\mu}{\sigma}}\sin(\omega t + 45^\circ - \beta z) \quad \text{(adjacent to upper surface)}$$

$$E_z(x_1) \approx \frac{-E_M}{\eta_0}\sqrt{\frac{\omega\mu}{\sigma}}\sin(\omega t + 45^\circ - \beta z) \quad \text{(adjacent to lower surface)} \tag{8-116}$$

Interpolation of E_z for the region between the two planes will not be attempted here. Higher-order approximations would take account of the finite skin depth and the propagation rates in air and metal normal to the surface, and these would modify E_x and $\boldsymbol{H}$, but the approximations given here suffice for metallic conductors.

The maximum value of E_z is infinitesimal compared to that of E_x, even at microwave frequencies (see Problem 8-10), but it should be noted that E_x and E_z are not in time phase. Thus the magnitude of their resultant does not drop to zero but varies between a maximum and a minimum which differ enormously, while the space orientation of the vector field rotates continuously, but not uniformly, in the xz plane. This is a form of elliptical polarization (compare with Eq. 8-24).

Because of the longitudinal component of electric field, the electric and magnetic field-direction lines are not confined to planes transverse to the direction of propagation. Since the deviation from the true TEM pattern is slight, this mode may appropriately be called a *quasi-TEM mode*. In practical usage, the mode is called simply the TEM mode, even though noninfinite conductivity is involved.

b. Power loss with quasi-TEM mode

Power dissipation in the conducting surfaces may be computed from the component of Poynting's vector normal to the surface:

$$P_x = -E_z H_y \tag{8-117}$$

Substitutions will be made for the lower surface; the result for the upper surface will be the negative of that shown because it is oppositely directed:

$$P_x = \left(\frac{E_M}{\eta_0}\right)^2 \sqrt{\frac{\omega\mu}{\sigma}} \sin(\omega t - \beta z)\sin(\omega t + 45° - \beta z)$$

$$= \left(\frac{E_M}{\eta_0\sqrt{2}}\right)^2 \sqrt{\frac{\omega\mu}{\sigma}} [\cos 45° - \cos(2\omega t + 45° - 2\beta z)]$$

If this is time-averaged over an integral number of cycles, the result $P_{x\text{av}}$ is

$$P_{x\text{av}} = \left(\frac{E_M}{\eta_0\sqrt{2}}\right)^2 \sqrt{\frac{\omega\mu}{2\sigma}}$$

Equation 8-79 may be substituted:

$$P_{x\text{av}} = \left(\frac{E_M}{\eta_0\sqrt{2}}\right)^2 R_S \qquad \textbf{(8-118)}$$

The squared quantity may be recognized as the rms value of the magnetic field tangent to the conducting surface (H_y), and that in turn as the rms value of the surface-current density.

8-5. CONCLUSIONS

Electromagnetic energy may be propagated in a homogeneous medium in the *transverse-electromagnetic*, or TEM, mode, in which the electric and magnetic fields are both directed in planes perpendicular to the direction of propagation and are perpendicular to each other. The propagation function for sinusoidal waves is analogous to that for a transmission line:

$$\alpha + j\beta = \sqrt{j\omega\mu(\sigma + j\omega\epsilon)} \qquad \textbf{(8-11)}$$

The magnitudes of sinusoidal $\boldsymbol{E}$ and $\boldsymbol{H}$ traveling-wave fields are related by the *intrinsic impedance* η:

$$\eta = \sqrt{\frac{j\omega\mu}{\sigma + j\omega\epsilon}} \qquad \textbf{(8-16)}$$

Reflections occur when a traveling-wave set strikes the bounding surface between two media of differing intrinsic impedances. Boundary conditions to relate the incident, reflected, and transmitted fields are derivable from Maxwell's equations. For waves which are normally incident on the reflecting surface, the reflection phenomena correspond to those on a transmission line. Obliquely incident waves are reflected in a manner which depends on the polarization of the waves relative to the plane of incidence.

The limiting-case concept of a current sheet on a surface of infinite conductivity gives an acceptable approximation for the boundary effect of a metallic surface on the fields adjacent to it. A quasi-TEM mode may propagate between two parallel planes of highly conducting metal. Such a mode has a minute longitudinal component in its electric field and differs but slightly from a true TEM mode.

PROBLEMS

8-1. Compute the propagation constant, velocity of propagation, and intrinsic impedance at a frequency of 550 megacycles per second for: (*a*) sea water (conductivity, 3.0 mhos per meter; relative permittivity, 80), and (*b*) copper (conductivity, 5.8×10^7 mhos per meter; assume relative permittivity unity).

8-2. Compute the energy stored in the electric field by charging each of the capacitors described below from zero to a maximum field intensity of E_0, and show that it is equal to the volume integral of w_ϵ. (*a*) A parallel-plane capacitor with plate areas of S and separation of d. Let $\epsilon = \epsilon_0$, and neglect fringing of the field at the edges. (*b*) A concentric-cylindrical capacitor, with inner radius r_a, outer radius r_b, and length l. Let $\epsilon = \epsilon_0$, and neglect fringing of the field at the ends.

8-3. Compute the energy stored per unit length in the magnetic field of a coaxial conductor, made of very thin cylinders, by increasing the current from zero to I_0, and show that it is equal to the volume integral of w_μ over a unit length. Radius of inner conductor, r_a; radius of outer conductor, r_b. Let $\mu = \mu_0$, and neglect end effects.

8-4. Find the divergence of the time-averaged Poynting's vector for a plane wave, Eq. 8-43, and verify that this is equal to the time-averaged value of $|\boldsymbol{E}_1|^2\sigma$.

8-5. A 550-megacycle-per-second plane wave moving through air is normally incident on sea water (see Problem 8-1). Write expressions for the incident, transmitted, and reflected electric and magnetic fields, and the conduction-current density and displacement-current density, with numerical substitutions for all quantities except t and z. Assume the incident electric field has a maximum value of 1000 microvolts per meter. Sketch a phasor diagram relating the various field magnitudes at the boundary surface. (This should correspond to Fig. 8-2.)

8-6. Repeat Problem 8-5, assuming that the fields are normally incident on copper rather than sea water.

8-7. Compute the time-averaged power flow into a metallic surface from normally incident waves using Poynting's vector, and bring the result into agreement with Eq. 8-77.

8-8. Derive Snell's law for the angle of refraction of a plane wave obliquely incident upon a nonconducting medium, Eq. 8-101, by adding an equiphase line in medium 2 in Fig. 8-3.

8-9. Find the resultant electric and magnetic fields (sum of incident and reflected components) for normal and oblique incidence upon an ideal conductor. Locate any surfaces on which either field is always zero, and, for the oblique-incidence case, find the phase velocity with which the pattern moves parallel to the reflecting surface.

8-10. Compute the ratio of the maximum value of E_z to the maximum value of E_x for a quasi-TEM mode between parallel-plane conductors at a frequency of 550 megacycles per second, if the surfaces are copper. (Coordinate directions as in Fig. 8-7.)

8-11. Write an expression for the displacement-current density of a TEM mode between two parallel planes of infinite conductivity, beginning with Eq. 8-113. Show that continuity of the current field (displacement current and conduction current together) is maintained at the conductor surfaces.

REFERENCES

1. BURROWS, C. R., "Radio Propagation Over a Plane Earth," *Bell System Tech. J.*, 16 (1937), 45–75.
2. JORDAN, EDWARD C., *Electromagnetic Waves and Radiating Systems.* New York: Prentice-Hall, Inc., 1950.
3. STRATTON, JULIUS ADAMS, *Electromagnetic Theory.* New York: McGraw-Hill Book Company, Inc., 1941.
4. TERMAN, FREDERICK EMMONS, *Radio Engineers' Handbook.* New York: McGraw-Hill Book Company, Inc., 1943.

CHAPTER 9

Conductor-Guided Fields: Two-Conductor Arrays

In the earlier chapters of this book, the inductance and capacitance parameters for a transmission line were postulated and used in the differential equations with no attempt to relate them to the cross-sectional dimensions or other physical properties of the line. It was mentioned that current is necessarily accompanied by a magnetic field and voltage by an electric field, and that those fields exist in the space between the conductors and possibly within them.

Electric and magnetic fields were discussed in the preceding two chapters, beginning with a derivation of Maxwell's equations and later considering the phenomena of sinusoidal traveling-wave trains when propagating in continuous media and when undergoing reflections at normal or oblique incidence. Conduction current of finite density, describable as a vector field, was found to be present whenever the propagation medium has a nonzero but finite conductivity.

Conducting surfaces parallel to the direction of field propagation influence the lateral extent of the field and other aspects of the process; in a sense all such conductors are wave guides, although usage often limits this term to hollow tubes of conducting material which enclose propagating fields.

Attention in this chapter will be directed toward two principal conductor-set cross sections, the circular coaxial line and the circular-wire parallel pair. As an example of versatility in mathematical and experimental technique, the parallel-slab-type equivalent of the coaxial line will be considered briefly in Appendix A.

9-1. COAXIAL LINE

A geometrically simple form of conductor-set cross section, one which yields algebraically simple expressions for the fields, is the coaxial cable, sketched in Fig. 9-1, The cylindrical coordinate system, with the $\boldsymbol{a}_z$ direction coincident with the axis of the conductor set, is an obvious choice here.

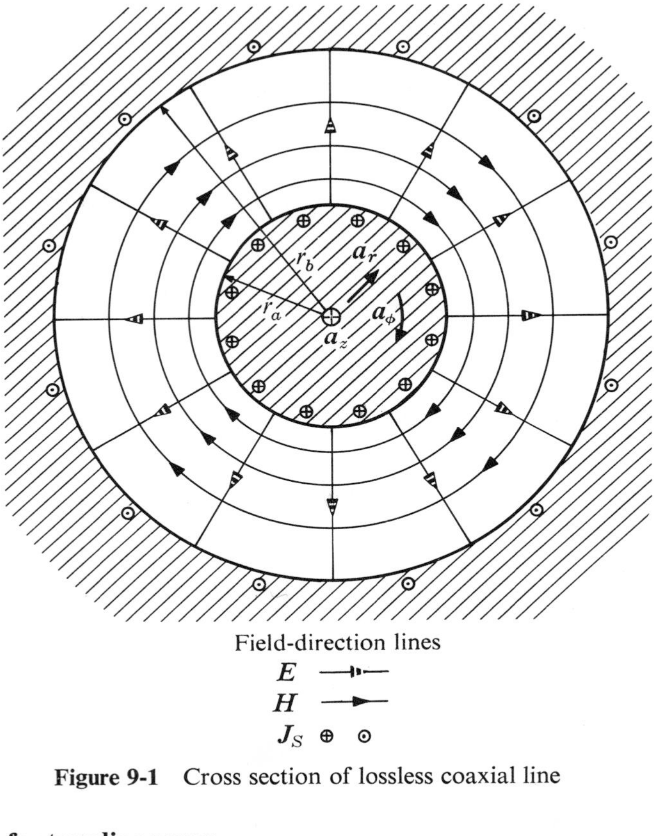

Figure 9-1 Cross section of lossless coaxial line

a. Fields for traveling waves

If one assumes (1) current flow in opposite directions in the two conductors at any given longitudinal location, (2) current flow uniformly distributed circumferentially, and (3) charge uniformly distributed circumferentially on each conductor, one may surmise from symmetry that the resulting fields will be independent of ϕ and that one possible field configuration will have a purely radial $\boldsymbol{E}$ field and a purely circumferential $\boldsymbol{H}$ field. (It should be noted that this is not the only mode which is possible in a coaxial line,[13] although it is the mode of principal importance for signal propagation.) It will be further assumed that the fields may propagate longitudinally as traveling waves. Strictly, it is necessary that the conductors be lossless (infinite conductivity) for the **E** field to be purely radial, and that will be assumed for investigation of the fields between the conductors.

(1) SOLUTION FOR **E** AND **H** FIELDS. In accordance with the foregoing assumptions, let the following traveling-wave electric-field function be postulated:

$$\boldsymbol{E}_1 = E_{1r}(r)\sin(\omega t - \beta z)\boldsymbol{a}_r \tag{9-1}$$

The functional variation of **E** with respect to r may be determined with the aid of Maxwell's equation involving the divergence of **D**; the accompanying **H** field and the parameter β may then be found with Maxwell's curl equations.

The space between the conductors will be assumed to be charge-free, so that, from Eq. 7-28,

$$\nabla \cdot \boldsymbol{D} = 0$$

The divergence of **D** may be found by multiplying Eq. 9-1 by ϵ and using Eq. 7-55:

$$\frac{1}{r}\frac{\partial[r\epsilon E_{1r}(r)\sin(\omega t - \beta z)]}{\partial r} = 0$$

This reduces to

$$\frac{\partial[rE_{1r}(r)]}{\partial r} = 0 \tag{9-2}$$

Equation 9-2 may be integrated directly; a constant of integration A_1 is introduced thereby:

$$\begin{aligned} rE_{1r}(r) &= A_1 \\ E_{1r}(r) &= \frac{A_1}{r} \end{aligned} \tag{9-3}$$

Hence, by substituting in Eq. 9-1,

$$\boldsymbol{E}_1 = \frac{A_1}{r}\sin(\omega t - \beta z)\boldsymbol{a}_r \tag{9-4}$$

Thus the magnitude of the **E** field varies inversely with r.

One may continue by testing this function in Maxwell's curl equations.

$$\nabla \times \boldsymbol{E} = -\mu\frac{\partial \boldsymbol{H}}{\partial t} \tag{7-34}$$

The curl of $\boldsymbol{E}_1$ is obtained with Eq. 7-55:

$$\nabla \times \boldsymbol{E}_1 = -\frac{\beta A_1}{r}\cos(\omega t - \beta z)\boldsymbol{a}_\phi \tag{9-5}$$

Substitution of this into Eq. 7-34 and integration with respect to time yields

$$\boldsymbol{H}_1 = \frac{\beta A_1}{\omega r \mu} \sin(\omega t - \beta z)\boldsymbol{a}_\phi \tag{9-6}$$

Thus the $\boldsymbol{H}_1$ field is, at all times and locations, (1) perpendicular to $\boldsymbol{E}_1$, (2) directly proportional to it in magnitude, and (3) in time phase with it.

$$\nabla \times \boldsymbol{H} = \epsilon \frac{\partial \boldsymbol{E}}{\partial t} \tag{7-32}$$

The parameter β may be found by taking the curl of $\boldsymbol{H}_1$, substituting in Eq. 7-32, and solving for $\boldsymbol{E}$:

$$\nabla \times \boldsymbol{H}_1 = \frac{-\beta^2 A_1}{\omega r \mu} \cos(\omega t - \beta z)\boldsymbol{a}_r$$

$$\boldsymbol{E}_1 = \frac{\beta^2 A_1}{\omega^2 r \mu \epsilon} \sin(\omega t - \beta z)\boldsymbol{a}_r$$

This result may be equated to Eq. 9-4:

$$\frac{A_1}{r} \sin(\omega t - \beta z)\boldsymbol{a}_r = \frac{\beta^2 A_1}{\omega^2 r \mu \epsilon} \sin(\omega t - \beta z)\boldsymbol{a}_r$$

After cancelling like terms the latter reduces to

$$1 = \frac{\beta^2}{\omega^2 \mu \epsilon}$$

$$\beta = \omega\sqrt{\mu\epsilon} \tag{9-7}$$

This result is identical with Eq. 8-27 for infinite plane waves propagating in a lossless medium. As before, the velocity of propagation is

$$v = \frac{1}{\sqrt{\mu\epsilon}} \tag{8-28}$$

Substitution of Eq. 9-7 for the first β in Eq. 9-6 yields

$$\boldsymbol{H}_1 = \frac{A_1}{r}\sqrt{\frac{\epsilon}{\mu}} \sin(\omega t - \beta z)\boldsymbol{a}_\phi$$

Intrinsic impedance as defined for the infinite-plane-wave case is appropriate here, too:

$$\eta = \sqrt{\frac{\mu}{\epsilon}} \tag{8-27}$$

$$\boldsymbol{H}_1 = \frac{A_1}{\eta r} \sin(\omega t - \beta z)\boldsymbol{a}_\phi \tag{9-8}$$

(2) FIELD MAGNITUDES IN PROPORTION TO CURRENT. The constant A_1 in Eqs. 9-4 and 9-8 for $\boldsymbol{E}_1$ and $\boldsymbol{H}_1$ is yet to be related to the current in the conductors. Ampere's law, Eq. 7-17, may be used for this purpose. Since for this assumed mode $\boldsymbol{D}$ has no longitudinal component, no such component of displacement current is present. Hence only conduction current will be encircled if the path of integration is confined to a plane perpendicular to $\boldsymbol{a}_z$. If the path of integration is further confined to the space between the two conductors, the instantaneous transmission-line current $i_1(z,t)$ is obtained. The simplest path is a circle concentric with the conductor.

$$\boldsymbol{dL} = r\,d\phi\boldsymbol{a}_\phi \tag{7-49}$$

$$\oint \boldsymbol{H}_1 \cdot \boldsymbol{dL} = \int_0^{2\pi} \frac{A_1}{\eta} \sin(\omega t - \beta z)\,d\phi$$

$$= \frac{2\pi A_1}{\eta} \sin(\omega t - \beta z)$$

Let

$$i_1(z,t) = I_{1M} \sin(\omega t - \beta z) \tag{9-9}$$

Equating the last two expressions yields:

$$A_1 = \frac{I_{1M}\eta}{2\pi} \tag{9-10}$$

Equations 9-4 and 9-8 may be rewritten, after substituting Eq. 9-10,

$$\boldsymbol{E}_1 = \frac{I_{1M}\eta}{2\pi r} \sin(\omega t - \beta z)\boldsymbol{a}_r \tag{9-11}$$

$$\boldsymbol{H}_1 = \frac{I_{1M}}{2\pi r} \sin(\omega t - \beta z)\boldsymbol{a}_\phi \tag{9-12}$$

(3) CONDUCTION-CURRENT FIELDS. A consequence of assuming infinite conductivity is that conduction current concentrates into sheets of infinitesimal thickness at the conductor surfaces, as discussed in Sec. 8-2*d*(1) and 8-4. Such a sheet maintains a magnetic-field difference between the field immediately above the conductor surface [$\boldsymbol{H}_1(r_a,z,t)$ or $\boldsymbol{H}_1(r_b,z,t)$] and the field immediately below the surface, which is zero. The conduction-current field may be regarded as a pair of surface-current densities; the symbols $\boldsymbol{J}_{S1a}$ and $\boldsymbol{J}_{S1b}$ may be used for the inner and outer conductors, respectively.

$$\boldsymbol{J}_{S1a} = \frac{I_{1M}}{2\pi r_a} \sin(\omega t - \beta z)\boldsymbol{a}_z \tag{9-13}$$

$$\boldsymbol{J}_{S1b} = \frac{-I_{1M}}{2\pi r_b} \sin(\omega t - \beta z)\boldsymbol{a}_z \tag{9-14}$$

(4) $\boldsymbol{E}$ AND $\boldsymbol{H}$ PAIR FOR OTHER DIRECTION OF TRAVEL. In Chapter 1 it was noted that a second voltage-and-current traveling-wave pair, moving in

the negative direction, would also satisfy the transmission-line differential equations. Equations for the fields and current of this wave pair, corresponding to those just derived in Eqs. 9-1 through 9-12, are

$$\boldsymbol{H}_2 = \frac{I_{2M}}{2\pi r}\sin(\omega t + \beta z)\boldsymbol{a}_\phi \tag{9-15}$$

$$\boldsymbol{E}_2 = \frac{-I_{2M}\eta}{2\pi r}\sin(\omega t + \beta z)\boldsymbol{a}_r \tag{9-16}$$

$$i_2(z,t) = I_{2M}\sin(\omega t + \beta z) \tag{9-17}$$

The reader should verify these expressions by comparison with the derivation just given for the $\omega t - \beta z$ wave functions, noting in particular the reversal of sign for $\boldsymbol{E}_2$.

b. Derivation of transmission-line parameters

The field-configuration mode just examined for the coaxial line is, like the infinite plane wave in a uniform medium, an instance of transverse electromagnetic (TEM) propagation. When TEM-mode fields are bounded by conducting surfaces, as in this instance, the concept of voltage as the line integral of $\boldsymbol{E}$ may be used. The expressions already derived for electric field are directly proportional to current, and this will enable one to find the characteristic impedance in terms of the radii r_a and r_b and the properties of the medium between.

(1) Voltage in time-varying TEM fields. The line integral of $\boldsymbol{E}$ was mentioned in the description of electric fields in Sec. 7-2*b*(2). Because the line integral between two conductor surfaces in a non-time-varying field is independent of path, it is a meaningful measure of the "resultant" strength of the intervening field. Known as *voltage*, it is a key element in the concept of the electric circuit as an approximate means of analyzing an electromagnetic-field problem.

The curl function was defined in Sec. 7-3*c*(1) in terms of the line integral around a small closed path. Unless the curl of a given vector field vanishes throughout a given region, the line integral of that vector field will not be independent of path. According to Eq. 7-34 (one of Maxwell's equations), the curl of $\boldsymbol{E}$ does not vanish if the fields are time-varying, and hence the concept of voltage as a path-independent line integral is not, in general, realizable for the dynamic $\boldsymbol{E}$ field.

For the TEM mode, however, independence of path for the line integral exists on a limited basis. Specifically, if one confines the paths of integration to planes perpendicular to the direction of wave propagation, line integrals of $\boldsymbol{E}$ in each such plane are independent of path. The z component of the curl of $\boldsymbol{E}_1$ as given in Eq. 9-11 vanishes, and that is all that is required if the path is restricted as just described. This is the basis for the voltage concept as commonly used in alternating-current circuit theory.

$$v_1(z,t) = -\int_{r_b}^{r_a} \boldsymbol{E}_1 \cdot (dr\, \boldsymbol{a}_r) \tag{9-18}$$

$$v_1(z,t) = -\int_{r_b}^{r_a} \frac{I_{1M}\eta}{2\pi r} \sin(\omega t - \beta z)\, dr$$

$$= \frac{I_{1M}\eta}{2\pi} \ln\left(\frac{r_b}{r_a}\right) \sin(\omega t - \beta z) \tag{9-19}$$

Similarly, for the wave traveling in the $-\boldsymbol{a}_z$ direction,

$$v_2(z,t) = \frac{-I_{2M}\eta}{2\pi} \ln\left(\frac{r_b}{r_a}\right) \sin(\omega t + \beta z) \tag{9-20}$$

(2) CHARACTERISTIC IMPEDANCE. In Chapter 1 it was indicated that the voltage and current functions of a traveling-wave pair should be related by the characteristic impedance, a function which for a lossless line was purely resistive. Comparison of Eqs. 9-9 and 9-19 indicates that the characteristic impedance of a coaxial line is as follows:

$$Z_0 = \frac{\eta}{2\pi} \ln\left(\frac{r_b}{r_a}\right)$$

$$= \frac{1}{2\pi} \sqrt{\frac{\mu}{\epsilon}} \ln\left(\frac{r_b}{r_a}\right) \tag{9-21}$$

(3) DISTRIBUTED INDUCTANCE AND CAPACITANCE. Characteristic impedance and velocity of propagation are related to the inductance and capacitance per unit length of a lossless transmission line as follows:

$$Z_0 = \sqrt{\frac{l}{c}} \tag{1-20}$$

$$v = \frac{1}{\sqrt{lc}} \tag{1-21}$$

Since expressions have been obtained for Z_0 and v in terms of the physical properties of the cable (μ, ϵ, r_a, and r_b), it is appropriate to solve Eqs. 1-20 and 1-21 for l and c:

$$l = \frac{Z_0}{v} \tag{9-22}$$

$$c = \frac{1}{Z_0 v} \tag{9-23}$$

Substitution of Eqs. 8-28 for v and 9-21 for Z_0 yields

$$l = \frac{\mu}{2\pi} \ln\left(\frac{r_b}{r_a}\right) \tag{9-24}$$

$$c = \frac{2\pi\epsilon}{\ln\left(\frac{r_b}{r_a}\right)} \tag{9-25}$$

Equations 9-24 and 9-25 define the distributed inductance and capacitance of a lossless coaxial cable in terms of its cross-sectional dimensions and the properties of the medium between the conductors. Equation 9-21 similarly defines the characteristic impedance. In each instance the cross-sectional dimensions appear solely in the form of the ratio r_b/r_a. A change in scale of the cross section leaves these derived parameters unchanged.

c. Standing waves with short-circuit termination

The existence of traveling waves which may move in either direction gives rise to the possibility of standing waves. The simplest instance is that of a short-circuited termination, that in which a highly conducting plate is fastened solidly across the end of the line. This has been examined from a voltage-and-current point of view in Chapter 3, where it was noted that for a lossless line, the phasors of the incident and reflected components were of equal magnitude at all points and times, and that at the short-circuited point, the incident and reflected voltage waves would be in phase opposition, whereas the incident and reflected current waves would be in phase with each other. Corresponding relationships are found among the field components; the resulting $\boldsymbol{E}$ field (which is purely radial, as previously noted) must vanish over the short-circuiting end surface. Let the origin in z be taken at the short-circuited end, with the line extending in the positive z direction. Then $\boldsymbol{E}_1$ and $\boldsymbol{H}_1$ are reflected waves, whereas $\boldsymbol{E}_2$ and $\boldsymbol{H}_2$ are incident components:

$$I_{1M} = I_{2M} \tag{9-26}$$

$$\begin{aligned}\boldsymbol{E}_{\text{sc}} &= \boldsymbol{E}_2 + \boldsymbol{E}_1 \\ &= \frac{I_{2M}}{2\pi r}\sqrt{\frac{\mu}{\epsilon}}\,[-\sin(\omega t + \beta z) + \sin(\omega t - \beta z)]\boldsymbol{a}_r \\ &= \frac{-I_{2M}}{\pi r}\sqrt{\frac{\mu}{\epsilon}}\,\sin\beta z\cos\omega t\,\boldsymbol{a}_r\end{aligned} \tag{9-27}$$

$$\begin{aligned}\boldsymbol{H}_{\text{sc}} &= \boldsymbol{H}_2 + \boldsymbol{H}_1 \\ &= \frac{I_{2M}}{2\pi r}[\sin(\omega t + \beta z) + \sin(\omega t - \beta z)]\boldsymbol{a}_\phi \\ &= \frac{I_{2M}}{\pi r}\cos\beta z\sin\omega t\,\boldsymbol{a}_\phi\end{aligned} \tag{9-28}$$

The properties indicated in Eqs. 3-30 through 3-33 and in Fig. 3-9 regarding standing waves of voltage and current on a short-circuited lossless line (alternation of nulls and maxima along the line, and time-quadrature relationship between voltage and current) apply to the field equations.

The accompanying surface-current density is the subject of Problem 9-1.

9-2. CIRCULAR-WIRE PARALLEL PAIR

A set of two circular conductors parallel to each other, as shown in Fig. 9-2, is an arrangement commonly used in transmission-line practice. From the standpoint of field analysis, it is less symmetrical than the coaxial cable, but amenable nevertheless.

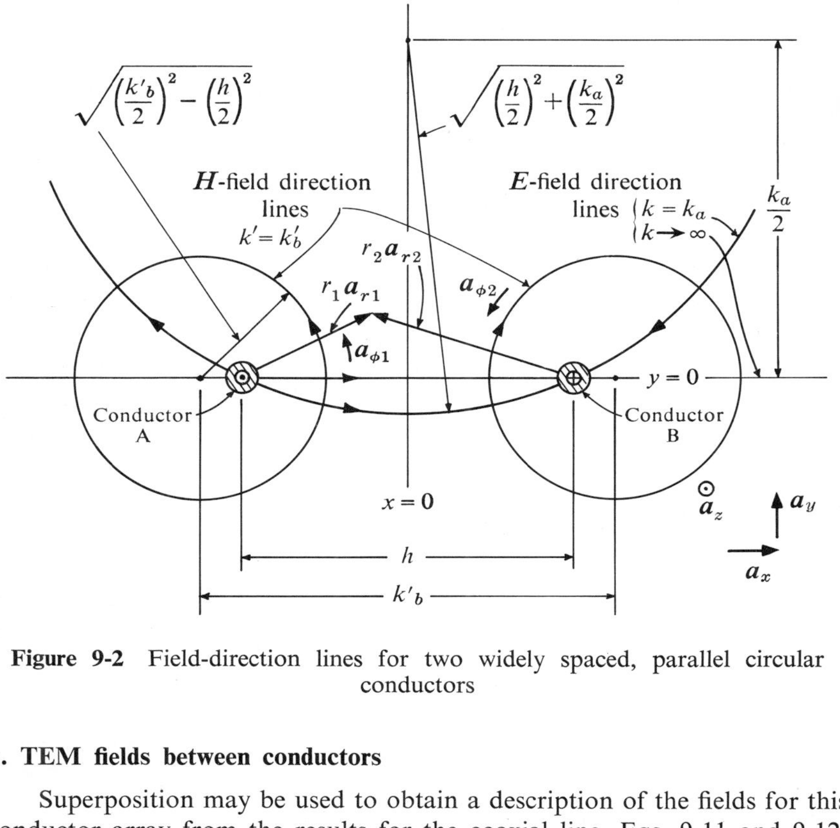

Figure 9-2 Field-direction lines for two widely spaced, parallel circular conductors

a. TEM fields between conductors

Superposition may be used to obtain a description of the fields for this conductor array from the results for the coaxial line, Eqs. 9-11 and 9-12. Initially it will be assumed that the conductor centers are at $-h/2,0$ and $h/2,0$ and that the conductor radii are extremely small compared to the distance h. (As is shown in Sec. 9-2a(3), the results may be generalized to conductors of any diameter, provided their centers are offset by appropriate distances from $-h/2,0$ and $h/2,0$.)

One may first visualize the fields which would exist between conductor A and a coaxial return path with a radius very much larger than h, with conductor B removed. A traveling-wave set moving in the $\boldsymbol{a}_z$ direction will be assumed, and will be designated by $\boldsymbol{E}_A$ and $\boldsymbol{H}_A$. Equations 9-11 and 9-12 will be applicable if r is replaced by r_1. If conductor B has an infinitesimal diameter and is uncharged, it may be replaced without disturbing fields $\boldsymbol{E}_A$ and $\boldsymbol{H}_A$. In like manner a circuit may be formed through conductor B and a coaxial return, and this may be assumed to carry a traveling-wave set also moving in the $\boldsymbol{a}_z$ direction, but in phase opposition to that between conductor A and its coaxial return. For these fields, which will be designated by $\boldsymbol{E}_B$ and $\boldsymbol{H}_B$, Eqs. 9-11 and 9-12 are applicable if r is replaced by r_2 and I_{1M} by $-I_{1M}$. Strictly the coaxial return paths would not be coincident (their centers are separated by h), but as their radii approach infinity, the resultant $\boldsymbol{H}$ field in their vicinity would approach zero (see Problem 9-2), and hence they would effectively cancel each other. Thus the only conduction currents remaining would be those in conductors A and B, and the resultant fields would be:

$$\boldsymbol{E} = \boldsymbol{E}_A + \boldsymbol{E}_B \tag{9-29}$$

$$\boldsymbol{H} = \boldsymbol{H}_A + \boldsymbol{H}_B \tag{9-30}$$

(The foregoing is essentially what is inferred in derivations given in terms of the fields of single, isolated conductors. Every current must have a return path, and for the TEM mode this must be a conduction current. Furthermore, both ends of nonclosing lines of the $\boldsymbol{D}$ field must terminate on charges. The *per-conductor* concept of inductance and capacitance is a mathematical fiction, although a useful one for computations dealing with multiconductor lines, as is indicated in Chapter 12.)

(1) ELECTRIC FIELD. The vector fields $\boldsymbol{E}_A$ and $\boldsymbol{E}_B$ at a point (x,y) due to a traveling-wave set moving in the $\boldsymbol{a}_z$ direction are, if one adapts Eq. 9-11 in the manner noted above,

$$\boldsymbol{E}_A = \frac{I_{1M}\eta}{2\pi r_1}\sin(\omega t - \beta z)\boldsymbol{a}_{r1} \tag{9-31}$$

$$\boldsymbol{E}_B = \frac{-I_{1M}\eta}{2\pi r_2}\sin(\omega t - \beta z)\boldsymbol{a}_{r2} \tag{9-32}$$

To put these expressions in terms of the common coordinate system shown in Fig. 9-2, a rectangular one, the following substitutions are needed:

$$r_1 = \sqrt{\left(x + \frac{h}{2}\right)^2 + y^2} \tag{9-33}$$

$$r_2 = \sqrt{\left(x - \frac{h}{2}\right)^2 + y^2} \tag{9-34}$$

The partial $\boldsymbol{E}$ fields will be resolved into components:

$$E_{Ax} = \frac{I_{1M}\eta[x + (h/2)] \sin(\omega t - \beta z)}{2\pi r_1^2} \tag{9-35}$$

$$E_{Ay} = \frac{I_{1M}\eta y \sin(\omega t - \beta z)}{2\pi r_1^2} \tag{9-36}$$

$$E_{Bx} = \frac{-I_{1M}\eta[x - (h/2)] \sin(\omega t - \beta z)}{2\pi r_2^2} \tag{9-37}$$

$$E_{By} = \frac{-I_{1M}\eta y \sin(\omega t - \beta z)}{2\pi r_2^2} \tag{9-38}$$

A helpful technique for describing a vector field is that of *direction lines*, which were introduced from the field-exploration point of view in Sec. 7-2*b*. Such lines are loci which are continuously tangent to the field. Thus at any point x,y in a transverse plane, the directional tangent of an incremental segment of such a line, or the ratio of Δy to Δx, is equal to the ratio of the y component of the field to the x component at that point. If the length of the segment is reduced to differential size, the ratio $\Delta y/\Delta x$ approaches, as a limit, the derivative dy/dx. Thus

$$\frac{dy}{dx} = \frac{E_y}{E_x} \tag{9-39}$$

In this instance Eq. 9-39 becomes

$$\frac{dy}{dx} = \frac{E_{Ay} + E_{By}}{E_{Ax} + E_{Bx}}$$

$$= \frac{(y/r_1^2) - (y/r_2^2)}{\{[x + (h/2)]/r_1^2\} - \{[x - (h/2)]/r_2^2\}}$$

Clearing the fractions within the numerator and denominator of the main expression and substituting Eqs. 9-33 and 9-34 reduces it to the following:

$$\frac{dy}{dx} = \frac{2xy}{x^2 - y^2 - (h/2)^2}$$

This is a nonlinear differential equation of the first order. It is not one for which the variables may be separated, but it proves to be convertible into an exact differential:

$$2xy\, dx + [y^2 + (h/2)^2 - x^2]\, dy = 0 \tag{9-40}$$

Given a first-order differential equation of the following form,

$$M\,dx + N\,dy = 0 \tag{9-41}$$

The necessary and sufficient condition that it be an exact differential is

$$\frac{\partial M}{\partial y} = \frac{\partial N}{\partial x} \tag{9-42}$$

This condition is not met by Eq. 9-40 as it stands, but if that equation is multiplied by the integrating factor $1/y^2$, the resulting equation will meet the requirement just given.

$$\frac{2x\,dx}{y} + \left[1 + \left(\frac{h}{2}\right)^2 \frac{1}{y^2} - \left(\frac{x}{y}\right)^2\right] dy = 0$$

or

$$\frac{2x}{y} + \left[1 + \left(\frac{h}{2}\right)^2 \frac{1}{y^2} - \left(\frac{x}{y}\right)^2\right] \frac{dy}{dx} = 0 \tag{9-43}$$

The expression which, if differentiated with respect to x (considering y to be a function of x) would yield Eq. 9-43, is

$$\frac{x^2}{y} + y - \left(\frac{h}{2}\right)^2 \frac{1}{y} = k \tag{9-44}$$

Here k is an arbitrary constant. Equation 9-44 may be reduced to the usual form for the equation of a circle by (1) multiplying it by y, (2) moving the two terms nearest the equality sign to their respective opposite sides, and (3) adding the quantity $(k/2)^2$ to both sides:

$$x^2 + y^2 - \left(\frac{h}{2}\right)^2 = ky$$

$$x^2 + y^2 - ky = \left(\frac{h}{2}\right)^2$$

$$x^2 + \left(y - \frac{k}{2}\right)^2 = \left(\frac{h}{2}\right)^2 + \left(\frac{k}{2}\right)^2 \tag{9-45}$$

Hence the direction lines of the $\boldsymbol{E}$ field are circles of radii $\sqrt{(h/2)^2 + (k/2)^2}$, with centers located on the Y axis but offset from the origin by amount $k/2$; the relation between the offset and the radius of each circle is such that every field line will pass through the points $(h/2,0)$ and $(-h/2,0)$. The arbitrary constant k may be assigned any value from $-\infty$ to $+\infty$, and each such value defines a direction line of the $\boldsymbol{E}$ field.

(2) MAGNETIC FIELD. Direction lines for the magnetic field may be found similarly:

$$\boldsymbol{H}_A = \frac{I_{1M}\sin(\omega t - \beta z)}{2\pi r_1}\boldsymbol{a}_{\phi 1} \tag{9-46}$$

$$\boldsymbol{H}_B = \frac{-I_{1M}\sin(\omega t - \beta z)}{2\pi r_2}\boldsymbol{a}_{\phi 2} \tag{9-47}$$

$$H_{Ax} = \frac{-I_{1M}y\sin(\omega t - \beta z)}{2\pi r_1^2} \tag{9-48}$$

$$H_{Ay} = \frac{I_{1M}[x + (h/2)]\sin(\omega t - \beta z)}{2\pi r_1^2} \tag{9-49}$$

$$H_{Bx} = \frac{I_{1M}y\sin(\omega t - \beta z)}{2\pi r_2^2} \tag{9-50}$$

$$H_{By} = \frac{-I_{1M}[x - (h/2)]\sin(\omega t - \beta z)}{2\pi r_2^2} \tag{9-51}$$

The differential equation for the direction lines is

$$\frac{dy}{dx} = \frac{H_{Ay} + H_{By}}{H_{Ax} + H_{Bx}} \tag{9-52}$$

The clearing of fractions after the appropriate terms have been substituted parallels the procedure used for the electric field and results in the following:

$$\frac{dy}{dx} = \frac{x^2 - y^2 - (h/2)^2}{-2xy}$$

$$[x^2 - y^2 - (h/2)^2]\,dx + 2xy\,dy = 0 \tag{9-53}$$

In this instance the integrating factor which will convert the differential equation into an exact differential is $1/x^2$. The result of integrating is

$$x + \frac{y^2}{x} + \left(\frac{h}{2}\right)^2\frac{1}{x} = k' \tag{9-54}$$

Here k' is an arbitrary constant. This result may be changed to the standard form for a circle by multiplying by x, rearranging terms, and adding $(k'/2)^2$ to both sides:

$$x^2 + y^2 - k'x = -\left(\frac{h}{2}\right)^2$$

$$\left(x - \frac{k'}{2}\right)^2 + y^2 = \left(\frac{k'}{2}\right)^2 - \left(\frac{h}{2}\right)^2 \tag{9-55}$$

Direction lines of the $\boldsymbol{H}$ field are circles, with centers on the X axis but offset from the origin by distances $k'/2$, which distances are necessarily greater than $h/2$. Each value of $k'/2$ defines a separate field-direction line. The radius of each circle is $\sqrt{(k'/2)^2 - (h/2)^2}$, a quantity which approaches zero for values of k' approaching h.

(3) GENERAL PROPERTIES AND BOUNDARY CONDITIONS. The $\boldsymbol{E}$ and $\boldsymbol{H}$ fields are mutually perpendicular; this may be demonstrated by showing that the scalar product $\boldsymbol{E} \cdot \boldsymbol{H}$ vanishes (see Problem 9-3).

As was true of the coaxial line, the mode of propagation is transverse-electromagnetic (TEM), and the concept of voltage as a path-independent

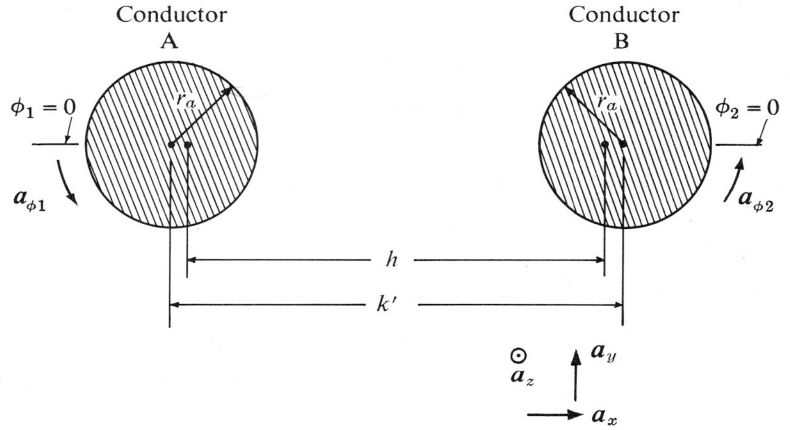

Figure 9-3 Closely spaced parallel conductors (see also Problems 9-4 and 9-5)

line integral is applicable on a limited basis, namely, if one restricts each line integral of $\boldsymbol{E}$ to a single plane perpendicular to the direction of propagation.

Curves faired so as to be everywhere *normal to the electric-field-direction lines* (but in a given transverse plane) have the property that the line integral along any such curve is zero. Because the line integral of $\boldsymbol{E}$ in a transverse plane is independent of path, its value from one such curve to another will be independent of the particular terminal points, and these curves are called *equipotential lines*. As has been noted, the $\boldsymbol{H}$ field-direction lines lie in transverse planes and are everywhere perpendicular to the $\boldsymbol{E}$ field-direction lines, hence they have the same geometric pattern as do equipotentials of the $\boldsymbol{E}$ field.

Thus, so far as the $\boldsymbol{E}$ field is concerned, the initially postulated conductors of infinitesimally small radii can be replaced by larger circular conductors, as indicated in Fig. 9-3, provided the center of each is displaced from the infinitesimal-conductor location so that the perimeter coincides with a locus (in this instance a circle) of constant potential. The field pattern between the new, larger conductors is the same as before, but the field within each conductor becomes zero.

Surface-charge density is equal in magnitude to the normal component of $\boldsymbol{D}$ field touching the conductor and hence will not be uniform around the circumference of the conductor. It will be highest at the point closest to the other conductor and weakest at the diametrically opposite point (see Problem 9-4).

Under the limiting condition of lossless conductors, as assumed here, the conduction current consists of a surface-current sheet, and no penetration of the conductor surface by magnetic flux will occur. The surface current will distribute itself over the perimeter of each conductor so that the resultant $\boldsymbol{H}$ field is tangent to the surface of each. The particular current distribution which will achieve this at each point on the perimeter is equal in magnitude to the strength of the $\boldsymbol{H}$ field immediately adjacent to it. Since $|\boldsymbol{H}|$ and $|\boldsymbol{E}|$ are in the same proportion throughout the field, the surface-current density is in direct proportion, with respect to circumferential position, to the surface-charge distribution just mentioned.[1] The resulting circumferential nonuniformity in surface-charge distribution and in current density is called *proximity effect* (see Problem 9-5).

b. Derivation of transmission-line parameters

The voltage function $v(z,t)$ may be found by integrating $\boldsymbol{E}$ from the surface of one conductor to the other, restricting the path to the XY plane. The easiest path to use is along the X axis. Let the radius of each conductor be r_a, as shown in Fig. 9-3:

$$v(z,t) = -\int_{(k'/2)-r_a}^{-(k'/2)+r_a} (\boldsymbol{E}_A + \boldsymbol{E}_B)\cdot(-dx\,\boldsymbol{a}_x) \tag{9-56}$$

In accordance with Eq. 9-55,

$$r_a^2 = \left(\frac{k'}{2}\right)^2 - \left(\frac{h}{2}\right)^2 \tag{9-57}$$

Let

$$v(z,t) = V_M \sin(\omega t - \beta z) \tag{9-58}$$

$$V_M = -\int_{(k'/2)-r_a}^{-(k'/2)+r_a} \left(\frac{I_{1M}}{2\pi[x + (h/2)]} - \frac{I_{1M}}{2\pi[x - (h/2)]}\right)\boldsymbol{a}_x\cdot(-dx\,\boldsymbol{a}_x) \tag{9-59}$$

Integration of the right-hand side, substitution of limits, and elimination of h by means of Eq. 9-57 will yield the following:

$$V_M = \frac{I_{1M}\eta}{\pi}\ln\left[\frac{k'}{2r_a} + \sqrt{\left(\frac{k'}{2r_a}\right)^2 - 1}\right] \tag{9-60}$$

The following identity may be used:

$$\cosh^{-1} u = \ln(u + \sqrt{u^2 - 1}) \tag{9-61}$$

Thus

$$V_M = \frac{I_{1M}\eta}{\pi}\cosh^{-1}\left(\frac{k'}{2r_a}\right) \tag{9-62}$$

If $r_a \ll k'$, a series expansion may be used for the radical in Eq. 9-60:

$$\sqrt{\left(\frac{k'}{2r_a}\right)^2 - 1} = \frac{k'}{2r_a}\sqrt{1 - \left(\frac{2r_a}{k'}\right)^2}$$

$$\approx \frac{k'}{2r_a}\left[1 - \frac{1}{2}\left(\frac{2r_a}{k'}\right)^2\right] \qquad \textbf{(9-63)}$$

$$V_M \approx \frac{I_{1M}\eta}{\pi}\ln\left(\frac{k'}{r_a}\right) \qquad \textbf{(9-64)}$$

Equations 9-62 and 9-64 may be substituted into Eq. 9-58.

$$\left.\begin{aligned} v(z,t) &= \frac{I_{1M}\eta}{\pi}\cosh^{-1}\left(\frac{k'}{2r_a}\right)\sin(\omega t - \beta z) \\ &\approx \frac{I_{1M}\eta}{\pi}\ln\left(\frac{k'}{r_a}\right)\sin(\omega t - \beta z) \end{aligned}\right\} \qquad \textbf{(9-65)}$$

The expressions for the component electric fields, Eq. 9-31 and 9-32, were based on the following traveling-wave current function:

$$i(z,t) = I_{1M}\sin(\omega t - \beta z) \qquad \textbf{(9-9)}$$

The characteristic impedance, which relates the voltage and current of a traveling-wave pair, is, therefore:

$$Z_0 = \frac{\eta}{\pi}\cosh^{-1}\left(\frac{k'}{2r_a}\right)$$

$$\approx \frac{\eta}{\pi}\ln\left(\frac{k'}{r_a}\right)$$

The intrinsic impedance of a lossless medium is

$$\eta = \sqrt{\frac{\mu}{\epsilon}} \qquad \textbf{(8-27)}$$

Hence

$$Z_0 = \frac{1}{\pi}\sqrt{\frac{\mu}{\epsilon}}\cosh^{-1}\left(\frac{k'}{2r_a}\right) \qquad \textbf{(9-66)}$$

$$Z_0 \approx \frac{1}{\pi}\sqrt{\frac{\mu}{\epsilon}}\ln\left(\frac{k'}{r_a}\right) \qquad \textbf{(9-67)}$$

The distributed parameters l and c may be related to Z_0 in the same manner as for the TEM mode in the coaxial line:

$$l = \frac{Z_0}{v} \qquad \textbf{(9-22)}$$

$$c = \frac{1}{Z_0 v} \qquad \textbf{(9-23)}$$

The velocity of propagation ν for the TEM mode in a lossless medium was found to be

$$\nu = \frac{1}{\sqrt{\mu\epsilon}} \tag{8-28}$$

Substitution of Eqs. 9-66 or 9-67, and 8-28, in Eqs. 9-22 and 9-23 yields

$$l = \frac{\mu}{\pi}\cosh^{-1}\left(\frac{k'}{2r_a}\right) \tag{9-68}$$

$$\approx \frac{\mu}{\pi}\ln\left(\frac{k'}{r_a}\right) \tag{9-69}$$

$$c = \frac{\epsilon\pi}{\cosh^{-1}(k'/2r_a)} \tag{9-70}$$

$$\approx \frac{\epsilon\pi}{\ln(k'/r_a)} \tag{9-71}$$

These results for the distributed inductance and capacitance of a lossless two-parallel-wire line correspond to Eqs. 9-24 and 9-25 for the lossless coaxial line.

9-3. EFFECTS OF FINITE CONDUCTIVITY

Conductivity which is less than infinite changes the field patterns of transmission lines from the forms just described: (1) the $\boldsymbol{E}$ field has a small longitudinal component which is not in time phase with the transverse component (see Sec. 8-4); (2) the current distribution is not a surface sheet; hence (3) magnetic flux exists within the conductors.

These effects are accompanied by a power loss per unit length. In terms of distributed-circuit parameters, the resistance becomes non-zero and the inductance increases slightly.

a. Coaxial lines

Derivations of equations for the resistances and incremental inductances of the conductors of a coaxial line are rather involved, and are detailed in Appendix B.

The following is an asymptotic approximation for the resistance of a uniform coaxial line, valid at high frequencies:

$$r \approx \frac{m_a}{2\sqrt{2}\,\pi r_a\sigma_a} + \frac{m_b}{2\sqrt{2}\,\pi r_b\sigma_b} + \frac{1}{4\pi r_a^2\sigma_a} - \frac{1}{4\pi r_b^2\sigma_b} \qquad \begin{pmatrix} m_a r_a \gg 1 \\ m_b r_b \gg 1 \end{pmatrix} \tag{9-72}$$

Here

$$\left.\begin{aligned} m_a &= \sqrt{\omega\sigma_a\mu_a} \\ m_b &= \sqrt{\omega\sigma_b\mu_b} \end{aligned}\right\} \tag{9-73}$$

The subscripts a and b indicate the inner and outer conductors respectively, and r_a and r_b are as shown in Fig. 9-1.

The quantity m is related to skin depth δ, Eq. 8-83, as follows:

$$m = \frac{\sqrt{2}}{\delta} \tag{9-74}$$

Lines composed of stranded, composite, braided, or corrugated conductors are more difficult to attack mathematically than the uniform, circularly symmetrical one considered in Appendix B and for which Eq. 9-72 applies. But such structures are often used in commercial lines in the interest of bending flexibility. A common arrangement is that of a stranded inner conductor and a braided outer one.[15,16,18]

A reasonable estimate of the effective resistance of stranded conductors may be obtained on the basis of an equivalent solid conductor, one which has the same d-c resistance and permeability.[10,11] The wires of a stranded conductor are spiralled together; this increases the effective length of the current paths slightly and hence increases the resistance. The inductance is also increased slightly, because a longitudinal solenoid is formed.[23]

Composite conductors are widely used. Copper wire may be silvered or tinned, or steel wire may be overlaid with copper ("Copperweld").[21] (Composite conductors for power-transmission lines are commented on in Sec. 12-1*b*.)

Wire braid is an inexpensive form of flexible outer conductor but does not provide the degree of shielding which a solid outer conductor does. Accordingly in some cables in which a braided outer conductor is used, it is surrounded by a separate braid for shielding.

Hollow conductors with circumferential corrugation may be used for semi-flexible cables. Such a conductor has the shielding properties of a tubular outer conductor and almost as low attenuation.

b. Parallel-wire pairs

If the spacing between parallel wires is many times the conductor radius, or if $\sqrt{\omega\mu\sigma}\,r_a$ (Fig. 9-3) is small, say less than unity, the current-density distribution may be considered symmetrical within each conductor. Then the effective resistance may be computed for each conductor in the same manner as for the inner conductor of a coaxial cable.

On the other hand, if the center-to-center spacing is only a few times the conductor radius, and the quantity $\sqrt{\omega\mu\sigma}\,r_a$ is large enough to cause a noticeable increase in resistance on the basis of skin-effect calculations, the current-density distribution will not be circularly symmetrical. This is an aspect of proximity effect, which was introduced in Sec. 9-2*a*. It will further increase the resistance. A formal mathematical solution to the general problem has been obtained, but numerical evaluation is practical only with some simplifications.[2] Sim[20] gives the following asymptotic approximation for the a-c resistance of a two-conductor pair consisting of solid circular conductors of radius r_a, with a center-to-center spacing of r_a/χ:

$$\frac{r_{\mathrm{ac}}}{r_{\mathrm{dc}}} \approx \frac{Bmr_a}{2\sqrt{2}} + \frac{B(2 - B^2)}{4} + \frac{B(9 - 10B^2 + 4B^4)}{16\sqrt{2}\, mr_a} \tag{9-75}$$

Here

$$B = \frac{1}{\sqrt{1 - 4\chi^2}}$$

This approximation is valid if $r_{\mathrm{ac}}/r_{\mathrm{dc}} > 2$.

For spacing approaching infinity, χ approaches zero and Eq. 9-75 approaches the asymptotic approximation for skin-effect resistance in a circular conductor with symmetrical current distribution (see Eq. B-59 and footnote).

Computed current-density magnitudes and relative phase angles for two illustrative cases are shown in Fig. 9-4.

If skin effect is so pronounced that the current distribution is representable by a surface-current density, the effective resistance may be readily found[1] (see Problem 9-6).

9-4. CONDUCTOR-SUPPORT TECHNIQUES AND THEIR ELECTRICAL PROPERTIES

Supports for the conductors are obviously necessary, and these often modify the assumption of line uniformity in the longitudinal direction. Because of their differing geometries, coaxial lines and parallel-wire lines will be considered separately.

a. Coaxial lines

The aspect of interest here is that of supporting the inner conductor in a centered position.

The simplest method, from the standpoint of electrical theory, is to fill the space between the conductors with a solid dielectric material. This technique is commonly used, especially in flexible cables, but dielectric hysteresis losses become objectionably high at microwave frequencies. A porous or "foam" type of dielectric is sometimes used instead.

If the line is to consist of mechanically rigid sections, sufficient centering support and a great reduction in losses may be obtained by means of spaced circular discs or "beads" of various shapes. An alternative form of support consists of resonant stubs, or short-circuited sections of coaxial cable with

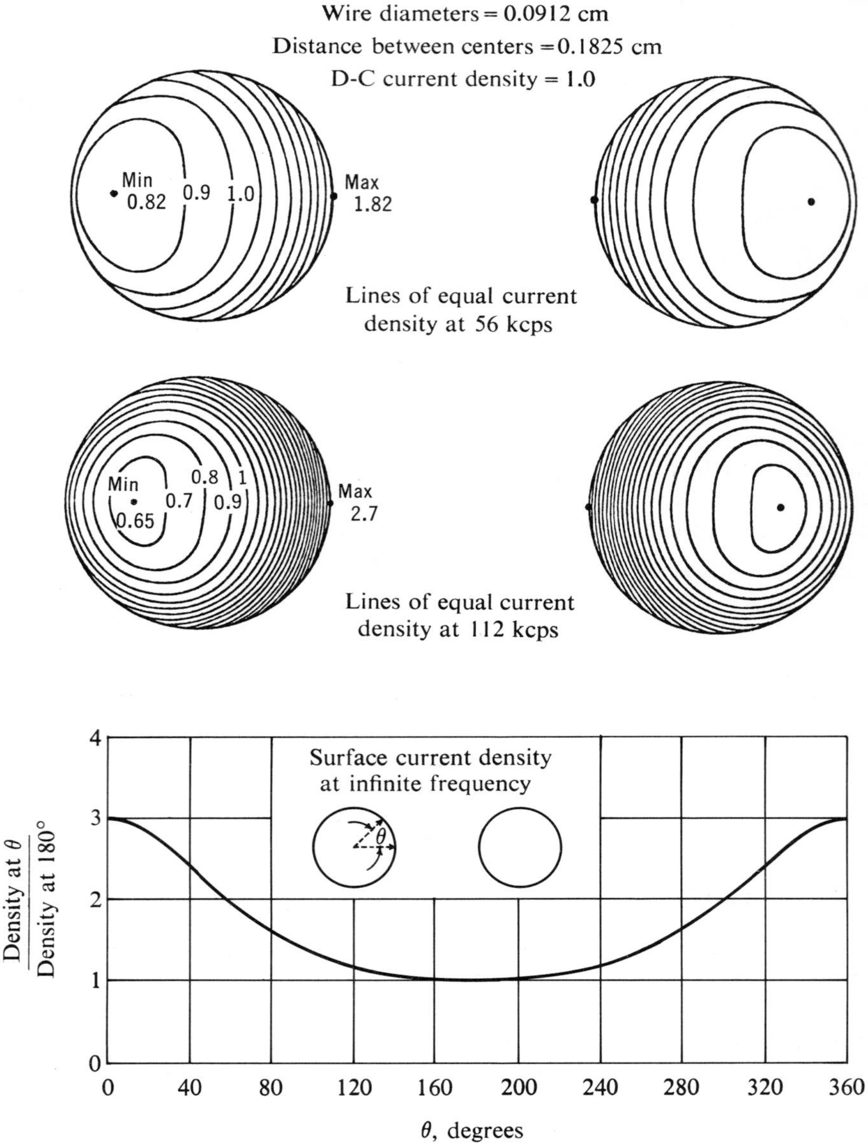

(*a*) Current-density magnitude contours

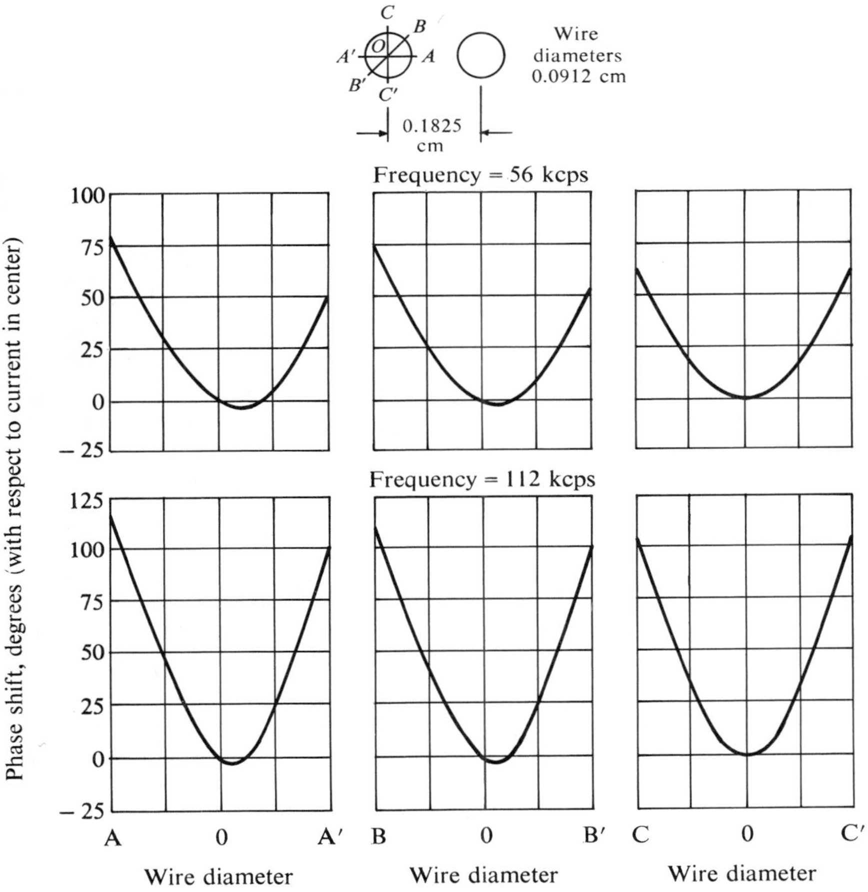

(*b*) Current density relative phase

Figure 9-4 Computed current-density loci showing proximity effect (from *Bell System Tech. J.*, 14 (1935), 184, 185, by permission)

nominal lengths of one-quarter wavelength. For semiflexible cables, a reduction in losses with acceptable mechanical properties may be had by using a continuous helical bar or rod of dielectric material between the two conductors. These methods complicate the wave-propagation phenomena.

(1) Disc or bead supports. An elementary form of disc support is a short cylinder with flat ends, illustrated in Fig. 9-5. Practical dielectric materials have permittivities two or more times that of air, and hence each such disc will constitute a short section of transmission line with a lower characteristic impedance than the air-filled sections. Each air-to-dielectric interface is a

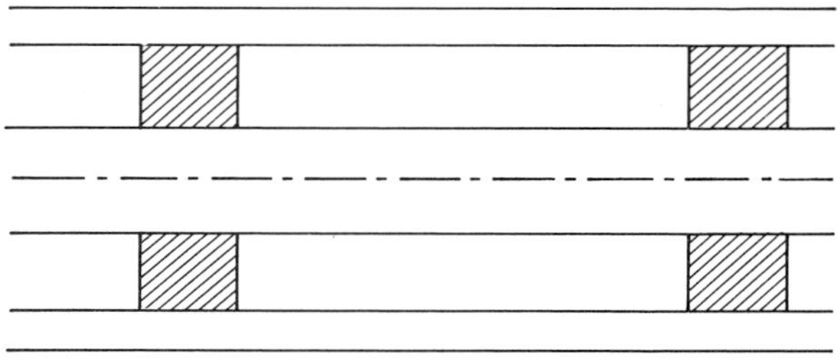

Figure 9-5 Disc-supported coaxial line

source of reflected waves with respect to waves incident from either direction. The minimum thickness of a disc is set by the need for mechanical rigidity, and this yields, at microwave frequencies, an electrical length which is sufficient to cause intolerably large standing waves.

Cancellation may be effected among the waves sent by two or more reflecting surfaces toward the generator by (1) making the thickness of each disc one-half wavelength (see Problem 9-7), or (2) by fixing both the disc thickness and the spacings between discs according to some selected pattern of electrical distances. Such arrangements have the disadvantage of being frequency-sensitive.

Reflections might be avoided by making the characteristic impedance of the dielectric-filled sections the same as for the air-filled sections. It would seem that this could be done by undercutting the inner conductor as illustrated in Fig. 9-6, such that its radius r_a' satisfied the following relationship (see Problem 9-8):

$$r_a' = r_b\left(\frac{r_a}{r_b}\right)^{\sqrt{\epsilon_d/\epsilon_0}} \qquad \textbf{(9-76)}$$

Abrupt changes in inner-conductor radius distort the fields from the TEM pattern however, and cause some reflections. These discontinuities are described in equivalent-circuit terminology as *fringing capacitances*. If the undercut radius is made slightly smaller than the predicted r_a', and the disc

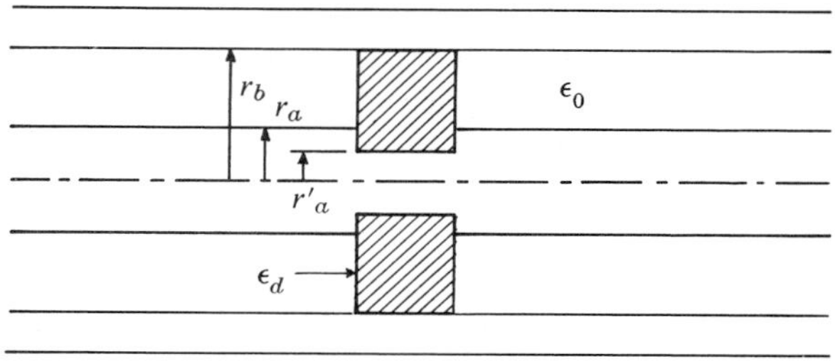

Figure 9-6 Undercut disc-supported coaxial line

thickness is appropriately chosen, a workable broad-band design may be arrived at.[4]

More elaborate disc supports have been devised to minimize standing waves,[17] but fabrication costs must be weighed against improvements in performance.

Dielectric supports in commercially produced line are often perforated discs or pegs, but the undercut-conductor principle is still used to obtain broad-band uniformity.

(2) RESONANT STUBS. The input admittance to a quarter-wavelength lossless short-circuited transmission line is zero. Thus it would appear that such a section of rigid coaxial line could be used as a support for the center conductor of the transmission line proper, as indicated in Fig. 9-7. Because the

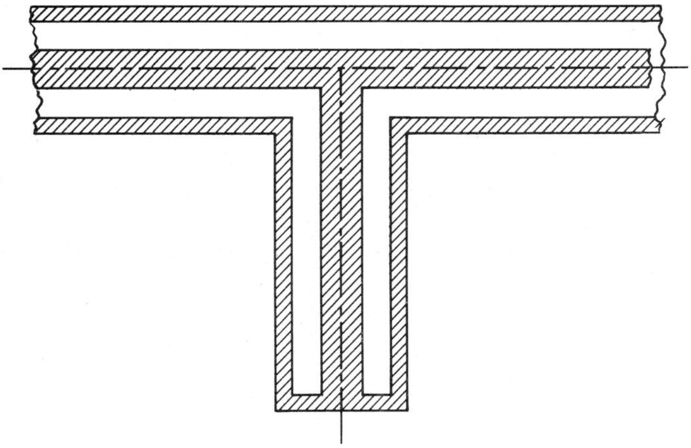

Figure 9-7 Resonant-stub-supported coaxial line

radius of the outer conductor is an appreciable fraction of a wavelength, and because the fields are distorted in the vicinity of the junction, the stub length from line center to short-circuiting plate which will yield resonance may be expected to differ slightly from $\lambda/4$.

Any deviation from the design frequency, as for example the side bands of a modulated signal, would change the electrical length of the stub and yield the following input admittance:

$$Y = \frac{1}{jZ_0} \cot \beta z_{st}$$

$$= \frac{1}{jZ_0} \cot(\omega\sqrt{lc}\, z_{st}) \qquad \textbf{(9-77)}$$

Let

$$\omega = \omega_0 + \Delta\omega \qquad \left(\frac{\Delta\omega}{\omega_0} \ll 1\right)$$

$$\omega_0\sqrt{lc}\, z_{st} = \frac{\pi}{2}$$

$$\omega\sqrt{lc}\, z_{st} = \frac{\pi}{2}\left(1 + \frac{\Delta\omega}{\omega_0}\right)$$

$$\cot(\omega\sqrt{lc}\, z_{st}) = -\tan\left(\frac{\pi\,\Delta\omega}{2\omega_0}\right)$$

$$\approx -\frac{\pi\,\Delta\omega}{2\omega_0}$$

$$Y \approx \frac{j\pi\,\Delta\omega}{Z_0 2\omega_0} \tag{9-78}$$

This simple form of stub is obviously frequency-sensitive.

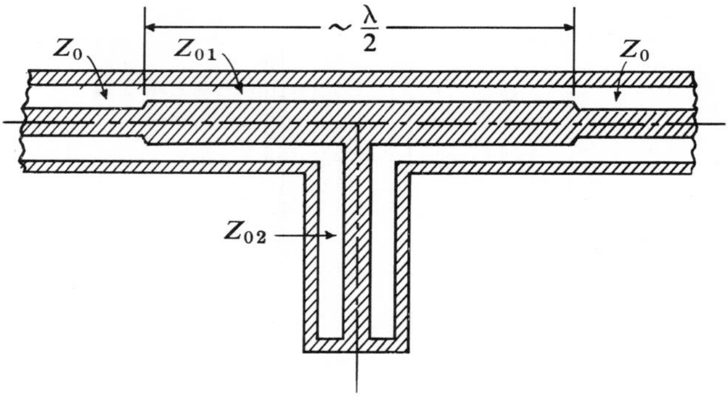

Figure 9-8 Broad-banded stub-supported coaxial line

The design indicated in Fig. 9-8 may be made much less sensitive to frequency variations than that in Fig. 9-7 by suitable choices of Z_{01} and Z_{02} in proportion to Z_0.[14]

(3) HELICAL SUPPORT. The traveling-wave fields within a coaxial cable with a helical dielectric bar or rod (see Fig. 9-9) have been analyzed by Griemsmann[7] in terms of two quasi-TEM modes of propagation. One of these follows the dielectric helix and the other follows a helical path at right angles to the dielectric helix. The path of the latter mode consists of alternate sections of air and solid dielectric, and, within certain frequency bands, propagation properties vary markedly. The behavior is comparable to that of a filter, and the cable will have frequencies of increased attenuation. The lowest such frequency has as its half wavelength the helical distance between

Culman 356

Stanley 354

9:00 Tues.

2nd

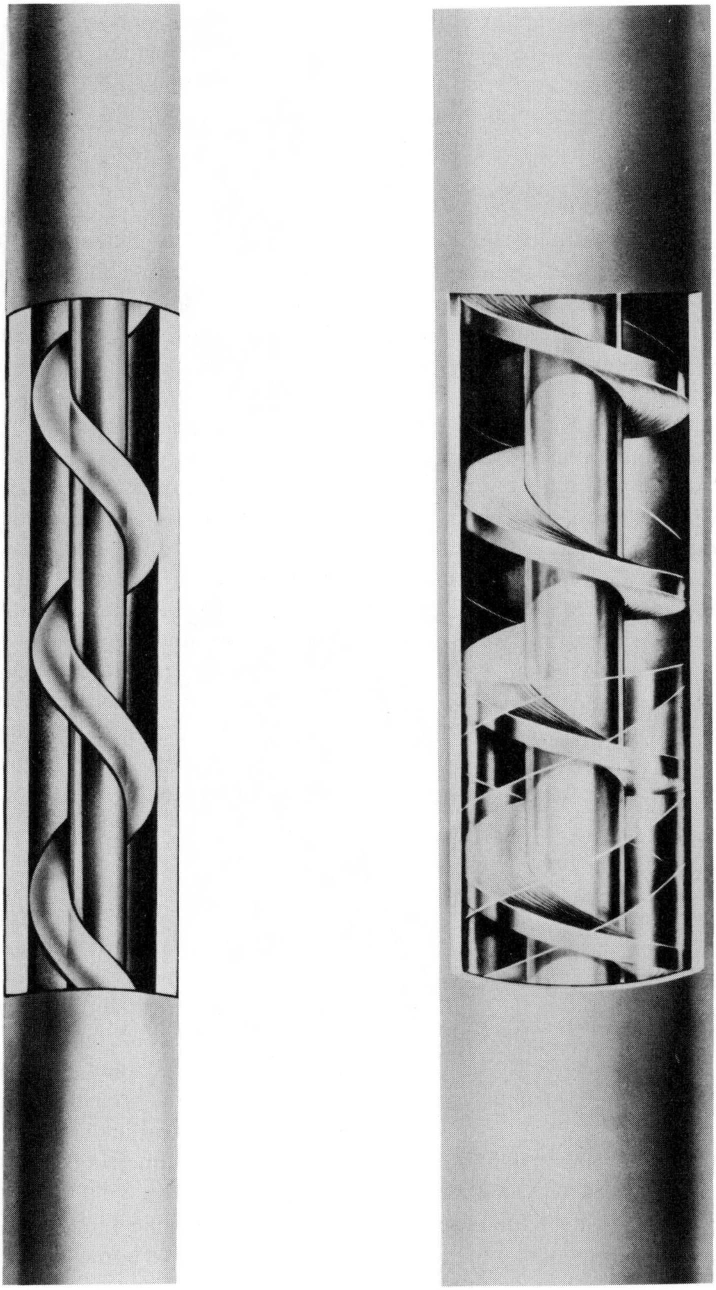

Figure 9-9 Coaxial lines with helical supports (Phelps Dodge Electronic Products, by permission)

centers of the dielectric at the mean of radii r_a and r_b. At frequencies below about 35 per cent of the lowest critical frequency, performance may be predicted to good approximation on the basis of an assumed TEM mode and a uniform dielectric medium of averaged permittivity.

b. Parallel-wire arrangements

From the point of view of this section, three types of parallel-wire arrangements will be commented on: (1) open-wire-and-pole construction, (2) shielded cables, and (3) plastic-embedded wire pairs without shielding. Parallel-wire sets are subject to more or less intense coupling with other circuits; this is examined briefly in Chapter 12.

(1) OPEN-WIRE-AND-POLE CONSTRUCTION. For telephone lines of this type, the parallel conductors are bare wires supported by glass insulators at intervals of perhaps 100 feet. At 150 kc the wavelength is 2000 m, or about 6500 feet. Most open-wire carrier channels use frequencies below this value, and under these circumstances the lumped-discontinuity effect of the insulators is negligible. The insulators have the effect of increasing the distributed capacitance of the line slightly, and they are the principal cause of losses dependent upon voltage. Most of these losses are related to displacement-current effects and hence are dependent on frequency. The nominal value of distributed shunt conductance is selected to account for them.[22]

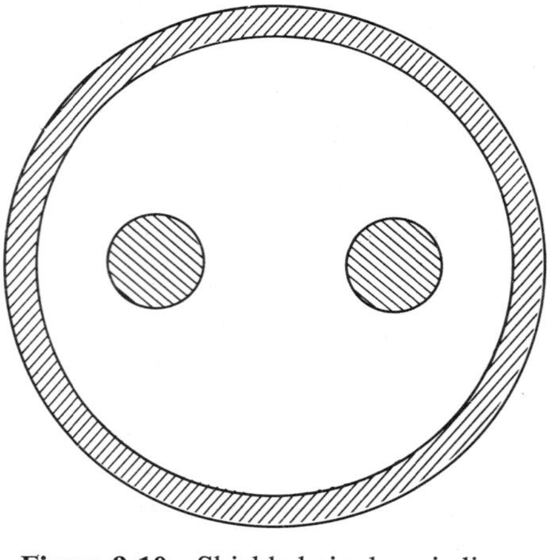

Figure 9-10 Shielded single-pair line

(2) SHIELDED CABLES. Where several telephone circuits are to follow the same route, a multipair cable is commonly used. Here the wires are individually insulated and twisted together in pairs, and usually sets of pairs are twisted together to form "quads." A lead-compound sheath is formed around the entire assembly. Such a line may be considered uniform in the longitudinal direction for the frequencies at which it is ordinarily used.

The single-pair shielded cable (see Fig. 9-10) is often used in short lengths in communication work. Two shielding braids are used in some designs, and for video-frequency applications the shield may consist of two strips of copper, spiral wound in opposing directions.[15] If the conductor diameters are assumed small compared to the shield diameter, the method of images gives a good approximation for analysis of the fields.* Successive-approximation solutions have been developed from that technique for cables of commercial-design proportions.[5]

(3) PLASTIC-EMBEDDED WIRE PAIRS. This form of line is convenient for short lead-in sections; a typical cross section is shown in Fig. 9-11. In the absence of a metallic shield over the plastic, the fields will extend into the air, where TEM waves would have a higher velocity of propagation than in the plastic. As a result the transmission mode will not be TEM but one in which both $\boldsymbol{E}$ and $\boldsymbol{H}$ may be expected to have longitudinal components.

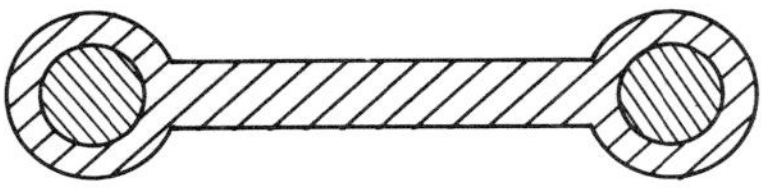

Figure 9-11 Plastic-embedded wire pair

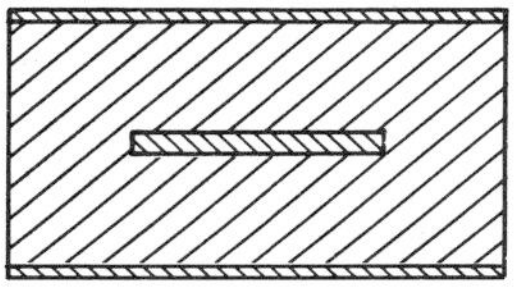

Figure 9-12 Strip line

c. "Strip line"

A modification of the coaxial cable which is simpler to fabricate and has almost as good shielding properties is the "strip line"; a cross section for one type is sketched in Fig. 9-12. Papers by Cohn[3] and Harvey[8] contain an extensive bibliography.

Here the two outer metallic strips correspond to the outer conductor of the coaxial cable, much as if it were split longitudinally at two diametrically opposite locations and the segments then flattened. Again, as in the plastic-embedded wire pair, the transmission mode would not be TEM, because the fields are not confined to the homogeneous dielectric slab.

9-5. CONCLUSIONS

Propagation in the TEM mode is possible in a lossless coaxial line and a lossless two-parallel-wire line. The fields in the space between the conductors are accompanied by a surface-current-density field on each conductor, equal in magnitude at every point on the surfaces to that of the $\boldsymbol{H}$ field tangential there.

Voltage in a two-conductor set conveying energy in the TEM mode is defined as the line integral of $\boldsymbol{E}$ from one conductor to the other, with the path restricted to a transverse plane. Current in either conductor is equal to the line integral of $\boldsymbol{H}$, confined to a transverse plane, around the conductor.

* The method of images is applied in Sec. 12-4 to a plane conducting surface; a more general treatment which includes the circularly cylindrical surface is given by Rogers.[19]

The following transmission-line parameters were derived for the TEM mode from the electromagnetic fields, using the line integrals just mentioned.

For the coaxial line (Fig. 9-1),

$$Z_0 = \frac{1}{2\pi}\sqrt{\frac{\mu}{\epsilon}}\ln\left(\frac{r_b}{r_a}\right) \tag{9-21}$$

$$l = \frac{\mu}{2\pi}\ln\left(\frac{r_b}{r_a}\right) \tag{9-24}$$

$$c = \frac{2\pi\epsilon}{\ln(r_b/r_a)} \tag{9-25}$$

For the two-parallel-wire line (Fig. 9-3, $r_a \ll k'$),

$$Z_0 \approx \frac{1}{\pi}\sqrt{\frac{\mu}{\epsilon}}\ln\left(\frac{k'}{r_a}\right) \tag{9-67}$$

$$l \approx \frac{\mu}{\pi}\ln\left(\frac{k'}{r_a}\right) \tag{9-69}$$

$$c \approx \frac{\epsilon\pi}{\ln(k'/r_a)} \tag{9-71}$$

The fields between physical metallic conductors are approximately those of a TEM mode. Within the conductors the current is distributed in depth in a manner dependent on frequency, conductivity, and permeability, and the effective resistance is a function of those variables.

Physical structures which support the conductors commonly cause discontinuities which, at the higher frequencies, may make the electromagnetic performance significantly different from that of a uniform line.

PROBLEMS

9-1. Write expressions for the surface-current density (as functions of r, z, and t) on a short-circuiting plate at the end of a coaxial line and on the conductors (see Eqs. 9-27 and 9-28).

9-2. Show that the $\boldsymbol{H}$ field of the two-parallel wire set, as described in Eqs. 9-30 and 9-46 through 9-51, is proportional to $1/x^2$ for $y = 0$ and $x \to \infty$.

9-3. Verify that $\boldsymbol{E} \cdot \boldsymbol{H}$ vanishes in the region between two parallel circular conductors, using Eq. 9-35 through 9-38 and 9-48 through 9-51 for the field components.

9-4. Find the resultant $\boldsymbol{E}$ field impinging on a conductor of radius r_a in a parallel pair as shown in Fig. 9-3. Give the result as a function of angle ϕ_2 and the voltage $v(z, t)$. What is the corresponding surface-charge density on the conductor?

9-5. Find the surface-current density on the conductors in Fig. 9-3 as functions of angles ϕ_1 and ϕ_2, assuming that the conductors are lossless.

9-6. Find, as a function of k'/r_a, the ratio between the loss caused in a conductor of high conductivity for which the surface-current-density distribution found in Problem 9-5 may be assumed valid and the loss caused by the same current uniformly distributed around the conductor periphery.

9-7. A solid-disc coaxial support like those shown in Fig. 9-5 has an electrical length of $\lambda/2$ at ω_0. Assume that the characteristic impedance of the air-filled sections of the line is Z_0, and that of the disc sections is Z_{0D}. If the right-hand line is terminated in its characteristic impedance, find the input impedance to the disc at its left-hand face as a function of $\Delta\omega$, where $\omega = \omega_0 + \Delta\omega$.

9-8. Verify Eq. 9-76 for the inner radius r_a' of an undercut disc support for a coaxial line.

REFERENCES

1. Adams, E. P., "The Resistance of Cylindrical Conductors at High Frequencies," *Proc. Am. Phil. Soc.*, 78 (1937), 271–85.
2. Arnold, A. H. M., "The Alternating-Current Resistance of Parallel Conductors of Circular Cross Section," *J. IEE (London)*, 77 (1935), 49–58, disc. 571–73.
3. Cohn, S. B., "A Reappraisal of Strip Transmission Line," *Microwave J.*, 3, No. 3 (1960), 17–27.
4. Cornes, R. W., "A Coaxial-Line Support for 0 to 4000 Mc." *Proc. IRE*, 37 (1949), 94–97.
5. Gent, A. W., "Capacitance of Shielded Balanced-Pair Transmission Line," *Elec. Commun.*, 33 (1956), 234–40.
6. Green, E. I., F. A. Leibe, and H. E. Curtis, "The Proportioning of Shielded Circuits for Minimum High-Frequency Attenuation," *Bell System Tech. J.*, 15 (1936), 248–83.
7. Griemsmann, J. W. E., "An Approximate Analysis of Coaxial Line with a Helical Dielectric Support," *IRE Trans. Microwave Theory Tech.*, MTT-4 (1956), 13–23.
8. Harvey, A. F., "Parallel-Plate Transmission Systems for Microwave Frequencies," *Proc. IEE (London)*, 106, Part B (1959) 129–40.
9. Higgins, T. J., "The Design of Bus-Bar Industrial Distribution Systems: An Epitomization of Available Data," *AIEE Trans.*, 64 (1945), 385–400.
10. Kennelly, A. E. and H. A. Affel, "Skin-Effect Resistance Measurements of Conductors at Radio Frequencies Up to 100,000 Cycles per Second," *Proc. IRE*, 4, No. 6 (1916), 523–74.
11. Kennelly, A. E., F. A. Laws, and P. H. Pierce, "Experimental Researches on Skin Effect in Conductors," *AIEE Trans.*, 35 (1915), 1953–2018.
12. King, B. G., J. McKenna, and G. Raisbeck, "Experimental Check of Formulas for Capacitance of Shielded Balanced-Pair Transmission Line," *Proc. IRE*, 46 (1958), 922–23.
13. Marcuvitz, N., *Waveguide Handbook*, pp. 72–80, New York: McGraw-Hill Book Company, Inc., 1951.
14. *The Microwave Engineer's Handbook and Buyer's Guide*, p. T–71, Brookline, Mass.: Horizon-House Microwave, Inc., 1963.

15. National Association of Broadcasters, Inc., *NAB Engineering Handbook*, 5th ed. pp. 2–184 to 2–196, 4–13 to 4–15, A. PROSE WALKER, ed. New York: McGraw-Hill Book Company, Inc., 1960.

16. PACKARD, K. S. and RODERICK V. LOWMAN, "Transmission Lines and Waveguides," *Antenna Engineering Handbook*, chap. 30, H. JASIK, ed. New York: McGraw-Hill Book Company, Inc., 1961.

17. PETERSON, D. W., "Notes on a Coaxial Line Bead," *Proc. IRE*, 37 (1949), 1294.

18. *Reference Data for Radio Engineers*, (4th ed.). New York: International Telephone and Telegraph Corporation, 1956.

19. ROGERS, WALTER E., *Introduction to Electric Fields*, pp. 152–71, New York: McGraw-Hill Book Company, Inc., 1954.

20. SIM, A. C., "New High-Frequency Proximity-Effect Formula," *Wireless Engr.*, 30, No. 8 (1953), 204–7; reprinted in *Elec. Commun.*, 131, No. 1 (1954), 63–66.

21. *Standard Handbook for Electrical Engineers*, 9th ed., p. 230, A. E. KNOWLTON, ed. New York: McGraw-Hill Book Company, Inc., 1957.

22. WILSON, L. T., "A Study of Telephone Line Insulators," *Bell System Tech. J.*, 9 (1930), 697–729.

23. ZABORSKY, J., "Skin Effect and Spiralling Effect in Stranded Conductors," *AIEE Trans.*, 72, Part III (1953), 599–609.

CHAPTER 10

Conductor-guided Fields: Hollow Rectangular Wave Guides

The two preceding chapters have emphasized one particular type of electromagnetic wave propagation, the TEM mode, in which the electric and magnetic fields are everywhere perpendicular to the direction of propagation. Propagation is also possible in modes in which one field has a component parallel to that direction, and such modes are important in that they may convey energy through hollow tubes of conducting material.

For the sake of mathematical simplicity, a particular traveling-wave mode for the wave guide with a rectangular cross section will be studied first. The same general technique employed for the coaxial cable, that of postulating a solution and testing it by substituting in Maxwell's equations, will be used initially. Afterward a more general mathematical approach will be tried. Figure 10-1 shows the geometry of the rectangular wave guide.

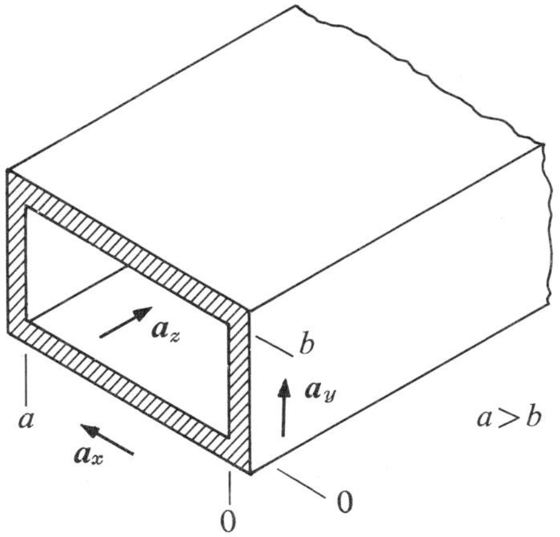

Figure 10-1 Dimensions and coordinates for rectangular wave guide

10-1. TE_{m0} PROPAGATING MODES

The simplest and also the most commonly used mode in a rectangular wave guide has these properties: (1) the electric field is confined to planes perpendicular to the direction of propagation, whereas the magnetic field has both transverse and longitudinal components, and (2) the electric field is directed from one of the guide surfaces straight across to the opposite surface. Actually an infinite number of modes possess these properties in common; they are referred to as TE_{m0} modes by which the following is meant: (1) TE designates *transverse electric* (property 1 above) (2) the second subscript, 0, indicates an absence of variation in field configuration as a function of the shorter transverse direction (y direction in Fig. 10-1), and (3) the first subscript, m, which is an integer, designates the particular mode of this class. This third item will be described specifically in Sec. 10-1*a* (2), after the TE_{m0} field patterns have been derived.

a. Electric and magnetic fields

For the ordinarily used approximation of the electric and magnetic fields, the wave-guide walls may be assumed to be of infinite conductivity, in which case a traveling wave should propagate without attenuation.

(1) TRAVELING-WAVE SOLUTION. In view of the success experienced in finding traveling-wave solutions in unbounded space and in a coaxial cable, such a solution will be postulated here. The phase function β will be regarded as an unknown and may well differ from that for the TEM mode. In accordance with the properties just listed for the TE_{m0} mode, the $\boldsymbol{E}$ field will be assumed to consist solely of a y-directed component. However, because the component of $\boldsymbol{E}$ tangential to a perfectly conducting surface must vanish (Sec. 8-2*b*) and, as shown in Fig. 10-1, such surfaces exist at $x = 0$ and at $x = a$, $[\boldsymbol{E}]_y$ will be assumed to be a function of x. The requirement that the divergence of $\boldsymbol{D}$ should vanish (Eq. 7-28, with $\rho = 0$) will be met if the $\boldsymbol{E}$ thus chosen is not a function of y. The trial solution may be stated as follows:

$$\boldsymbol{E}_1 = \text{Im}[E_y(x)\epsilon^{j(\omega t-\beta z)}]\boldsymbol{a}_y \tag{10-1}$$

Sequential substitution of Eq. 10-1 into Maxwell's curl equations, 7-34 and 7-32, will be made with a view to fixing β:

$$\nabla \times \boldsymbol{E}_1 = \text{Im}\left[j\beta E_y(x)\epsilon^{j(\omega t-\beta z)}\boldsymbol{a}_x + \frac{dE_y(x)}{dx}\epsilon^{j(\omega t-\beta z)}\boldsymbol{a}_z\right]$$

$$\boldsymbol{H}_1 = \text{Im}\left[\frac{-\beta}{\omega\mu}E_y(x)\epsilon^{j(\omega t-\beta z)}\boldsymbol{a}_x - \frac{1}{j\omega\mu}\frac{dE_y(x)}{dx}\epsilon^{j(\omega t-\beta z)}\boldsymbol{a}_z\right] \tag{10-2}$$

$$\nabla \times \boldsymbol{H}_1 = \operatorname{Im}\left\{\left[\frac{j\beta^2}{\omega\mu} E_y(x) + \frac{1}{j\omega\mu}\frac{d^2E_y(x)}{dx^2}\right]\epsilon^{j(\omega t-\beta z)}\right\}\boldsymbol{a}_y$$

$$\boldsymbol{E}_1 = \operatorname{Im}\left\{\left[\frac{\beta^2}{\omega^2\mu\epsilon} E_y(x) + \frac{1}{(j\omega)^2\mu\epsilon}\frac{d^2E_y(x)}{dx^2}\right]\epsilon^{j(\omega t-\beta z)}\right\}\boldsymbol{a}_y \tag{10-3}$$

Comparing Eq. 10-3 with Eq. 10-1 indicates that $E_y(x)$ must satisfy the following differential equation:

$$\frac{1}{(j\omega)^2\mu\epsilon}\frac{d^2E_y(x)}{dx^2} + \left[\frac{\beta^2}{\omega^2\mu\epsilon} - 1\right]E_y(x) = 0 \tag{10-4}$$

Equation 10-4 may be solved as follows:

$$\frac{d^2E_y(x)}{dx^2} + (\omega^2\mu\epsilon - \beta^2)E_y(x) = 0$$

$$E_y(x) = A_1 \sin(\sqrt{\omega^2\mu\epsilon - \beta^2}x) + B_1 \cos(\sqrt{\omega^2\mu\epsilon - \beta^2}x) \tag{10-5}$$

Here A_1 and B_1 are arbitrary constants which are determined by boundary conditions, and the phase function β is also fixed by boundary conditions.

(2) Boundary conditions. As was mentioned at the start of the derivation, a perfectly conducting surface will support no tangential component of the $\boldsymbol{E}$ field, so E_y must vanish along the surfaces at $x = 0$ and $x = a$. From Eq. 10-5,

$$E_y(0) = B_1$$

Therefore,

$$B_1 = 0$$

Then

$$E_y(a) = A_1 \sin(\sqrt{\omega^2\mu\epsilon - \beta^2}a)$$

This can equal zero only by choosing β so that

$$\sqrt{\omega^2\mu\epsilon - \beta^2}a = m\pi$$

Here m is any integer, and β may be subscripted as β_{m0} to emphasize its functional dependence on the assumed mode features:

$$\beta_{m0}^2 = \omega^2\mu\epsilon - \left(\frac{m\pi}{a}\right)^2 \tag{10-6}$$

Equation 10-5 may be rewritten with these results substituted:

$$E_y(x) = A_1 \sin\left(\frac{m\pi x}{a}\right) \tag{10-7}$$

The constant A_1 has the same dimensions as E_y and is simply a measure of its magnitude.

Complete expressions for the $\boldsymbol{E}$ and $\boldsymbol{H}$ fields may now be written by substitution in Eqs. 10-1 and 10-2:

$$\begin{aligned}\boldsymbol{E}_1 &= \operatorname{Im}\left[A_1 \sin\left(\frac{m\pi x}{a}\right)\epsilon^{j(\omega t-\beta_{m0}z)}\right]\boldsymbol{a}_y \\ &= A_1 \sin\left(\frac{m\pi x}{a}\right)\sin(\omega t - \beta_{m0}z)\boldsymbol{a}_y\end{aligned} \tag{10-8}$$

$$\begin{aligned}\boldsymbol{H}_1 = \operatorname{Im}\Bigg[&-\frac{A_1\beta_{m0}}{\omega\mu}\sin\left(\frac{m\pi x}{a}\right)\epsilon^{j(\omega t-\beta_{m0}z)}\boldsymbol{a}_x \\ &- \frac{A_1 m\pi}{j\omega\mu a}\cos\left(\frac{m\pi x}{a}\right)\epsilon^{j(\omega t-\beta_{m0}z)}\boldsymbol{a}_z\Bigg] \\ = &-\frac{A_1\beta_{m0}}{\omega\mu}\sin\left(\frac{m\pi x}{a}\right)\sin(\omega t-\beta_{m0}z)\boldsymbol{a}_x \\ &+ \frac{A_1 m\pi}{\omega\mu a}\cos\left(\frac{m\pi x}{a}\right)\cos(\omega t-\beta_{m0}z)\boldsymbol{a}_z\end{aligned} \tag{10-9}$$

Equations 10-8 and 10-9, supplemented by Eq. 10-6, describe an electromagnetic traveling-wave system, or mode, which satisfies Maxwell's equations and appears to be capable of propagating energy in the rectangular wave guide. The field configuration for $m = 1$ is sketched in Fig. 10-2.

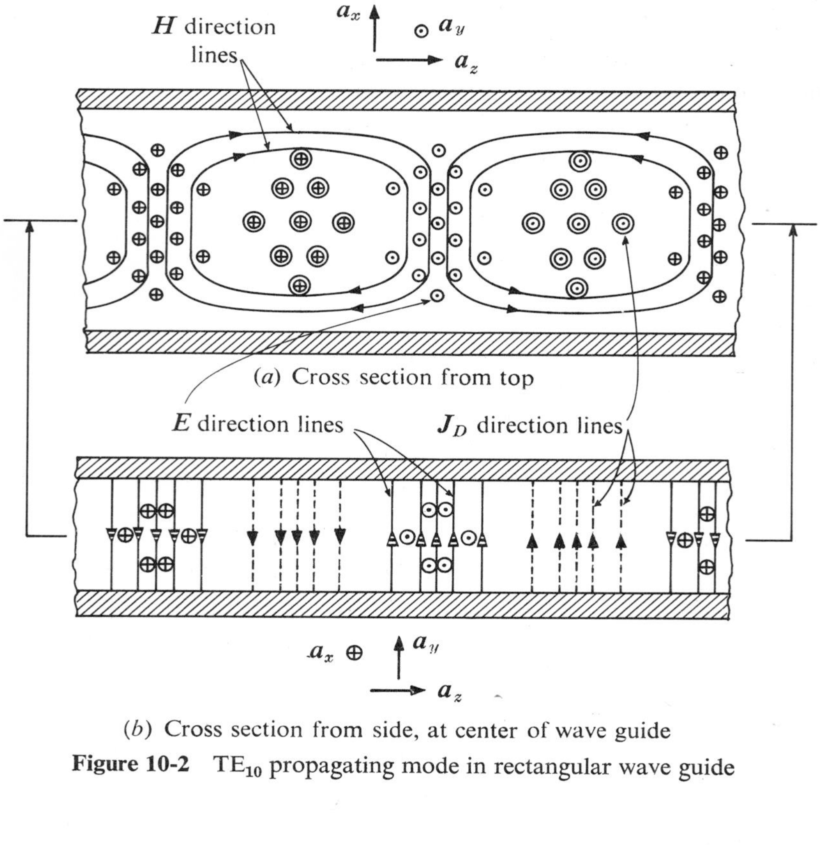

Figure 10-2 TE_{10} propagating mode in rectangular wave guide

It has been assumed, in going from the first to the second forms of Eqs. 10-8 and 10-9, that β_{m0} is a real quantity. In accordance with the definition for β_{m0} in Eq. 10-6, it follows that, for the solution just given to be valid, the frequency must be greater than the following limiting value, which is known as the *cutoff frequency* and is designated by f_{cm0}:

$$f_{cm0} = \frac{1}{2\pi} \frac{m\pi}{a\sqrt{\mu\epsilon}}$$

$$= \frac{m}{2a\sqrt{\mu\epsilon}} \qquad \textbf{(10-10)}$$

At frequencies below cutoff, β_{m0} is imaginary. The solution is then not of the traveling-wave type; appropriate equations are developed in Sec. 10-2. (It is shown there that such modes do not propagate but exist only in the vicinity of the guide discontinuity or other source which excites them.)

Since m may be any integer, Eqs. 10-8 and 10-9 actually describe a multiplicity of modes. For a given width a and with excitation at a stated frequency, only a limited number of these TE_{m0} modes will have cutoff frequencies which are below the excitation frequency, and only those modes (among those in the TE_{m0} class) may propagate. In accordance with the principle of superposition, however, all such possible modes may exist simultaneously without influencing one another. As a subscript in the mode designator, m indicates the number of half-period variations in the electric field along the longer transverse direction, the x direction in Fig. 10-1.

(3) TE_{10} MODE AS THE DOMINANT MODE. For a given size of wave guide, the TE_{10} mode has a lower cutoff frequency than any other TE_{m0} mode, and, as is shown in Sec. 10-3*a* and *b*, it has the lowest cutoff frequency of any possible mode. It can exist on a propagating basis at the same frequencies as any other modes can, and it can exist at a lower frequency than any of the others can; hence it is called the *dominant* mode. For most applications it is undesirable to have propagation taking place in more than one mode. Multimoding may be prevented by selecting the wave-guide size for a particular installation such that only the TE_{10} mode has a cutoff frequency which is lower than the excitation frequency.

From the design point of view, if f_{ex} is the excitation frequency and the TE_{10} mode is to be a propagating mode but the TE_{20} and higher TE_{m0} modes are not, the width a should satisfy the following inequality, which is derivable from Eq. 10-10:

$$\frac{1}{f_{ex}\sqrt{\mu\epsilon}} > a > \frac{1}{2f_{ex}\sqrt{\mu\epsilon}} \qquad \textbf{(10-11)}$$

This may be stated more conveniently in terms of the TEM-mode wavelength

λ_{ex} of the frequency f_{ex}:

$$\lambda_{\text{ex}} = \frac{v_0}{f_{\text{ex}}} = \frac{1}{f_{\text{ex}}\sqrt{\mu\epsilon}}$$

$$\lambda_{\text{ex}} > a > \frac{\lambda_{\text{ex}}}{2} \tag{10-12}$$

(4) Parametric equation of *H*-field direction lines. A parametric equation for the ***H***-field-direction lines (see the paragraph preceding Eq. 9-39) may be found by solving the following differential equation:

$$\frac{dx}{dz} = \frac{H_x}{H_z} = \frac{-\beta_{m0}a \sin\left(\frac{m\pi x}{a}\right)\sin(\omega t - \beta_{m0}z)}{m\pi \cos\left(\frac{m\pi x}{a}\right)\cos(\omega t - \beta_{m0}z)} \tag{10-13}$$

The separation of variables and integration of this equation is left as Problem 10-2. The result is as follows:

$$\sin\left(\frac{m\pi x}{a}\right)\cos(\omega t - \beta_{m0}z) = C \tag{10-14}$$

Here C is an arbitrary constant. Inspection of the equation indicates that C must have a magnitude of unity or less in order to correspond to real values of x and z, but that each value of C within that range would represent a different field-direction line. For C slightly less than unity in magnitude, the field-direction lines are approximately elliptical (see Problem 10-3).

b. Complementary field functions

The equations just given for ***E*** and ***H*** may be supplemented by expressions for displacement-current density, surface-current density, and power density. These help to unify the field and-circuit-theory aspects of wave-guide propagation.

(1) Displacement-current field. Displacement current is present wherever the electric field is changing; it is defined mathematically as follows:

$$\boldsymbol{J}_D = \epsilon\frac{\partial \boldsymbol{E}}{\partial t} \tag{10-15}$$

Equation 10-8 may be substituted here:

$$\boldsymbol{J}_{D1} = A_1\omega\epsilon \sin\left(\frac{m\pi x}{a}\right) \cos(\omega t - \beta_{m0}z)\boldsymbol{a}_y \tag{10-16}$$

The following observations may be made from Fig. 10-2 and from the equations it illustrates: (1) the magnetic-field-direction lines encircle, in accordance with the right-hand rule, portions of the displacement-current field within the half-wavelength sections between displacement-current nulls; (2) the displacement-current density is maximum where the electric field is zero, and is so directed as to be changing the direction of the electric field from that of the electric-field maximum which has just passed the given location to that of the electric-field maximum which is next approaching; and (3) the transverse component of magnetic field is a maximum at the same locations as the electric field, and is so directed that the z component of the cross product $\boldsymbol{E} \times \boldsymbol{H}$ points in the direction of wave propagation.

(2) SURFACE-CURRENT FIELD. Currents may be expected to flow in the side walls and in the top and bottom of the wave guide because: (1) continuity of the current field can be maintained only if the displacement-current field in the wave-guide interior joins to a conduction-current field at the top and bottom of the wave guide, and (2) a difference in the magnetic-field strengths inside and outside the wave-guide interior can be maintained only by means of currents in the wave-guide conductor material. At wave-guide frequencies (about 3×10^9 cps and higher), skin effect is so pronounced that skin depth is negligible compared to the wave guide cross-sectional dimensions, and one may properly reason in terms of a surface-current density, the magnitude of which is everywhere equal to the magnitude of the $\boldsymbol{H}$ field tangent to the conducting surface in question and which flows at right angles to that field.

On the basis of the magnetic-field requirements the following expressions for surface-current density may be written; immediately afterward it will be shown that those expressions also satisfy the requirement of continuity between surface-current density in the conducting surfaces and displacement-current density in the wave-guide interior:

$$\boldsymbol{J}_{S1}(0,y,z) = \boldsymbol{J}_{S1}(a,y,z) = \frac{-A_1 m\pi}{\omega\mu a} \cos(\omega t - \beta_{m0}z)\boldsymbol{a}_y \qquad \text{(sidewalls)} \tag{10-17}$$

$$\begin{aligned} \boldsymbol{J}_{S1}(x,0,z) &= H_{1z}\boldsymbol{a}_x - H_{1x}\boldsymbol{a}_z && \text{(bottom)} \\ \boldsymbol{J}_{S1}(x,b,z) &= -H_{1z}\boldsymbol{a}_x + H_{1x}\boldsymbol{a}_z && \text{(top)} \end{aligned} \tag{10-18}$$

Finding the parametric equation for the field-direction lines of the surface-current density on the top and bottom surfaces is left as Problem 10-4.

Two important observations may be made concerning the surface-current patterns: (1) no current flows across the longitudinal centerlines of the top and bottom surfaces, and (2) no longitudinal component of current flows in the sidewalls. Item 1 is of particular value in measurement techniques in that a narrow longitudinal slit of any desired length may be cut through the middle of the top without interfering with propagation of the TE_{10} mode. A probe may be inserted in the slit, and with the aid of suitable detecting equipment, a series of measurements made of relative field strength.

The divergence of surface-current density would have the units amperes per meter squared, the same as those of displacement-current density:

$$\nabla \cdot \boldsymbol{J}_{S1}(0,y,z) = 0 \qquad \text{(sidewall)}$$

$$\nabla \cdot \boldsymbol{J}_{S1}(a,y,z) = 0 \qquad \text{(sidewall)}$$

$$\begin{aligned}\nabla \cdot \boldsymbol{J}_{S1}(x,0,z) &= \frac{-A_1(m\pi)^2}{\omega\mu a^2}\sin\left(\frac{m\pi x}{a}\right)\cos(\omega t - \beta_{m0}z) \\ &\quad + \frac{-A_1\beta_{m0}^2}{\omega\mu}\sin\left(\frac{m\pi x}{a}\right)\cos(\omega t - \beta_{m0}z) \qquad \text{(bottom)} \qquad \textbf{(10-19)}\end{aligned}$$

$$\nabla \cdot \boldsymbol{J}_{S1}(x,b,z) = -\nabla \cdot \boldsymbol{J}_{S1}(x,0,z)$$

Substitution of Eq. 10-6 reduces Eq. 10-19 to

$$\nabla \cdot \boldsymbol{J}_{S1}(x,0,z) = -A_1\omega\epsilon \sin\left(\frac{m\pi x}{a}\right)\cos(\omega t - \beta_{m0}z) \qquad \textbf{(10-20)}$$

Comparison of these results with Eq. 10-16 for displacement-current density indicates an exact agreement in magnitude. The divergence of the surface-current-density function is positive when the function is *increasing* in strength because of a distributed source, and inflowing displacement-current flux has the nature of such a source with respect to the surface current. Hence the current density leaving the bottom surface [the negative of the divergence of $\boldsymbol{J}_{S1}(x,0,z)$] corresponds to the upward-directed displacement-current density, and it in turn corresponds to that entering the top surface.

(3) POYNTING'S VECTOR: POWER FLOW. Poynting's vector for this traveling-wave set may be readily written from Eqs. 10-8 and 10-9:

$$\begin{aligned}\boldsymbol{P}_1 &= \boldsymbol{E}_1 \times \boldsymbol{H}_1 \\ &= \frac{A_1^2\beta_{m0}}{\omega\mu}\sin^2\left(\frac{m\pi x}{a}\right)\sin^2(\omega t - \beta_{m0})\boldsymbol{a}_z \\ &\quad + \frac{A_1^2 m\pi}{\omega\mu a}\sin\left(\frac{m\pi x}{a}\right)\cos\left(\frac{m\pi x}{a}\right)\sin(\omega t - \beta_{m0}z)\cos(\omega t - \beta_{m0}z)\boldsymbol{a}_x \\ &= \frac{A_1^2\beta_{m0}}{4\omega\mu}\left[1 - \cos\left(\frac{2m\pi x}{a}\right)\right][1 - \cos 2(\omega t - \beta_{m0}z)]\boldsymbol{a}_z \\ &\qquad + \frac{A_1^2 m\pi}{4\omega\mu a}\sin\left(\frac{2m\pi x}{a}\right)\sin 2(\omega t - \beta_{m0}z)\boldsymbol{a}_x \qquad \textbf{(10-21)}\end{aligned}$$

If this quantity is time-averaged over an integral number of cycles, the following is obtained:

$$\boldsymbol{P}_{1\text{av}}(x) = \frac{A_1^2\beta_{m0}}{4\omega\mu}\left[1 - \cos\left(\frac{2m\pi x}{a}\right)\right]\boldsymbol{a}_z \tag{10-22}$$

Average power flow through the wave guide may be found by taking the surface integral of $\boldsymbol{P}_{1\text{av}}(x)$ over a transverse cross-section of the wave guide.

$$P_{1SI} = \int_0^b \int_0^a \boldsymbol{P}_{1\text{av}}(x) \cdot (dx\, dy\, \boldsymbol{a}_z)$$

$$= \frac{A_1^2\beta_{m0}ab}{4\omega\mu} \tag{10-23}$$

Examination of Eqs. 10-21 through 10-23 indicates (1) that power flow in the longitudinal direction is pulsating—it varies, at any given location, from zero up to twice the average value and back down to zero again in a half-cycle period; and (2) that power flow in the transverse direction is reactive in nature—it varies at any given location, from maximum in one direction to maximum in the opposite direction and back to maximum in the first direction in a half-cycle period.

c. Wave set traveling in reverse direction

With the two-wire transmission line it was found that waves could propagate with equal ease in either direction. One may surmise that the same should be true of wave guides, and this may be checked by postulating an $\boldsymbol{E}$ field which travels in the $-\boldsymbol{a}_z$ direction, and substituting in Maxwell's equations. Let

$$\boldsymbol{E}_2 = A_2 \sin\left(\frac{m\pi x}{a}\right) \sin(\omega t + \beta_{m0}z)\boldsymbol{a}_y \tag{10-24}$$

The reader is urged to carry out the algebraic work for practice; the phase function β_{m0} proves to be the same as for the $+\boldsymbol{a}_z$-moving wave (Eq. 10-6), and the $\boldsymbol{H}$ field is as follows:

$$\boldsymbol{H}_2 = \frac{A_2\beta_{m0}}{\omega\mu} \sin\left(\frac{m\pi x}{a}\right) \sin(\omega t + \beta_{m0}z)\boldsymbol{a}_x + \frac{A_2 m\pi}{\omega\mu a} \cos\left(\frac{m\pi x}{a}\right) \cos(\omega t + \beta_{m0}z)\boldsymbol{a}_z \tag{10-25}$$

If Poynting's vector is computed, the longitudinal component proves to be pointed in the $-\boldsymbol{a}_z$ direction, as one would expect.

The sketching of field patterns for this traveling-wave set is the substance of Problem 10-5.

d. Standing-wave fields in short-circuited wave guide

With expressions available for waves traveling in the two directions, one is prepared for a simple problem involving a discontinuity in the wave guide, that of a guide with a short-circuiting end plate. The boundary conditions require that the **E** field should vanish over the surface of the highly conducting plate. If one chooses the value of $z = 0$ for the location of the end plate, the following results:

$$\boldsymbol{E}_1(x,0,t) = -\boldsymbol{E}_2(x,0,t)$$

Hence

$$A_1 = -A_2 \tag{10-26}$$

If $\boldsymbol{E}_1$, Eq. 10-8, is added to $\boldsymbol{E}_2$, 10-24, and $\boldsymbol{H}_1$, 10-9, to $\boldsymbol{H}_2$, 10-25, expressions are obtained for the resultant fields. These may be reduced, by substituting Eq. 10-26 and appropriate trigonometric identities, to the following:

$$\boldsymbol{E}_{\text{sc}} = -2A_1 \sin\left(\frac{m\pi x}{a}\right) \sin \beta_{m0} z \cos \omega t \, \boldsymbol{a}_y \tag{10-27}$$

$$\boldsymbol{H}_{\text{sc}} = \frac{-2A_1\beta_{m0}}{\omega\mu} \sin\left(\frac{m\pi x}{a}\right) \cos \beta_{m0} z \sin \omega t \, \boldsymbol{a}_x - \frac{2A_1 m\pi}{\omega\mu a} \cos\left(\frac{m\pi x}{a}\right) \sin \beta_{m0} z \sin \omega t \, \boldsymbol{a}_z \tag{10-28}$$

Important points concerning these results are (1) the **E** and **H** fields are in time quadrature with each other at every location in the wave guide, (2) the **E** field is always zero on the transverse planes located at half-wavelength intervals (π/β_{m0}) from the end plate, (3) the longitudinal component of the **H** field is always zero on the transverse planes at half-wavelength intervals from the end plate, (4) the transverse component of the **H** field is always zero on the transverse planes at odd multiples of a quarter wavelength from the endplate, (5) at every point between each adjacent pair of nulls the intensity of the **E** field rises and falls in synchronism, and (6) at every point between each adjacent pair of nulls the intensities of both components of the **H** field rise and fall in synchronism. These characteristics, excepting those aspects relating to the longitudinal component of the **H** field, correspond to those for the short-circuited coaxial cable (see Eqs. 9-27 and 9-28).

The displacement-current density may also be found:

$$\boldsymbol{J}_{D\text{sc}} = 2A_1\omega\epsilon \sin\left(\frac{m\pi x}{a}\right) \sin \beta_{m0} z \sin \omega t \, \boldsymbol{a}_y \tag{10-29}$$

The displacement-current field has the same configuration in space as does the **E** field but is in time quadrature with it. The magnetic field is in time phase with the displacement-current field and encircles it spacewise in accordance with the right-hand rule. Problems 10-6 and 10-7 amplify on the standing-wave phenomena caused by a short-circuiting endplate.

10-2. DISCONTINUITIES AND NONPROPAGATING OR EVANESCENT TE_{m0} MODES

Many types of discontinuities other than the short-circuiting end plate are present in wave-guide equipment, and these lack the symmetry and simplicity which that particular example possesses. Among the discontinuities of interest are bends in the wave guide, irises (transverse conducting sheets extending over a part of the wave-guide cross section—one type is shown in Fig. 10-3), junctions with wave-guide stubs, and antenna structures to couple

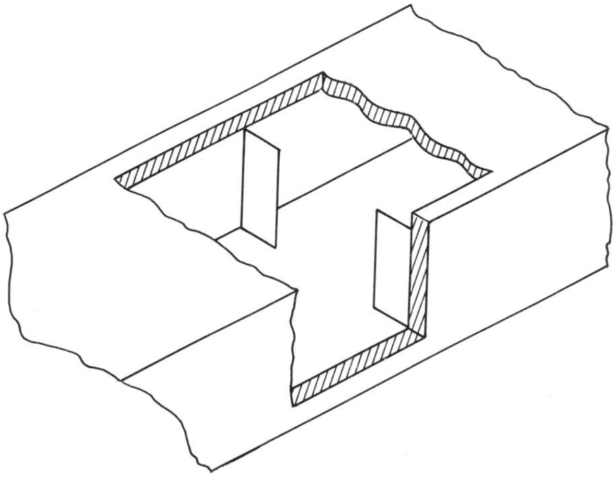

Figure 10-3 Vertical iris in rectangular wave guide

the wave-guide to a coaxial cable. At such discontinuities the boundary conditions cannot be satisfied by means of one reflected and one transmitted traveling wave set, each of the same mode as the incident traveling wave. Rather, a multiplicity of modes, each of appropriate magnitude proportion and phase relationship with respect to the incident wave, is needed. In a rectangular wave guide of the usual proportions these additional, parasitic modes will all have cutoff frequencies which are above that of the mode of the incident wave, and presumably above the excitation frequency; hence they will be nonpropagating or *evanescent*. Accordingly it is desirable to investigate briefly the structure and properties of nonpropagating modes.

a. Properties of nonpropagating TE_{m0} modes

The phase function β_{m0} as given in Eq. 10-6, which relates it to the wave-guide width and the frequency, will be imaginary if the frequency is below the cutoff value given in Eq. 10-10. For this case let

$$\beta_{m0} = -j\alpha_{m0} \tag{10-30}$$

With this substitution the two forms of Eqs. 10-8 and 10-9 may be rewritten as follows:

$$\begin{aligned} \boldsymbol{E}_1 &= \text{Im}\left[A_1 \sin\left(\frac{m\pi x}{a}\right)\epsilon^{-\alpha_{m0}z}\epsilon^{j\omega t}\right]\boldsymbol{a}_y \\ &= A_1 \sin\left(\frac{m\pi x}{a}\right)\epsilon^{-\alpha_{m0}z} \sin \omega t\, \boldsymbol{a}_y \end{aligned} \tag{10-31}$$

$$\begin{aligned} \boldsymbol{H}_1 &= \text{Im}\left[\frac{A_1 j\alpha_{m0}}{\omega\mu} \sin\left(\frac{m\pi x}{a}\right)\epsilon^{-\alpha_{m0}z}\epsilon^{j\omega t}\boldsymbol{a}_x - \frac{A_1 m\pi}{j\omega\mu a} \cos\left(\frac{m\pi x}{a}\right)\epsilon^{-\alpha_{m0}z}\epsilon^{j\omega t}\boldsymbol{a}_z\right] \\ &= \frac{A_1\alpha_{m0}}{\omega\mu} \sin\left(\frac{m\pi x}{a}\right)\epsilon^{-\alpha_{m0}z} \cos \omega t\, \boldsymbol{a}_x + \frac{A_1 m\pi}{\omega\mu a} \cos\left(\frac{m\pi x}{a}\right)\epsilon^{-\alpha_{m0}z} \cos \omega t\, \boldsymbol{a}_z \end{aligned} \tag{10-32}$$

This, like the one described by Eqs. 10-27 and 10-28, is a standing-wave pattern, since (1) $\boldsymbol{E}$ and $\boldsymbol{H}$ are in time quadrature at every location, (2) the $\boldsymbol{E}$ field changes in synchronism at every point, and (3) the $\boldsymbol{H}$ field changes in synchronism at every point. In this pattern neither field has any nulls with respect to z; rather each diminishes in magnitude with increase in distance in the $+\boldsymbol{a}_z$ direction. The magnitude appears to increase indefinitely for increasingly negative values of z, but in a physical problem the mode would exist only because it was excited by a discontinuity having mode-conversion characteristics and would be defined only for locations on the $+\boldsymbol{a}_z$ side of the discontinuity.

A parametric equation for the $\boldsymbol{H}$-field direction lines may be derived (see Problem 10-8), and expressions written for the surface-current density and for the parametric equation of its direction lines (Problem 10-9). A second solution may be obtained by making the following substitution in Eqs. 10-8 and 10-9:

$$\beta_{m0} = j\alpha_{m0} \tag{10-33}$$

$$\boldsymbol{E}_2 = A_1 \sin\left(\frac{m\pi x}{a}\right)\epsilon^{\alpha_{m0}z} \sin \omega t\, \boldsymbol{a}_y \tag{10-34}$$

$$\boldsymbol{H}_2 = \frac{-A_1\alpha_{m0}}{\omega\mu} \sin\left(\frac{m\pi x}{a}\right)\epsilon^{\alpha_{m0}z} \cos \omega t\, \boldsymbol{a}_x + \frac{A_1 m\pi}{\omega\mu a} \cos\left(\frac{m\pi x}{a}\right)\epsilon^{\alpha_{m0}z} \cos \omega t\, \boldsymbol{a}_z \tag{10-35}$$

This pair of equations also describes a standing-wave pattern, but in this case the magnitude decreases exponentially in the $-\boldsymbol{a}_z$ direction. Thus evanescent modes may exist in both the transmitted and reflected directions of any given incident wave.

b. Illustration: boundary-value problem using only one nonpropagating mode

As a preliminary illustration of boundary-value problems involving parasitic modes, consider the following: A rectangular wave guide is filled with a dielectric medium of permittivity ϵ_1 for $z < 0$, and the permittivity is ϵ_0 for $z > 0$. Here $\epsilon_1 > \epsilon_0$. The frequency is such that the TE_{10} mode will propagate in the portion with permittivity ϵ_1 but not in the portion with permittivity ϵ_0. Using Eq. 10-10, the foregoing restriction may be stated thus:

$$\frac{\pi}{a\sqrt{\mu\epsilon_1}} < \omega < \frac{\pi}{a\sqrt{\mu\epsilon_0}} \tag{10-36}$$

The following incident wave in the high-permittivity medium impinges on the discontinuity at $z = 0$:

$$\boldsymbol{E}_I = \text{Im}\left[E_{IM}\sin\left(\frac{\pi x}{a}\right)\epsilon^{j(\omega t - \beta_{10}z)}\right]\boldsymbol{a}_y \tag{10-37}$$

Find the reflected and transmitted fields.

Continuity of the tangential components of the $\boldsymbol{E}$ and $\boldsymbol{H}$ fields, and of the normal components of the $\boldsymbol{D}$ and $\boldsymbol{B}$ fields, must be maintained across any boundary surface. For the given mode, the $\boldsymbol{D}$ field has no component normal to the surface in question. Locations on the two sides of the interface surface will be designated by $z = 0-$ and $z = 0+$:

$$\begin{aligned}
[\boldsymbol{E}_I(x,0-,t)]_y + [\boldsymbol{E}_R(x,0-,t)]_y &= [\boldsymbol{E}_T(x,0+,t)]_y \\
[\boldsymbol{H}_I(x,0-,t)]_x + [\boldsymbol{H}_R(x,0-,t)]_x &= [\boldsymbol{H}_T(x,0+,t)]_x \\
[\mu\boldsymbol{H}_I(x,0-,t)]_z + [\mu\boldsymbol{H}_R(x,0-,t)]_z &= [\mu\boldsymbol{H}_T(x,0+,t)]_z
\end{aligned} \tag{10-38}$$

The following forms for the reflected and transmitted $\boldsymbol{E}$-field components may be postulated; the angles θ_K and θ_T are introduced in anticipation that those fields will not be in time phase with each other nor with the incident field at the boundary:

$$\begin{aligned}
\boldsymbol{E}_R &= \text{Im}\left[E_{RM}\sin\left(\frac{\pi x}{a}\right)\epsilon^{j(\omega t + \theta_K + \beta_{10}z)}\right]\boldsymbol{a}_y \\
\boldsymbol{E}_T &= \text{Im}\left[E_{TM}\sin\left(\frac{\pi x}{a}\right)\epsilon^{-\alpha_{10}z}\epsilon^{j(\omega t + \theta_T)}\right]\boldsymbol{a}_y
\end{aligned} \tag{10-39}$$

Here

$$\begin{aligned}
\beta_{10} &= \sqrt{\omega^2\mu\epsilon_1 - \left(\frac{\pi}{a}\right)^2} \\
\alpha_{10} &= \sqrt{\left(\frac{\pi}{a}\right)^2 - \omega^2\mu\epsilon_0}
\end{aligned} \tag{10-40}$$

Substitution of Eqs. 10-37 and 10-39 in the first equation of set 10-38 yields the following, after cancelling the common factors—Im operator, $\sin(\pi x/a)$, and $\epsilon^{j\omega t}$:

$$E_{IM} + E_{RM}\epsilon^{j\theta_K} = E_{TM}\epsilon^{j\theta_T} \tag{10-41}$$

The $\boldsymbol{H}$-field components will not be given here in full, but by comparison with Eqs. 10-9, 10-25, and 10-32 one may assemble the terms for the remaining two equations in set 10-38:

$$\frac{-E_{IM}\beta_{10}}{\omega\mu} + \frac{E_{RM}\beta_{10}\epsilon^{j\theta_K}}{\omega\mu} = \frac{jE_{TM}\alpha_{10}\epsilon^{j\theta_T}}{\omega\mu} \tag{10-42}$$

$$\frac{-E_{IM}\pi}{j\omega a} - \frac{E_{RM}\pi\epsilon^{j\theta_K}}{j\omega a} = \frac{-E_{TM}\pi\epsilon^{j\theta_T}}{j\omega a} \tag{10-43}$$

If the latter equation is multiplied by $-j\omega a/\pi$, it proves to be identical with Eq. 10-41 and hence is redundant. Substitution of Eq. 10-41 in Eq. 10-42 yields, after cancellation of like quantities and grouping terms,

$$E_{RM}\epsilon^{j\theta_K}(\beta_{10} - j\alpha_{10}) = E_{IM}(\beta_{10} + j\alpha_{10})$$

$$E_{RM}\epsilon^{j\theta_K} = E_{IM}\epsilon^{j[2\tan^{-1}(\alpha_{10}/\beta_{10})]} \tag{10-44}$$

$$E_{TM}\epsilon^{j\theta_T} = \frac{2E_{IM}\beta_{10}}{\beta_{10} - j\alpha_{10}} \tag{10-45}$$

Equation 10-44 is reminiscent of the results obtained in Sec. 3-2*e* for reflections on a lossless transmission line with a purely reactive termination, but caution must be used in drawing analogies between the two problems, since important differences exist.

The writing of equations for the magnetic fields is left as Problem 10-10.

c. Vertical iris and accompanying nonpropagating modes

The vertical iris sketched in Fig. 10-3 possesses a high degree of symmetry, yet its fields are far more difficult to compute than those of the problem just considered. The boundary requirements are (1) that E_y vanish on both sides of the iris sheet, and (2) that continuity of E_y and H_x be maintained in the plane of the iris over the area between the conducting surfaces. Because the iris structure is uniform in the y direction, it does not tend to induce E_x or E_z field components when a TE_{10} mode is incident upon it. Hence reflected and transmitted fields are limited to the TE_{m0} type. Furthermore, because it is symmetrical with respect to the center of the guide in the x direction, it does not tend to induce even-ordered TE_{m0} modes (they are antisymmetric with respect to that axis).

In spite of restriction to odd-ordered TE_{m0} modes when the incident field is in the TE_{10} mode, an infinite number of modes within that class may be expected in the reflected and transmitted fields. A complete solution for the magnitude and relative phase of each would involve an infinite number of simultaneous linear equations. In wave-guide applications the aspect of primary interest is the effect on the TE_{10} mode itself—the magnitude and phase of its reflected and transmitted components. Approximate solutions have been derived for these.[2,4,5,8]

By analogy with the corresponding standing-wave effects on two-conductor lines, *equivalent impedances* for irises and other wave-guide discontinuities may be defined.[9] The equivalent impedance of the iris shown in Fig. 10-3 is an inductive reactance connected in shunt.

10-3. GENERAL SOLUTION FOR TE AND TM MODES

A more comprehensive approach to the finding of wave-guide modes is that of reducing Maxwell's equations to a general wave equation. The two equations involving the curl function form the starting point:

$$\nabla \times \boldsymbol{H} = \epsilon \frac{\partial \boldsymbol{E}}{\partial t} \tag{10-46}$$

$$\nabla \times \boldsymbol{E} = -\mu \frac{\partial \boldsymbol{H}}{\partial t} \tag{7-34}$$

Equation 10-46 corresponds to Eq. 7-32 with conductivity σ set equal to zero. $\boldsymbol{H}$ may be eliminated from this set by differentiating Eq. 10-46 with respect to time, taking the curl of Eq. 7-34, and substituting:

$$\nabla \times (\nabla \times \boldsymbol{E}) = -\mu\epsilon \frac{\partial^2 \boldsymbol{E}}{\partial t^2} \tag{10-47}$$

a. Reduction to scalar wave equations

Equation 10-47 is a *vector wave equation*; it may be reduced to a set of scalar wave equations by means of the following formal identity from vector analysis:

$$-\nabla \times (\nabla \times \boldsymbol{E}) + \nabla(\nabla \cdot \boldsymbol{E}) = \nabla^2 \boldsymbol{E} \tag{10-48}$$

This is actually the definition of the *laplacian* of a *vector field.* For rectangular coordinates, a routine substitution of Eqs. 7-44, 7-45, 7-47, and 7-48 into the left-hand side of Eq. 10-48 (see Problem 10-12) will yield the following:

$$\nabla^2 \boldsymbol{E} = \nabla^2 E_x \boldsymbol{a}_x + \nabla^2 E_y \boldsymbol{a}_y + \nabla^2 E_z \boldsymbol{a}_z \tag{10-49}$$

(This simple result cannot be generalized intuitively to other coordinate systems; see Sec. 11-1*a* regarding the outcome in cylindrical coordinates.)

Since the space within the wave guide is assumed to be free of electric charge, the divergence of $\boldsymbol{E}$ vanishes, and Eq. 10-47 may be replaced by three scalar equations, each representing the electric-field magnitude in one of the coordinate directions:

$$\nabla^2 E_x = \mu\epsilon \frac{\partial^2 E_x}{\partial t^2}$$

$$\nabla^2 E_y = \mu\epsilon \frac{\partial^2 E_y}{\partial t^2} \tag{10-50}$$

$$\nabla^2 E_z = \mu\epsilon \frac{\partial^2 E_z}{\partial t^2}$$

Each of these may be written in expanded form to show the functional dependence on x, y, and z explicitly. Thus for the equation in E_z,

$$\frac{\partial^2 E_z}{\partial x^2} + \frac{\partial^2 E_z}{\partial y^2} + \frac{\partial^2 E_z}{\partial z^2} = \mu\epsilon \frac{\partial^2 E_z}{\partial t^2} \tag{10-51}$$

Wave equations for the cartesian components of $\boldsymbol{H}$ may be obtained by taking the curl of Eq. 10-46, differentiating Eq. 7-34 with respect to time and making substitutions paralleling those of Eqs. 10-47, 10-48, and 10-49. The expanded form for the wave equation in H_z is

$$\frac{\partial^2 H_z}{\partial x^2} + \frac{\partial^2 H_z}{\partial y^2} + \frac{\partial^2 H_z}{\partial z^2} = \mu\epsilon \frac{\partial^2 H_z}{\partial t^2} \tag{10-52}$$

Equations 10-51 and 10-52 were written for the z components because that is the longitudinal direction of the wave guide shown in Fig. 10-1, and the longitudinal components of field prove to be useful as reference functions.

b. Interrelationships among field components—mode types

Expressions may be derived for E_x, E_y, H_x, and H_y in terms of E_z and H_z. To find such an equation for H_x, take the y component of Eq. 10-46 and the x component of Eq. 7-34:

y comp. of curl

$$\frac{\partial H_x}{\partial z} - \frac{\partial H_z}{\partial x} = \epsilon \frac{\partial E_y}{\partial t} \tag{10-53}$$

$$\frac{\partial E_z}{\partial y} - \frac{\partial E_y}{\partial z} = -\mu \frac{\partial H_x}{\partial t} \tag{10-54}$$

If the first of these is differentiated with respect to z and the second with respect to t, E_y may be eliminated:

$$\frac{\partial^2 H_x}{\partial z^2} - \mu\epsilon \frac{\partial^2 H_x}{\partial t^2} = \frac{\partial}{\partial z}\left(\frac{\partial H_z}{\partial x}\right) + \frac{\epsilon\,\partial}{\partial t}\left(\frac{\partial E_z}{\partial y}\right) \tag{10-55}$$

This equation may be greatly simplified if the variation of each field component with respect to z and t is assumed to be that of a sinusoidal traveling wave:

$$\begin{aligned} H_x &= \text{Im}[H_{0x}(x,y)\epsilon^{j(\omega t-\beta z)}] \\ H_z &= \text{Im}[H_{0z}(x,y)\epsilon^{j(\omega t-\beta z)}] \\ E_z &= \text{Im}[E_{0z}(x,y)\epsilon^{j(\omega t-\beta z)}] \end{aligned} \tag{10-56}$$

It should be anticipated that $H_{0x}(x,y)$, $H_{0z}(x,y)$, and $E_{0z}(x,y)$ may be complex.

Equations 10-56 may be substituted into Eq. 10-55 and the Im operator and the factor $\epsilon^{j(\omega t-\beta z)}$, which are common to every term, cancelled:

$$(-\beta^2 + \mu\epsilon\omega^2)H_{0x}(x,y) = -j\beta\frac{\partial H_{0z}(x,y)}{\partial x} + j\omega\epsilon\frac{\partial E_{0z}(x,y)}{\partial y} \tag{10-57}$$

Corresponding equations for the other components are

$$\begin{aligned} (-\beta^2 + \mu\epsilon\omega^2)H_{0y}(x,y) &= -j\beta\frac{\partial H_{0z}(x,y)}{\partial y} - j\omega\epsilon\frac{\partial E_{0z}(x,y)}{\partial x} \\ (-\beta^2 + \mu\epsilon\omega^2)E_{0x}(x,y) &= -j\beta\frac{\partial E_{0z}(x,y)}{\partial x} - j\omega\mu\frac{\partial H_{0z}(x,y)}{\partial y} \\ (-\beta^2 + \mu\epsilon\omega^2)E_{0y}(x,y) &= -j\beta\frac{\partial E_{0z}(x,y)}{\partial y} + j\omega\mu\frac{\partial H_{0z}(x,y)}{\partial x} \end{aligned} \tag{10-58}$$

Wave equations 10-51 and 10-52 separate E_z from H_z and, in accordance with Eqs. 10-57 and 10-58, H_x, H_y, E_x, and E_y may each be divided into two separate functions, one proportional to a derivative of E_z and the other proportional to a derivative of H_z. Thus, by the principle of superposition, a general sinusoidal traveling-wave field may be split into two parts, one of which has an E_z component but no H_z component, and the other of which has an H_z component but no E_z component. Functions of the first type are known as *transverse-magnetic* (TM) modes, because the magnetic field is confined to planes perpendicular to the direction of propagation; similarly, functions of the second type are known as *transverse electric* (TE) modes.

c. Solution by product-function method

Substitution of the appropriate parts of Eq. 10-56 in Eqs. 10-51 and 10-52 gives the following:

$$\frac{\partial^2 E_{0z}(x,y)}{\partial x^2} + \frac{\partial^2 E_{0z}(x,y)}{\partial y^2} = (\beta^2 - \mu\epsilon\omega^2)E_{0z}(x,y) \tag{10-59}$$

$$\frac{\partial^2 H_{0z}(x,y)}{\partial x^2} + \frac{\partial^2 H_{0z}(x,y)}{\partial y^2} = (\beta^2 - \mu\epsilon\omega^2)H_{0z}(x,y) \tag{10-60}$$

The product-function method may be used to obtain the functions $E_{0z}(x,y)$ and $H_{0z}(x,y)$. Let

$$E_{0z}(x,y) = X_{Ez}(x)\,Y_{Ez}(y) \tag{10-61}$$

$$\frac{d^2X_{Ez}(x)}{dx^2}\,Y_{Ez}(y) + X_{Ez}(x)\,\frac{d^2Y_{Ez}(y)}{dy^2} = (\beta^2 - \mu\epsilon\omega^2)X_{Ez}(x)\,Y_{Ez}(y)$$

Variables may be separated by dividing this by $X_{Ez}(x)\,Y_{Ez}(y)$.

$$\frac{d^2X_{Ez}(x)}{dx^2}\,\frac{1}{X_{Ez}(x)} + \frac{1}{Y_{Ez}(y)}\,\frac{d^2Y_{Ez}(y)}{dy^2} = \beta^2 - \mu\epsilon\omega^2 \tag{10-62}$$

This must be satisfied for independently chosen values of x and y, and such can result only if (1) the first term, which is not a function of y, but is the only part of the equation which is a function of x, is equal to a constant, say, $-C_1^2$; and (2) the second term, which is not a function of x, but is the only part of the equation which is a function of y, is equal to another constant, say, $-C_2^2$:

$$\frac{d^2X_{Ez}(x)}{dx^2}\,\frac{1}{X_{Ez}(x)} = -C_1^2 \tag{10-63}$$

$$\frac{d^2Y_{Ez}(y)}{dy^2}\,\frac{1}{Y_{Ez}(y)} = -C_2^2 \tag{10-64}$$

Equation 10-62 imposes the following constraint on C_1 and C_2:

$$-C_1^2 - C_2^2 = \beta^2 - \mu\epsilon\omega^2 \tag{10-65}$$

Equations 10-63 and 10-64 yield the following, in which A_1, etc., are arbitrary constants:

$$X_{Ez}(x) = A_1 \sin C_1x + A_2 \cos C_1x \tag{10-66}$$

$$Y_{Ez}(y) = A_3 \sin C_2y + A_4 \cos C_2y \tag{10-67}$$

Similarly,

$$H_{0z}(x,y) = X_{Hz}(x)Y_{Hz}(y) \qquad \text{(10-68}$$

$$X_{Hz}(x) = A_5 \sin C_3x + A_6 \cos C_3x \tag{10-69}$$

$$Y_{Hz}(y) = A_7 \sin C_4y + A_8 \cos C_4y \tag{10-70}$$

Where

$$-C_3^2 - C_4^2 = \beta^2 - \mu\epsilon\omega^2 \tag{10-71}$$

d. Application of boundary conditions

The permissible values for the C's and some of the A's are fixed by the boundary condition that the tangential component of the electric field vanish along the conductor surfaces. The phase function is then fixed by Eq. 10-65 or 10-71.

(1) TM MODES. The TM case may be examined more directly, since E_z is parallel to the surfaces of the wave guide and hence must vanish at $x = 0$ and $x = a$ and at $y = 0$ and $y = b$. In accordance with Eq. 10-61,

$$E_{0z}(x,y) = (A_1 \sin C_1x + A_2 \cos C_1x)(A_3 \sin C_2y + A_4 \cos C_2y) \tag{10-72}$$

Setting x equal to zero

$$E_{0z}(0,y) = A_2(A_3 \sin C_2y + A_4 \cos C_2y)$$

Therefore, $$A_2 = 0$$

After substituting this in Eq. 10-72, x is set equal to a, where $\boldsymbol{E}$ must also vanish:

$$E_{0z}(a,y) = A_1 \sin C_1a(A_3 \sin C_2y + A_4 \cos C_2y)$$

Therefore, $$C_1a = m\pi$$

Here m may be any integer. Substituting this in Eq. 10-72 gives

$$E_{0z}(x,y) = A_1 \sin\left(\frac{m\pi x}{a}\right)(A_3 \sin C_2y + A_4 \cos C_2y)$$

Similarly,

$$E_{0z}(x,0) = A_1A_4 \sin\left(\frac{m\pi x}{a}\right)$$

Therefore, $$A_4 = 0$$

$$E_{0z}(x,b) = A_1A_3 \sin\left(\frac{m\pi x}{a}\right) \sin C_2b$$

Therefore, $$C_2b = n\pi$$

Here n may be any integer.

The product A_1A_3 may be replaced by a single constant C_{mn}, which corresponds to the particular mode defined by a given choice of m and n:

$$E_{0z}(x,y) = C_{mn} \sin\left(\frac{m\pi x}{a}\right) \sin\left(\frac{n\pi y}{b}\right) \tag{10-73}$$

From Eq. 10-65, the phase function is as follows:

$$\beta_{mn}^2 = \mu\epsilon\omega^2 - \left(\frac{m\pi}{a}\right)^2 - \left(\frac{n\pi}{b}\right)^2 \tag{10-74}$$

Let $$h^2 = \left(\frac{m\pi}{a}\right)^2 + \left(\frac{n\pi}{b}\right)^2 \tag{10-75}$$

The functions of x, y for the remaining field components may be written after substituting in Eqs. 10-57 and 10-58:

$$
\begin{aligned}
H_{0x}(x,y) &= \frac{j\omega\epsilon n\pi}{h^2 b} C_{mn} \sin\left(\frac{m\pi x}{a}\right) \cos\left(\frac{n\pi y}{b}\right) \\
H_{0y}(x,y) &= \frac{-j\omega\epsilon m\pi}{h^2 a} C_{mn} \cos\left(\frac{m\pi x}{a}\right) \sin\left(\frac{n\pi y}{b}\right) \\
E_{0x}(x,y) &= \frac{-j\beta_{mn} m\pi}{h^2 a} C_{mn} \cos\left(\frac{m\pi x}{a}\right) \sin\left(\frac{n\pi y}{b}\right) \\
E_{0y}(x,y) &= \frac{-j\beta_{mn} n\pi}{h^2 b} C_{mn} \sin\left(\frac{m\pi x}{a}\right) \cos\left(\frac{n\pi y}{b}\right)
\end{aligned}
\qquad \textbf{(10-76)}
$$

One may verify by inspection that E_{0x}, which is tangential to the wave guide at $y = 0$ and $y = b$, vanishes there, and that E_{0y} vanishes at $x = 0$ and $x = a$. One may also note that the normal component of $\boldsymbol{H}$, and hence $\boldsymbol{B}$, vanishes at the conductor surface.

Complete expressions as functions of time and the three distance coordinates may now be written, following the definitions of Eq. 10-56:

$$
\begin{aligned}
E_z &= C_{mn} \sin\left(\frac{m\pi x}{a}\right) \sin\left(\frac{n\pi y}{b}\right) \sin(\omega t - \beta_{mn} z) \\
E_x &= \frac{-C_{mn}\beta_{mn} m\pi}{h^2 a} \cos\left(\frac{m\pi x}{a}\right) \sin\left(\frac{n\pi y}{b}\right) \cos(\omega t - \beta_{mn} z) \\
E_y &= \frac{-C_{mn}\beta_{mn} n\pi}{h^2 b} \sin\left(\frac{m\pi x}{a}\right) \cos\left(\frac{n\pi y}{b}\right) \cos(\omega t - \beta_{mn} z) \\
H_x &= \frac{C_{mn}\omega\epsilon n\pi}{h^2 b} \sin\left(\frac{m\pi x}{a}\right) \cos\left(\frac{n\pi y}{b}\right) \cos(\omega t - \beta_{mn} z) \\
H_y &= \frac{-C_{mn}\omega\epsilon m\pi}{h^2 a} \cos\left(\frac{m\pi x}{a}\right) \sin\left(\frac{n\pi y}{b}\right) \cos(\omega t - \beta_{mn} z)
\end{aligned}
\qquad \textbf{(10-77)}
$$

The TM_{11} mode is illustrated in Fig. 10-4.

An equation for the cutoff frequency f_{cmn} may be found from Eq. 10-74:

$$\omega_{cmn}^2 \mu\epsilon = \left(\frac{m\pi}{a}\right)^2 + \left(\frac{n\pi}{b}\right)^2$$

$$f_{cmn} = \frac{1}{2\pi\sqrt{\mu\epsilon}} \sqrt{\left(\frac{m\pi}{a}\right)^2 + \left(\frac{n\pi}{b}\right)^2} \qquad \textbf{(10-78)}$$

For the $\boldsymbol{H}$-field to have direction lines which are closed curves, both H_x and H_y functions are needed, so m and n must both be nonzero. Comparison of Eq. 10-78 with Eq. 10-10 indicates that the cutoff frequencies of all TM modes are higher than that of the TE_{10} mode.

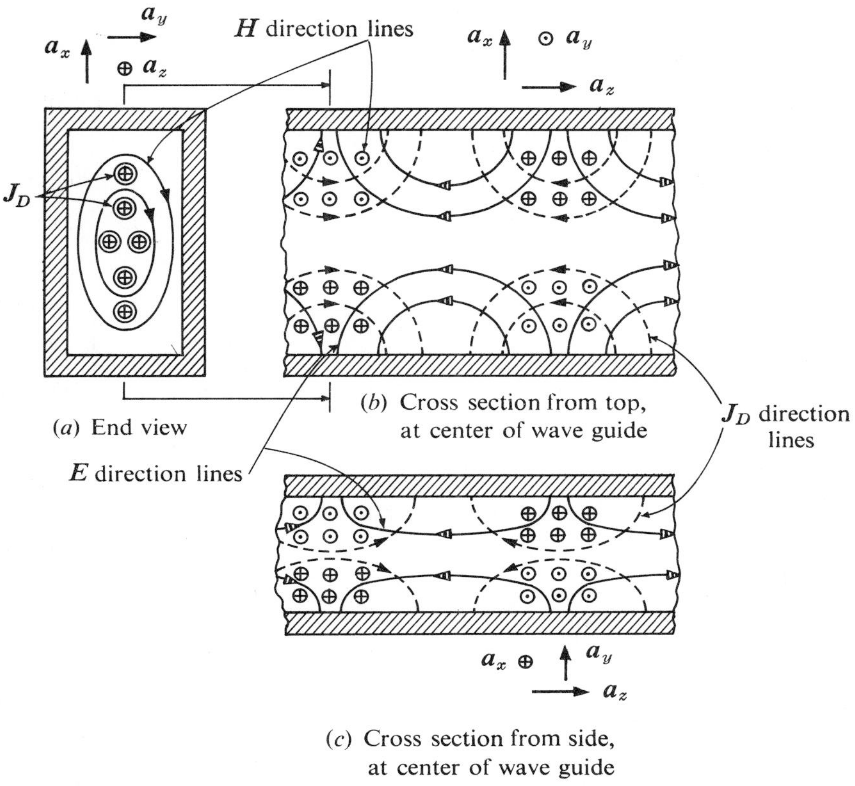

Figure 10-4 TM_{11} propagating mode in rectangular wave guide

In usual applications of rectangular wave guides, transmission in the TE_{10} mode alone is sought, and the guide dimensions are chosen with respect to frequency so as to ensure this. Hence transverse-magnetic modes will exist only in evanescent form in the vicinity of guide discontinuities. The compiling of descriptive equations for TM modes at frequencies below cutoff is left as Problem 10-13.

(2) TE MODES. For general analysis of TE modes one substitutes Eqs. 10-69 and 10-70 in Eq. 10-68, and that in turn in Eq. 10-58, so that the E-field components parallel to the guide surfaces may be found:

$$E_{0x}(x,y) = \frac{-j\omega\mu C_4}{-\beta^2 + \mu\epsilon\omega^2}(A_5 \sin C_3x + A_6 \cos C_3x)(A_7 \cos C_4y - A_8 \sin C_4y)$$

(10-79)

$$E_{0y}(x,y) = \frac{-j\omega\mu C_3}{-\beta^2 + \mu\epsilon\omega^2}(A_5 \cos C_3x - A_6 \sin C_3x)(A_7 \sin C_4y + A_8 \cos C_4y)$$

The boundary condition that the tangential components of $\boldsymbol{E}$ vanish along the guide surfaces fixes most of these constants:

$$E_{0x}(x,0) = 0 \qquad \text{therefore } A_7 = 0$$

$$E_{0x}(x,b) = 0 \qquad \text{therefore } C_4 b = n\pi$$

$$E_{0y}(0,y) = 0 \qquad \text{therefore } A_5 = 0$$

$$E_{0y}(a,y) = 0 \qquad \text{therefore } C_3 a = m\pi$$

From Eq. 10-71,

$$\beta_{mn}^2 = \mu\epsilon\omega^2 - \left(\frac{m\pi}{a}\right)^2 - \left(\frac{n\pi}{b}\right)^2$$

This is the same as the equation for the phase function of TM modes, Eq. 10-74; Eq. 10-78 for cutoff frequencies of TM modes is also applicable here for TE modes.

The results just found may be combined with Eqs. 10-75, 10-79, 10-68, 10-57, and 10-58 to yield expressions for the field components.

Let $$A_6 A_8 = A_{mn}$$

$$E_{0x}(x,y) = \frac{j\omega\mu n\pi}{h^2 b} A_{mn} \cos\left(\frac{m\pi x}{a}\right) \sin\left(\frac{n\pi y}{b}\right)$$

$$E_{0y}(x,y) = \frac{j\omega\mu m\pi}{h^2 a} A_{mn} \sin\left(\frac{m\pi x}{a}\right) \cos\left(\frac{n\pi y}{b}\right)$$

$$H_{0z}(x,y) = A_{mn} \cos\left(\frac{m\pi x}{a}\right) \cos\left(\frac{n\pi y}{b}\right) \qquad \textbf{(10-80)}$$

$$H_{0x}(x,y) = \frac{j\beta_{mn} m\pi}{h^2 a} A_{mn} \sin\left(\frac{m\pi x}{a}\right) \cos\left(\frac{n\pi y}{b}\right)$$

$$H_{0y}(x,y) = \frac{j\beta_{mn} n\pi}{h^2 b} A_{mn} \cos\left(\frac{m\pi x}{a}\right) \sin\left(\frac{n\pi y}{b}\right)$$

It should be noted that either m or n (but not both) may be set equal to zero for TE modes and still yield nontrivial results, but that both m and n must be nonzero for TM modes. Setting n equal to zero reduces the TE solution just given to the form developed in Eqs. 10-8 and 10-9. TE_{0n}-mode patterns resemble the TE_{m0} ones, except that they are turned 90 degrees in space (in terms of Fig. 10-1) such that the $\boldsymbol{E}$-field variation takes place in the shorter transverse direction.

Except for a square wave guide, the TE_{10} mode has a lower cutoff frequency than the TE_{01} mode; in any case it has a lower cutoff frequency than any other TE mode, and, as noted in Sec. 10-3*a*, than any TM mode. Hence it is properly called the dominant mode.

10-4. VELOCITIES AND SIGNAL PROPAGATION

Velocity is an important measure of wave-propagation phenomena. For the TEM mode in a lossless medium, this was found to be equal to $1/\sqrt{\mu\epsilon}$ for all frequencies, but for wave-guide modes (TE and TM) velocity is a more complicated function. More than one concept of "velocity of the fields" will prove useful. The simplest of these is the *phase velocity*, or apparent velocity of a given sinusoidal wave, and it proves to be dependent on the ratio between the wave frequency and the cutoff frequency.

As was mentioned in Sec. 2-3, actual communication signals cover the frequency spectrum. Variation of phase velocity with frequency, which occurs in a wave guide even if the guide is lossless, causes *phase distortion*, or relative shifting of the sinusoidal components. (In the TEM mode in a two-conductor line, phase distortion does not occur if the line is lossless.) However, it was also mentioned that the intelligence put into a signal is in practice recoverable if distortion is kept small within some limited band of frequencies. With due regard for the restrictions thereby imposed, a wave guide can be used efficiently for signal transmission.

Modulation is a technique for adapting a signal so as to take best advantage of the characteristics of the transmission system. Several types of modulation have been exploited; *amplitude modulation*, illustrated in Fig. 10-5, is perhaps the simplest to analyze and will serve as the example in the

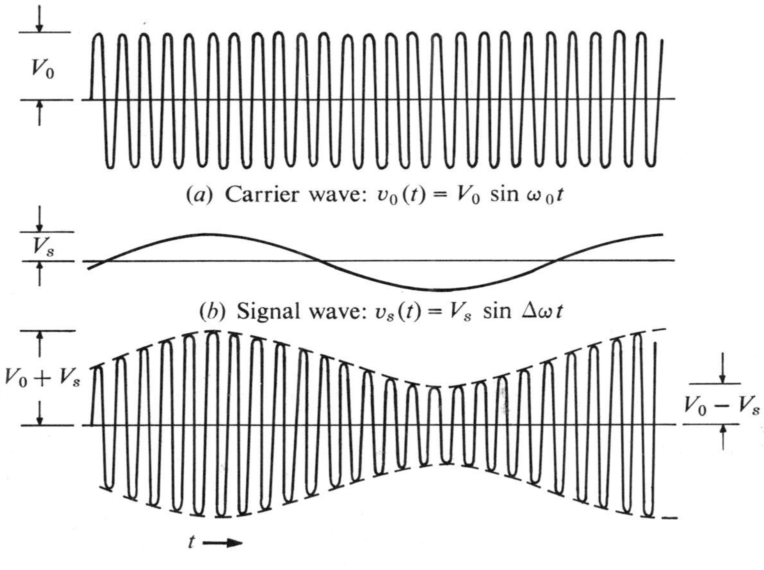

(*a*) Carrier wave: $v_0(t) = V_0 \sin \omega_0 t$

(*b*) Signal wave: $v_s(t) = V_s \sin \Delta\omega t$

(*c*) Modulated wave: $v(t) = (V_0 + V_s \sin \Delta\omega t) \sin \omega_0 t$

Figure 10-5 Amplitude modulation with sinusoidal signal

discussion which follows. The signal contained in an amplitude-modulated wave may be sensed graphically by means of the *envelope*, which is a pair of curves faired so that one touches all the positive maxima of the modulated wave and the other touches all the negative maxima. This is indicated by the dashed lines in Fig. 10-5(*c*). Insight as to the "performance" of a transmission system may be obtained by studying particular envelopes for apparent speed of movement (group velocity) and for any progressive change in shape.

Two approaches to the "signal-transmitting performance" of a wave guide will be examined; these differ greatly in mathematical complexity and in the scope of information obtained. An elementary analysis is possible if amplitude modulation by a uniform sinusoidal signal is assumed; in audio terminology this signal would be an uninterrupted tone of constant pitch and loudness. Such a signal would not convey any intelligence. On the other hand, the step function and the isolated rectangular pulse embody much of the essential nature of practical communication, but mathematical analysis of the wave-guide propagation of waves modulated by those signals is difficult. In keeping with the mathematical level of this text, a compromise will be made; the sinusoidal-signal case will be derived in detail, and a semiquantitative summary of results will be given for the step-function and rectangular-pulse signals.

a. Phase-velocity function

As has been noted in Chapter 2, the phase velocity of a sinusoidal traveling wave (steady state) is related to the phase function as follows:

$$v = \frac{\omega}{\beta} \qquad \textbf{(2-15)}$$

The cutoff frequency for both TE and TM modes in a rectangular wave guide is

$$\omega_{cmn}^2 \mu\epsilon = \left(\frac{m\pi}{a}\right)^2 + \left(\frac{n\pi}{b}\right)^2 \qquad \textbf{(10-78)}$$

Substitution of this into Eq. 10-74 yields

$$\beta = \sqrt{\mu\epsilon(\omega^2 - \omega_c^2)} \qquad \textbf{(10-81)}$$

The subscripts *m* and *n* have been dropped. Substituting Eq. 10-81 in Eq. 2-15 yields

$$\begin{aligned} v &= \frac{\omega}{\sqrt{\mu\epsilon(\omega^2 - \omega_c^2)}} \\ &= \frac{1}{\sqrt{\mu\epsilon\left[1 - \left(\dfrac{\omega_c}{\omega}\right)^2\right]}} \end{aligned} \qquad \textbf{(10-82)}$$

At frequencies much greater than cutoff, v approaches $1/\sqrt{\mu\epsilon}$, the same as for TEM waves, but as frequency is reduced toward the cutoff value, v increases without limit. Thus v may exceed $1/\sqrt{\mu_0\epsilon_0}$, the speed of light in vacuum. (If $\mu = \mu_0$ and $\epsilon = \epsilon_0$, v is never less than the speed of light in vacuum.) This appears to contradict the principles of relativity, but an examination of the energy distribution and movement in a wave-guide mode in comparison to that in the TEM mode will relieve the difficulty.

Let the *energy-density functions* w_ϵ and w_μ, introduced in connection with Poynting's vector in Sec. 8-1*e*, be used here:

$$w_\epsilon = \frac{\epsilon\,|\boldsymbol{E}|^2}{2} \tag{8-37}$$

$$w_\mu = \frac{\mu\,|\boldsymbol{H}|^2}{2} \tag{8-38}$$

Let

$$w = w_\epsilon + w_\mu \tag{10-83}$$

$$\boldsymbol{P} = \boldsymbol{E} \times \boldsymbol{H} \tag{8-42}$$

(1) ENERGY DISTRIBUTION AND POYNTING VECTOR FOR TEM MODE. Equations 8-7 and 8-18 for the $\boldsymbol{E}$ and $\boldsymbol{H}$ fields in an unbounded medium may be adapted to the lossless case by setting α equal to zero and η equal to $\sqrt{\mu/\epsilon}$:

$$\boldsymbol{E} = E_{xM}\sin(\omega t - \beta z)\boldsymbol{a}_x \tag{10-84}$$

$$\boldsymbol{H} = E_{xM}\sqrt{\frac{\epsilon}{\mu}}\sin(\omega t - \beta z)\boldsymbol{a}_y \tag{10-85}$$

Substituting these into Eqs. 8-37 and 8-38 yields the following:

$$\begin{aligned} w &= \frac{\epsilon}{2}E_{xM}^2\sin^2(\omega t - \beta z) + \frac{\mu}{2}E_{xM}^2\frac{\epsilon}{\mu}\sin^2(\omega t - \beta z) \\ &= \epsilon E_{xM}^2\sin^2(\omega t - \beta z) \end{aligned} \tag{10-86}$$

Similarly, substitution in Eq. 8-42 yields

$$\boldsymbol{P} = E_{xM}^2\sqrt{\frac{\epsilon}{\mu}}\sin^2(\omega t - \beta z)\boldsymbol{a}_z \tag{10-87}$$

The total energy density w is zero over the transverse planes corresponding to $\omega t - \beta z$ equal to an integral multiple of π, and the same is true of Poynting's vector. Furthermore Poynting's vector contains only a z-directed component. To maintain the given energy distribution with respect to the $\boldsymbol{E}$ and $\boldsymbol{H}$ field patterns, the energy must move at the same speed as the fields do, or $1/\sqrt{\mu\epsilon}$.

(2) ENERGY DISTRIBUTION AND POYNTING VECTOR FOR TE_{10} MODE. The TE_{10} wave-guide mode is of practical interest and is also the easiest to illustrate

in sketches, so it will be used here. The second forms of Eqs. 10-8 and 10-9, with m set equal to unity, may be used for the wave-guide fields:

$$\boldsymbol{E} = A \sin\left(\frac{\pi x}{a}\right) \sin(\omega t - \beta_{10} z)\boldsymbol{a}_y \tag{10-88}$$

$$\boldsymbol{H} = -\frac{A\beta_{10}}{\omega\mu} \sin\left(\frac{\pi x}{a}\right) \sin(\omega t - \beta_{10} z)\boldsymbol{a}_x + \frac{A\pi}{\omega\mu a} \cos\left(\frac{\pi x}{a}\right) \cos(\omega t - \beta_{10} z)\boldsymbol{a}_z \tag{10-89}$$

As before, the field expressions are substituted into Eqs. 8-37 and 8-38:

$$w = \frac{\epsilon}{2} A^2 \sin^2\left(\frac{\pi x}{a}\right) \sin^2(\omega t - \beta_{10} z) + \frac{A^2\beta_{10}^2}{2\omega^2\mu} \sin^2\left(\frac{\pi x}{a}\right) \sin^2(\omega t - \beta_{10} z) + \frac{A^2\pi^2}{2\omega^2\mu a^2} \cos^2\left(\frac{\pi x}{a}\right) \cos^2(\omega t - \beta_{10} z) \tag{10-90}$$

From Eq. 10-6

$$\beta_{10}^2 = \omega^2\mu\epsilon - \left(\frac{\pi}{a}\right)^2 \tag{10-91}$$

The terms in Eq. 10-90 may be rearranged by substituting Eq. 10-91:

$$w = A^2\left[\epsilon - \frac{\pi^2}{2\omega^2\mu a^2}\right] \sin^2\left(\frac{\pi x}{a}\right) \sin^2(\omega t - \beta_{10} z) + \frac{A^2\pi^2}{2\omega^2\mu a^2} \cos^2\left(\frac{\pi x}{a}\right) \cos^2(\omega t - \beta_{10} z) \tag{10-92}$$

The function w is zero at the following locations:

$$\begin{aligned} &\left.\begin{array}{l} x = 0 \\ x = a \end{array}\right\} \quad \omega t - \beta_{10} z = k\pi \qquad (k \text{ is any integer}) \\ &x = \frac{a}{2} \quad \omega t - \beta_{10} z = \frac{(k+1)}{2}\pi \end{aligned} \tag{10-93}$$

It has maxima at the following locations:

$$\begin{aligned} &x = \frac{a}{2} \quad \omega t - \beta_{10} z = k\pi \qquad (w_{M1}) \\ &\left.\begin{array}{l} x = 0 \\ x = a \end{array}\right\} \quad \omega t - \beta_{10} z = \frac{(k+1)}{2}\pi \qquad (w_{M2}) \end{aligned} \tag{10-94}$$

These are indicated in Fig. 10-6. If desired, the form of the scalar field w could be shown in greater detail by means of contours, but such lines tend to be confusing in a diagram in which magnetic-field lines have been drawn.

Poynting's vector is

$$\boldsymbol{P} = \frac{A^2\beta_{10}}{\omega\mu}\sin^2\left(\frac{\pi x}{a}\right)\sin^2(\omega t - \beta_{10}z)\boldsymbol{a}_z$$
$$+ \frac{A^2\pi}{\omega\mu a}\sin\left(\frac{\pi x}{a}\right)\cos\left(\frac{\pi x}{a}\right)\sin(\omega t - \beta_{10}z)\cos(\omega t - \beta_{10}z)\boldsymbol{a}_x \quad \textbf{(10-95)}$$

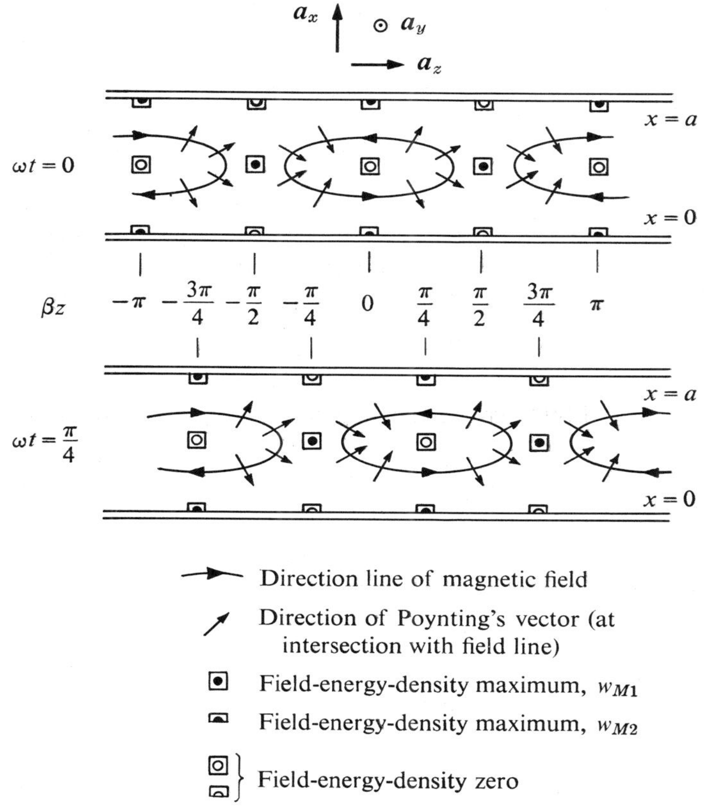

Figure 10-6 Locations of maxima and zeros of field-energy-density function relative to Poynting's vector field for TE_{10} mode (see Eqs. 10-88 through 10-95)

Arrows indicating the direction of Poynting's vector at a number of locations in the field are shown in Fig. 10-6. By comparing Poynting vector directions and the location of maximum energy densities at consecutive time intervals, it may be seen that the outward components of energy movement in the range $-\pi/2 < (\omega t - \beta_{10}z) < 0$ weaken the trailing portion of the energy "hump" in the center of the guide and strengthen the leading portions of the humps at the sidewalls, whereas the inward components of energy movement in the range $0 < (\omega t - \beta_{10}z) < \pi/2$ weaken the trailing portion of the humps at the sidewalls and strengthen the leading portion of the hump at the center. The result is apparent longitudinal movement at the phase velocity.

The limiting situation occurs when the frequency approaches the cutoff value; then β approaches zero and the phase velocity infinity. Under these circumstances the energy movement is purely transverse and the field pattern changes simultaneously at all values of z (see Problem 10-16).

b. Traveling envelope of sinusoidally modulated wave

An amplitude-modulated wave may be resolved mathematically into uniform sinusoidal components of differing frequencies which travel in a wave guide at differing phase velocities. If the frequency of the modulating signal is small compared to the carrier frequency, the envelope which characterizes the resultant wave at the sending end remains identifiable as the wave travels along the wave guide. The envelope appears to travel at a lower speed than do its sinusoidal components, and furthermore its shape is gradually but progressively changed with increase in the distance traveled.

The analysis which follows is applicable to any wave-guide mode, and for convenience the modulated wave will be described in terms of an output voltage $v(z,t)$ (assuming a suitable termination-and-conversion device at the particular location in z). For TE modes in a rectangular wave guide, for example, $v(z,t)$ would be proportional to $|\boldsymbol{E}(x,y,z,t)|$.

(1) EQUATIONS FOR MODULATED WAVE. In accordance with Fig. 10-5, let $v_0(t)$ be the carrier wave and $v_s(t)$ be the signal by which it is amplitude-modulated:

$$v_0(t) = V_0 \sin \omega_0 t \tag{10-96}$$

$$v_s(t) = V_s \sin \Delta\omega t \tag{10-97}$$

Let

$$M = \frac{V_s}{V_0} \tag{10-98}$$

The modulated wave at $z = 0$ is

$$v(0,t) = V_0(1 + M \sin \Delta\omega t) \sin \omega_0 t$$

This may be changed by means of a trigonometric identity into the following:

$$v(0,t) = V_0\left[\sin \omega_0 t + \frac{M}{2}\cos(\omega_0 t - \Delta\omega t) - \frac{M}{2}\cos(\omega_0 t + \Delta\omega t)\right]$$

Each of the three frequency components will travel at its respective phase velocity, and the corresponding phase constants will be designated by

β_0, β_-, and β_+. As a general function of z and t the traveling modulated wave is

$$v(z,t) = V_0\left[\sin(\omega_0 t - \beta_0 z) + \frac{M}{2}\cos(\omega_0 t - \Delta\omega t - \beta_- z) - \frac{M}{2}\cos(\omega_0 t + \Delta\omega t - \beta_+ z)\right] \quad \textbf{(10-99)}$$

(2) GROUP VELOCITY. If it is assumed that $\Delta\omega \ll \omega_0$, β_- and β_+ may be related to β_0 by Taylor's series and the principal effects of this variation brought into clear focus.

$$\beta_+ = \beta_0 + \Delta\omega\left(\frac{d\beta}{d\omega}\right)_{\omega_0} + \frac{(\Delta\omega)^2}{2}\left(\frac{d^2\beta}{d\omega^2}\right)_{\omega_0} + \cdots \quad \textbf{(10-100)}$$

Let

$$\Delta\beta = \Delta\omega\left(\frac{d\beta}{d\omega}\right)_{\omega_0} \quad \textbf{(10-101)}$$

and

$$\Delta'\beta = \frac{(\Delta\omega)^2}{2}\left(\frac{d^2\beta}{d\omega^2}\right)_{\omega_0} \quad \textbf{(10-102)}$$

Then

$$\begin{aligned} \beta_+ &\approx \beta_0 + \Delta\beta + \Delta'\beta \\ \beta_- &\approx \beta_0 - \Delta\beta + \Delta'\beta \end{aligned} \quad \textbf{(10-103)}$$

Substitution of Eq. 10-103 in Eq. 10-99 gives the following:

$$v(z,t) = V_0\left[\sin(\omega_0 t - \beta_0 z) + \frac{M}{2}\cos(\omega_0 t - \beta_0 z - \Delta'\beta z - \Delta\omega t + \Delta\beta z) - \frac{M}{2}\cos(\omega_0 t - \beta_0 z - \Delta'\beta z + \Delta\omega t - \Delta\beta z)\right]$$

The cosine terms may be combined to yield the following:

$$v(z,t) = V_0[\sin(\omega_0 t - \beta_0 z) + M\sin(\Delta\omega t - \Delta\beta z)\sin(\omega_0 t - \beta_0 z - \Delta'\beta z)] \quad \textbf{(10-104)}$$

For locations z for which $\Delta'\beta z \ll 1$ (see below), this may be simplified to

$$v(z,t) \approx V_0\left[1 + M\sin\Delta\omega\left(t - \frac{\Delta\beta}{\Delta\omega}z\right)\right]\sin(\omega_0 t - \beta_0 z) \quad \textbf{(10-105)}$$

Let

$$v_g = \left(\frac{\Delta\omega}{\Delta\beta}\right)_{\Delta\omega\to 0} = \frac{1}{\left(\dfrac{d\beta}{d\omega}\right)_{\omega_0}} \quad \textbf{(10-106)}$$

The bracketed terms in Eq. 10-105 describe the envelope of the traveling wave; it appears to move, without change of shape, at velocity v_g. This is known as the *group velocity*. Differentiation of Eq. 10-81 for β gives

$$\frac{d\beta}{d\omega} = \frac{\omega\mu\epsilon}{\sqrt{\mu\epsilon(\omega^2 - \omega_c^2)}} \tag{10-107}$$

Substitution of Eq. 10-107 in Eq. 10-106 yields

$$v_g = \frac{\sqrt{\mu\epsilon(\omega_0^2 - \omega_c^2)}}{\omega_0\mu\epsilon}$$

This may be simplified by substituting the phase velocity of the carrier frequency ω_0 as given by Eq. 10-82.

$$v_g = \frac{1}{v\mu\epsilon}$$

The TEM velocity v_0 may also be substituted.

$$v_g = \frac{v_0^2}{v} \tag{10-108}$$

(3) ENVELOPE DISTORTION. The effect of neglecting $\Delta'\beta z$ in Eq. 10-105 should be investigated. Equation 10-107 may be differentiated to obtain $d^2\beta/d\omega^2$, which is related to $\Delta'\beta z$ by Eq. 10-102.

$$\frac{d^2\beta}{d\omega^2} = \frac{\mu\epsilon}{\sqrt{\mu\epsilon(\omega^2 - \omega_c^2)}} - \frac{\omega^2\mu^2\epsilon^2}{[\mu\epsilon(\omega^2 - \omega_c^2)]^{3/2}}$$

$$= \frac{-\omega_c^2\mu^2\epsilon^2}{[\mu\epsilon(\omega^2 - \omega_c^2)]^{3/2}}$$

$$\Delta'\beta = -\frac{(\Delta\omega)^2}{2}\frac{\omega_c^2\sqrt{\mu\epsilon}}{(\omega_0^2 - \omega_c^2)^{3/2}} \tag{10-109}$$

For given values of ω_0 and $\Delta\omega$, $\Delta'\beta z$ will exceed any stated finite magnitude if z is made sufficiently large. The result is a change in envelope shape, which will be demonstrated in an approximate manner. The last term of Eq. 10-104 may be expanded as follows:

$$\sin(\omega_0 t - \beta_0 z - \Delta'\beta z) = \sin(\omega_0 t - \beta_0 z)\cos\Delta'\beta z - \cos(\omega_0 t - \beta_0 z)\sin\Delta'\beta z$$

Equation 10-104 may be rewritten as follows:

$$v(z,t) = V_0\{[1 + M\sin(\Delta\omega t - \Delta\beta z)\cos\Delta'\beta z]\sin(\omega_0 t - \beta_0 z) - M\sin(\Delta\omega t - \Delta\beta z)\sin\Delta'\beta z\cos(\omega_0 t - \beta_0 z)\} \tag{10-110}$$

The sine and cosine functions of $\omega_0 t - \beta_0 z$ may be combined by use of the following identity:

$$a \sin \theta + b \cos \theta = \sqrt{a^2 + b^2} \sin\left[\theta + \tan^{-1}\left(\frac{b}{a}\right)\right] \qquad \textbf{(10-111)}$$

Direct substitution of the terms of Eq. 10-110 into Eq. 10-111 would yield a bulky and unilluminating expression. If M is assumed to be small compared to unity, an approximate solution may be obtained:

$$\sqrt{a^2 + b^2} \approx a + \left(\frac{b^2}{2a}\right)$$

$$\approx a \qquad (b \ll a) \qquad \textbf{(10-112)}$$

$$\tan^{-1}\left(\frac{b}{a}\right) \approx \frac{b}{a} \qquad (b \ll a) \qquad \textbf{(10-113)}$$

$$v(z,t) \approx V_0[1 + M \sin(\Delta\omega t - \Delta\beta z) \cos \Delta'\beta z] \sin(\omega_0 t - \beta_0 z - \phi) \qquad \textbf{(10-114)}$$

$$\phi \approx M \sin(\Delta\omega t - \Delta\beta z) \sin \Delta'\beta z \qquad \textbf{(10-115)}$$

Thus the envelope appears to travel at the group velocity v_g defined in Eq. 10-106, but the envelope changes shape meanwhile. The signal amplitude is $M \cos \Delta'\beta z$ rather than M, and at those values of z at which $\Delta'\beta z$ is an odd multiple of $\pi/2$, the envelope shows no modulation.

If higher-order terms had been carried in approximation 10-100, additional modes of variation would have been brought into the description of the moving envelope.

c. Rectangular-step modulating function

Karbowiak[7] has investigated by contour-integral methods the propagation of a signal whose modulating function is a rectangular step. The following aspects of the results are of interest (see Fig. 10-7):

(1) No signal is sensed at distance z from the source until time $t_0 = z/v_0$, has elapsed.

(2) At time t_0 the "B precursor" envelope appears. This is a surge which abruptly reaches a crest of appreciable magnitude, but which quickly drops to a lower value and then diminishes in proportion to $t^{-1/4}$. (The designator "B," adopted by Karbowiak, indicates "branch cut.")

(3) Simultaneous with the B precursor is another component, the "P precursor"; it is initially much smaller and increases slowly until shortly before $t_1 = z/v_g$. (Here v_g is the group velocity, Eq. 10-106.) Then the P precursor begins to rise more rapidly. (The designator "P" indicates "pole integral.")

(4) The P precursor leads into the wave front of the main pulse envelope.

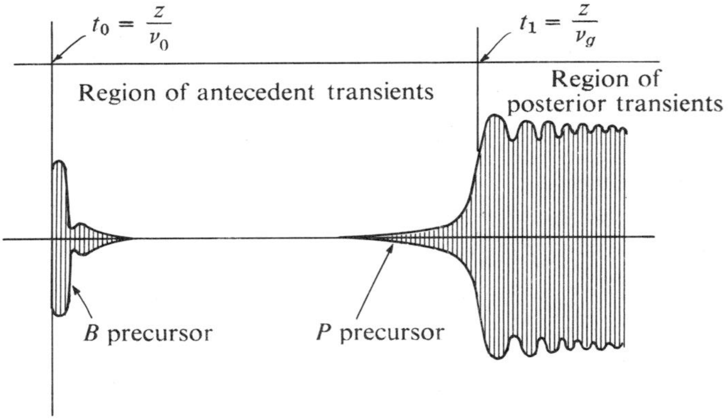

Figure 10-7 The response of a wave guide to a rectangular-step-modulated carrier (from *Proc. IEE (London)*, by permission[7])

This wave front rises at a time rate proportional to $z^{-1/2}$, and at time t_1 it reaches one-half of the steady-state asymptote.

(5) The wave front of the main pulse envelope reaches a crest somewhat above the steady-state asymptote, then oscillates about that asymptote with an amplitude which diminishes in proportion to $t^{-1/2}$. This oscillation is the resultant of two components, the *B* sequel and the *P* sequel.

d. Single-rectangular-pulse modulating function

A rectangular pulse may be considered as the superposition of two step functions of opposite polarities, with one delayed with respect to the other. Envelope shapes based on the analysis just described, but with omission of the *B* precursor and the *B* sequel (this is reasonable in most practical situations) are shown in Fig. 10-8 for a pulse of duration Δt. These show the progressive change in envelope shape with distance of travel in the wave guide.

Elliott[3] has presented a more approximate analysis for the rectangular-pulse form of modulating signal in a wave guide.

10-5. ATTENUATION OF TE_{10} PROPAGATING MODE

Physical materials used for the conducting surfaces of wave guides have finite conductivities, but much effort has been directed toward fabrication techniques which will minimize losses.[1,6] Power will be absorbed from the traveling fields and their magnitudes will thereby be attenuated with distance traveled. As indicated earlier, the usual metals for this purpose, copper, silver, or brass, have such high conductivities that the field configurations are

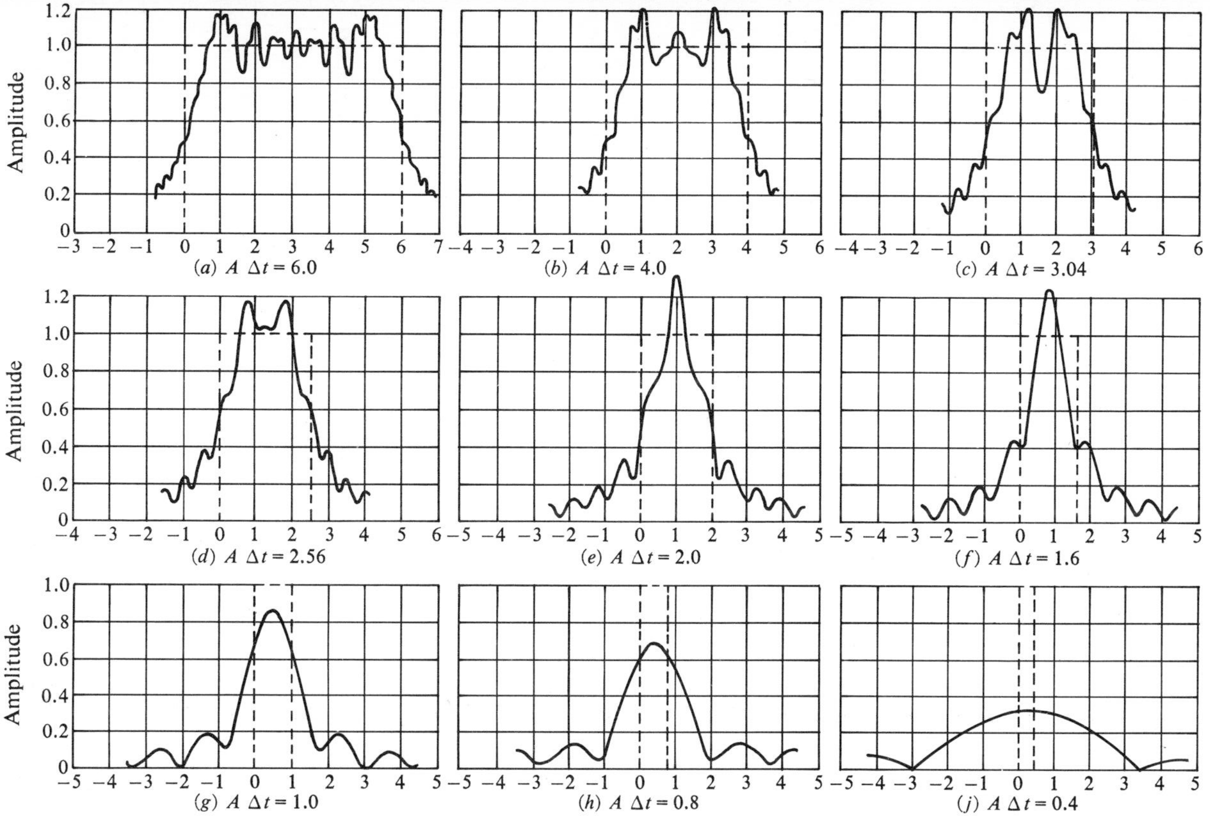

Figure 10-8 Envelope of the received pulse after transmission through a wave guide $A = \frac{\omega_0 v_0}{2_z} \frac{\omega_0}{\omega_c} \left[1 - \left(\frac{\omega_c}{\omega_0} \right)^2 \right]$ (from *Proc. IEE* (*London*), by permission[7])

Note: Abscissae are in terms of the dimensionless variable $A(t - t_1)$. Here $t_1 = z/v_g$

essentially the same as if the conductivity were infinite, and this simplifies the solution greatly.

The procedure which will be followed is to compare the power loss for a short length Δz with the power transmitted. In the discussion of Poynting's vector it was shown (Eq. 8-43) that the time-averaged power diminishes with distance traveled in proportion to $\epsilon^{-2\alpha z}$. Hence

$$\frac{P_{\text{loss}} + P_{\text{tr}}}{P_{\text{tr}}} = \epsilon^{2\alpha\,\Delta z}$$

If $P_{\text{loss}} \ll P_{\text{tr}}$,

$$\frac{P_{\text{loss}}}{P_{\text{tr}}} + 1 \approx 1 + 2\alpha\,\Delta z$$

$$\alpha \approx \frac{P_{\text{loss}}}{2P_{\text{tr}}\,\Delta z} \tag{10-116}$$

The expressions for $\boldsymbol{E}$ and $\boldsymbol{H}$ given in Eqs. 10-8 and 10-9 will be the bases for substitutions in the equations which follow. The time-averaged transmitted power for this wave set was found to be

$$P_{\text{tr}} = \frac{A_1^2\beta_{10}ab}{4\omega\mu} \tag{10-23}$$

Loss per unit of wave-guide length may be computed by means of Poynting's vector normal to each conducting surface, as in Sec. 8-4. Equation 8-42 reduces to the following:

$$P_{\text{nor}} = E_{\tan}H_{\tan} \tag{10-117}$$

The expression for the $\boldsymbol{E}$ field in the ideally conducting wave guide, Eq. 10-8, contains no tangential component at the conducting surface; for the surface of high, yet finite, conductivity it may be approximated by the following relationship to $H_{\tan}$:

$$E_{\tan} = \operatorname{Im}[H_{0\tan}\eta_M\epsilon^{j\omega t}] \tag{10-118}$$

where

$$H_{\tan} = \operatorname{Im}[H_{0\tan}\epsilon^{j\omega t}]$$

$$\eta_M = \sqrt{\frac{\omega\mu}{\sigma}}\,\epsilon^{j\pi/4} \tag{8-30}$$

$$= R_S + jR_S$$

Here R_S is the surface resistance, Eq. 8-79. Poynting's vector may be written separately for the sidewalls and the horizontal surfaces.

Because of symmetry, Poynting's vector will have the same magnitude on both sidewalls; the vector for the wall for which $x = 0$ will be designated by $\boldsymbol{P}_W$. The tangential $\boldsymbol{E}$ field found from Eqs. 10-9 and 10-118, is

$$E_y = \frac{-A_1\pi}{\omega\mu a}\,|\eta_M|\cos(\omega t + 45° - \beta z) \tag{10-119}$$

Substitution of Eqs. 10-9 and 10-119 into Eq. 8-42 gives

$$\begin{aligned}\boldsymbol{P}_W &= E_y H_z \boldsymbol{a}_x \\ &= -\left(\frac{A_1\pi}{\omega\mu a}\right)^2 |\eta_M| \cos(\omega t + 45° - \beta z)\cos(\omega t - \beta z)\boldsymbol{a}_x \\ &= -\left(\frac{A_1\pi}{\omega\mu a}\right)^2 |\eta_M| [\cos 45° \cos^2(\omega t - \beta z) \\ &\qquad - \sin 45° \sin(\omega t - \beta z)\cos(\omega t - \beta z)]\boldsymbol{a}_x \\ &= -\left(\frac{A_1\pi}{\omega\mu a}\right)^2 |\eta_M| \left\{\frac{\cos 45°}{2}[1 + \cos 2(\omega t - \beta z)] \right. \\ &\qquad \left. - \frac{\sin 45°}{2} \sin 2(\omega t - \beta z)\right\}\boldsymbol{a}_x\end{aligned}$$

The time-averaged value $\boldsymbol{P}_{W\text{av}}$ is

$$\begin{aligned}\boldsymbol{P}_{W\text{av}} &= -\left(\frac{A_1\pi}{\omega\mu a}\right)^2 |\eta_M| \frac{\cos 45°}{2} \boldsymbol{a}_x \\ &= -\left(\frac{A_1\pi}{\omega\mu a}\right)^2 \frac{R_S}{2} \boldsymbol{a}_x\end{aligned}$$

This should be integrated over a strip extending from 0 to b in the $\boldsymbol{a}_y$ direction and from z_1 to $z_1 + \Delta z$ in the $\boldsymbol{a}_z$ direction:

$$\begin{aligned}P_{\text{wall}} &= \int_0^b \int_{z_1}^{z_1+\Delta z_1} \boldsymbol{P}_{W\text{av}} \cdot (-dy\, dz\, \boldsymbol{a}_x) \\ &= \left(\frac{A_1\pi}{\omega\mu a}\right)^2 \frac{R_S b\, \Delta z}{2}\end{aligned} \tag{10-120}$$

For a point on the top or bottom surface, Poynting's vector ($\boldsymbol{P}_T$ or $\boldsymbol{P}_B$, respectively) is more complicated. The tangential component of $\boldsymbol{H}$ includes both H_x and H_z:

$$\boldsymbol{P}_T = (E_z H_x - E_x H_z)\boldsymbol{a}_y \qquad (y = b)$$

The expression for $\boldsymbol{P}_B$ is the negative of that for $\boldsymbol{P}_T$ because they are oppositely directed. Let

$$\begin{aligned}H_x &= \text{Im}[H_{0x}\epsilon^{j\omega t}] \\ E_z &= \text{Im}[\eta_M H_{0x}\epsilon^{j\omega t}] \\ H_z &= \text{Im}[H_{0z}\epsilon^{j\omega t}] \\ E_x &= \text{Im}[-\eta_M H_{0z}\epsilon^{j\omega t}]\end{aligned}$$

Terms from Eq. 10-9 may be substituted for H_{0x} and H_{0z}, and E_x and E_z written in forms corresponding to Eq. 10-119. The time-averaged value for $\boldsymbol{P}_T$ may be obtained by steps paralleling those for $\boldsymbol{P}_W$:

$$\boldsymbol{P}_{T\text{av}} = \frac{1}{4}\left(\frac{A_1}{\omega\mu}\right)^2 \left\{\beta^2\left[1 - \cos\left(\frac{2\pi x}{a}\right)\right] + \left(\frac{\pi}{a}\right)^2\left[1 + \cos\left(\frac{2\pi x}{a}\right)\right]\right\} R_S \boldsymbol{a}_y$$

This is to be integrated over a strip extending from 0 to a in the $\boldsymbol{a}_x$ direction and from z_1 to $z_1 + \Delta z$ in the $\boldsymbol{a}_z$ direction:

$$P_{\text{top}} = \int_0^a \int_{z_1}^{z_1+\Delta z} \boldsymbol{P}_{T\text{av}} \cdot (dx\, dz\, \boldsymbol{a}_y)$$

$$= \frac{1}{4}\left(\frac{A_1}{\omega\mu}\right)^2 \left[\beta^2 a\,\Delta z + \left(\frac{\pi}{a}\right)^2 a\,\Delta z\right] R_S$$

Substitution of Eq. 10-6 reduces this to the following:

$$P_{\text{top}} = \frac{1}{4}\left(\frac{A_1}{\omega\mu}\right)^2 \omega^2\mu\epsilon a\,\Delta z R_S$$

$$= \frac{A_1^2\epsilon R_S a\,\Delta z}{4\mu} \tag{10-121}$$

The power loss on the bottom surface is equal to that on the top, and the losses in the two walls are equal. Hence the total loss in distance Δz along the wave guide is

$$P_{\text{loss}} = 2P_{\text{top}} + 2P_{\text{wall}}$$

$$= A_1^2 R_S\left[\frac{a\epsilon}{2\mu} + \frac{\pi^2 b}{\omega^2\mu^2 a^2}\right]\Delta z \tag{10-122}$$

Equations 10-23 and 10-122 may be substituted in Eq. 10-116 to yield an expression for α:

$$\alpha = \left[\frac{a\epsilon\omega}{ab\beta} + \frac{\pi^2}{\omega\mu a^3\beta}\right] R_S \tag{10-123}$$

By substitution of Eqs. 10-6, 10-10, and 8-27, this may be reduced to the following:

$$\alpha = \frac{R_S}{\eta\sqrt{1-(f_c/f)^2}}\left[\frac{1}{b} + \frac{2}{a}\left(\frac{f_c}{f}\right)^2\right] \tag{10-124}$$

For frequencies much greater than cutoff, Eq. 10-124 approaches the following asymptote:

$$\alpha \approx \frac{1}{b}\sqrt{\frac{\pi\epsilon f}{\sigma}} \qquad (f \gg f_c) \tag{10-125}$$

The value of f/f_c which yields the minimum attenuation for given values of a and b may be found by differentiation (see Problem 10-17); the result is as follows:

$$\left(\frac{f}{f_c}\right)^2 = \frac{3}{2}\left(1 + \frac{2b}{a}\right) + \sqrt{\frac{9}{4}\left(1 + \frac{2b}{a}\right)^2 - \frac{2b}{a}} \tag{10-126}$$

Commercially standardized designs for rectangular wave guides fix dimension b at equal to or slightly less than $a/2$. For $b = a/2$, the ratio f/f_c for minimum attenuation becomes 2.41.

In the interest of preventing multiple moding, it is desirable to operate a wave guide at a frequency somewhat less than twice the cutoff value, even though this is appreciably less than the minimum-attenuation frequency just noted. Recommended frequency ranges given in current commercial literature are from about 1.25 to 1.90 times the cutoff frequency.[9]

10-6. CONCLUSIONS

Electromagnetic waves may be transmitted through hollow rectangular metallic wave guides in field configurations in which either the magnetic field or the electric field has a longitudinal component. Each distinct configuration is known as a *mode* and is characterized by a *cutoff frequency* below which it cannot exist as a traveling wave. The number of possible modes is infinite, but they may be classified as *transverse electric* (TE) or *transverse magnetic* (TM). In the former class the electric field is confined to planes perpendicular to the wave guide axis, but a longitudinal component of magnetic field is necessary. Conversely, in TM modes the magnetic field is confined to planes perpendicular to the wave-guide axis, but a longitudinal component of electric field is present.

The *dominant* mode, the one with the lowest cutoff frequency, is the TE_{10} mode. In this mode the fields are independent of distance in the shorter transverse direction in the wave guide, although the $\boldsymbol{E}$ field is everywhere parallel to the shorter transverse dimension and is proportional to $\sin \pi x/a$. Here a is the longer transverse dimension and x is the corresponding coordinate. This is the usual mode for signal transmission.

Standing-wave field patterns may be formed by superposition of traveling-wave fields moving in opposite directions.

Traveling-wave or standing-wave fields in a wave guide are accompanied by surface-current-density fields in the walls, which are directed perpendicular to the tangential magnetic field. For the TE_{10} mode, no current flows across the longitudinal axis of either of the wider surfaces.

Modes of higher cutoff frequency than the excitation frequency may exist in the vicinity of wave-guide discontinuities in *evanescent* or *nonpropagating* form. In such modes the electric and magnetic fields are in time quadrature with each other.

The apparent velocity of each sinusoidal component, or *phase velocity*, depends on frequency, and exceeds that for a TEM wave in the same medium as that enclosed in the wave guide. Amplitude-modulated-signal envelopes appear to travel at a lower speed, known as the *group velocity*, and also undergo progressive changes in shape.

PROBLEMS

10-1. Verify that the expression for the magnetic field of the TE_{m0} mode given in Eq. 10-9 satisfies Maxwell's equation in div $\boldsymbol{B}$.

10-2. Solve Eq. 10-13 by separation of variables, and reduce the answer to Eq. 10-14.

10-3. Show, for $m = 1$, by means of series expansions, that the magnetic-field-direction lines described in Eq. 10-14 are approximately elliptical for C slightly less than unity in magnitude. The following change of variables may be helpful:

$$\frac{\pi x}{a} = \frac{\pi}{2} + \frac{\pi\,\Delta x}{a}$$

10-4. Write the differential equation for the direction lines of the surface-current-density field on the top and bottom surfaces of a rectangular wave guide with a TE_{10} propagating mode in it. Separate the variables and solve. Determine what range of values of the arbitrary constant corresponds to lines which connect to the side walls. Sketch several direction lines for the case $\beta_{10}a/\pi = 1$.

10-5. Sketch the field patterns (direction lines) for $\boldsymbol{E}_2$ and $\boldsymbol{H}_2$ as given in Eqs. 10-24 and 10-25. Write an expression for the displacement-current-density field and add its direction lines to the sketch. Compare with Fig. 10-2.

10-6. Write Poynting's vector for the rectangular wave guide with a TE_{10} propagating mode and a short-circuiting end plate (Eqs. 10-27 and 10-28). Find the time-averaged value, if any.

10-7. Sketch the direction-line patterns for the $\boldsymbol{E}_{sc}$, $\boldsymbol{H}_{sc}$ and $\boldsymbol{J}_{Dsc}$ fields (Eqs. 10-27, 10-28, and 10-29) at ωt equal to (*a*) zero, (*b*) 45°, (*c*) 90°, and (*d*) 135°.

10-8. Write the differential equation for the direction lines of the magnetic field for a TE_{10} nonpropagating mode in a rectangular wave guide (Eq. 10-32). Separate variables and solve. Investigate by means of series expansions and the change of variables suggested in Problem 10-3 the direction lines near the centerline of the wave guide. Sketch the direction-line patterns of the electric and magnetic fields for ωt equal to (*a*) zero, (*b*) 45°, (*c*) 90°, and (*d*) 135°.

10-9. Write expressions for the surface-current-density function for the sidewalls and the top and bottom surfaces of a rectangular wave guide with a TE_{10} nonpropagating mode present. Write the differential equation for the direction lines, separate variables, and solve.

10-10. Write complete expressions for the incident and reflected magnetic fields in the range $z < 0$ and for the magnetic field in the range $z > 0$ in the problem discussed in Sec. 10-2*b*.

10-11. Rework the problem discussed in Sec. 10-2*b* if the following is true rather than Eq. 10-36:

$$\frac{\pi}{a\sqrt{\mu\epsilon_1}} < \frac{\pi}{a\sqrt{\mu\epsilon_0}} < \omega$$

10-12. Given the function $\boldsymbol{E}(x, y, z, t) = E_x\boldsymbol{a}_x + E_y\boldsymbol{a}_y + E_z\boldsymbol{a}_z$. Find, by substituting in Eqs. 7-44, 7-45, and 7-47, the laplacian of the vector field $\boldsymbol{E}$, as given by Eq. 10-48. Verify, with the aid of Eq. 7-48, the identity stated in Eq. 10-49.

10-13. Modify the expression for E_z in Eq. 10-56 so that it will describe a nonpropagating TM mode. Make corresponding modifications in set 10-76, and write complete expressions, similar to Eq. 10-77, for all field components. Compare these results with Eqs. 10-31 and 10-32 and the discussion concerning nonpropagating TE_{m0} modes.

10-14. Find the parametric equations for the direction lines of the $\boldsymbol{E}$ field of the TM_{11} mode in the plane $x = a/2$.

10-15. Rewrite the equations in set 10-80 for the general TE mode as explicit functions of time (as in Eq. 10-77).

10-16. Examine the TE_{10} fields as given in Eqs. 10-88 through 10-95 for frequency (*a*) approaching the cutoff value, and (*b*) equal to the cutoff value.

10-17. Verify Eq. 10-126 for the frequency of minimum attenuation for the TE_{10} mode.

REFERENCES

1. ALLISON, J. and F. A. BENSON, "Surface Roughness and Attenuation of Precision Drawn, Chemically Polished, Electropolished, Electroplated and Electroformed Waveguides," *Proc. IEE* (*London*), 102, Part B (1955), 251–59.
2. COLLIN, ROBERT E., *Field Theory of Guided Waves*, chap. 8. New York: McGraw-Hill Book Company, Inc., 1960.
3. ELLIOTT, R. S., "Pulse Waveform Degradation Due to Dispersion in Waveguides," *IRE Trans. Microwave Theory Tech.*, MTT-5, No. 4 (1957), 254–57.
4. GHOSE, RABINDRA N., *Microwave Circuit Theory and Analysis*. New York: McGraw-Hill Book Company, Inc., 1963.
5. HARRINGTON, ROGER F., *Time-Harmonic Electromagnetic Fields*. New York: McGraw-Hill Book Company, Inc., 1961.
6. HARVEY, A. F., "Mechanical Design and Manufacture of Microwave Structures," *IRE Trans. Microwave Theory Tech.*, MTT-7, No. 4 (1959), 402–22.
7. KARBOWIAK, A. E., "Propagation of Transients in Waveguides," *Proc. IEE* (*London*), 104, Part C (1957), 339–48 (also Monograph No. 224R).
8. MARCUVITZ, N., *Waveguide Handbook*. New York: McGraw-Hill Book Company, Inc., 1951.
9. *The Microwave Engineer's Handbook and Buyer's Guide*. Brookline, Mass.: Horizon House-Microwave, Inc., 1963.

CHAPTER 11

Conductor-Guided Fields: Circular Wave Guides

Electromagnetic-wave propagation is possible within tubular circular conductors in modes similar to those in hollow rectangular wave guides; several other types of guides of circular cross section will also propagate waves. Among the latter are closely wound wire helices, wires coated with dielectric material, and solid or hollow dielectric rods.[1] Detailed mathematical derivations will, for simplicity, be limited to the hollow metallic wave guide of high conductivity. These derivations will follow the same general approach as for the rectangular wave guide. The circular cylindrical coordinate system is the most suitable here because of the ease in fitting boundary conditions.

In a hollow metallic circular wave guide both transverse magnetic and transverse electric modes are possible; the former are characterized by a longitudinal component of $\boldsymbol{E}$, the latter by a longitudinal component of $\boldsymbol{H}$. Modes which have *circularly symmetrical* field patterns exist in both the TM and TE types, and the simplest of these modes are the modes of interest as vehicles for transmitting signals.

The *helical* wave guide is in essence a modification of the tubular circular wave guide. It has a mode-discrimination quality in its attenuation function which favors the circularly symmetrical TE modes.

11-1. SOLUTION OF MAXWELL'S EQUATIONS IN CYLINDRICAL COORDINATES

The circular wave guide will be assumed to be a perfectly conducting cylindrical tube with internal radius r_a.

a. Equation of traveling-wave function

Derivation of the scalar wave equation for the propagating fields in a circular wave guide may begin with the vector wave equation, 10-47.

$$\nabla \times (\nabla \times \boldsymbol{E}) = -\mu\epsilon \frac{\partial^2 \boldsymbol{E}}{\partial t^2} \qquad \textbf{(10-47)}$$

The following identity used in Chapter 10 is useful here:

$$-\nabla \times (\nabla \times \boldsymbol{E}) + \nabla(\nabla \cdot \boldsymbol{E}) = \nabla^2 \boldsymbol{E} \qquad \textbf{(10-48)}$$

If one inserts the cylindrical-coordinate expressions for curl 7-56, divergence 7-55, gradient 7-57 and laplacian of a scalar field 7-58 into Eq. 10-48 and separates the coefficients of $\boldsymbol{a}_z$, the following immediately useful result is obtained:

$$-[\nabla \times (\nabla \times \boldsymbol{E})]_z + [\nabla(\nabla \cdot \boldsymbol{E})]_z = \nabla^2 E_z \qquad \textbf{(11-1)}$$

The r component of Eq. 10-48 is a function of both E_r and E_ϕ, and the same is true of the ϕ component. In other words, the variables do not separate for those components. (Should $\boldsymbol{E}$ not be a function of ϕ, the variables will separate, but the remaining terms will not reduce to $\nabla^2 E_r$ or $\nabla^2 E_\phi$; see Problem 11-1.)

The procedure here will be to find the functional form of E_z and to derive, from Maxwell's equations, supplementary equations which will enable one to find the other field components from E_z.

The region within the wave guide is assumed to be free of charge; hence $\nabla \cdot \boldsymbol{E} = 0$. Substituting Eq. 11-1 in Eq. 10-47 gives

$$\nabla^2 E_z = \mu\epsilon \frac{\partial^2 E_z}{\partial t^2} \qquad \textbf{(11-2)}$$

E_z by itself is a scalar field, and Eq. 7-58, giving the laplacian in terms of cylindrical coordinates, may be substituted:

$$\frac{1}{r}\frac{\partial}{\partial r}\left(r\frac{\partial E_z}{\partial r}\right) + \frac{1}{r^2}\frac{\partial^2 E_z}{\partial \phi^2} + \frac{\partial^2 E_z}{\partial z^2} = \mu\epsilon\frac{\partial^2 E_z}{\partial t^2} \qquad \textbf{(11-3)}$$

As in the preceding chapter, it is convenient to assume that E_z is a sinusoidal traveling-wave function:

$$E_z = \text{Im}[E_{0z}(r,\phi)\epsilon^{j(\omega t - \beta z)}] \qquad \textbf{(11-4)}$$

Equation 11-4 may be substituted in Eq. 11-3, the Im operator deleted from all terms, and the factor $\epsilon^{j(\omega t - \beta z)}$ cancelled throughout:

$$\frac{1}{r}\frac{\partial}{\partial r}\left(r\frac{\partial E_{0z}(r,\phi)}{\partial r}\right) + \frac{1}{r^2}\frac{\partial^2 E_{0z}(r,\phi)}{\partial \phi^2} - \beta^2 E_{0z}(r,\phi) = -\mu\epsilon\omega^2 E_{0z}(r,\phi) \qquad \textbf{(11-5)}$$

b. Solution by separation of variables

This partial differential equation in E_{0z} may be solved by separation of variables with the product-function technique. Let

$$E_{0z}(r,\phi) = R(r)\Phi(\phi) \tag{11-6}$$

The procedure is similar to that followed in Sec. 10-3. Equation 11-6 is substituted into Eq. 11-5, and the resulting equation is divided by $R(r)$ and $\Phi(\phi)$ and multiplied by r^2 to separate the variables:

$$\frac{r}{R(r)}\frac{d}{dr}\left(r\frac{dR(r)}{dr}\right) + \frac{1}{\Phi(\phi)}\frac{d^2\Phi(\phi)}{d\phi^2} = (\beta^2 - \mu\epsilon\omega^2)r^2 \tag{11-7}$$

The term immediately to the left of the equality sign is the only one which is a function of ϕ, and it is not a function of r. For the equation to be satisfied for independently chosen combinations of r and ϕ, this term must equal a constant. Let

$$\frac{1}{\Phi(\phi)}\frac{d^2\Phi(\phi)}{d\phi^2} = -m^2 \tag{11-8}$$

This may be reduced to

$$\frac{d^2\Phi(\phi)}{d\phi^2} + m^2\Phi(\phi) = 0 \tag{11-9}$$

(1) SOLUTION FOR Φ FUNCTION. Equation 11-9 may be recognized as a homogeneous linear differential equation of the second order with constant coefficients, the solution to which is the following:

$$\Phi(\phi) = C_1 \sin m\phi + C_2 \cos m\phi \tag{11-10}$$

Here C_1 and C_2 are arbitrary constants.

The possible values of the assumed constant m are limited by the boundary condition that the function E_{0z}, and hence $\Phi(\phi)$, must recur at intervals of 2π in ϕ

$$\Phi(\phi + 2\pi) = \Phi(\phi) \tag{11-11}$$

This will be satisfied if the constant m is any integer.

(2) SOLUTION FOR $R(r)$ FUNCTION. Substitution of Eq. 11-8 in Eq. 11-7 leaves the following ordinary differential equation:

$$\frac{r}{R(r)}\frac{d}{dr}\left(r\frac{dR(r)}{dr}\right) - m^2 = (\beta^2 - \mu\epsilon\omega^2)r^2 \tag{11-12}$$

This is a form of Bessel's differential equation. It may be reduced to standard form by multiplying it by $R(r)/r^2$ and making the following change of variable:

$$p = r\sqrt{\mu\epsilon\omega^2 - \beta^2} \tag{11-13}$$

Then
$$\frac{d^2R(p)}{dp^2} + \frac{1}{p}\frac{dR(p)}{dp} + R(p)\left(1 - \frac{m^2}{p^2}\right) = 0 \tag{11-14}$$

The general solution to this equation may be written as follows:

$$R(p) = A_m J_m(p) + B_m Y_m(p) \tag{11-15}$$

The functions J_m and Y_m, known as Bessel functions of the first and second kinds, of order m, are derivable from infinite series and have been tabulated extensively. They are discussed in some detail in Sec. B-1*b*. Functions J_0 and J_1 are of particular interest in the study of the circular wave guide and are plotted in Fig. 11-1. A_m and B_m are constants which are chosen in accordance with boundary conditions.

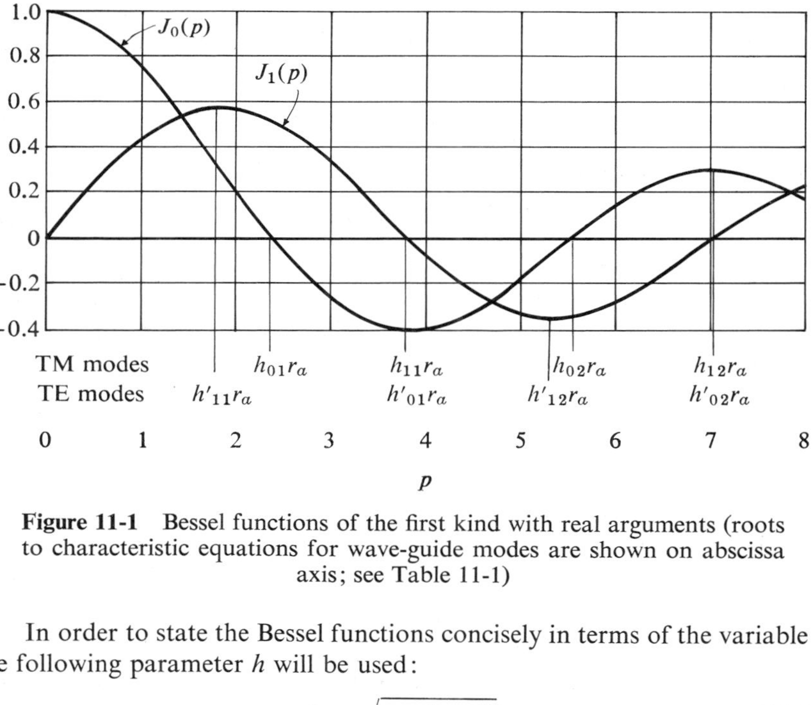

Figure 11-1 Bessel functions of the first kind with real arguments (roots to characteristic equations for wave-guide modes are shown on abscissa axis; see Table 11-1)

In order to state the Bessel functions concisely in terms of the variable r, the following parameter h will be used:

$$h = \sqrt{\mu\epsilon\omega^2 - \beta^2} \tag{11-16}$$

Thus
$$R(r) = A_m J_m(hr) + B_m Y_m(hr) \tag{11-17}$$

The function $Y_m(hr)$ will approach minus infinity as the argument approaches zero. Within the hollow wave guide the fields must be finite; hence this function is excluded from the solution:

$$B_m = 0 \tag{11-18}$$

c. Longitudinal-component functions

If the results obtained from Eqs. 11-10, 11-17 and 11-18 are substituted in Eq. 11-6, the following results:

$$E_{0z}(r,\phi) = A_m J_m(hr)(C_1 \sin m\phi + C_2 \cos m\phi) \tag{11-19}$$

The solution to this point may be duplicated, step for step, in terms of the longitudinal component of a postulated $\boldsymbol{H}$ field:

$$H_z = \text{Im}[H_{0z}(r,\phi)\epsilon^{j(\omega t - \beta z)}] \tag{11-20}$$

$$H_{0z}(r,\phi) = A'_m J_m(hr)(C'_1 \sin m\phi + C'_2 \cos m\phi) \tag{11-21}$$

A longitudinal $\boldsymbol{E}$ component, such as E_z in Eq. 11-4, is characteristic of transverse-magnetic modes, whereas a longitudinal $\boldsymbol{H}$ component (Eq. 11-20) is characteristic of transverse-electric modes. The values of the parameters h and β in both cases are fixed by the boundary condition that the components of $\boldsymbol{E}$ which are parallel to the conducting guide wall shall vanish along that conducting surface. The mathematical application of this boundary condition to the two types of modes differs, so they will be considered separately.

d. Transverse components as related to longitudinal components

Expressions for the radial and circumferential components of the fields in terms of the longitudinal components may be derived from Maxwell's equations involving the curl of $\boldsymbol{H}$, Eq. 10-46, and the curl of $\boldsymbol{E}$, Eq. 7-34. The r and ϕ components of those vector equations are

$$\frac{1}{r}\frac{\partial H_z}{\partial \phi} - \frac{\partial H_\phi}{\partial z} = \epsilon \frac{\partial E_r}{\partial t} \tag{11-22}$$

$$\frac{\partial H_r}{\partial z} - \frac{\partial H_z}{\partial r} = \epsilon \frac{\partial E_\phi}{\partial t} \tag{11-23}$$

$$\frac{1}{r}\frac{\partial E_z}{\partial \phi} - \frac{\partial E_\phi}{\partial z} = -\mu \frac{\partial H_r}{\partial t} \tag{11-24}$$

$$\frac{\partial E_r}{\partial z} - \frac{\partial E_z}{\partial r} = -\mu \frac{\partial H_\phi}{\partial t} \tag{11-25}$$

If Eq. 11-22 is differentiated with respect to z, and Eq. 11-25 is differentiated with respect to t and multiplied by ϵ, the derivative involving E_r may be eliminated from the pair of equations, and the following expression for H_ϕ results:

$$\frac{\partial^2 H_\phi}{\partial z^2} - \mu\epsilon \frac{\partial^2 H_\phi}{\partial t^2} = \frac{1}{r}\frac{\partial}{\partial z}\left(\frac{\partial H_z}{\partial \phi}\right) - \epsilon \frac{\partial}{\partial t}\left(\frac{\partial E_z}{\partial r}\right) \tag{11-26}$$

As with the rectangular wave-guide analysis, this equation may be greatly simplified if the fields are assumed to be sinusoidal traveling-wave functions, in accordance with Eqs. 11-4 and 11-20. The remaining components will be assumed to have the same form, and the functions $E_{0r}(r,\phi)$, $E_{0\phi}(r,\phi)$, $H_{0\phi}(r,\phi)$, and $H_{0\phi}(r,\phi)$ will be introduced for that purpose.

Equation 11-26 may then be restated as follows:

$$(\mu\epsilon\omega^2 - \beta^2)H_{0\phi} = -\frac{j\beta}{r}\frac{\partial H_{0z}}{\partial\phi} - j\omega\epsilon\frac{\partial E_{0z}}{\partial r} \tag{11-27}$$

The left-hand side of this equation may be simplified by substituting Eq. 11-16:

$$h^2 H_{0\phi} = -\frac{j\beta}{r}\frac{\partial H_{0z}}{\partial\phi} - j\omega\epsilon\frac{\partial E_{0z}}{\partial r} \tag{11-28}$$

Corresponding equations for the other components are

$$\begin{aligned} h^2 E_{0r} &= -\frac{j\omega\mu}{r}\frac{\partial H_{0z}}{\partial\phi} - j\beta\frac{\partial E_{0z}}{\partial r} \\ h^2 E_{0\phi} &= -\frac{j\beta}{r}\frac{\partial E_{0z}}{\partial\phi} + j\omega\mu\frac{\partial H_{0z}}{\partial r} \\ h^2 H_{0r} &= \frac{j\omega\epsilon}{r}\frac{\partial E_{0z}}{\partial\phi} - j\beta\frac{\partial H_{0z}}{\partial r} \end{aligned} \tag{11-29}$$

11-2. PROPAGATION MODES IN HOLLOW WAVE GUIDE

The remaining boundary conditions for the hollow wave guide apply at the surface $r = r_a$. Here the tangential components of the electric field, E_z, and E_ϕ, and the normal component of the magnetic field, H_r, all vanish.

a. TM modes: general

For TM modes, E_z is described by Eqs. 11-4 and 11-19, and H_z is zero. Components E_ϕ and H_r may be found from Eqs. 11-29, and 11-19:

$$E_{0\phi}(r,\phi) = -\frac{j\beta m A_m}{h^2 r} J_m(hr)(C_1 \cos m\phi - C_2 \sin m\phi) \tag{11-30}$$

$$H_{0r}(r,\phi) = \frac{jm\omega\epsilon A_m}{h^2 r} J_m(hr)(C_1 \cos m\phi - C_2 \sin m\phi) \tag{11-31}$$

All three will vanish at radius r_a if the following is true:

$$J_m(hr_a) = 0 \tag{11-32}$$

Values of the argument hr_a which will satisfy Eq. 11-32 are known as *zeros* or *roots* of the Bessel function, and have been tabulated extensively.[2] Some are presented in Table 11-1 and those within the scope of Fig. 11-1 have been marked there. They are transcendental numbers and are not related to one another by any simple arithmetic rule. For each function order m, an infinite number of zeros exist, and they are conventionally

Table 11-1 ZEROS OF BESSEL FUNCTIONS*

$J_m(h_{mn}r_a) = 0$ (TM *modes*)

m	n	$h_{mn}r_a$
0	1	2.404826
1	1	3.831706
2	1	5.135622
0	2	5.520078
3	1	6.380162
1	2	7.015587
4	1	7.588342
2	2	8.417244
0	3	8.653728

$\left[\dfrac{dJ_m(h'_{mn}r)}{dr}\right]_{r=r_a} = 0$ (TE *modes*)

m	n	$h'_{mn}r_a$
1	1	1.841184
2	1	3.054237
0	1	3.831706
3	1	4.201189
4	1	5.317553
1	2	5.331443
5	1	6.415616
2	2	6.706133
0	2	7.015587
6	1	7.501266
3	2	8.015237
1	3	8.536316
7	1	8.577836

* Adapted from Reference 2. Reprinted by permission.

designated by counting them in sequence of location n from the origin. The designator $n = 1$ is assigned to the zero which is closest to, but not at, the origin. Field-descriptive equations may be made specific in this regard by attaching the subscripts m and n to h, β, and related quantities, and the same subscripts are used in the mode designator, TM_{mn}.

The minimum frequency which will yield a real rather than an imaginary value for β, in other words, the cutoff frequency, is determined, in accordance with Eq. 11-16, by the parameter h. It in turn is fixed by the wave-guide radius r_a and the Bessel function root of the mode selected.

$$\omega_{cmn} = \frac{h_{mn}}{\sqrt{\mu\epsilon}} \tag{11-33}$$

As with the rectangular wave guide,

$$\beta = \sqrt{\mu\epsilon(\omega^2 - \omega_c^2)} \tag{11-34}$$

b. TE modes: general

The only $\boldsymbol{E}$ component which is tangential to the wave-guide surface in a TE mode is E_ϕ, From Eqs. 11-29, and 11-21,

$$E_{0\phi} = \frac{j\omega\mu A'_m}{h^2}\frac{dJ_m(hr)}{dr}(C_1 \sin m\phi + C_2 \cos m\phi) \tag{11-35}$$

$$H_{0r} = \frac{-j\beta A'_m}{h^2}\frac{dJ_m(hr)}{dr}(C_1 \sin m\phi + C_2 \cos m\phi) \tag{11-36}$$

These components will vanish along the wave-guide surface if the following is true*:

$$\left[\frac{dJ_m(hr)}{dr}\right]_{r=ra} = 0 \tag{11-37}$$

To distinguish the argument values which satisfy Eq. 11-37 from those for the zeros of $J_m(hr_a)$, the prime mark will be added as a superscript: h'_{mn}, β'_{mn}, etc. The corresponding mode designator is TE_{mn}. Some values of $h'r_a$ are listed in Table 11-1, and those within the scope of Fig. 11-1 have been marked there.

In accordance with Eq. 11-16, the cutoff frequency of a TE mode is

$$\omega'_{cmn} = \frac{h'_{mn}}{\sqrt{\mu\epsilon}} \tag{11-42}$$

$$\beta' = \sqrt{\mu\epsilon(\omega^2 - \omega_c'^2)} \tag{11-43}$$

* The derivative of the zero-order Bessel function is as follows:

$$\frac{dJ_0(hr)}{dr} = -hJ_1(hr) \tag{11-38}$$

For higher-order functions, the following are applicable:

$$\frac{dJ_m(hr)}{dr} = [J_{m-1}(hr) - J_{m+1}(hr)]\,\frac{h}{2} \tag{11-39}$$

$$\frac{dJ_m(hr)}{dr} = \frac{m}{r}J_m(hr) - hJ_{m+1}(hr) \tag{11-40}$$

$$\frac{dJ_m(hr)}{dr} = -\frac{m}{r}J_m(hr) + hJ_{m-1}(hr) \tag{11-41}$$

c. Circularly symmetrical modes: TE_{01} mode

Circular symmetry of the fields is a potential advantage of circular wave guides, and is a property of the TM_{0n} and TE_{0n} modes.

Within the former class, the TM_{01} mode has been used as a means of transferring microwave signals between a fixed base and a rotating antenna; its field pattern is sketched in Fig. 11-2, and it is the subject of Problem 11-3.

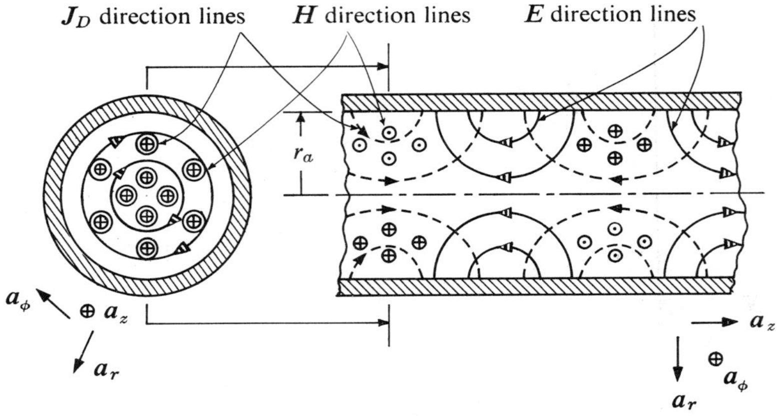

Figure 11-2 TM_{01}-mode field pattern in circular wave guide

The simplest circularly symmetrical mode of the other type, the TE_{01} mode, has been the subject of considerable development work as a means of transmitting microwave signals over distances of many miles. This is because of its peculiar attenuation function, one which drops continuously as frequency is raised. The TE_{01} mode is also used in one form of resonant-cavity wavemeter.[3]

(1) FIELD PATTERN OF THE TE_{01} MODE. Equation 11-37 is satisfied for $m = 0$ and $n = 1$ by the following argument value:

$$J_1(3.8317) = 0 \qquad h'_{01}r_a = 3.8317 \tag{11-44}$$

Equation 11-21 may be rewritten

$$H_{0z} = A'_{01}J_0(h'_{01}r) \tag{11-45}$$

From Eqs. 11-29 and 11-38,

$$E_{0\phi} = \frac{-j\omega\mu A'_{01}}{h'_{01}} J_1(h'_{01}r) \tag{11-46}$$

$$H_{0r} = \frac{j\beta'_{01}A'_{01}}{h'_{01}} J_1(h'_{01}r) \tag{11-47}$$

These may be rewritten as explicit functions of time:

$$H_z = A'_{01}J_0(h'_{01}r)\sin(\omega t - \beta'_{01}z) \tag{11-48}$$

$$E_\phi = \frac{-\omega\mu A'_{01}}{h'_{01}} J_1(h'_{01}r)\cos(\omega t - \beta'_{01}z) \tag{11-49}$$

$$H_r = \frac{\beta'_{01}A'_{01}}{h'_{01}} J_1(h'_{01}r)\cos(\omega t - \beta'_{01}z) \tag{11-50}$$

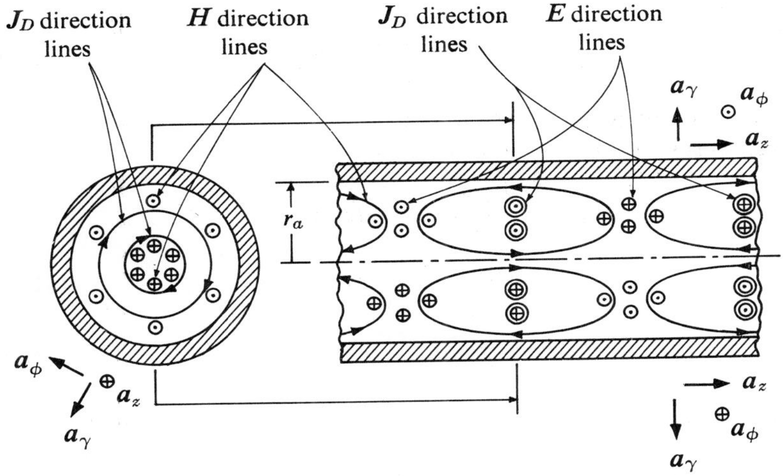

Figure 11-3 TE_{01}-mode field pattern in circular wave guide

The surface-current-density field is of particular interest in that it is purely circumferential. It is equal in magnitude to the magnetic field at radius r_a:

$$\boldsymbol{J_S} = A'_{01}J_0(h'_{01}r_a)\sin(\omega t - \beta'_{01}z)\boldsymbol{a}_\phi \tag{11-51}$$

$$\begin{aligned} J_0(h'_{01}r_a) &= J_0(3.8317) \\ &= -0.4028 \end{aligned} \tag{11-52}$$

Thin transverse cuts may be made in the wave guide without interfering with the propagation of TE_{0n} modes, and this is one method of obstructing the propagation of modes outside this class.

The TE_{01} field pattern is illustrated in Fig. 11-3.

(2) Attenuation function of TE_{01} mode. The attenuation function of the TE_{01} mode may be derived on the same basis as for the rectangular wave guide in Sec. 10-5. To determine the transmitted power, the longitudinal

component of Poynting's vector may be written:

$$\begin{aligned} P_{1z} &= -E_\phi H_r \\ &= \frac{\beta'_{01}\omega\mu A'^2_{01}}{h'^2_{01}} J_1^2(h'_{01}r)\cos^2(\omega t - \beta'_{01}z) \\ &= \frac{\beta'_{01}\omega\mu A'^2_{01}}{2h'^2_{01}} J_1^2(h'_{01}r)[1 + \cos 2(\omega t - \beta'_{01}z)] \end{aligned} \qquad \textbf{(11-53)}$$

When this function is time-averaged over an integral number of cycles it reduces to

$$\boldsymbol{P}_{1\text{av}} = \frac{\beta'_{01}\omega\mu A'^2_{01}}{2h'^2_{01}} J_1^2(h'_{01}r)\boldsymbol{a}_z \qquad \textbf{(11-54)}$$

The transmitted power P_{tr} may be found by integrating this over the transverse cross section of the wave guide:

$$\begin{aligned} P_{\text{tr}} &= \int_0^{2\pi}\int_0^{r_a} \boldsymbol{P}_{1\text{av}} \cdot (r\,dr\,d\phi\,\boldsymbol{a}_z) \\ &= \frac{\beta'_{01}\omega\mu A'^2_{01}\pi}{h'^2_{01}} \int_0^{r_a} J_1^2(h'_{01}r)\,r\,dr \end{aligned} \qquad \textbf{(11-55)*}$$

$$= \frac{\beta'_{01}\omega\mu A'^2_{01}\pi r_a^2 J_0^2(h'_{01}r_a)}{2h'^2_{01}} \qquad \textbf{(11-56)}$$

The power dissipated in a short section Δz of the wave-guide wall is found in the same general manner as for the rectangular wave guide. Thus by squaring Eq. 11-48, with $r = r_a$, and multiplying by R_S, the time-averaged value of Poynting's vector directed into the guide wall is found to be

$$\boldsymbol{P}_{W\text{av}} = \tfrac{1}{2}A'^2_{01}J_0^2(h'_{01}r_a)R_S\boldsymbol{a}_r \qquad \textbf{(11-57)}$$

This should be integrated over a cylindrical strip of length Δz:

$$\begin{aligned} P_{\text{loss}} &= \int_0^{2\pi}\int_{z_1}^{z_1+\Delta z} \boldsymbol{P}_{W\text{av}} \cdot (r_a\,d\phi\,dz\,\boldsymbol{a}_r) \\ &= \pi r_a A'^2_{01}J_0^2(h'_{01}r_a)R_S\,\Delta z \end{aligned} \qquad \textbf{(11-58)}$$

* The integral in Eq. 11-55 may be evaluated as follows:

$$\int_0^{r_a} J_1^2(h'_{01}r)r\,dr = \frac{r^2}{2}\left\{\left(\frac{dJ_1(h'_{01}r)}{dr}\frac{1}{h'_{01}}\right)^2 - \left(1 - \frac{1}{h'^2_{01}r^2}\right)J_1^2(h'_{01}r)\right\}\Bigg]_0^{r_a}$$

[McLachlan, N. W., *Bessel Functions for Engineers*, 2nd ed. (London: Oxford University Press, 1961), p. 104.]

The second term vanishes at the upper limit in accordance with the boundary condition of Eq. 11-44, and the derivative of J_1 may be replaced by Eq. 11-41, which also contains $J_1(h'_{01}r)$. Thus the integral reduces to the following:

$$\int_0^{r_a} J_1^2(h'_{01}r)r\,dr = \frac{r_a^2}{2}J_0^2(h'_{01}r_a)$$

Substitution of Eqs. 11-56 and 11-58 into Eq. 10-116 gives the following expression for the attenuation function:

$$\alpha = \frac{R_S h_{01}'^2}{\omega\mu\beta_{01}' r_a} \tag{11-59}$$

Equation 11-42 may be substituted for h_{01}' in the numerator and Eq. 11-43 for β_{01}' in the denominator:

$$\begin{aligned} \alpha &= \frac{R_S \omega_{c01}'^2}{\omega\sqrt{\omega^2 - \omega_{c01}'^2}} \sqrt{\frac{\epsilon}{\mu}} \\ &= R_S \left(\frac{\omega_{c01}'}{\omega}\right)^2 \sqrt{\frac{\epsilon}{\mu}} \frac{1}{\sqrt{1 - (\omega_{c01}'/\omega)^2}} \end{aligned} \tag{11-60}$$

$$R_S = \sqrt{\frac{\omega\mu}{2\sigma}} \tag{8-79}$$

At frequencies much greater than cutoff, the second radical in Eq. 11-60 approaches unity, and hence the attenuation function approaches the following asymptote, after substitution of Eq. 8-79:

$$\alpha \approx \sqrt{\frac{\epsilon}{2\sigma}} \frac{\omega_{c01}'^2}{\omega^{3/2}} = \sqrt{\frac{\pi\epsilon}{\sigma}} \frac{f_{c01}'^2}{f^{3/2}} \tag{11-61}$$

Thus the attenuation drops continuously as the frequency is raised above the cutoff value.

d. Low-attenuation transmission: mode conversion

Equation 11-61 suggests that if the TE_{01} mode were utilized at a carrier frequency many times the cutoff frequency, an exceedingly low attenuation could be reached.

Realization of a practical communication system of this type has been the object of extensive development work during recent years.[4,5,6,7] A major problem is that of *mode conversion*, or the transfer of part of the signal energy from the intended TE_{01} mode into other modes, followed by partial transfer back to the TE_{01} mode at near or distant locations. As may be inferred by reference to Table 11-1, many modes would have cutoff frequencies that are lower than the signal frequency and hence would be *propagating* parasitic modes rather than evanescent ones.

One specific example is that of conversion from the TE_{01} mode to the TM_{11} mode and back. This effect is pronounced in the vicinity of bends in a circular wave guide; it is fostered by the fact that those modes have the same phase velocity. In addition, almost every type of discontinuity or variation from the simple, straight circular-cylindrical shape will cause some mode conversion. Such external circumstances as mechanical flexing of the wave guide will vary the degree of conversion at each location. For any line long enough to make the low-attenuation property worthwhile, the composite result of the mode-conversion processes is likely to be an erratically varying, degraded output signal.

In the hope of (1) reducing the degree of mode conversion, or (2) increasing the attenuation of undesired modes, several modifications of the basic wave-guide structure have been tested. Interruption of longitudinally directed surface current is an obvious means of obstructing the propagation of modes inherently dependent on such current; of various forms of construction which will accomplish this, the closely wound wire helix is probably the most practical to fabricate.

11-3. HELICAL WAVE GUIDES: GENERAL[6,8,9]

A practical helical wave guide consists of a narrow strip or wire of conducting material formed into a closely spaced circular helix, as sketched in Fig. 11-4. To obtain mechanical support it is surrounded by a layer of

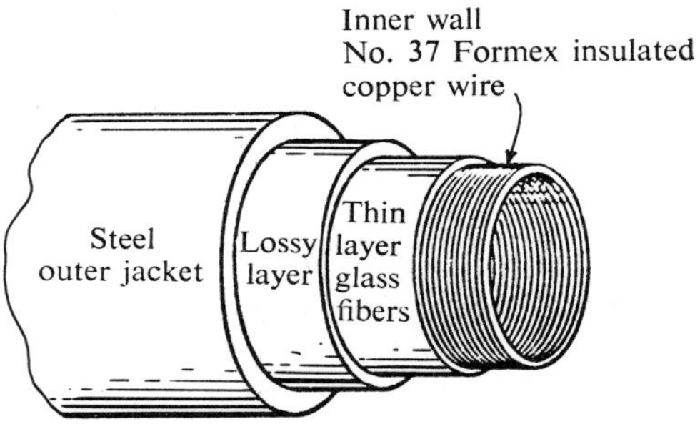

Figure 11-4 Helical wave guide (from *Micro-wave J.*, by permission, p. 103 of Ref. 7)

insulating or poorly conducting material. Such a structure has an anisotropic surface impedance, one which is very low along the conducting strip or wire but which may be much higher in the direction normal to the strip or wire, depending on the properties of the surrounding layer.

The propagation modes which may exist in a helical wave guide will necessarily differ from those which exist in a continuous cylindrical wave guide, but the TE_{0n}-mode configurations are approached very closely if the pitch or ratio of center-to-center distance between successive turns compared to the perimeter is very small and if the metal has a high conductivity.

An ideal helical wave guide on this basis would have zero pitch, zero surface impedance in the circumferential direction, and a longitudinal surface impedance $Z_{SL}\epsilon^{j\theta}$ which could be chosen arbitrarily. The boundary conditions would be

$$\begin{aligned} E_{0\phi}(r_a) &= 0 \\ E_{0z}(r_a) &= -Z_{SL}\epsilon^{j\theta}H_{0\phi}(r_a) \end{aligned} \tag{11-62}$$

The characteristic equation for the parameters γ and h has been found to be

$$\left[\frac{m^2\gamma^2}{h^2r_a^2\omega^2\mu\epsilon} J_m^2(hr_a) + J_m'^2(hr_a)\right] j\omega\epsilon r_a Z_{SL}\epsilon^{j\theta} - hr_aJ_m(hr_a)J'_m(hr_a) = 0 \tag{11-63}$$

It may be noted that if $Z_{SL} = 0$, the resulting equation may be satisfied by either Eq. 11-32 or 11-37, the characteristic equations for TM or TE modes in a homogeneous, lossless circular wave guide.

The transmission property of the circularly symmetrical TE modes may be checked by setting m in Eq. 11-63 equal to zero. Equation 11-37 may be factored from the remainder; hence the TE_{0n} modes are not affected by Z_{SL}, and all have zero attenuation in the ideal helical wave guide.

In a practical helical wave guide (circumferential surface impedance not zero) the attenuation constants of the TE_{0n} modes are somewhat higher than in a circular wave guide made of the same conducting material.

Modes of other than the TE_{0n} type in an ideal helical wave guide will differ progressively from those in a circular cylinder as the longitudinal surface impedance is increased. Such modes will have longitudinal components of both $\boldsymbol{E}$ and $\boldsymbol{H}$ and hence will be *mixed modes* rather than transverse electric or transverse magnetic. Contour charts have been prepared for the complex propagation function over a limited range of parameters.[9] An interesting feature disclosed by those charts is the existence of low-attenuation modes (in addition to those of the TE_{0n} class) for all values of Z_{SL}.

11-4. CONCLUSIONS

A circular tube of highly conducting material will transmit electromagnetic waves of sufficiently high frequency much as a rectangular tube or wave guide will. Both transverse-electric (TE) and transverse-magnetic (TM) modes are possible.

Maxwell's curl equations in cylindrical coordinates may be reduced to a scalar wave equation in terms of the longitudinal component of $\boldsymbol{E}$ or $\boldsymbol{H}$. The solution involves Bessel functions dependent on radial distance; boundary conditions restrict the solution to integral-order functions of the first kind.

The cutoff frequency ω_c for each mode is inversely proportional to the wave-guide radius r_a and is fixed by the boundary condition that the tangential component of $\boldsymbol{E}$ vanish at the cylindrical conducting surface. (The radial component of $\boldsymbol{B}$ also vanishes there, but this is not an independent constraint.) Specifically, the Bessel function argument at $r = r_a$ is $\omega_c\sqrt{\mu\epsilon}r_a$; for TM_{mn} modes this argument must have a value which will make the mth-order Bessel function equal to zero, and for TE_{mn} modes the argument must have a value which will make the derivative of the mth-order Bessel function equal to zero.

Modes for which $m = 0$ have circularly symmetrical fields, whereas the fields of other modes vary circumferentially. The TE_{0n} modes are characterized by surface-current patterns which are purely circumferential in direction, and attenuation functions which decrease indefinitely with increasing frequency. Mode conversion at wave-guide discontinuities has been an impediment to commercial exploitation of this property.

PROBLEMS

11-1. Expand the function $-\nabla \times (\nabla \times \boldsymbol{E}) + \nabla(\nabla \cdot \boldsymbol{E})$ in cylindrical coordinates to verify Eq. 11-1 and the statements following it.

11-2. Verify that the change of variables given in Eq. 11-13 will reduce Eq. 11-12 to the form of Bessel's equation given in Eq. 11-14.

11-3. Write expressions for (*a*) the electric and magnetic fields of the TM_{01} mode as explicit functions of time, (*b*) the surface-current density, and (*c*) the displacement-current density. Make a sketch supplementing Fig. 11-2 to show the surface-current field. May thin slits be cut in the wave guide without interfering with the TM_{01} mode? If so, in what direction?

11-4. At what value of $h_{01}r$ is the magnetic field in the TM_{01} mode most intense?

11-5. Equation 11-31 for H_r for a TM mode contains the factor $1/r$. Investigate the behavior of H_r in the vicinity of $r = 0$ for (*a*) $m = 0$, (*b*) $m = 1$, (*c*) $m = 2$, and (*d*) $m = 3$. $[J_m(p) \approx (1/m!)(p/2)^m \quad (p \ll 1).]$

11-6. Sketch patterns for the TE_{02} mode, and evaluate the proportions of the following radii with respect to the wave-guide radius r_a: (*a*) those radii at which any field component is zero, and (*b*) those radii at which any field component has a maximum.

11-7. Compute the cutoff frequency for the TE_{01} mode in a circular wave guide with an inside diameter of 2 in. Find the attenuation in the TE_{01} mode for (*a*) 35 kmc per sec, and (*b*) 75 kmc per sec, if the wave guide is made of copper.

REFERENCES

1. Barlow, H. M. and J. Brown, *Radio Surface Waves.* London: Oxford Univ. Press, 1962.

2. Beattie, C. L., "Table of the First 700 Zeros of Bessel Functions—$J_l(x)$ and $J_l'(x)$," *Bell System Tech. J.*, 37, No. 3 (1958), 689–97. (Table reprinted in

The Microwave Engineer's Handbook and Buyer's Guide, pp. T–226 to T–229. Brookline, Mass.: Horizon House-Microwave, Inc., 1963.)

3. GINZTON, EDWARD L., *Microwave Measurements*. New York: McGraw-Hill Book Company, Inc., 1957.

4. KARBOWIAK, A. E., "System Aspects of Long Distance Communication by Waveguide," *Proc. IEE (London)*, 109, Part B (1962), 336–44.

5. KARBOWIAK, A. E. and L. SOLYMAR, "Characteristics of Waveguide for Long-Distance Transmission," *J. Res. Natl. Bur. Std.* (U.S.), Sec. D, Radio Propagation, 65D, No. 1 (1961), 75–88; reprinted in *Elec. Commun.*, 37, No. 1 (1961), 27–36.

6. KING, ARCHIE P., "Status of Low-Loss Waveguide and Components at Millimeter Wavelengths," *Microwave J.*, 7, No. 3 (1964), 102–6.

7. MILLER, S. E., "Waveguide as a Communication Medium," *Bell System Tech. J.*, 33, No. 6 (1954), 1209–65.

8. MORGAN, S. P. and J. A. YOUNG, "Helix Waveguide," *Bell System Tech. J.*, 35, No. 6 (1956), 1347–84.

9. UNGER, H. G., "Normal Modes and Mode Conversion in Helix Waveguide," *Bell System Tech. J.*, 40, No. 1 (1961), 255–80.

CHAPTER 12

Multiconductor Systems

More than two conductors are effectively present in all transmission systems except the wave guide and the coaxial line at microwave frequencies. In some instances the transmission-line proper consists of more than two conductors, and in any event inductive and capacitive coupling interlink a given line with all wires and conducting media in the vicinity. Some specific manifestations of this situation are (1) three-phase lines for power transmission (three wires); (2) "phantom" telephone circuits (four wires); (3) telephone circuits paralleled with one another and with power lines; (4) "ground wires" on power-transmission lines, strung parallel to but above the power conductors (to intercept lightning discharges); and (5) the physical ground, including both the natural soil, rock, and water, and man-built conducting structures, such as pipes and rails.

Elementary features of interest from the standpoint of transmission theory include (1) the resistance, self-inductance, and capacitance, assuming that they can be defined in a consistent manner, for a set of more than two wires which is operated as a single circuit; (2) the mutual inductance between two paralleled two-wire lines; (3) the pattern of currents induced in the ground by a nearby transmission line; and (4) the behavior of a transmission line and ground when they are short-circuited together. This list is incomplete and even these topics will not be examined exhaustively, but attenuation will be directed to the less complicated aspects.

The discussion of three-phase systems will be abbreviated; other texts present the technique of applying symmetrical components to short-circuit calculations, and compendia of formulas for impedance calculations.[4,14,16] Reference 9 presents a tabular summary of design features of 280 lines constructed during 1943–53, and a condensation of that material is given in Ref. 13.

12-1. THREE-PHASE-POWER TRANSMISSION: SOME HIGHLIGHTS

Advisable preliminaries to the development of topics 1 and 4 above are the following: (1) the definition of symmetrical-component sets for voltage and current, and (2) consideration of practical conductor-types and the bases for their selection, because the transmission-line parameters of distributed resistance, inductance, and capacitance are all functions of the conductor design.

a. Voltage-and-current concepts

Electrically a three-phase transmission line consists of three power-carrying wires (or cables) and a ground. As noted in the introductory paragraph, the natural ground may be supplemented by conductors buried in it

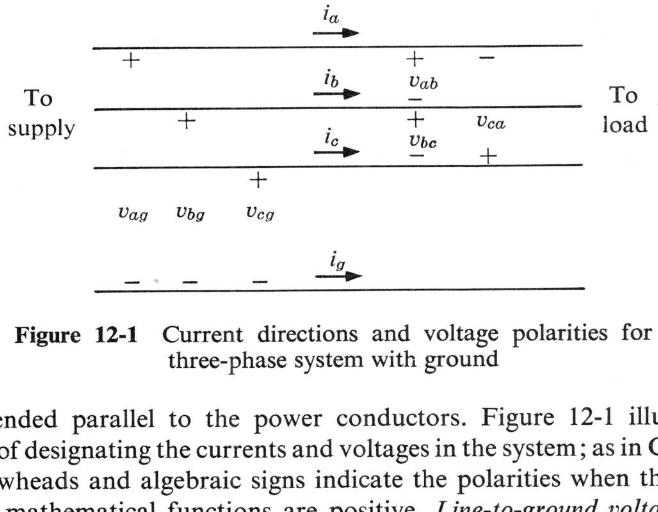

Figure 12-1 Current directions and voltage polarities for three-phase system with ground

or suspended parallel to the power conductors. Figure 12-1 illustrates a method of designating the currents and voltages in the system; as in Chapter 1, the arrowheads and algebraic signs indicate the polarities when the accompanying mathematical functions are positive. *Line-to-ground voltages*, such as v_{ag}, and *line-to-line voltages*, such as v_{ab}, are both useful. The following relationships are in accordance with Kirchhoff's laws:

$$\begin{aligned} v_{ab} &= v_{ag} - v_{bg} \\ v_{bc} &= v_{bg} - v_{cg} \\ v_{ca} &= v_{cg} - v_{ag} \end{aligned} \qquad \textbf{(12-1)}$$

$$-i_g = i_a + i_b + i_c \qquad \textbf{(12-2)}$$

The set of power conductors may be conductively connected to the physical ground through the neutral points of transformer banks or by other means, or it may be "ungrounded," but it is inductively and capacitively coupled to ground in any case. In many transmission-line "faults" one or more power conductors are short-circuited to ground.

The method of *symmetrical components* is an expedient means of network analysis for unsymmetrical-fault situations. In this method the actual currents and voltages are resolved into "symmetrical sets" designated as *positive sequence*, *negative sequence*, and *zero sequence*. For example,

$$i_a = i_{a+} + i_{a-} + i_{a0} \tag{12-3}$$

In actual systems the current-to-voltage relationships within each sequence set are, to a good degree of approximation, independent of the other sequence sets, except at the unsymmetrical-fault location.

(1) POSITIVE-SEQUENCE AND NEGATIVE-SEQUENCE QUANTITIES. A *symmetrical three-phase set* consists of three sinusoidal voltages or currents which are equal to one another in rms values and are mutually separated by 120 degrees in time phase. Two independent *phase sequences* may be specified, as indicated in Fig. 12-2: *a-b-c* and *c-b-a*. The generated voltages in a utility system form a symmetrical three-phase set; their sequence is considered to be positive, whereas the reverse sequence is designated as negative. The positive-sequence and negative-sequence components of the currents shown in Fig. 12-1 may be written as follows, if *a-b-c* is the positive sequence:

$$\begin{aligned}
i_{a+} &= I_{M+} \sin(\omega t + \phi_+) \\
&= \mathrm{Im}[\sqrt{2}\, I_{a+}\epsilon^{j\omega t}] \\
I_{a+} &= \frac{I_{M+}}{\sqrt{2}}\,\epsilon^{j\phi_+} \\
i_{b+} &= I_{M+} \sin(\omega t + \phi_+ - 120^\circ) \\
I_{b+} &= I_{a+}\epsilon^{-j120^\circ} \\
i_{c+} &= I_{M+} \sin(\omega t + \phi_+ - 240^\circ) \\
I_{c+} &= I_{a+}\epsilon^{-j240^\circ}
\end{aligned} \tag{12-4}$$

$$\begin{aligned}
i_{a-} &= I_{M-} \sin(\omega t + \phi_-) \\
I_{a-} &= \frac{I_{M-}}{\sqrt{2}}\,\epsilon^{j\phi_-} \\
I_{b-} &= I_{a-}\epsilon^{j120^\circ} \\
I_{c-} &= I_{a-}\epsilon^{j240^\circ}
\end{aligned} \tag{12-5}$$

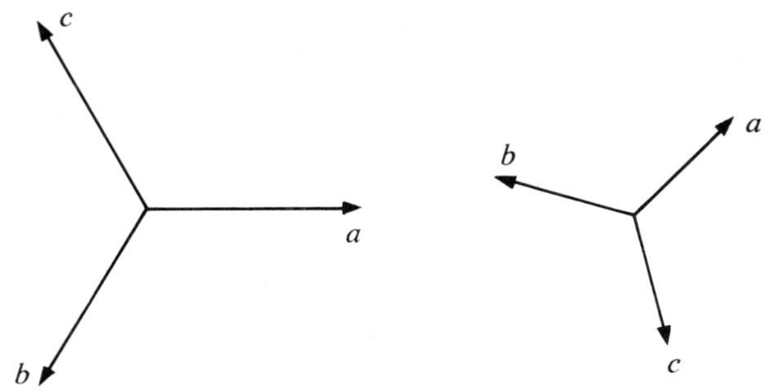

(*a*) Symmetrical three-phase set—*a*-*b*-*c* sequence

(*b*) Symmetrical three-phase set—*c*-*b*-*a* sequence

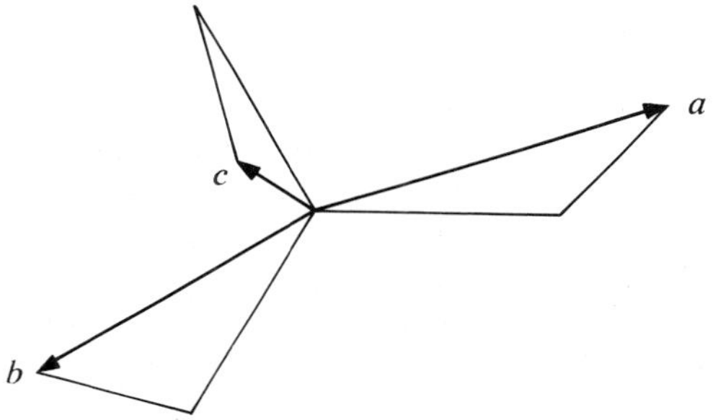

(*c*) Unsymmetrical set formed by adding oppositely sequenced symmetrical sets

Figure 12-2 Sequences of voltages or currents in three-phase systems

The following may be readily verified:

$$
\begin{aligned}
i_{a+} + i_{b+} + i_{c+} &= 0 \\
i_{a-} + i_{b-} + i_{c-} &= 0
\end{aligned}
\qquad \textbf{(12-6)}
$$

(2) Zero-sequence quantities. The *zero-sequence-set* components of given currents or voltages are equal and in time phase with one another:

$$
\begin{aligned}
i_{a0} &= I_{M0}\sin(\omega t + \phi_0) \\
&= \mathrm{Im}[\sqrt{2}\, I_{a0}\epsilon^{j\omega t}] \\
i_{a0} &= i_{b0} = i_{c0} \\
I_{a0} &= I_{b0} = I_{c0}
\end{aligned}
\qquad \textbf{(12-7)}
$$

The zero-sequence current set is thought of as flowing in one direction in the transmission line, divided equally among the three wires and returning through the ground:

$$\begin{aligned} -i_g &= i_{a0} + i_{b0} + i_{c0} \\ &= 3i_{a0} \end{aligned} \tag{12-8}$$

This is in agreement with Eqs. 12-2 and 12-6.

The zero-sequence component of line-to-ground voltage may be found by adding together the three line-to-ground voltages (as instantaneous functions or in phasor form) and dividing by three, and may be called the *neutral-to-ground voltage*:

$$v_{ng} = \tfrac{1}{3}(v_{ag} + v_{bg} + v_{cg}) \tag{12-9}$$

(3) LINE-TO-NEUTRAL VOLTAGES AND "PER-PHASE" CONCEPT. *Line-to-neutral voltages* are defined by the elimination of the zero-sequence component from the line-to-ground voltages:

$$\begin{aligned} v_{an} &= v_{ag} - v_{ng} \\ v_{bn} &= v_{bg} - v_{ng} \\ v_{cn} &= v_{cg} - v_{ng} \end{aligned} \tag{12-10}$$

Addition of the equations in set 12-10, followed by substitution of Eq. 12-9 to eliminate v_{ng}, leaves this constraint on the line-to-neutral voltages:

$$v_{an} + v_{bn} + v_{cn} = 0 \tag{12-11}$$

It is convenient to reason mathematically on a *per-phase* basis for computations related to symmetrical operation of a three-phase system; one uses the current in one conductor, the corresponding line-to-neutral voltage, the "wye" or line-to-neutral form for shunt impedance or admittance, and, for power or volt-amperes or vars, one-third of the corresponding three-phase quantity.

b. Conductor types: effective resistance

The design of conductors for power-transmission lines is influenced by the following principal requirements: (1) high conductivity and sufficient cross-sectional area to carry the intended load current without excessive loss and without overheating, (2) bending flexibility for convenient transporting and installing, (3) high tensile strength in proportion to weight per unit length, and (4), avoidance of corona-type interference with radio or television signals.

In most designs the cross section consists largely or entirely of circular strands. Cross-sectional views of several types are shown in Fig. 12-3.

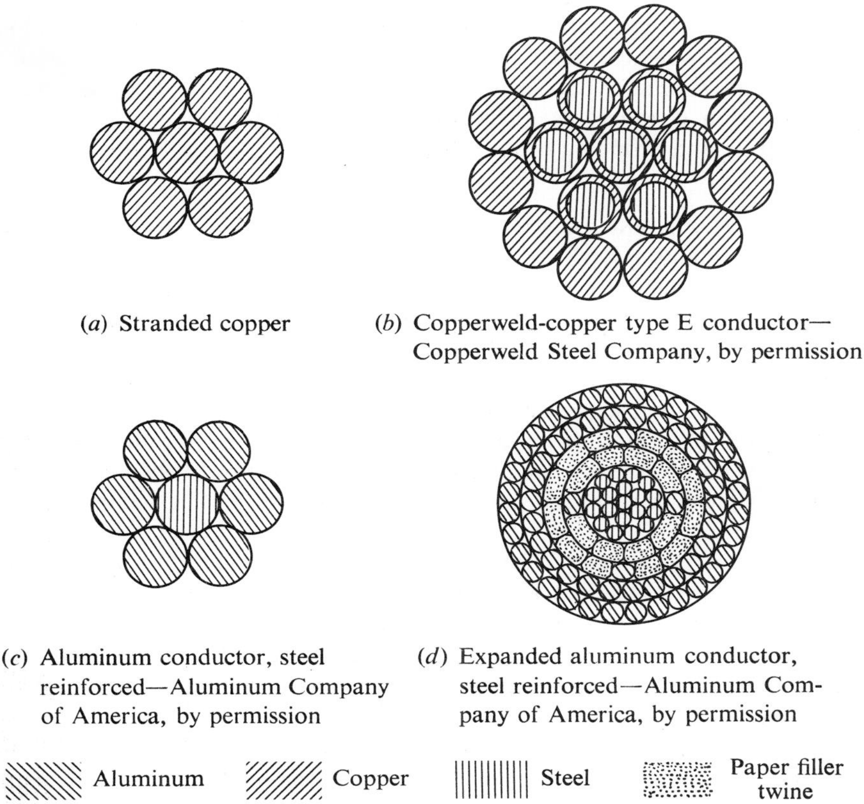

(*a*) Stranded copper

(*b*) Copperweld-copper type E conductor—Copperweld Steel Company, by permission

(*c*) Aluminum conductor, steel reinforced—Aluminum Company of America, by permission

(*d*) Expanded aluminum conductor, steel reinforced—Aluminum Company of America, by permission

Figure 12-3 Cross sections of power conductors

(1) MATERIALS AND MECHANICAL PROPERTIES. Copper and aluminum are the standard current-carrying materials. For wires of the same resistance and same length, an aluminum wire would have a cross-sectional area 1.60 times that of a copper wire but would weigh only 0.483 times as much. Hard-drawn stranded copper has good tensile strength, but aluminum is less satisfactory in this regard.

For higher tensile strength, steel strands may be used as the core of a stranded conductor, as in ACSR (aluminum conductor, steel reinforced)[7,8] or CCSR (copper conductor, steel reinforced).[10] Alternatively, some of the strands may be steel overlaid with copper or aluminum ("Copperweld"[13] or "Alumoweld"[6]). Most overhead ground wires are galvanized steel.*

* Special high-strength galvanized steel by itself has been used for the conductors of extra-long spans, such as that across the Sognefiord in Norway (15,847 feet, erected in the fall of 1955). The line spanning Messina Straits, between Italy and Sicily (11,832 feet, also erected in the fall of 1955) has a cross-sectional area which is 12.6 per cent aluminum and the remainder steel.[5]

Tensile-strength requirements include not only the supporting of conductor dead weight from a set of towers (and these must be of economic height and spacing), but such factors as (1) wind-induced vibration, (2) variations in conductor sag due to temperature changes, and (3) the accumulating and dropping of ice coatings.[13]

(2) CORONA AND ITS PREVENTION.[2,4,13] Corona is an electric discharge caused by intense electric fields; it is random in the timing of its occurrence and in its frequency spectrum, and it causes "noise" or interference in the radio and television broadcast spectrums. For a given voltage and spacing between two conductors, the existence or nonexistence of localized fields of such intensity as to cause corona depends primarily on the radius of each conductor and on the presence of irregularities, such as burrs and scratches, on the outer surface. (Conductor-supporting clamps, vibration dampers, and other hardware attached to the conductors are also likely sources; they must be shaped such that corona-generating fields will not be created on their surfaces.)

A minimum diameter for the conductors on a given line is fixed by corona characteristics; at the higher voltages this diameter is commonly larger than that corresponding to a stranded conductor of adequate conducting cross-sectional area. "Expanded" conductors (Fig. 12-3) may then meet the corona requirement more economically than the stranded type. "Bundle" conductors, or sets of two, three, or four conductors per phase, with spacings in the order of 18 inches, have been used on many lines built for 345 kv or higher.[1] This arrangement keeps the field intensity sufficiently low and at the same time gives a lower reactance than a single, larger conductor for each phase.

(3) RESISTANCE PARAMETER. Skin effect causes a noticeable increase in effective resistance at 60 cps in the larger, compactly arranged, all-copper stranded conductors, but very little increase in resistance in the expanded types. Theoretical calculation of resistance change due to skin effect in stranded conductors was commented on in Sec. 9-3*a*.

Resistance is also a function of temperature in the metal, which may vary widely depending on ambient conditions and the current in the conductor. Effective resistances for zero, 25, 50, and 60 cps, at temperatures of 25°C and either 50° or 75°C have been tabulated for many commercially available types of conductors.[4,7,13,14,16]

Under balanced-load conditions the three line currents have equal rms values. In accordance with the per-phase concept described in Sec. 12-1*a*(3), the current in each conductor is the per-phase current; that current and the conductor resistance account for the per-phase resistive loss; hence the resistance of one conductor is the *per-phase resistance.*

12-2. INDUCTANCE CALCULATIONS FOR SINGLE-PHASE AND THREE-PHASE LINES

In Chapter 9 the parameter of distributed self-inductance for a two-wire line was derived by interrelating the traveling-wave functions for the $\boldsymbol{E}$ and $\boldsymbol{H}$ fields with those from Chapter 1 for voltage and current. The magnetic-field magnitude was proportional to current, and the electric-field magnitude related to it in turn by intrinsic impedance. Voltage was found by evaluating the line integral of the electric field from one conductor to the other.

The concept of *flux linkages* provides another approach to the calculation of inductance, one which is particularly convenient for finding mutual inductance. It is based on direct application of Faraday's law, Eq. 7-18. This principle, together with the conventional definition of inductance, may be stated in lumped-parameter terminology as follows:

$$v_L = -N\frac{d\phi}{dt} - L\frac{di}{dt} \tag{12-12}$$

a. Mutual inductance between two parallel two-wire lines

Inductive coupling between two balanced circuits is a simple example of intercircuit coupling and is a cause of "cross talk" in telephony. The cross section is shown in Fig. 12-4; conductor spacings will be assumed large in comparison to conductor diameters. Current in the upper circuit gives rise to flux, some of which links one of the conductors in the lower circuit but not both. Changing of that flux will induce a voltage within the lower circuit

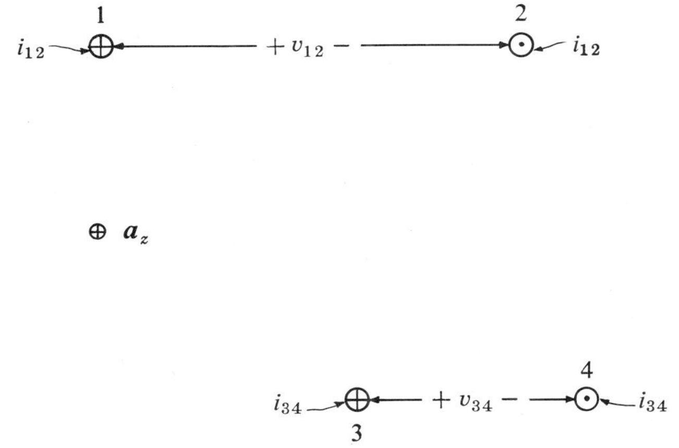

Figure 12-4 Mutual inductance between 2 two-wire lines

in each longitudinal element of the line. The coefficient of proportionality is the *distributed mutual inductance* l_m, which is defined as follows:

$$\Delta z\left[\frac{\partial v_{34}(z,t)}{\partial z}\right]_{z=z_1} = -\Delta z\, l_m \frac{\partial i_{12}(z_1,t)}{\partial t} \tag{12-13}$$

This should be compared with Eq. 1-5 for the voltage drop in a transmission line because of self inductance.

The rate of change of magnetic flux may be related to voltage by the following equation, which is the distributed-parameter form of Eq. 12-12:

$$\Delta z\left[\frac{\partial v_{34}(z,t)}{\partial z}\right]_{z=z_1} = -\iint \frac{\partial \boldsymbol{B}_{12}}{\partial t}\cdot d\boldsymbol{S}_{34} \tag{12-14}$$

Here $\boldsymbol{B}_{12}$ is the magnetic field created by current i_{12}, and the area for the surface integral is the rectangle in the plane of conductors 3 and 4 which is bounded by the opposing surfaces of those conductors and by the lines $z = z_1 - (\Delta z/2)$ and $z = z_1 + (\Delta z/2)$. Substituting Eq. 12-13 in Eq. 12-14 gives

$$\Delta z\, l_m \frac{\partial i_{12}(z_1,t)}{\partial t} = \iint \frac{\partial \boldsymbol{B}_{12}}{\partial t}\cdot d\boldsymbol{S}_{34} \tag{12-15}$$

Direct evaluation of the integral would be arduous, but the task may be greatly simplified by use of the component fields $\boldsymbol{H}_A$ and $\boldsymbol{H}_B$ (Eqs. 9-30, 9-46, and 9-47). Since the direction lines of each of these component fields are circles concentric with the respective conductors, the result could be obtained by taking the sum of two scalar integrals for which the limits are radial distances as indicated in Fig. 12-5:

$$\begin{aligned}\iint \boldsymbol{B}_{12}\cdot d\boldsymbol{S}_{34} &= \iint \mu\boldsymbol{H}_A\cdot d\boldsymbol{S}_{34} + \iint \mu\boldsymbol{H}_B\cdot d\boldsymbol{S}_{34}\\ &= \mu\,\Delta z\int_{r_{13}}^{r_{14}} \frac{i_{12}(z_1,t)}{2\pi r_1}\,dr_1 + \mu\,\Delta z\int_{r_{23}}^{r_{24}} \frac{-i_{12}(z_1,t)}{2\pi r_2}\,dr_2\\ &= \Delta z\,\frac{\mu}{2\pi}\,i_{12}(z_1,t)\ln\left(\frac{r_{14}r_{23}}{r_{13}r_{24}}\right)\end{aligned} \tag{12-16}$$

Equation 12-16 is differentiated with respect to time and substituted in Eq. 12-15. Then Δz and the time derivative of $i_{12}(z_1,t)$ are divided from both sides:

$$l_m = \frac{\mu}{2\pi}\ln\left(\frac{r_{14}r_{23}}{r_{13}r_{24}}\right) \tag{12-17}$$

The same result will be obtained if one evaluates the flux which is created by current in the lower circuit and which also links the upper circuit.

A drastic reduction in inductive coupling may be achieved by *transposing* one pair with respect to the other at regular intervals Δz_T, which distances

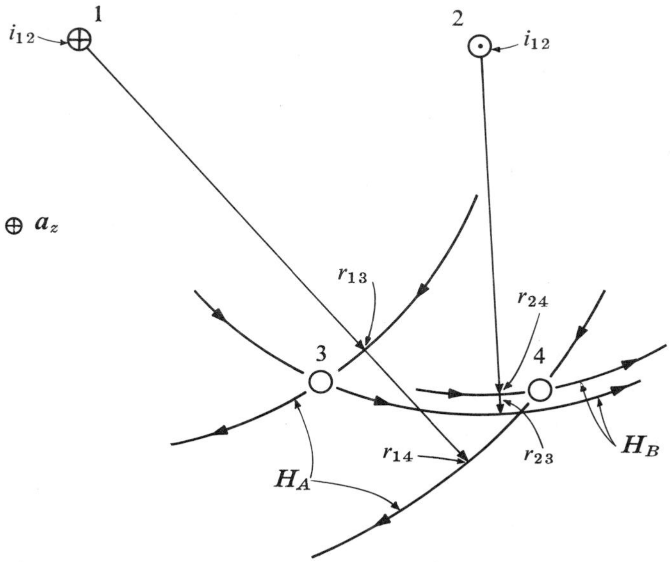

Figure 12-5 Equivalent radii for evaluation of integrals for mutual inductance

should be short compared to the wavelengths used, although long compared to the interconductor spacings. This is indicated in Fig. 12-6. Problem 12-2 is concerned with the residual mutual inductance between two transposed lines as a function of the interval length Δz_T.

Open-wire construction of telephone lines may involve a dozen or more wire pairs paralleling one another physically and with all interconductor spacings in the order of inches or a few feet. Each pair must be transposed with respect to every other pair if cross talk is to be minimized; elaborate transposition patterns have been prepared to accomplish this.[3]

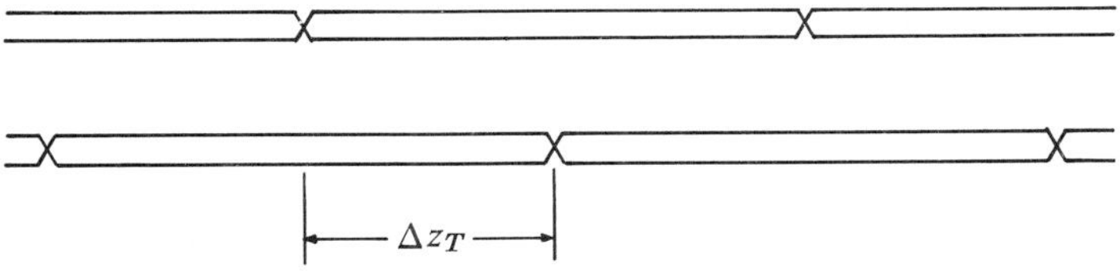

Figure 12-6 Transposition of 2 two-wire lines

b. Inductance of transposed three-phase lossless line

The cross section of a general three-phase line, in which the interconductor spacings are all different, is sketched in Fig. 12-7. The variation of line-to-neutral voltage in each phase because of inductive effects depends on

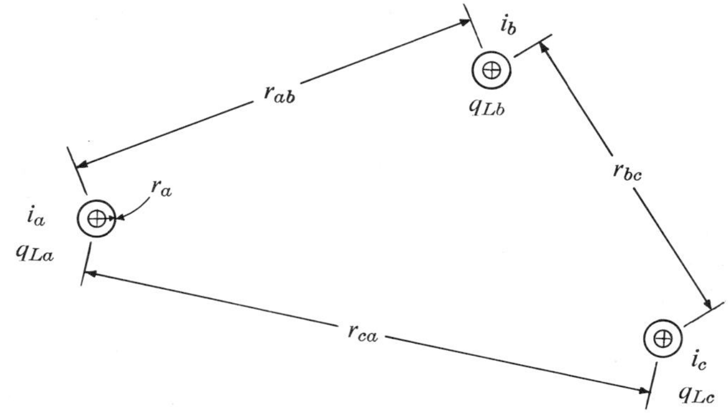

Figure 12-7 Cross section of three-phase line with general spacing

the spacings among the conductors and on the current in each conductor. Even if the current pattern were constrained to a symmetrical three-phase set the three voltages would be affected differently. In general a matrix consisting of both self and mutual terms is needed to describe the inductance property. A welcome exception occurs when the configuration is that of an equilateral triangle, as sketched in Fig. 12-8. With this highly symmetrical arrangement the "distributed inductance of the line" may be expressed on a per-phase basis with one self-inductance.

The equilateral-triangular cross section is rarely used, but its property of inductive symmetry may be achieved on a distance-averaged basis for

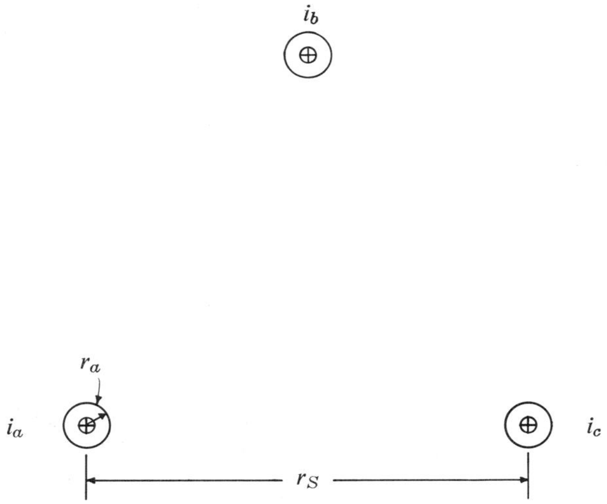

Figure 12-8 Equilateral-triangular spacing of conductors

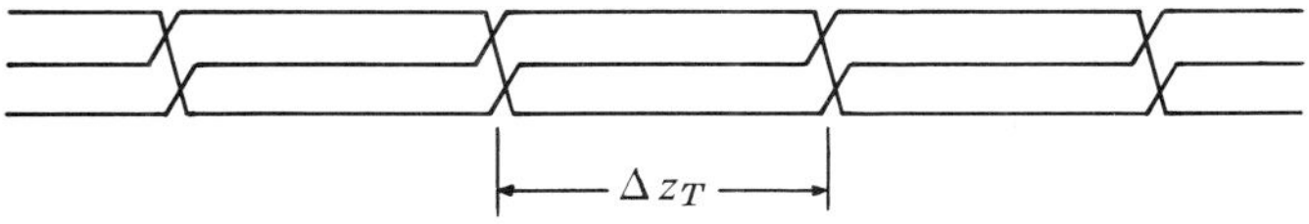

Figure 12-9 Transposition of three-phase line

other configurations by transposition or cyclically changing the positions of the conductors with respect to the three locations in the cross section, as suggested in Fig. 12-9.

(1) DERIVATION FOR GENERAL THREE-WIRE LINE. The conductor-set cross section shown in Fig. 12-7 will be used. As in part (*a*), conductor spacings will be assumed large in comparison to conductor diameter. Only conduction current will flow longitudinally, and it is restricted to the three conductors shown. Hence

$$i_a = -i_b - i_c \tag{12-18}$$

All conductors will be assumed to have the same radii, r_a.

Equations for rate of change of voltage with distance may be written as follows:

$$\Delta z \frac{\partial v_{ab}}{\partial z} = -\int_{r_a}^{r_{ab}} \frac{\partial i_a}{\partial t} \frac{\mu}{2\pi r_1} \Delta z \, dr_1 + \int_{r_a}^{r_{ab}} \frac{\partial i_b}{\partial t} \frac{\mu}{2\pi r_2} \Delta z \, dr_2 + \int_{r_{bc}}^{r_{ac}} \frac{\partial i_c}{\partial t} \frac{\mu}{2\pi r_3} \Delta z \, dr_3 \tag{12-19}$$

$$\Delta z \frac{\partial v_{ac}}{\partial z} = -\int_{r_a}^{r_{ac}} \frac{\partial i_a}{\partial t} \frac{\mu}{2\pi r_1} \Delta z \, dr_1 + \int_{r_{bc}}^{r_{ab}} \frac{\partial i_b}{\partial t} \frac{\mu}{2\pi r_2} \Delta z \, dr_2 + \int_{r_a}^{r_{ac}} \frac{\partial i_c}{\partial t} \frac{\mu}{2\pi r_3} \Delta z \, dr_3 \tag{12-20}$$

The line-to-line voltages are related to the line-to-neutral voltages as follows:

$$\begin{aligned} v_{ab} &= v_{an} - v_{bn} \\ v_{ac} &= v_{an} - v_{cn} \end{aligned} \tag{12-1}$$

The line-to-neutral voltages are constrained as follows:

$$v_{an} + v_{bn} + v_{cn} = 0 \tag{12-11}$$

(A voltage may exist between the neutral point and the physical ground.)

Addition of the two equations just given from set 12-1, followed by substitution of 12-11, gives this result:

$$v_{an} = \tfrac{1}{3}(v_{ab} + v_{ac}) \tag{12-21}$$

Equations 12-19 and 12-20 may be substituted into the time derivative of Eq. 12-21 and i_a eliminated by means of Eq. 12-18:

$$\frac{\partial v_{an}}{\partial z} = \frac{\mu}{6\pi}\left\{\left[2\ln\left(\frac{r_{ab}}{r_a}\right) + \ln\left(\frac{r_{ab}r_{ac}}{r_a r_{bc}}\right)\right]\frac{\partial i_b}{\partial t} + \left[2\ln\left(\frac{r_{ac}}{r_a}\right) + \ln\left(\frac{r_{ab}r_{ac}}{r_a r_{bc}}\right)\right]\frac{\partial i_c}{\partial t}\right\} \quad \textbf{(12-22)}$$

Similar equations may be written for v_{bn} and v_{cn}.

(2) LINE WITH EQUAL SPACING. Under the condition of equilateral-triangular spacing the coefficients of the derivatives of i_b and i_c in Eq. 12-22 are equal, and Eq. 12-18 may be substituted to replace those two currents with i_a. Let

$$r_{ab} = r_{ac} = r_{bc} = r_s$$

$$\frac{\partial v_{an}}{\partial z} = -\frac{\mu}{6\pi}\ln\left(\frac{r_s^3}{r_a^3}\right)\frac{\partial i_a}{\partial t}$$

$$= -\frac{\mu}{2\pi}\ln\left(\frac{r_s}{r_a}\right)\frac{\partial i_a}{\partial t} \quad \textbf{(12-23)}$$

In accordance with the concept of Eq. 1-7, the per-phase distributed self-inductance of an equilateral triangularly spaced line is

$$l_Y = \frac{\mu}{2\pi}\ln\left(\frac{r_s}{r_a}\right) \quad \textbf{(12-24)}$$

Comparison of this with Eq. 9-69 shows that l_Y is one-half of the inductance of a two-wire line in which the same-sized conductors and same spacing have been used. On a "per-conductor" basis the two transmission lines would have equal inductances.

(3) TRANSPOSED THREE-WIRE LINE. For a line with an arbitrary conductor-set cross section, but in which the line is transposed one full cycle in each length of $3\Delta z_T$ (see Fig. 12-9), the interconductor spacings may be designated as r_{ab}, r'_{ab}, r''_{ab}, etc., for the three consecutive sections of lengths Δz_T each:

$$r'_{ab} = r_{ac} = r''_{bc} \quad \textbf{(12-25)}$$

$$r'_{ac} = r_{bc} = r''_{ab} \quad \textbf{(12-26)}$$

$$r'_{bc} = r_{ab} = r''_{ac} \quad \textbf{(12-27)}$$

Equations corresponding to 12-22 may be written in terms of the r' and r'' spacings; Eq. 12-22 and each of the two new equations may be multiplied by Δz_T, the three equations added together and then divided by $3\Delta z_T$ to obtain an average value for the derivative of v_{an} over the transposition cycle. Substitution of Eqs. 12-25, 12-26, 12-27, and 12-18 will permit the result to be reduced to the following:

$$\frac{\partial v_{an}}{\partial z} = -\frac{\mu}{6\pi}\ln\left(\frac{r_{ab}r_{bc}r_{ac}}{r_a^3}\right)\frac{\partial i_a}{\partial t} \tag{12-28}$$

An average, per-phase distributed self-inductance may be defined as follows:

$$l_{Y\text{av}} = \frac{\mu}{2\pi}\ln\left(\frac{\sqrt[3]{r_{ab}r_{bc}r_{ac}}}{r_a}\right) \tag{12-29}$$

If one compares this result with Eq. 12-24 for the equilateral triangularly spaced line, it appears that lines of the two types with the same conductor radii r_a would have equal inductances if r_s were equal to the geometric mean of the three interconductor spacings of the transposed line.

The constraints of Eqs. 12-18 and 12-11 did not distinguish between positive-sequence and negative-sequence currents or voltages, although they did exclude zero-sequence currents and voltages. Accordingly the distributed inductance of a transposed transmission line is the same for positive-sequence and for negative-sequence currents and voltages. (This principle is not true for the impedances of rotating machines.) Zero-sequence inductance will be discussed in Sec. 12-4*c*.

c. Effect of resistance and internal flux

The analyses of inductance in this chapter have assumed that the conductors are circular and that they are small in diameter compared to spacings, and further that the current in each conductor is concentrated in a sheet at its surface. Skin effect is not that pronounced at 60 cycles per second, and the result is time-varying flux within the conductor which increases the per-phase inductance above that given in Eqs. 12-24 and 12-29. This additional inductance depends on the cross-sectional geometry of the conductor.

For conductors that are homogeneous circular cylinders, general results are available. The additional inductance caused by flux within a solid conductor with a circularly symmetrical current-density distribution will be investigated in Appendix B. Numerical values based on the exact solution (Eq. B-50) have been tabulated.[7,11] Equation B-55 gives a low-frequency approximation; internal-flux inductance l_a approaches a maximum of $\mu/8\pi$ henrys per meter as frequency approaches zero. As indicated in the discussion of proximity effect in Sec. 9-3*b*, the current distribution within each conductor may be regarded as circularly symmetrical for the spacings used in open-wire construction—hence the results just noted give the additional per-phase inductance. Thus if skin effect is negligible:

$$l_\phi = l_a + l_Y$$
$$= \frac{\mu}{8\pi} + \frac{\mu}{2\pi}\ln\left(\frac{r_s}{r_a}\right)$$
$$= \frac{\mu}{2\pi}\left[\frac{1}{4} + \ln\left(\frac{r_s}{r_a}\right)\right] \quad \text{(henrys per meter)} \tag{12-30}$$

Because the inductance of any line is proportional to the logarithm of the spacing, it may be stated as the sum of two mathematical components, one (l'_a) which depends on the conductor cross section and on the frequency (because of skin effect), and another (l_d) which depends solely on the spacing*:

$$l_\phi = l'_a + l_d \tag{12-31}$$

Let

$$l_d = \frac{\mu}{2\pi}\ln r_s \tag{12-32}$$

For the solid circular conductor with negligible skin effect (see Eq. 12-30), l'_a would be as follows:

$$l'_a = \frac{\mu}{2\pi}\left[\frac{1}{4} + \ln\left(\frac{1}{r_a}\right)\right] \tag{12-33}$$

In Eq. 12-30 the units used for r_s and r_a are immaterial so long as the same units are used for both. However, numerical values of l_d and l'_a separately would be functions of the units used for r_s and r_a.

As noted in Sec. 12-1*b*, power-line conductors are almost always either (1) stranded, or (2) of composite construction, in which the effective conducting cross section is approximately annular. If skin effect is ignored, the concept of *self-geometric-mean distance*[7,14,16] may be used to compute the component inductance l'_a for such a conductor.

Spiralling of strands causes a significant increase in inductance for one class of conductor, namely, a steel-reinforced type with a single layer of conducting strands. A longitudinal ferromagnetic solenoid is formed thereby. This effect is slight when two or more layers of conducting strands are used, because successive layers are spiralled in opposing directions and hence the respective ***H*** fields largely offset one another.[8]

Convenient tables present the inductive reactances per mile corresponding to l'_a and l_d at 25, 50, and 60 cps, giving (1) values for x_a for each of those frequencies for each of a multiplicity of commercially available types and sizes of conductors, and (2) x_d at each of those frequencies for a number of values of r_s stated in feet.[4,7,13,14,16]

* This method was devised by W. A. Lewis.[4]

12-3. CAPACITANCE CALCULATIONS FOR THREE-PHASE LINE

A basic definition of capacitance in lumped-circuit theory is

$$C = \frac{Q}{V} \tag{12-34}$$

This may be applied to the TEM mode on a transmission line. When three wires are involved, as illustrated in Fig. 12-7, the voltage between each pair of conductors depends on the charge per unit length (q_L) on each of the three conductors. Each of these line charges may be considered to create a component $\boldsymbol{E}$ field, radially directed and proportional to the inverse of the radial distance:

$$\begin{aligned} \boldsymbol{E}_a &= \frac{q_{La}}{2\pi\epsilon_0 r_1}\,\boldsymbol{a}_{r1} \\ \boldsymbol{E}_b &= \frac{q_{Lb}}{2\pi\epsilon_0 r_2}\,\boldsymbol{a}_{r2} \\ \boldsymbol{E}_c &= \frac{q_{Lc}}{2\pi\epsilon_0 r_3}\,\boldsymbol{a}_{r3} \end{aligned} \tag{12-35}$$

The system will be assumed to be in charge equilibrium, that is,

$$q_{La} + q_{Lb} + q_{Lc} = 0 \tag{12-36}$$

The summation of these fields is the resultant $\boldsymbol{E}$ field, but the operation of line integration to find voltages between conductors may be performed on each component field separately.

Conductor diameters will be assumed small compared to the spacings, such that the distortion produced, for example, in the component field $\boldsymbol{E}_a$ by the finite extent of the conducting surfaces of lines b and c, is negligible:

$$v_{ab} = \frac{q_{La}}{2\pi\epsilon_0}\int_{r_a}^{r_{ab}}\left(\frac{1}{r_1}\,\boldsymbol{a}_{r1}\right)\cdot(dr_1\boldsymbol{a}_{r1}) + \frac{q_{Lb}}{2\pi\epsilon_0}\int_{r_a}^{r_{ab}}\left(\frac{1}{r_2}\,\boldsymbol{a}_{r2}\right)\cdot(dr_1\boldsymbol{a}_{r1}) + \frac{q_{Lc}}{2\pi\epsilon_0}\int_{r_a}^{r_{ab}}\left(\frac{1}{r_3}\,\boldsymbol{a}_{r3}\right)\cdot(dr_1\boldsymbol{a}_{r1})$$

Because the line integral of $\boldsymbol{E}$ in a transverse plane is independent of path, this may be reduced to the following:

$$v_{ab} = \frac{q_{La}}{2\pi\epsilon_0}\int_{r_a}^{r_{ab}}\frac{dr}{r} + \frac{q_{Lb}}{2\pi\epsilon_0}\int_{r_a}^{r_{ab}}\frac{-dr}{r} + \frac{q_{Lc}}{2\pi\epsilon_0}\int_{r_{ac}}^{r_{bc}}\frac{dr}{r}$$

$$\begin{aligned} v_{ab} &= \frac{q_{La}}{2\pi\epsilon_0}\ln\left(\frac{r_{ab}}{r_a}\right) + \frac{q_{Lb}}{2\pi\epsilon_0}\ln\left(\frac{r_a}{r_{ab}}\right) + \frac{q_{Lc}}{2\pi\epsilon_0}\ln\left(\frac{r_{bc}}{r_{ac}}\right) \\ v_{ac} &= \frac{q_{La}}{2\pi\epsilon_0}\ln\left(\frac{r_{ac}}{r_a}\right) + \frac{q_{Lb}}{2\pi\epsilon_0}\ln\left(\frac{r_{bc}}{r_{ab}}\right) + \frac{q_{Lc}}{2\pi\epsilon_0}\ln\left(\frac{r_a}{r_{ac}}\right) \end{aligned} \tag{12-37}$$

As with the inductance calculations, line-to-neutral voltage will be used to obtain a per-phase capacitance:

$$v_{an} = \tfrac{1}{3}(v_{ab} + v_{ac}) \tag{12-21}$$

$$v_{an} = \frac{1}{6\pi\epsilon_0}\left[q_{La}\ln\left(\frac{r_{ab}r_{ac}}{r_a^2}\right) + q_{Lb}\ln\left(\frac{r_a r_{bc}}{r_{ab}^2}\right) + q_{Lc}\ln\left(\frac{r_a r_{bc}}{r_{ac}^2}\right)\right] \tag{12-38}$$

If the conductor-set cross section is an equilateral triangle of sides r_s, Eq. 12-38 may be reduced to the following with the aid of Eq. 12-36:

$$V_{1-n} = \frac{q_{La}}{6\pi\epsilon_0}\left[\ln\left(\frac{r_s^2}{r_a^2}\right) - \ln\left(\frac{r_a}{r_s}\right)\right]$$

$$= \frac{q_{La}}{2\pi\epsilon_0}\ln\left(\frac{r_s}{r_a}\right) \tag{12-39}$$

In accordance with the principle indicated in Eq. 12-34, a per-phase distributed capacitance may be defined as follows:

$$c = \frac{2\pi\epsilon_0}{\ln\left(\dfrac{r_s}{r_a}\right)} \qquad \text{(farads per meter)} \tag{12-40}$$

In the inductance calculations, the transposed line was treated by adding the voltage drops incurred by the line currents flowing in three consecutive short sections of line Δz_T each. The analogous procedure is inexact here, because the three line sections would have the same voltages rather than the same charges per unit length. Nevertheless a fictitious capacitance computed on the basis of geometric mean spacing yields results of engineering accuracy for the transposed line.

If the capacitance property is stated in terms of the shunt reactance of a unit length of line x_c, tabular presentation of data for specific conductors at arbitrary spacings may be organized in the same manner as for inductive reactance:

$$x_c = \frac{\ln\left(\dfrac{r_s}{r_a}\right)}{2\pi\epsilon_0\omega} \tag{12-41}$$

$$x_c = \frac{\ln\left(\dfrac{1}{r_a}\right)}{2\pi\epsilon_0\omega} + \frac{\ln r_s}{2\pi\epsilon_0\omega} \tag{12-42}$$

Let

$$x_d' = \frac{\ln r_s}{2\pi\epsilon_0\omega} \tag{12-43}$$

and

$$x_a' = \frac{\ln\left(\dfrac{1}{r_a}\right)}{2\pi\epsilon_0\omega} \tag{12-44}$$

$$x_c = x_a' + x_d' \tag{12-45}$$

Equations 12-41 and 12-44 were derived for circular conductors; values for x_a' for many commercially available conductors are given in tables.[4,7,13,14,16]

12-4. GROUND CURRENTS: ANALYSIS BY IMAGES

The natural earth has a conductivity in the order of 10^{-1} to 10^{-3} mhos per meter, values which one may contrast with that of 5.8×10^7 mhos per meter for copper. But the earth has an enormous available cross section. Hence it may be anticipated that ground currents will take the form of diffuse current-density fields. Such currents may be induced by alternating currents in overhead conductors, or the ground may be conductively connected to the line by a short-circuited conductor and the grounded neutral point of a transformer bank. The conductivity of the ground affects not only the resistance to zero-sequence or ground-return currents but also the inductive reactance associated with such a path.

In general the current field is greatly constricted where it enters or leaves a metallic conductor, and hence most of the resistance associated with ground-return paths is localized in the neighborhood of the grounded terminals. A "ground resistance" may be allocated to each on this basis.*

The current-density field parallel to the line will tend to be concentrated near the surface (close to the wire carrying current in the opposite direction) if the conductivity is high, and distributed to greater depths if the conductivity is low. Mathematical analyses are highly approximate because of the inhomogeneity of the earth, and even if a uniform, finite conductivity is assumed, the work is tedious.[12,15] A measure of insight may be gained rather easily, however, from the limiting case of a plane surface of infinite conductivity, for which the technique of *images* may be used.

a. Single conductor with ground return

The simplest example is that of a single conductor with ground return, as illustrated in Fig. 12-10(*a*). The boundary conditions at an infinitely conducting surface are the same as those derived for oblique reflection, namely: (1) that the tangential component of $\boldsymbol{E}$ vanish at the conducting surface; (2) that the normal component of $\boldsymbol{B}$ vanish at the conducting surface; (3) that a surface-current density, equal in magnitude to the tangential component of $\boldsymbol{H}$ at the conducting surface, flow at right angles to the $\boldsymbol{H}$ field

* In the interest of lightning protection, it is desirable that the ground resistance associated with each transmission-line tower be low, in the order of 10 ohms or less. In event that the tower-footing surface area and the soil conductivity are too small to achieve this, additional ground-contacting conductors may be installed. These may be rods, driven vertically, or counterpoises, consisting of buried wires paralleling the line or extending radially from the towers.

in the direction required by the right-hand rule; and (4) that a surface-charge density, equal in magnitude to the normal component of $\boldsymbol{D}$ leaving the conducting surface, be present.

It may be seen from the symmetry of the equivalent image system in Fig. 12-10(*b*) that if line 1-1′ is perpendicular to the plane corresponding to

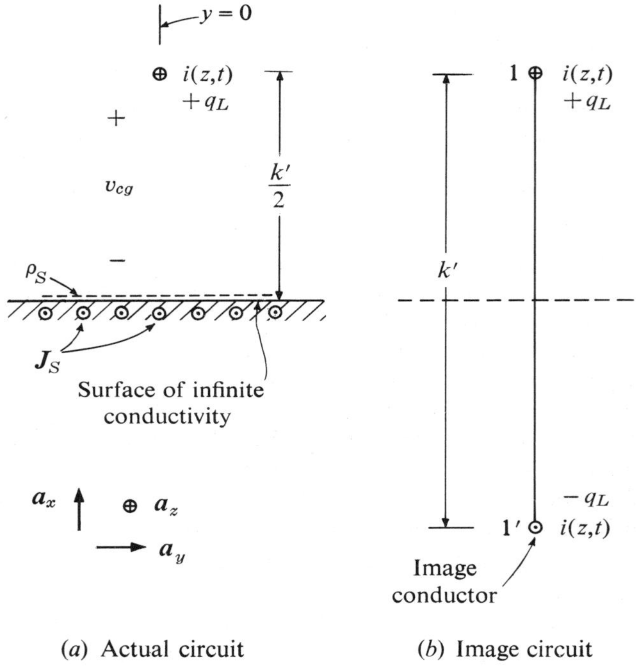

Figure 12-10 Single conductor with ideal ground return

ground, if the image conductor 1′ is at the same distance from that surface as the real conductor 1 is, and if the image conductor carries a current equal in magnitude but directed oppositely to that in the real conductor, the magnetic field at the midplane will be purely tangential. Likewise, if the charge per unit length of the image conductor is the negative of that on the real conductor, the electric field at the midplane will be purely normal. Thus conditions 1 and 2 have been satisfied, and the field configurations between the real conductor and the conducting surface are the same as those found in Sec. 9-2 for the space between two parallel circular conductors. From the results of that section, expressions may be derived for surface-current density and surface-charge density to satisfy conditions 3 and 4:

$$i(z,t) = I_M \sin(\omega t - \beta z) \qquad \text{(amperes)} \qquad \textbf{(12-46)}$$

For the surface-current density, Eqs. 9-49 and 9-51 may be used, with $x = 0$:

$$J_S = \frac{-I_M h \sin(\omega t - \beta z)}{2\pi\left[\left(\frac{h}{2}\right)^2 + y^2\right]} \boldsymbol{a}_z \qquad \text{(amperes per meter)} \qquad \textbf{(12-47)}$$

It is assumed that r_a is much smaller than k'; hence, in accordance with Eq. 9-57, $h \approx k'$.

The surface-charge density may be found with the aid of Eqs. 9-35 and 9-37, with x set equal to zero.

$$\rho_S = \frac{-I_M \epsilon_0 \eta h \sin(\omega t - \beta z)}{2\pi\left[\left(\frac{h}{2}\right)^2 + y^2\right]} \qquad \text{(coulombs per square meter)} \qquad \textbf{(12-48)}$$

The voltage from the conductor to the ground plane is one-half of that between the two conductors of Fig. 12-10(*b*). In the traveling-wave situation it is related to the current as indicated in Eqs. 9-62 and 9-64:

$$\begin{aligned} v_{cg}(z,t) &= \frac{I_M \eta}{2\pi} \cosh^{-1}\left(\frac{k'}{2r_a}\right) \sin(\omega t - \beta z) \\ &\approx \frac{I_M \eta}{2\pi} \ln\left(\frac{k'}{r_a}\right) \sin(\omega t - \beta z) \qquad \text{(volts)} \qquad \textbf{(12-49)} \end{aligned}$$

The characteristic impedance, distributed inductance and distributed capacitance for the conductor and its ground return are related to the corresponding values for the real-and-image conductor pair (see Eqs. 9-66 through 9-71) in the following manner:

$$\begin{aligned} Z_{0cg} &= \frac{Z_{011'}}{2} \\ l_{cg} &= \frac{l_{11'}}{2} \\ c_{cg} &= 2c_{11'} \end{aligned} \qquad \textbf{(12-50)}$$

b. Ground currents induced by two-wire line

When more than one current-carrying conductor is in the presence of an infinitely conducting surface, the boundary condition of zero normal component of $\boldsymbol{B}$ at that surface may be satisfied if an image conductor is envisioned for each of the real conductors. This is illustrated for the two-wire line in Fig. 12-11. An expression for surface-current density may be adapted from Eq. 12-47 by allowing for the offsets in the $\boldsymbol{a}_y$ direction:

$$J_S = \frac{-I_M h}{2\pi}\left[\frac{1}{(h/2)^2 + (y-a)^2} - \frac{1}{(h/2)^2 + (y+a)^2}\right] \sin(\omega t - \beta z)\boldsymbol{a}_z \qquad \textbf{(12-51)}$$

Since this current field in the ground plane necessarily accompanies the flow of current in the wire pair, one may surmise that the magnetic-field pattern in the vicinity of the conductors is altered by the introduction of the ground plane and hence the value of flux linkages obtained for the calculation of inductance would be changed. By using the image line and the principle

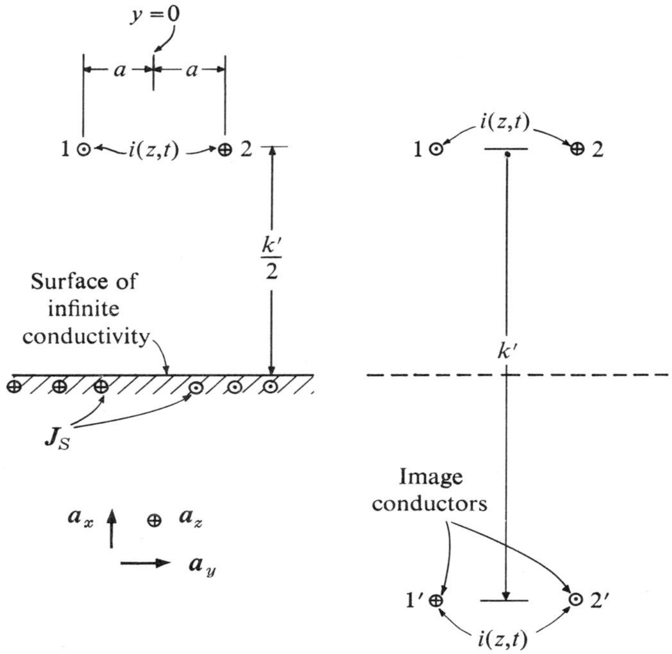

(*a*) Actual circuit (*b*) Image circuit

Figure 12-11 Two-wire line above ideal ground

of superposition, the effective inductance per unit length of line may be shown to be

$$l_{\text{eff}} = l_{12} - l_{12,1'2'} \tag{12-52}$$

The latter term is the mutual inductance (Eq. 12-17) between the real line and the image line.

c. Zero-sequence inductance of three-phase line

As noted earlier, the concept of zero-sequence current is a current set which flows through the transmission line, divided equally among the three conductors, and returns through the ground. Zero-sequence voltages are those component voltages with respect to ground which are common to all three conductors; in other words, they are equal and in time phase. The zero-sequence inductance and capacitance are derived line parameters which relate those sets.

If the ground is assumed to have infinite conductivity, the method of images may be used, as indicated in Fig. 12-12. The surface-current density

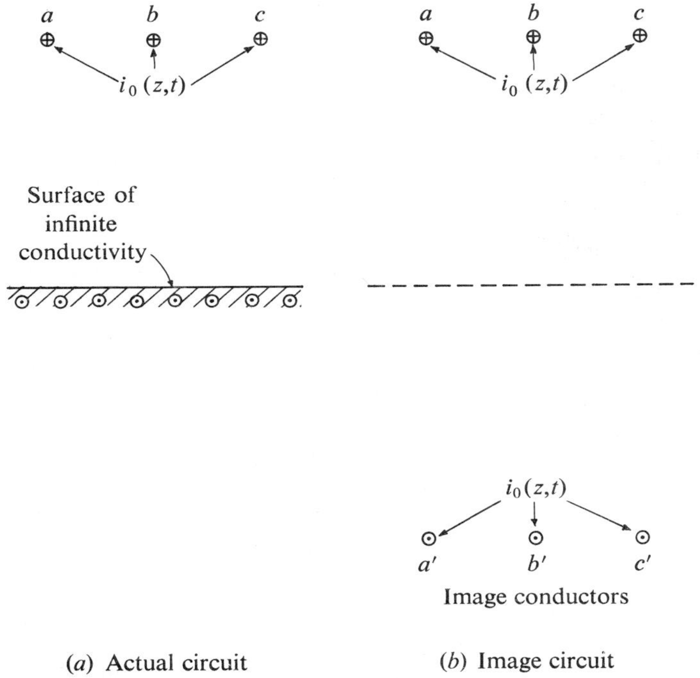

Figure 12-12 Zero-sequence currents in three-phase line with ideal ground return

function could be written by superposing three components of the form of Eq. 12-47, with appropriate heights and horizontal offsets for each.

The derivatives of voltage with respect to z may be related to the current in each real-and-image conductor pair as follows:

$$\begin{aligned}
\frac{\partial v_{aa'}}{\partial z} &= (-l_{aa'} - l_{aa',bb'} - l_{aa',cc'})\frac{\partial i_0}{\partial t} \\
\frac{\partial v_{bb'}}{\partial z} &= (-l_{bb'} - l_{aa',bb'} - l_{bb',cc'})\frac{\partial i_0}{\partial t} \qquad \textbf{(12-53)} \\
\frac{\partial v_{cc'}}{\partial z} &= (-l_{cc'} - l_{aa',cc'} - l_{bb',cc'})\frac{\partial i_0}{\partial t}
\end{aligned}$$

The various self and mutual inductances correspond to Eqs. 9-69 and 12-17.

If the line is transposed, the averaged zero-sequence voltage between the real line and the image line is related to the time rate of change of current as follows:

$$\frac{\partial v_{nn'}}{\partial z} = \tfrac{1}{3}\left(\frac{\partial v_{aa'}}{\partial z} + \frac{\partial v_{bb'}}{\partial z} + \frac{\partial v_{cc'}}{\partial z}\right)$$
$$= \tfrac{1}{3}(-l_{aa'} - l_{bb'} - l_{cc'} - 2l_{aa',bb'} - 2l_{aa',cc'} - 2l_{bb',cc'})\frac{\partial i_0}{\partial t} \qquad \textbf{(12-54)}$$

The zero-sequence voltage between the line and the ground plane is one-half as much. The zero-sequence inductance per unit length is then the following in terms of the indicated self-inductances and mutual inductances.

$$l_0 = \tfrac{1}{6}(l_{aa'} + l_{bb'} + l_{cc'} + 2l_{aa',bb'} + 2l_{aa',cc'} + 2l_{bb',cc'}) \qquad \textbf{(12-55)}$$

Approximate formulas for the zero-sequence inductive reactance, allowing for uniform, finite conductivity, are available.[4,7]

12-5. CONCLUSIONS

In many transmission lines composed of more than two conductors, the currents and voltages may be resolved into component sets which possess a high degree of symmetry and which are physically meaningful in terms of the usual performance of the system. The positive-sequence, negative-sequence, and zero-sequence sets of symmetrical-component theory are of this type. Each has a current pattern and a voltage pattern, and if the line is transposed, the relationship between current and voltage for each set can be expressed with an equivalent distributed resistance, distributed self-inductance, and distributed capacitance, independently of the other sets. The symmetrical-component method yields a good approximation in many systems containing nontransposed lines.

Transposition is also important as a means of reducing coupling between lines, such as telephone circuits, which are intended to function independently of each other.

The method of images may be used to analyze the currents which flow in an ideal ground plane which is in the vicinity of a transmission line and possibly connected to it.

PROBLEMS

12-1. Use the concept of flux linkages to derive an expression for the distributed self-inductance of a two-wire line. Assume that the conductor diameters are small compared to the spacing, and that the current is distributed uniformly over the cross section of each conductor.

12-2. Derive an expression for the resultant mutual inductance between two transposed two-wire lines for a length of $2\Delta z_T$ as a function of Δz_T and the wavelength ($\lambda = 2\pi/\beta$). Restate the result as an average distributed mutual inductance.

12-3. Derive an expression for the distributed self-inductance of a "phantom circuit" on a telephone line, consisting of four wires each of radius r_a arranged as shown in Fig. 12-13. The current in one direction is divided equally between the two upper conductors, and that in the return direction is divided equally between the two lower conductors.

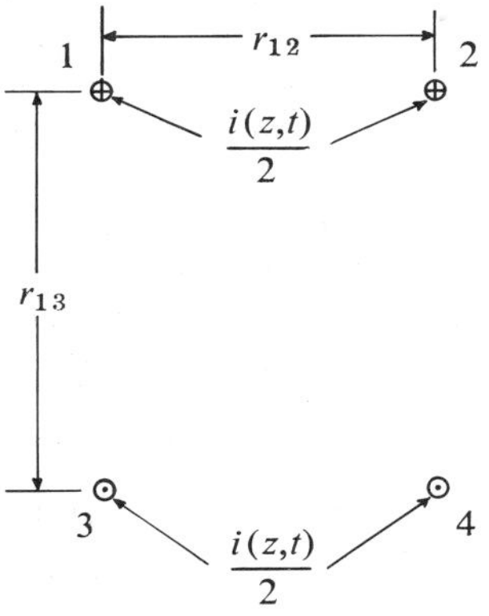

Figure 12-13 Cross section for one type of phantom circuit on telephone line (see Problem 12-3)

12-4. A two-wire line is built with solid conductors 0.258 in. in diameter, spaced 4 ft horizontally, and strung 25 ft above the ground. Compute the self-inductance per mile and the mutual inductance per mile between the line and its image.

12-5. A transposed three-phase line has the following characteristics:

Conductor type: 795,000 circular mil ACSR

$x_a = 0.401$ ohms per mile (60 cps)

$x_a' = 0.0917$ megohms for one mile

Spacing: 26 feet, flat ($r_{ab} = r_{bc} = r_{ac}/2$)

Average height above ground: 55 feet

Length: 40 miles

Compute the positive-sequence inductive and capacitive reactances. Assuming that the ground has infinite conductivity, compute the zero-sequence inductive reactance.

REFERENCES

1. Abetti P. A., C. B. Lindh, and H. O. Simmons, Jr., "Economics of Single and Bundle Conductors for Extra-High-Voltage Transmission," *AIEE Trans.*, 79, Part III (1960), 138–47.
2. Adams, G. E., "Radio Interference from High-Voltage Transmission Lines as Influenced by the Line Design," *AIEE Trans.*, 77, Part III (1958), 54–62.

3. Babcock, W. C., Esther Rentrop, and C. S. Thaeler, *Crosstalk on Open-Wire Lines*, Bell Telephone System Tech. Publs., Monograph 2520, 1955.

4. *Electrical Transmission and Distribution Reference Book*. Pittsburgh: Central Station Engineers of the Westinghouse Electric Corporation, 1950.

5. "Fiord Span is 3 Miles Long," *Elec. World*, 145, No. 20 (1956), 100, 203.

6. Jensen, C. H., R. E. DeMuth, and R. W. Mowery, "The Electrical Properties of Single-Layer Aluminum Conductors, Steel Reinforced (ACSR) Having Single Steel Core Wires With Heavy Aluminum Coating," *AIEE Trans.*, 81, Part III (1962), 27–32.

7. Kimbark, Edward W., *Electrical Transmission of Power and Signals*. New York: John Wiley & Sons, 1949.

8. Lewis, W. A. and P. D. Tuttle, "The Resistance and Reactance of Aluminum Conductors, Steel Reinforced," *AIEE Trans.*, 77, Part III (1959), 1189–1214.

9. "Modern Transmission Designs Adapt Engineering Advances," *Elec. World*, 140, No. 8 (1953), 121–50.

10. Preston, G. W. and H. G. Taylor, "Copper Conductors for Overhead Lines," *J. IEE (London)*, 91, Part II (1944), 451–68.

11. Rosa, Edward B. and Frederick W. Grover, "Formulas and Tables for the Calculation of Mutual and Self Inductance" (Sci. Paper 169), *Bull. Bur. Std. (U.S.)*, 8, No. 1 (1912), 1–237.

12. Rudenberg, Reinhold, *Transient Performance of Electric Power Systems*. New York: McGraw-Hill Book Company, Inc., 1950.

13. *Standard Handbook for Electrical Engineers*, 9th ed., pp. 218–98, 1156–1305, A. E. Knowlton, ed. New York: McGraw-Hill Book Company, Inc., 1957.

14. Stevenson, William D., *Power System Analysis*, (2nd ed.). New York: McGraw-Hill Book Company, Inc., 1962.

15. Sunde, E. D., *Earth Conduction Effects in Transmission Systems*. New York: D. Van Nostrand Company, Inc., 1949.

16. Zaborsky, John and J. W. Rittenhouse, *Electric Power Transmission*. New York: Ronald Press Company, 1954.

CHAPTER 13

Antennas and Radiating Fields

Transmission lines and wave guides have as their purpose the channeling of electromagnetic energy from one localized region to another, and their fields may be described as nonradiative. The traveling-wave fields for the coaxial line and for the rectangular and circular wave guides were, in each instance, contained within a finite cross section by an enclosing, highly conducting surface. For the open-wire line in the TEM mode the fields extended to infinity, but they diminished rapidly with increasing radial distance. On open-wire lines the interconductor spacing is small compared to wavelength, and this has the effect of thwarting the formation of modes which would transport energy away from the line rather than parallel to it.

Antennas are, in a sense, modified sections of transmission lines in which the "effective spacing" is comparable to wavelength. The electromagnetic fields of antennas, in contrast to those of transmission lines, are characterized by components which, on a time-averaged basis, convey energy ever-outward from the antenna structure. In most instances the "modified transmission line" comprising the antenna is, in effect, open-circuited at one end. Accordingly the field pattern includes pronounced standing waves in the immediate vicinity of the antenna.

Several textbooks deal intensively with antennas.[1–10] The present treatment will touch only some elementary aspects, ones which provide illustrations of electromagnetic theory on the level of the preceding chapters. Attention will be directed toward one basic type of antenna, the thin-wire dipole, which is illustrated in Fig. 13-1.

13-1. ANTENNA PROPERTIES: GENERAL

The properties usually studied may be grouped into two main classes: (1) the configuration of the electric and magnetic fields, and (2) the input impedance.

Field configuration is of theoretical interest from the standpoint of Maxwell's equations and boundary conditions; the aspect of greatest practical interest is the extent to which the radiated energy is focused into a directional pattern. The so-called far fields, or radiation fields, are of greater importance for that purpose than the fields close to the antenna. Directivity may be greatly enhanced by the coordinated use of two or more dipoles in an array.

The antenna input impedance influences the design of the transmission system linking a transmitter to the antenna. A good estimate of the resistive component may be made by assuming that the input power is equal to the radiated power, which in turn may be computed from Poynting's vector for the radiated fields. The calculation of input reactance[3,4] is beyond the scope of this book.

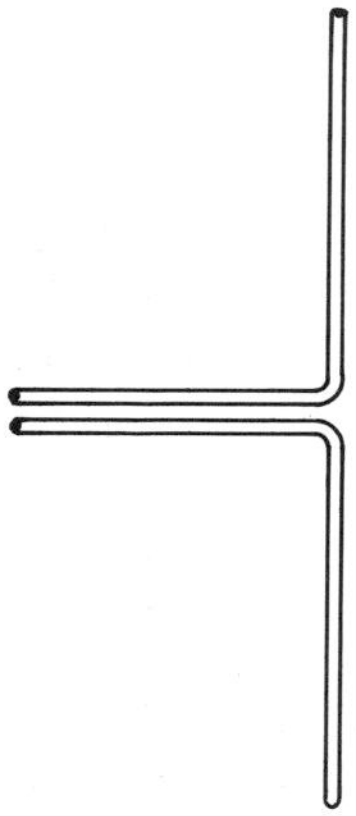

Figure 13-1 Thin-wire dipole antenna

13-2. FIELDS OF DIPOLE ANTENNA

Practical dipoles are usually cylindrical in shape and have some type of external supply. (A balanced two-wire line is indicated in Fig. 13-1, but other arrangements are common.) The resulting boundary surface is complicated, and a rigorous mathematical solution by separating variables and fitting boundary conditions is not feasible.

An approximate method will be used here, one which yields expressions for the fields outside the immediate vicinity of the antenna surface. In this method the incremental fields which would be produced by a short, isolated segment of alternating current are computed, and these incremental fields are summed with respect to an assumed current distribution along the antenna.

a. Incremental fields of isolated current segment

From the known variation of the magnetic field in the vicinity of a long conductor carrying direct current, the incremental magnetic field produced by a short segment of that current may be inferred. The fields of an alternating-current segment must satisfy Maxwell's equations, and a traveling-wave function seems plausible. Very close to the antenna, the alternating magnetic field may be expected to approach a pattern similar to that caused by direct current.

(1) MAGNETIC-FIELD CONTRIBUTION OF SHORT DIRECT-CURRENT SEGMENT. The magnetic field observed in the vicinity of a long cylindrical conductor carrying direct current in the $\boldsymbol{a}_z$ direction, with the return conductor coaxially shaped (or remotely located), is

$$\boldsymbol{H} = \frac{I}{2\pi r}\,\boldsymbol{a}_\phi \tag{13-1}$$

The contribution to this resultant field of a short segment dz of conductor carrying current I would be a useful mathematical quantity (1) as an element for antenna theory and (2) for the calculation of the resultant field and the inductance of conductors bent into such shapes as coils. Because of the requirement of continuity of current, an isolated current segment cannot be realized experimentally, but an expression for the incremental field due to a current segment may be inferred from the mathematical parallelism, or dualism, between the magnetic field of an infinitely long conductor which carries direct current and the electric field of a like conductor when uniformly charged. The two situations are sketched in Fig. 13-2. The magnitude of the electric field at point (r,z) due to the incremental charge $\rho_L\,dz$ is

$$|\boldsymbol{dE}| = \frac{\rho_L\,dz}{4\pi\epsilon(r^2 + z^2)} \tag{13-2}$$

This field may be resolved into r and z components:

$$\boldsymbol{dE} = \frac{r\rho_L\,dz}{4\pi\epsilon(r^2 + z^2)^{3/2}}\,\boldsymbol{a}_r + \frac{z\rho_L\,dz}{4\pi\epsilon(r^2 + z^2)^{3/2}}\,\boldsymbol{a}_z \tag{13-3}$$

For a charged line of infinite length, one may conclude from symmetry that the resultant z component of the $\boldsymbol{E}$ field will be zero. The net field is purely radial and has a magnitude equal to the integral of the r component of Eq. 13-3 with respect to z from $-\infty$ to ∞.

$$\boldsymbol{E} = \left.\frac{rz\rho_L}{4\pi r^2\epsilon\sqrt{r^2 + z^2}}\right]_{-\infty}^{\infty}\boldsymbol{a}_r$$

$$= \frac{\rho_L}{2\pi r\epsilon}\,\boldsymbol{a}_r \tag{13-4}$$

Comparison of the magnitudes in Eqs. 13-1 and 13-4 indicates that the following $\boldsymbol{dH}$ function, corresponding to $dE_r\boldsymbol{a}_r$, would be appropriate:

$$\boldsymbol{dH} = \frac{r(I\,dz)}{4\pi(r^2 + z^2)^{3/2}}\,\boldsymbol{a}_\phi \tag{13-5}$$

Integration of this with respect to z parallels the steps leading to Eq. 13-4 and gives Eq. 13-1.

Despite the intuitive origin of Eq. 13-5, solutions based on it have been found correct for all conductor configurations, provided integration is performed over the complete current path.

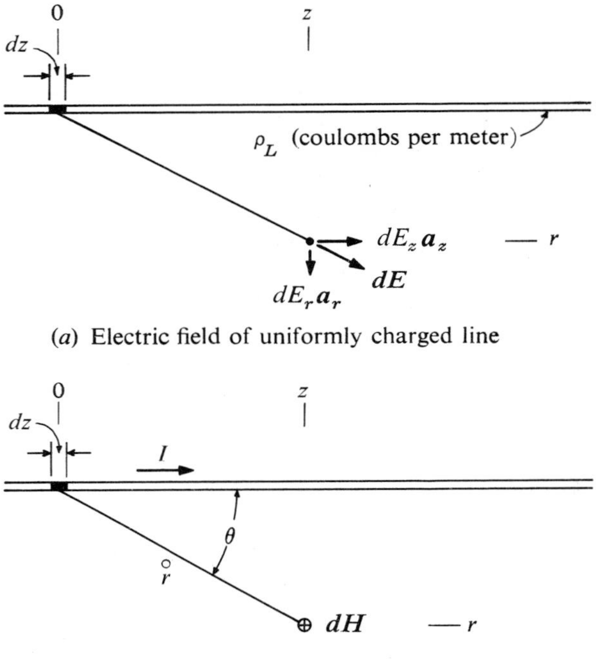

(b) Magnetic field of line carrying direct current

Figure 13-2 Field calculations for infinitely long conductor

For application to short-dipole antennas, Eq. 13-5 may be stated in spherical coordinates:

$$\boldsymbol{dH} = \frac{(I\,dz)\sin\theta}{4\pi\mathring{r}^2}\,\boldsymbol{a}_\phi \tag{13-6}$$

Equation 13-6 is sometimes spoken of as the "Law of Biot and Savart."

(2) SIMPLIFIED WAVE EQUATION IN SPHERICAL COORDINATES. The two curl equations of Maxwell's set may be reduced to a wave equation in $\boldsymbol{H}$ in a

manner corresponding to that for $\boldsymbol{E}$ in Chapter 10:

$$\nabla \times \boldsymbol{H} = \epsilon \frac{\partial \boldsymbol{E}}{\partial t} \quad \textbf{(7-32)}$$

$$\nabla \times (\nabla \times \boldsymbol{H}) = \epsilon\left(\nabla \times \frac{\partial \boldsymbol{E}}{\partial t}\right)$$

$$= \epsilon \frac{\partial}{\partial t}(\nabla \times \boldsymbol{E}) \quad \textbf{(13-7)}$$

$$\nabla \times \boldsymbol{E} = -\mu \frac{\partial \boldsymbol{H}}{\partial t} \quad \textbf{(7-34)}$$

The time derivative of Eq. 7-34 is substituted in Eq. 13-7.

$$\nabla \times (\nabla \times \boldsymbol{H}) = -\mu\epsilon \frac{\partial^2 \boldsymbol{H}}{\partial t^2} \quad \textbf{(13-8)}$$

On the basis of symmetry one may assume that $\boldsymbol{H}$ will have only a ϕ component and that that component will not vary circumferentially. Let

$$\boldsymbol{H} = H_\phi(\mathring{r},\theta,t)\boldsymbol{a}_\phi \quad \textbf{(13-9)}$$

Iterated substitution of Eq. 13-9 in Eq. 7-66, the expression for curl in spherical coordinates, yields

$$\nabla \times \boldsymbol{H} = \frac{1}{\mathring{r} \sin\theta} \frac{\partial(\sin\theta\, H_\phi)}{\partial\theta} \boldsymbol{a}_{\mathring{r}} - \frac{1}{\mathring{r}} \frac{\partial(\mathring{r} H_\phi)}{\partial \mathring{r}} \boldsymbol{a}_\theta$$

$$\nabla \times (\nabla \times \boldsymbol{H}) = \left\{-\frac{1}{\mathring{r}} \frac{\partial}{\partial\theta}\left[\frac{1}{\mathring{r}\sin\theta} \frac{\partial(\sin\theta\, H_\phi)}{\partial\theta}\right] - \frac{1}{\mathring{r}} \frac{\partial}{\partial \mathring{r}}\left[\frac{\partial(\mathring{r} H_\phi)}{\partial \mathring{r}}\right]\right\}\boldsymbol{a}_\phi \quad \textbf{(13-10)}$$

Substitution of Eq. 13-10 in Eq. 13-8 yields the following:

$$-\frac{1}{\mathring{r}^2} \frac{\partial}{\partial\theta}\left[\frac{1}{\sin\theta} \frac{\partial(\sin\theta\, H_\phi)}{\partial\theta}\right] - \frac{1}{\mathring{r}} \frac{\partial^2(\mathring{r} H_\phi)}{\partial \mathring{r}^2} = -\mu\epsilon \frac{\partial^2 H_\phi}{\partial t^2} \quad \textbf{(13-11)}$$

(3) SOLUTION OF WAVE EQUATION FOR ALTERNATING-CURRENT SEGMENT. Although the preceding expression is formidable, it may be reduced by postulating that $\boldsymbol{H}$ consists in part of factors which may be estimated (1) on the assumption that for small values of $\mathring{r}$, the solution should approach Eq. 13-5, if I is replaced by $I_M \sin \omega t$; and (2) on the assumption of a traveling-wave field moving radially outward. The estimated functional relationships will be checked by substitution into the wave equation.

First let it be assumed that the functional variation with θ is the same as in Eq. 13-6, namely, $\sin\theta$. Let

$$H_\phi(\mathring{r},\theta,t) = \sin\theta\, H'_\phi(\mathring{r},t) \quad \textbf{(13-12)}$$

After substitution of Eq. 13-12 in Eq. 13-11, the term sin θ may be cancelled and the following is left:

$$\frac{2H'_\phi}{\mathring{r}^2} - \frac{1}{\mathring{r}}\frac{\partial^2(\mathring{r}H'_\phi)}{\partial \mathring{r}^2} = -\mu\epsilon\frac{\partial^2 H'_\phi}{\partial t^2} \qquad \textbf{(13-13)}$$

Next it will be assumed that the function $H'_\phi(\mathring{r},t)$ consists of a sinusoidal traveling-wave function with phase function β. Let

$$H'_\phi(\mathring{r},t) = \text{Im}[H''_\phi(\mathring{r})\epsilon^{j(\omega t - \beta\mathring{r})}] \qquad \textbf{(13-14)}$$

After substitution of Eq. 13-14 in Eq. 13-13 the Im operator and the exponential may be cancelled, leaving

$$\frac{2H''_\phi}{\mathring{r}^2} - \frac{1}{\mathring{r}}\frac{d^2(\mathring{r}H''_\phi)}{d\mathring{r}^2} + \frac{2j\beta}{\mathring{r}}\frac{d(\mathring{r}H''_\phi)}{d\mathring{r}} + \frac{\beta^2(\mathring{r}H''_\phi)}{\mathring{r}} = \mu\epsilon\omega^2 H''_\phi \qquad \textbf{(13-15)}$$

The last two terms in Eq. 13-15 are independent of $\mathring{r}$. Together they will define the phase function β independently of H''_ϕ, which is in accordance with the assumed functional form of Eq. 13-14.

$$\beta = \omega\sqrt{\mu\epsilon} \qquad \textbf{(13-16)}$$

This is the same value as for the TEM mode and is reasonable because the geometry of the spherical wave front approaches that of a TEM wave front at large distances (many wavelengths) from the source. Substitution of this value for β in Eq. 13-15 leaves the following equation in $H''_\phi(\mathring{r})$:

$$\frac{2H''_\phi}{\mathring{r}^2} - \frac{1}{\mathring{r}}\frac{d^2(\mathring{r}H''_\phi)}{d\mathring{r}^2} + \frac{2j\beta}{\mathring{r}}\frac{d(H\mathring{r}''_\phi)}{d\mathring{r}} = 0 \qquad \textbf{(13-17)}$$

In accordance with Eq. 13-6 an inverse-square variation of H''_ϕ with $\mathring{r}$ may be expected, but, with excellent foresight, it will be anticipated that such a term alone will not satisfy Eq. 13-17. Hence, let

$$H''_\phi(\mathring{r}) = \frac{K}{\mathring{r}^2} + H'''_\phi(\mathring{r}) \qquad \textbf{(13-18)}$$

Eq. 13-17 then becomes

$$\frac{2K}{\mathring{r}^4} + \frac{2H'''_\phi}{\mathring{r}^2} - \frac{2K}{\mathring{r}^4} + \frac{1}{\mathring{r}}\frac{d^2(\mathring{r}H'''_\phi)}{d\mathring{r}^2} - \frac{2j\beta K}{\mathring{r}^3} + \frac{2j\beta}{\mathring{r}}\frac{d(\mathring{r}H'''_\phi)}{d\mathring{r}} = 0$$

This reduces to

$$\frac{2H'''_\phi}{\mathring{r}^2} + \frac{1}{\mathring{r}}\frac{d^2(\mathring{r}H'''_\phi)}{d\mathring{r}^2} - \frac{2j\beta K}{\mathring{r}^3} + \frac{2j\beta}{\mathring{r}}\frac{d(\mathring{r}H'''_\phi)}{d\mathring{r}} = 0 \qquad \textbf{(13-19)}$$

If $H'''_\phi(\mathring{r})$ is chosen proportional to $1/\mathring{r}$, the derivative terms in Eq. 13-19 will vanish, leaving the following:

$$\frac{2H'''_\phi(\mathring{r})}{\mathring{r}^2} - 2j\frac{\beta K}{\mathring{r}^3} = 0$$

or

$$H'''_\phi(\mathring{r}) = \frac{j\beta K}{\mathring{r}} \qquad \textbf{(13-20)}$$

Assembling the parts of the solution represented by Eqs. 13-12, 13-14, 13-16, 13-18, and 13-20 gives the following:

$$H_\phi(\mathring{r},\theta,t) = \sin\theta \,\mathrm{Im}\left[K\left(\frac{1}{\mathring{r}^2} + \frac{j\beta}{\mathring{r}}\right)\epsilon^{j(\omega t - \beta\mathring{r})}\right] \tag{13-21}$$

$$H_\phi(\mathring{r},\theta,t) = K\sin\theta\left[\frac{\sin(\omega t - \beta\mathring{r})}{\mathring{r}^2} + \frac{\beta\cos(\omega t - \beta\mathring{r})}{\mathring{r}}\right] \tag{13-22}$$

As $\mathring{r}$ approaches zero, the second term in the brackets becomes negligible compared to the first. By comparison with Eq. 13-6 for a direct-current segment, it appears that when $\mathring{r}$ approaches zero, the magnetic field of a segment of length Δz and current $I_M \sin\omega t$ should approach the following:

$$\boldsymbol{H} = \frac{(I_M\,\Delta z)\sin\theta\sin\omega t}{4\pi\mathring{r}^2}\,\boldsymbol{a}_\phi \qquad (\mathring{r}\to 0) \tag{13-23}$$

The following substitution will bring Eq. 13-22 into agreement with Eq. 13-23 for $\mathring{r} \to 0$:

$$K = \frac{I_M\,\Delta z}{4\pi} \tag{13-24}$$

(4) General properties of $\boldsymbol{H}$ and $\boldsymbol{E}$ fields. Equation 13-22 may be rewritten with Eqs. 13-16 and 13-24 substituted:

$$\boldsymbol{H} = \frac{I_M\,\Delta z\sin\theta}{4\pi}\left[\frac{\omega\sqrt{\mu\epsilon}}{\mathring{r}}\cos\omega(t - \mathring{r}\sqrt{\mu\epsilon}) + \frac{1}{\mathring{r}^2}\sin\omega(t - \mathring{r}\sqrt{\mu\epsilon})\right]\boldsymbol{a}_\phi \tag{13-25}$$

The $\boldsymbol{E}$ field may be found from the following equation:

$$\nabla\times\boldsymbol{H} = \epsilon\frac{\partial\boldsymbol{E}}{\partial t} \tag{7-32}$$

$$\begin{aligned}\boldsymbol{E} = {} & \frac{I_M\,\Delta z\cos\theta}{2\pi\epsilon}\left[\frac{\sqrt{\mu\epsilon}}{\mathring{r}^2}\sin\omega(t - \mathring{r}\sqrt{\mu\epsilon}) - \frac{1}{\omega\mathring{r}^3}\cos\omega(t - \mathring{r}\sqrt{\mu\epsilon})\right]\boldsymbol{a}_{\mathring{r}} \\ & + \frac{I_M\,\Delta z\sin\theta}{4\pi\epsilon}\left[\frac{\omega\mu\epsilon}{\mathring{r}}\cos\omega(t - \mathring{r}\sqrt{\mu\epsilon}) + \frac{\sqrt{\mu\epsilon}}{\mathring{r}^2}\sin\omega(t - \mathring{r}\sqrt{\mu\epsilon}) \right. \\ & \left. - \frac{1}{\omega\mathring{r}^3}\cos\omega(t - \mathring{r}\sqrt{\mu\epsilon})\right]\boldsymbol{a}_\theta\end{aligned} \tag{13-26}$$

This result may be checked by substituting it in Maxwell's equation involving curl $\boldsymbol{E}$, Eq. 7-34, and solving for $\boldsymbol{H}$, for comparison with Eq. 13-25 (see Problem 13-1).

Some insight may be gained by writing Poynting's vector as an instantaneous function and then taking the time average (see Problem 13-2). The final result is compact indeed:

$$\boldsymbol{P}_{\mathrm{av}}(\mathring{r},\theta) = \frac{(I_M\,\Delta z)^2\omega^2\mu\sqrt{\mu\epsilon}\sin^2\theta}{32\pi^2\mathring{r}^2}\,\boldsymbol{a}_{\mathring{r}} \tag{13-27}$$

This function arises from the term in H_ϕ involving $1/\mathring{r}$ and the corresponding term in E_θ. These parts of the total fields are known as the *radiation fields*, because Eq. 13-27 indicates a sustained movement of energy from the current element outward.

A criterion for sensing whether the radiation-field terms give a good approximation at a particular distance may be found by noting at what distance, for a given field component, the magnitudes of the terms in different powers of $1/\mathring{r}$ are equal. This distance proves to be the same in every instance and may be indicated by $\mathring{r}'$:

$$\begin{aligned} \mathring{r}' &= \frac{1}{\omega\sqrt{\mu\epsilon}} \\ &= \frac{1}{\beta} \\ &= \frac{\lambda}{2\pi} \end{aligned} \tag{13-28}$$

At radii greater than about $\frac{1}{6}$ wavelength the radiation-field terms are dominant in Eqs. 13-25 and 13-26; the complete expressions may reasonably be said to describe the *near field*, the radiation-field terms by themselves, the *far field*. It should be kept in mind when using the phrase "near field" that no attempt was made to satisfy boundary conditions at the "surface" of the current element, the length and diameter of which are assumed to be infinitesimal compared to wavelength.

The far-field approximations may be designated with a subscript f:

$$\boldsymbol{H}_f = \frac{I_M \Delta z\, \omega\sqrt{\mu\epsilon}\sin\theta}{4\pi\mathring{r}} \cos\omega(t - \mathring{r}\sqrt{\mu\epsilon})\boldsymbol{a}_\phi \tag{13-29}$$

$$\boldsymbol{E}_f = \frac{I_M \Delta z\, \omega\mu\sin\theta}{4\pi\mathring{r}} \cos\omega(t - \mathring{r}\sqrt{\mu\epsilon})\boldsymbol{a}_\theta \tag{13-30}$$

These fields are in time phase with each other and are related in magnitude by the intrinsic impedance of space:

$$\begin{aligned} \frac{E_{\theta f}}{H_{\phi f}} &= \sqrt{\frac{\mu}{\epsilon}} \\ &= \eta \end{aligned} \tag{13-31}$$

Equations 13-29 and 13-30 constitute a TEM-type wave pair. It may be noted, in accordance with Problem 13-3, that $\boldsymbol{E}_f$ does not satisfy Maxwell's equation for continuity of the $\boldsymbol{D}$ field; a radial component is necessary to meet that requirement. Figure 13-3 shows direction lines of the $\boldsymbol{E}$ and $\boldsymbol{H}$ fields, based on the far-field equations, 13-29 and 13-30, plus the $1/\mathring{r}^2$ term in $E\mathring{r}$ (see Eq. 13-26).

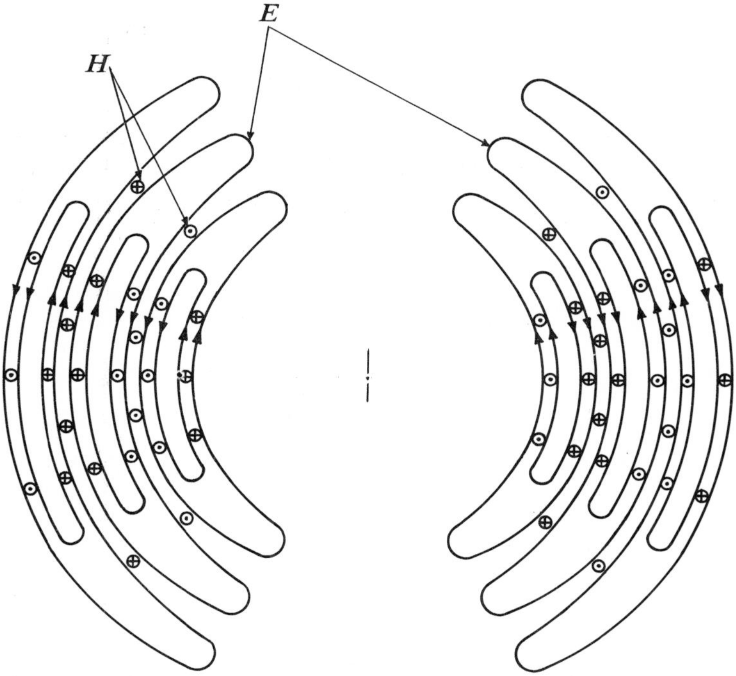

Figure 13-3 Direction lines of radiating fields of short dipole antenna

b. Current-distribution function and fields of general dipole

The current on an antenna and the displacement current touching it must satisfy the requirement of continuity; for a thin-wire dipole this means that the current, at any instant, will vary gradually with location along the wires and will approach zero at the ends. The actual distribution may be expected to depend on several minor factors, such as the shape of the wire ends, the wire thickness, and the lead-in configuration, but a good approximation for thin dipoles as a class is the standing-wave type of function described by the following equations[3,4,9]; it has the advantage of being tractable mathematically:

$$\begin{aligned} i(z) &= I_{LM} \sin \beta(h - z) \sin \omega t \qquad (0 < z < h) \\ i(z) &= I_{LM} \sin \beta(h + z) \sin \omega t \qquad (-h < z < 0) \end{aligned} \tag{13-32}$$

The length of the dipole is $2h$, and $i(z)$ will be considered positive in the $\boldsymbol{a}_z$ direction.

The term $I_{LM} \sin \omega t$ is called the *loop current*, because it is the largest value on the standing-wave pattern, assuming that $\beta h \geqslant \pi/2$. The maximum value of the current at the input terminals I_{IM} is related to I_{LM} as follows:

$$I_{IM} = I_{LM} \sin \beta h \tag{13-33}$$

The antenna is assumed to consist of a succession of current segments $i(z)\,dz$, and the resultant incremental fields are summed by integration. Attention here will be limited to the far fields. From Eq. 13-29, with $I_M \Delta z$

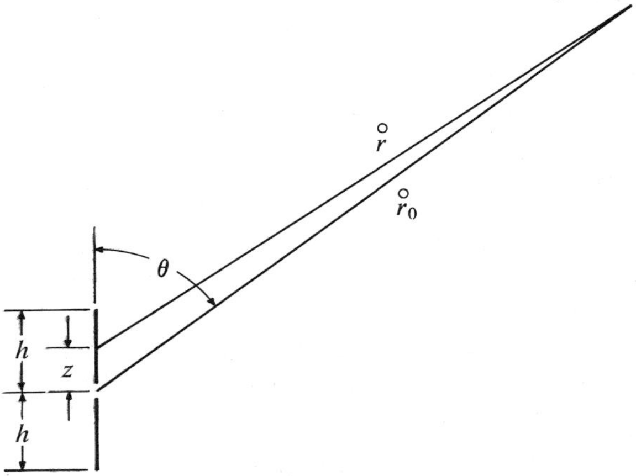

Figure 13-4 Radial distances as function of position on dipole

replaced by $I_{LM} \sin \beta(h - z)\,dz$ or $I_{LM} \sin \beta(h + z)\,dz$, the integral to be evaluated is

$$H_{\phi f} = \int_0^h \frac{I_{LM}\beta \sin \beta(h - z) \sin \theta \cos(\omega t - \beta \mathring{r})\,dz}{4\pi \mathring{r}} + \int_{-h}^0 \frac{I_{LM}\beta \sin \beta(h + z) \sin \theta \cos(\omega t - \beta \mathring{r})\,dz}{4\pi \mathring{r}} \tag{13-34}$$

As shown in Fig. 13-4, $\mathring{r}$ is a function of z:

$$\mathring{r} = \sqrt{\mathring{r}_0^2 - 2\mathring{r}_0 z \cos \theta + z^2} = \mathring{r}_0 \sqrt{1 + \frac{-2\mathring{r}_0 z \cos \theta + z^2}{\mathring{r}^2}} \tag{13-35}$$

The radical may be expanded in a power series; if only the first-order terms of $z/\mathring{r}$ are retained, the result is

$$\mathring{r} \approx \mathring{r}_0 \left[1 - \frac{\mathring{r}_0 z \cos \theta}{\mathring{r}_0^2}\right] \approx \mathring{r}_0 - z \cos \theta \tag{13-36}$$

Unless h is very short compared to wavelength, the time-phase differences between the incremental fields coming from various segment locations along the antenna may be expected to be important. On the other hand, the effect of a changing value of $\mathring{r}$ in the denominator, when $\mathring{r}_0 \gg h$, is slight. Equation 13-34 is accordingly simplified to the following:

$$H_{\phi f} = \int_0^h \frac{I_{LM}\beta \sin\beta(h - z)\sin\theta\cos(\omega t - \beta\mathring{r}_0 + \beta z\cos\theta)\,dz}{4\pi\mathring{r}_0} + \int_{-h}^0 \frac{I_{LM}\beta \sin\beta(h + z)\sin\theta\cos(\omega t - \beta\mathring{r}_0 + \beta z\cos\theta)\,dz}{4\pi\mathring{r}_0} \tag{13-37}$$

Evaluation of this integral is the substance of Problem 13-4:

$$H_{\phi f} = \frac{I_{LM}\cos(\omega t - \beta\mathring{r})[\cos(\beta h\cos\theta) - \cos\beta h]}{2\pi\mathring{r}_0\sin\theta} \tag{13-38}$$

If it is assumed that $\beta h \ll 1$, such that terms in βh and βz above the first order may be neglected, the integration of Eq. 13-37 is easier and a less cumbersome answer results.

$$\begin{aligned} \sin\beta(h - z) &\approx \beta(h - z) \\ \sin\beta(h + z) &\approx \beta(h + z) \end{aligned} \tag{13-39}$$

$$\begin{aligned} \cos(\omega t - \beta\mathring{r} + \beta z\cos\theta) &= \cos(\omega t - \beta\mathring{r})\cos(\beta z\cos\theta) \\ &\quad - \sin(\omega t - \beta\mathring{r})\sin(\beta z\cos\theta) \\ &\approx \cos(\omega t - \beta\mathring{r}) - \beta z\cos\theta\sin(\omega t - \beta\mathring{r}) \end{aligned}$$

Substitution of these approximations in Eq. 13-37 gives the following, after deletion of product terms involving hz or z^2:

$$\begin{aligned} H_{\phi f} &\approx \int_0^h \frac{I_{LM}\beta^2(h - z)\sin\theta\cos(\omega t - \beta\mathring{r}_0)\,dz}{4\pi\mathring{r}_0} + \int_{-h}^0 \frac{I_{LM}\beta^2(h + z)\sin\theta\cos(\omega t - \beta\mathring{r}_0)\,dz}{4\pi\mathring{r}_0} \\ &\approx \frac{I_{LM}\beta^2\sin\theta\cos(\omega t - \beta\mathring{r}_0)}{4\pi\mathring{r}_0}\left\{\left[hz - \frac{z^2}{2}\right]_0^h + \left[hz + \frac{z^2}{2}\right]_{-h}^0\right\} \\ &\approx \frac{I_{LM}\beta^2h^2\sin\theta\cos(\omega t - \beta\mathring{r}_0)}{4\pi\mathring{r}_0} \end{aligned} \tag{13-40}$$

For a short dipole the current is nowhere as large as I_{LM}, but the current at the input terminals is, in accordance with Eqs. 13-33 and 13-39, approximately the following:

$$I_{IM} \approx I_{LM}\beta h \tag{13-41}$$

Equation 13-38 will reduce to the approximation given in Eq. 13-40 if series expansions are substituted for the cosine terms involving βh (see Problem 13-5).

The electric far field may be found with the aid of Eq. 13-31, which relates it to the magnetic far field, Eq. 13-38:

$$E_{\theta f} = \sqrt{\frac{\mu}{\epsilon}} \frac{I_{LM} \cos(\omega t - \beta \mathring{r}_0)[\cos(\beta h \cos \theta) - \cos \beta h]}{2\pi \mathring{r}_0 \sin \theta} \quad \textbf{(13-42)}$$

If $\beta h \ll 1$, Eq. 13-31 is used with Eq. 13-40:

$$E_{\theta f} \approx \sqrt{\frac{\mu}{\epsilon}} \frac{I_{LM}\beta^2 h^2 \cos(\omega t - \beta \mathring{r}_0) \sin \theta}{4\pi \mathring{r}_0} \quad \textbf{(13-43)}$$

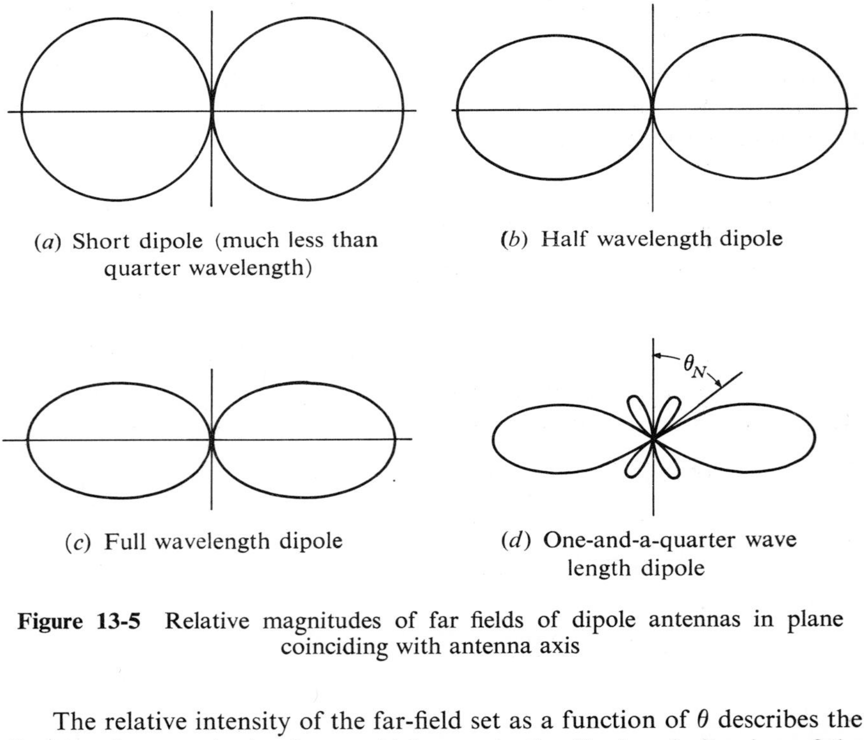

(*a*) Short dipole (much less than quarter wavelength)

(*b*) Half wavelength dipole

(*c*) Full wavelength dipole

(*d*) One-and-a-quarter wave length dipole

Figure 13-5 Relative magnitudes of far fields of dipole antennas in plane coinciding with antenna axis

The relative intensity of the far-field set as a function of θ describes the directional properties in planes which contain the dipole axis. In view of the complexity of Eqs. 13-38 and 13-42, graphical presentation of selected results is helpful. Figure 13-5 shows polar plots as functions of θ of far-field magnitude for four values of βh. Dipoles longer than 1 wavelength have zero far field at certain discrete values of θ in addition to 0 and 180 degrees, as indicated in Fig. 13-5(*d*) (see Problem 13-7).

13-3. RADIATION RESISTANCE

A useful property measure of an antenna is the *radiation resistance*, which is defined as the average power divided by the square of the effective current.

Average power may be found by evaluating the surface integral of the time-averaged Poynting's vector over a sphere which is concentric with the origin. This will be done for the simplified case of the short dipole (Eqs. 13-40 and 13-43):

$$\boldsymbol{P}_f = E_{\theta f} H_{\phi f} \boldsymbol{a}_{\mathring{r}}$$

$$\boldsymbol{P}_{\text{av}} \approx \sqrt{\frac{\mu}{\epsilon}} \frac{I_{LM}^2 \beta^4 h^4 \sin^2 \theta}{32\pi^2 \mathring{r}_0^2} \boldsymbol{a}_{\mathring{r}} \tag{13-44}$$

$$\boldsymbol{dS} = \mathring{r}_0^2 \sin \theta \, d\theta \, d\phi \, \boldsymbol{a}_{\mathring{r}} \tag{13-45}$$

$$\oiint \boldsymbol{P}_{\text{av}} \cdot \boldsymbol{dS} \approx \int_0^{2\pi} \int_0^{\pi} \sqrt{\frac{\mu}{\epsilon}} \frac{I_{LM}^2 \beta^4 h^4 \sin^3 \theta \, d\theta \, d\phi}{32\pi^2}$$

$$\approx \int_0^{\pi} \sqrt{\frac{\mu}{\epsilon}} \frac{I_{LM}^2 \beta^4 h^4 \sin^3 \theta \, d\theta}{16\pi}$$

$$\int_0^{\pi} \sin^3 \theta \, d\theta = \int_0^{\pi} \sin \theta (1 - \cos^2 \theta) \, d\theta$$

$$= -\cos \theta + \frac{\cos^3 \theta}{3} \Big]_0^{\pi}$$

$$= \frac{4}{3}$$

$$\oiint \boldsymbol{P}_{\text{av}} \cdot \boldsymbol{dS} \approx \sqrt{\frac{\mu}{\epsilon}} \frac{I_{LM}^2 \beta^4 h^4}{12\pi} \tag{13-46}$$

Conventionally the loop current is used in the calculation of radiation resistance; its effective value is $I_{LM}/\sqrt{2}$. The following is a general expression for the radiation resistance:

$$R_{\text{rad}} = \frac{\oiint \boldsymbol{P}_{\text{av}} \cdot \boldsymbol{dS}}{(I_{LM}/\sqrt{2})^2} \tag{13-47}$$

Equation 13-46 is substituted in Eq. 13-47 to yield the radiation resistance of a short dipole ($\beta h \ll 1$).

$$R_{\text{rad}} \approx \sqrt{\frac{\mu}{\epsilon}} \frac{\beta^4 h^4}{6\pi} \quad \text{(loop-current basis)} \tag{13-48}$$

For the short dipole the result may be more meaningful when referred to input current. In accordance with Eq. 13-41,

$$R_{\text{rad}} \approx \sqrt{\frac{\mu}{\epsilon}}\frac{\beta^2 h^2}{6\pi} \quad \text{(input-current basis)} \tag{13-49}$$

The corresponding integration with respect to θ for Poynting's vector based on the far fields of the general dipole, Eqs. 13-38 and 13-42, is much more complicated. The result may be stated as a lengthy combination of

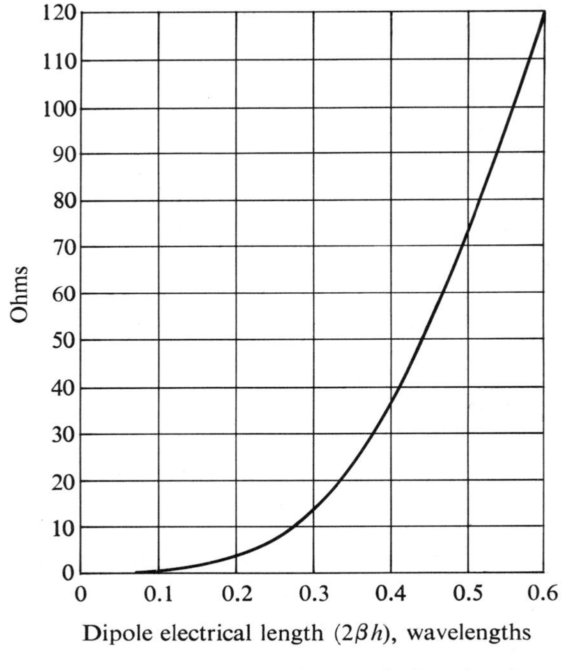

Figure 13-6 Radiation resistance (referred to loop current) of dipole as function of electrical length

tabulated functions,[1,3] or it may be evaluated numerically. A plot of radiation resistance versus dipole length is given in Fig. 13-6. Of particular interest for some applications is the radiation resistance of a half-wavelength dipole, 73 ohms.

13-4. EFFECT OF IDEAL GROUND PLANE

Low-frequency and medium-frequency broadcast antennas often consist of monopoles extending vertically upward from the earth. For the idealized situation of a perfectly conducting earth, the field patterns and radiation resistance may be found by the method of images. (This was used in Chapter 12 in connection with transmission lines above a perfectly conducting earth.)

Figure 13-7 shows a monopole antenna with ground and the dipole which corresponds to the monopole and its image. If a conducting sheet were inserted into the equatorial plane of the dipole, it would not tend to distort the fields, because it would be normal to the ***E*** field and parallel to the ***H*** field.

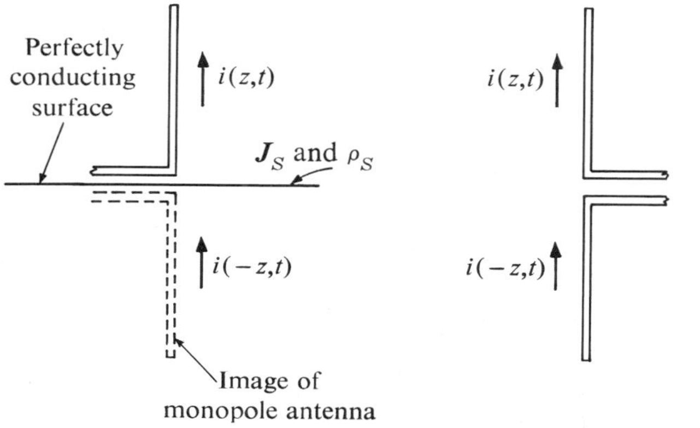

(*a*) Monopole with ground plane and image

(*b*) Equivalent dipole

Figure 13-7 Monopole with perfectly conducting ground plane

Surface currents, oppositely phased, would flow radially along each side of the sheet. These would be equal in magnitude to the magnitude of ***H*** just above the respective surfaces. Surface-charge distributions, of opposite polarities, would terminate the ***D*** field on each side of the sheet. Removal of the excitation from the lower half of the dipole would leave only the upper surface current and the upper surface-charge distribution. No fields would then exist below the conducting sheet. The resulting system is that of the monopole.

No power is dissipated in a perfectly conducting ground; hence the monopole power corresponding to a given current is one-half that for the dipole of equal height h, and, in accordance with Eq. 13-47, the monopole radiation resistance is one-half that of the dipole. Calculation of the fields of a monopole antenna with a ground of finite conductivity is far more complicated.

In the interest of decreasing propagation losses, a set of buried wires, arranged radially, may be used to lower the effective ground resistivity. *Ground wires*, as these are known, should extend about a third of a wavelength from the antenna base and should number 120 or more. This corresponds to an angular spacing of 3 degrees or less.[1,3,11]

13-5. DIRECTIVITY AND COMPOSITE ANTENNAS

All antenna patterns are directional to some extent, and in many applications it is desirable that they be highly directional. Antennas may be classified for this purpose as *broadcast* or *point-to-point* units. For broadcasting it is assumed that receivers are distributed over a substantial geographical area, which may or may not be within some well-defined sector in the horizontal direction ϕ as viewed from the antenna. In the vertical direction θ, a narrow sector will include the expected locations of receivers.

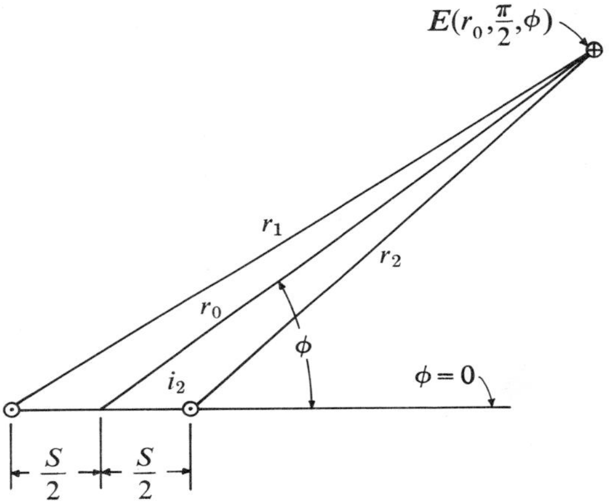

Figure 13-8 Two-dipole array (current i_2 lags i_1 by ψ radians)

In point-to-point applications, the radiated energy should be concentrated as much as possible toward the one intended receiver.

Some of the principle techniques for obtaining directionality are (1) *arrays*, consisting of two or more dipoles in a prescribed electrical spacing and with a controlled magnitude-and-phase relationship among the respective input currents; (2) *parasitic elements*, which are resonant lengths of conductor parallel to a dipole but excited solely by induction from it; (3) *metallic lenses*, or assemblies of closely spaced conducting surfaces parallel to the direction of propagation (these produce wave-guide modes locally); and (4) *reflecting surfaces* in conjunction with (a) a dipole, (b) an array of dipoles, or (c) a wave-guide *horn*, or flared ending on a wave guide. Wire grids may be used instead of continuous surfaces as reflectors. Methods 2, 3 and 4 are used largely at wavelengths in the order of a meter or less.

The resultant far field of one such type will be examined here, namely, the two-dipole array, which is sketched in Fig. 13-8. The pattern will be computed for the plane perpendicular to the dipole axes and passing through their centers. For this plane, $\theta = \pi/2$, and the equation for the electric far field of a single dipole, Eq. 13-42, will reduce to the following:

$$E_{\theta f}\left(r, \frac{\pi}{2}, t\right) = \text{Im}\left[\frac{jI_{LM}\epsilon^{j(\omega t - \beta \mathring{r}_0)}(1 - \cos \beta h)}{2\pi \mathring{r}_0}\right] \tag{13-50}$$

The radial direction will be restricted to the plane $\theta = \pi/2$ for the remainder of this derivation, and hence the symbol r will be used rather than $\mathring{r}$.

The dipoles in Fig. 13-8 are each displaced in location by $S/2$ from the origin, and their currents are displaced by ψ radians in time phase with respect to each other:

$$r_1 \approx r_0 + \frac{S}{2}\cos\phi$$
$$r_2 \approx r_0 - \frac{S}{2}\cos\phi \tag{13-51}$$

These approximations parallel the one made in Eqs. 13-35 and 13-36. Correspondingly, the effect of the difference between r_1 and r_0 and between r_2 and r_0 in the denominator, will be ignored here, too:

$$E_{\theta f1} = \text{Im}\left[\frac{jI_{LM}\epsilon^{j[\omega t - \beta r_0 - (\beta S/2)\cos\phi + (\psi/2)]}(1 - \cos\beta h)}{2\pi r_0}\right]$$
$$E_{\theta f2} = \text{Im}\left[\frac{jI_{LM}\epsilon^{j[\omega t - \beta r_0 + (\beta S/2)\cos\phi - (\psi/2)]}(1 - \cos\beta h)}{2\pi r_0}\right] \tag{13-52}$$

These may be added together and common terms factored out:

$$E_{\theta f1} + E_{\theta f2} = \text{Im}\left[\frac{jI_{LM}\epsilon^{j(\omega t - \beta r_0)}(1 - \cos\beta h)}{2\pi r_0} \times \left(\epsilon^{j[(\beta S/2)\cos\phi - (\psi/2)]} + \epsilon^{-j[(\beta S/2)\cos\phi - (\psi/2)]}\right)\right]$$

$$E_{\theta f1} + E_{\theta f2} = \text{Im}\left[\frac{2jI_{LM}\epsilon^{j(\omega t - \beta r_0)}(1 - \cos\beta h)\cos\left(\dfrac{\beta S}{2}\cos\phi - \dfrac{\psi}{2}\right)}{2\pi r_0}\right]$$
$$= \frac{I_{LM}\cos(\omega t - \beta r_0)(1 - \cos\beta h)\cos\left(\dfrac{\beta S}{2}\cos\phi - \dfrac{\psi}{2}\right)}{\pi r_0} \tag{13-53}$$

The rms value of the resultant field as a function of ϕ is proportional to $\cos[(\beta S/2)\cos\phi - (\psi/2)]$, and is usually shown as a polar plot for a particular combination of βS and ψ. Figure 13-9 shows this function for quarter-wavelength spacing and $\psi = \pi/2$. The principal features of this combination are the phase cancellation of the fields from the two dipoles in the $\phi = \pi$

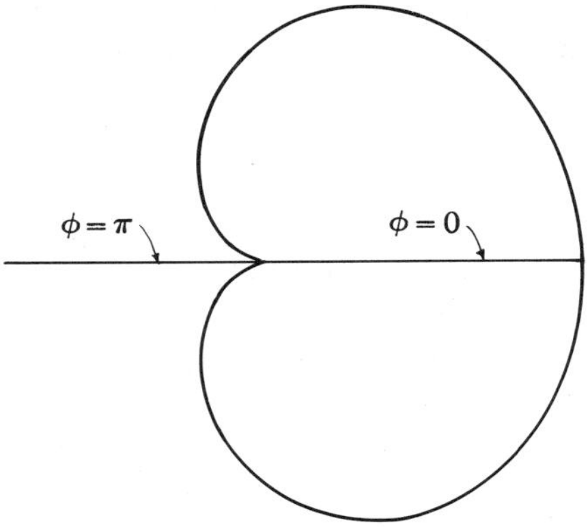

Figure 13-9 Relative magnitudes in equatorial plane of far fields of two-dipole array; quarter-wavelength spacing, currents at phase quadrature ($\psi = \pi/2$; see Fig. 13-8)

direction, and maximum phase reinforcement in the $\phi = 0$ direction. (Problem 13-10 calls for some additional plots.)

13-6. CONCLUSIONS

The electromagnetic fields of a dipole antenna travel radially outward at the same speed as plane waves in space and they transport energy in that direction. Components E_θ and H_ϕ each have a term which is proportional to the inverse first power of radial distance; these terms are known as the far fields or radiation fields. The far-field portions of E_θ and H_ϕ are in time phase with each other and are related in magnitude by the intrinsic impedance of space.

The far fields of a very short dipole are proportional to sin θ, and thus are strongest in the equatorial plane ($\theta = \pi/2$) and are zero along the dipole axis ($\theta = 0$ or π). As length is increased up to a full wavelength, the pattern becomes more θ directive in the vicinity of the equatorial plane.

Directivity with respect to ϕ may be obtained with an array of two or more dipoles. By controlling the relative phases of the input currents, pronounced phase cancellation or reinforcement among the fields from the separate sources may be obtained in selected sectors.

The field configuration of a vertical monopole of length h above a perfectly conducting earth would be the same as the upper half of that of a dipole of length $2h$ in space. Comparable behavior may be obtained from a monopole above ground of finite conductivity if a radial array of ground wires is added.

PROBLEMS

13-1. Find $\nabla \times \boldsymbol{E}$ from Eq. 13-26 and use the result in one of Maxwell's equations to find $\boldsymbol{H}$. Compare the result with Eq. 13-25.

13-2. Write Poynting's vector for a current segment in instantaneous form from Eqs. 13-25 and 13-26. Reduce all terms involving squares or products of sines and cosines of functions of t; then find the time-averaged value.

13-3. Find $\nabla \cdot \boldsymbol{E}$ from Eq. 13-26. Note that the far-field term by itself, Eq. 13-30, does not have zero divergence.

13-4. Evaluate the integral in Eq. 13-37.

13-5. Expand the cosine terms involving βH in Eq. 13-38 in power series for $\beta H \ll 1$, and show that the result approaches Eq. 13-40.

13-6. Investigate by series expansion the variation with respect to θ of $H_{\phi f}$ as given by Eq. 13-38, for θ approaching zero. Examine this in particular for $\beta H = \pi$.

13-7. Evaluate angle θ_N for the far-field null in Fig. 13-5(*d*).

13-8. Write expressions for surface-current density and surface-charge density on a perfectly conducting ground plane with a monopole antenna perpendicular to it. Use far-field equations 13-38 and 13-42 for $0 < \theta < \pi/2$. Draw a sketch similar to Fig. 13-3 and include $\boldsymbol{E}$, $\boldsymbol{H}$, displacement-current density, surface-current density, and surface-charge density.

13-9. You are an assistant engineer in a company which is designing a vertical-monopole broadcast antenna for which a ground-wire system will be necessary. The president of the company has suggested that the ground wires be laid out in concentric circles rather than radial lines, in the belief that "this will help to keep the wave front smooth." (The president started his career in the engineering section, but has been doing administrative work for about 15 years.) The chief engineer is to leave town on business in a few minutes and has just handed you the memorandum from the president. He hasn't had time to read it carefully but wants you to prepare a reply for him by the time he returns tomorrow. Examine the proposition and compose a memorandum setting forth, in a nice way, your analysis and conclusions.

13-10. Sketch polar plots of relative strength of $E_{\theta f}$ for a two-dipole array, similar to Fig. 13-9, for the following: (*a*) $\beta S = \pi/2$, $\psi = -\pi/2$; (*b*) $\beta S = \pi/2$, $\psi = 0$; (*c*) $\beta S = \pi$, $\psi = 0$; and (*d*) $\beta S = \pi$, $\psi = \pi$.

13-11. A dipole is located one-quarter wavelength from, and parallel to, a large, perfectly conducting sheet. Use the method of images to determine the far-field-magnitude function for the $\theta = \pi/2$ plane and sketch the result as a polar plot.

REFERENCES

1. *Antenna Engineering Handbook*, Henry Jasik, ed. New York: McGraw-Hill Book Company, Inc., 1961.

2. Hund, August, *Short-Wave Radiation Phenomena*, Vols. I and II. New York: McGraw-Hill Book Company, Inc., 1952.

3. JORDAN, EDWARD C., *Electromagnetic Waves and Radiating Systems*. New York: Prentice-Hall, Inc., 1950.

4. KING, RONOLD W. P., *The Theory of Linear Antennas*. Cambridge, Mass.: Harvard University Press, 1956.

5. KRAUS, JOHN D., *Antennas*. New York: McGraw-Hill Book Company, Inc., 1950.

6. SCHELKUNOFF, SERGEI A., *Advanced Antenna Theory*. New York: John Wiley & Sons, Inc., 1952.

7. SCHELKUNOFF, SERGEI A. and FRIIS, H. T., *Antennas: Theory and Practice*. New York: John Wiley & Sons, Inc., 1952.

8. SILVER, SAMUEL, *Microwave Antenna Theory and Design* (Radiation Laboratory Series No. 12). New York: McGraw-Hill Book Company, Inc., 1949.

9. SMITH, R. A., *Aerials for Metre and Decimetre Wave-Lengths*. London: Cambridge University Press, 1949.

10. THOUREL, L., *The Antenna* (trans. by H. de Laistre Banting). New York: John Wiley & Sons, Inc., 1960. (Originally published as *Les Antennes*, Paris, Dunod, 1956.)

11. WAIT, J. R. and POPE, W. A., "The Characteristics of a Vertical Antenna with a Radial Conductor Ground System," *IRE National Convention Record, pt.* 2, *Antennas and Propagation*, Vol. 2, pp. 79–86, 1954.

APPENDIX A

Parallel-Slab Equivalent of Slotted Coaxial Line

A transmission-line cross section of particular interest from the standpoints of mathematical analysis and experimental measurement technique is the *parallel-plane-equivalent* coaxial line,[3] which is sketched in Fig. A-1. This cross section, in which the side planes extend to infinity and the center conductor is approximately elliptical, corresponds in electrical properties to the circularly symmetrical cross section shown in Fig. 9-1. The mathematical relationship between the two geometrical shapes is known as a *conformal transformation.*

The cross section shown in Fig. A-1 is impractical, but for a considerable range of parameters it may be closely approximated by the one shown in Fig. A-2. Here the side conductors, which together represent the outer conductor of Fig. 9-1, are of finite cross-sectional extent, and the middle conductor is circular and hence much easier to fabricate than the corresponding conductor in Fig. A-1. This modified cross section has proved useful in the design of slotted-line units for microwave measurements.

A-1. SLOTTED LINES: GENERAL

A movable antenna-like probe, with suitable detecting and indicating equipment, is a practical means of obtaining standing-wave patterns and other field measurements at microwave frequencies.

The most obvious method of placing the probe in the electromagnetic field of a coaxial line is to cut a narrow longitudinal slot through the outer conductor and mount the probe on a longitudinally sliding carriage such that the probe projects through the slot some adjustable distance. This arrangement has the following disadvantages: (1) the characteristic impedance and the probe-unit output are sensitive to deviations in mechanical proportions, such as eccentric location of the inner conductor, or a slight bend in its axis, or nonparallelism between the probe movement and the inner conductor; and (2) a slot of practical width permits appreciable radiation of energy. This has the effect of adding a reactive component to the characteristic impedance and of altering the field patterns through attenuation, such that they are not precisely repetitive at half-wavelength intervals.

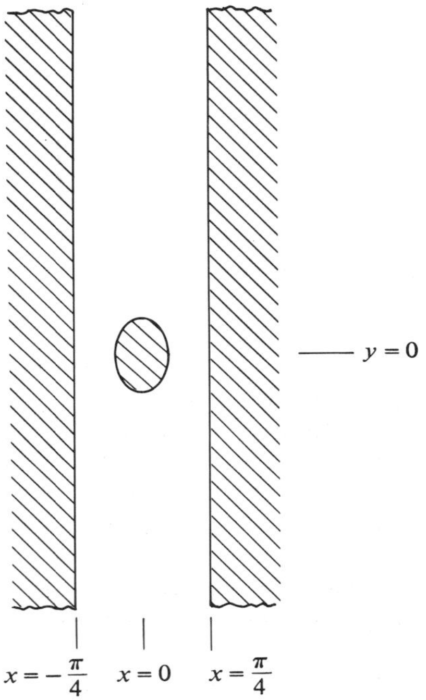

Figure A-1 Parallel-plane equivalent coaxial line—ideal

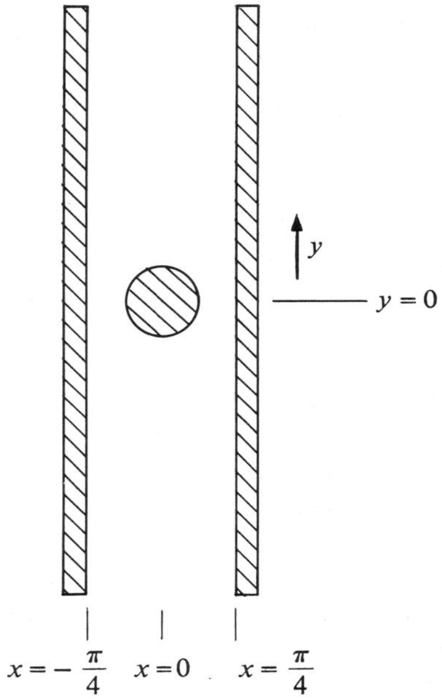

Figure A-2 Parallel-slab equivalent slotted coaxial line

The slab-type-equivalent slotted line has less severe requirements as to mechanical alignment and dimensional tolerances than its circular prototype, and it has the equivalent of an extremely narrow slot from the standpoint of radiation losses. The latter feature may be readily examined analytically.

A-2. CONFORMAL TRANSFORMATIONS: BASIC PROPERTIES[1]

In this method the transverse cross section of the circular coaxial line and its parallel-plane equivalent are represented in two two-dimensional fields, in which the coordinates of points are stated in complex-number form. The field representing the cross section of the circular coaxial line is known as the w plane, and that of its parallel-plane equivalent, the z plane. The respective cartesian coordinates are u and v, and x and y:

$$w = u + iv \tag{A-1}$$

$$z = x + iy \tag{A-2}$$

(Here the symbol i will be used for the complex operator rather than j, to minimize the possibility of confusing vectors and distances in two-dimensional space with phasors representing sinusoidal functions of time.)

If w is defined as some continuous function of z, each point in the z plane has a corresponding point in the w plane. For multiple-valued functions, a given point in one plane may correspond to more than one point (possibly an infinite number of points) in the other plane, but in those instances it is possible to divide one or both planes into regions such that a one-for-one correspondence exists between any point in a given region on one plane and a functionally related point in a specified region on the other plane.

By restricting the functional relationship between w and z such that the *Cauchy-Riemann criteria* are met, an important property of differential geometric correspondence is obtained between figures drawn on one plane and the respective "mapped" figures on the other. The transformation is then said to be *conformal.* The Cauchy-Riemann equations are

$$\frac{\partial u}{\partial x} = \frac{\partial y}{\partial y} \tag{A-3}$$

$$\frac{\partial u}{\partial y} = -\frac{\partial v}{\partial x} \tag{A-4}$$

The key concept in conformal mapping is that angles between intersecting lines in one plane are faithfully reproduced in the other plane on a "microscopic" basis. More specifically, if one (1) draws lines C_1 and C_2 (which may be curved) in the z plane such that they intersect at a point z_0, (2) locates the corresponding point w_0 and a succession of points in the w plane which will define curves C_1' and C_2' corresponding to curves C_1 and C_2, (3) draws straight lines through the point z_0 tangent to C_1 and C_2, and through point w_0 tangent to C_1' and C_2', then (4) the angles between the pairs of tangents are equal (see Fig. A-3). This property is applicable throughout the field except at points where dw/dz is zero or where w approaches infinity; no such points exist in the region of interest of the particular function to be investigated here.

Thus a geometric figure of differential extent in the neighborhood of point z_0 and the functionally corresponding figure in the neighborhood of point w_0 will be similar (corresponding angles equal, corresponding sides proportional), but they would not necessarily be of the same size nor would their corresponding sides bear the same orientation to the respective coordinate axes. Furthermore, if the first geometric figure were moved without rotation to the neighborhood of some other point z_1, the functionally corresponding figure in the neighborhood of point w_1 would in general differ in size from the previously mapped figure near w_0 and would be differently oriented.

A complementary feature pertains to two-dimensional vector fields. If the boundary requirements of such a field may be realized by a set of equipotential curves in the w plane, the corresponding lines in the z plane may likewise be regarded as equipotentials, and the complete pattern of equipotential lines and field-direction lines is transformable from the w plane to the z plane. This is applicable to the electric field of the TEM mode on a transmission line as viewed in any transverse plane; for the coaxial line studied in Sec. 9-1 the equipotential boundary curves are circles of radii r_a and r_b (Fig. 9-1).

A-3. TRANSFORMATION FUNCTION FOR COAXIAL LINE

Useful transformation functions have probably been found primarily by judicious trial-and-error prospecting. The following proved to yield results useful in the present physical problem[3]:

$$w = \tan z \tag{A-5}$$

This is a multiple-valued function in that an infinite number of values of z, separated by multiples of π, all have the same tangent. Accordingly attention will be limited to a single region within the z plane, namely, a strip defined by $-\pi/4 \leqslant x \leqslant \pi/4$ and $-\infty < y < \infty$.

Substitution of Eqs. A-1 and A-2 into Eq. A-5 yields

$$\begin{aligned} u + iv &= \tan(x + iy) \\ &= \frac{\tan x + \tan(iy)}{1 - \tan x \tan(iy)} \end{aligned}$$

As may be shown from Eq. 3-72, $\tan iy$ may be replaced by $i \tanh y$.

$$u + iv = \frac{\tan x + i \tanh y}{1 - i \tan x \tanh y} \tag{A-6}$$

If Eq. A-6 is multiplied by its conjugate, an expression is obtained for loci in the z plane corresponding to circles in the w plane, concentric with the origin:

$$u^2 + v^2 = \frac{\tan^2 x + \tanh^2 y}{1 + \tan^2 x \tanh^2 y} \tag{A-7}$$

It may be noted that if $\tan x$ is unity in magnitude, the right-hand side of Eq. A-7 becomes independent of y and, further, that it reduces to unity. Thus a circle of unit radius in the w plane transforms into two lines parallel to the y axis but displaced from it by $\pm \tan^{-1}(1)$ or $\pm\pi/4$. Circles of radii less than unity will be found to transform into closed curves which are symmetric about both coordinate axes and which have x intercepts of less than $\pi/4$.

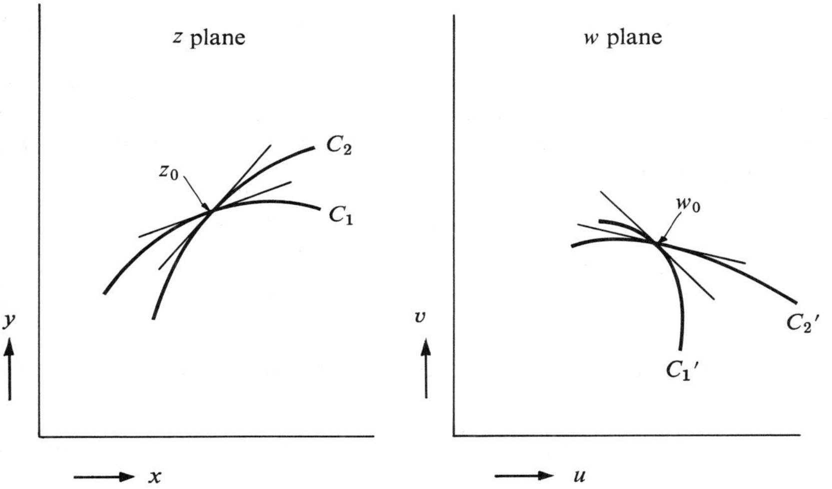

Figure A-3 Conformal transformation

The shape approached by the loci in the z plane for w-plane circles of radii approaching zero may be found by series expansions for $\tan x$ and $\tanh y$:

$$\tan x \approx x + \frac{x^3}{3}$$
$$\tan^2 x \approx x^2 + \frac{2x^4}{3} \tag{A-8}$$

$$\tanh y \approx y - \frac{y^3}{3}$$
$$\tanh^2 y \approx y^2 - \frac{2y^4}{3} \tag{A-9}$$

Let

$$u^2 + v^2 = r^2 \tag{A-10}$$

Substitution of Eqs. A-8, A-9, and A-10 into Eq. A-7 yields the following, in which terms of higher order than the fourth have been dropped from the denominator:

$$r^2 \approx \frac{x^2 + (2x^4/3) + y^2 - (2y^4/3)}{1 - x^2y^2} \tag{A-11}$$

If the denominator is multiplied out, the $r^2x^2y^2$ term which results on the left-hand side is discardable because it is of higher order than fourth (which is the highest order to which the numerator of the right-hand side is valid). The fourth-power terms in the numerator may be grouped and factored as follows:

$$r^2 \approx x^2 + y^2 + \tfrac{2}{3}(x^2 + y^2)(x^2 - y^2) \tag{A-12}$$

In terms of second-order quantities, $x^2 + y^2 \approx r^2$. This approximation may be substituted into the last term on the right-hand side without changing the accuracy of the approximation so far as second- and fourth-power terms are concerned. Hence

$$\begin{aligned} r^2 &\approx x^2 + y^2 + \tfrac{2}{3}r^2(x^2 - y^2) \\ &\approx x^2\left(1 + \frac{2r^2}{3}\right) + y^2\left(1 - \frac{2r^2}{3}\right) \end{aligned}$$

Or, in the standard form of equation for an ellipse:

$$1 \approx \frac{x^2}{r^2}\left(1 + \frac{2r^2}{3}\right) + \frac{y^2}{r^2}\left(1 - \frac{2r^2}{3}\right) \tag{A-13}$$

The semiminor and semimajor axes are $r/\sqrt{1 + (2r^2/3)}$ and $r/\sqrt{1 - (2r^2/3)}$, respectively.

From the standpoint of application to the coaxial-line problem, the quantity r is the normalized radius of the inner conductor, or the ratio of the radius of the inner conductor to the inner radius of the outer conductor.

Problems A-1 and A-2 deal with calculation of numerical proportions which should be used in a parallel-plane equivalent line to have the same characteristic impedance as a given coaxial line, and with the slot width in the coaxial line to which the openings at the top and bottom of the equivalent line correspond.

A circular middle conductor in the equivalent line transforms into an approximately elliptical figure in the w plane, and the characteristic impedance for that configuration may be computed by approximation methods.[3]

Necessary auxiliaries for a slab slotted-line section are transition sections[2] to change the field patterns from those of the circular coaxial line to those of the slab section and back again, without producing reflections.

PROBLEMS

A-1. A coaxial line with air dielectric has a characteristic impedance of 50 ohms. Compute the ratio of inner-conductor radius to inner radius of outer conductor. What should be the major and minor axes of the middle conductor of an exact slab-equivalent line, in proportion to the distance between the slabs?

A-2. The slab-equivalent line discussed in Problem A-1 has a ratio of slab width to slab separation of 4.0. What are the u and v coordinates corresponding to the upper edge of the right-hand slab? What is the angle between the edges of a slot in the circular line which is equivalent to the opening between the edges of the slabs in the z plane?

REFERENCES

1. CHURCHILL, RUEL V., *An Introduction to Complex Variables and Applications.* New York: McGraw-Hill Book Company, Inc., 1948.
2. GINZTON, EDWARD L., *Microwave Measurements*, pp. 253–57. New York: McGraw-Hill Book Company, Inc., 1957.
3. WHOLEY, W. B. and ELDRED, W. W., "A New Type of Slotted Line Section," *Proc. IRE*, 38 (1950), 244–48.

APPENDIX B

Skin Effect in Coaxial Conductors

In the wave-propagation analyses for the general transmission line in Chapters 2 and 5, resistance was assumed to be simply a constant per unit length of line. Dependence of effective resistance on the conductor material and its cross-sectional area and the frequency was mentioned, but not examined. The functional relationship among these quantities is best analyzed by means of the conduction-current fields and the accompanying magnetic fields. This will be done for the coaxial cable and will serve to extend the treatment given in Sec. 9-1 for lossless lines of that type.

An expression for the distributed inductance of a coaxial line was derived in Sec. 9-1, but non-infinite conductivity causes this to be increased somewhat. The incremental inductance is a function of the same parameters as the effective resistance.

High but finite conductivity will be assumed. As in Chapter 8, this will be taken to mean that $\omega\epsilon \ll \sigma$, or in other words that displacement-current density within the conductors will be assumed negligible compared to conduction-current density. Imperfect conductivity of the conductors will alter the field pattern such that $\boldsymbol{E}$ will have a small longitudinal component similar to that for plane conductors discussed in Sec. 8-4. This component will be ignored so far as the fields between the conductors are concerned, but within the conducting regions it is significantly related to the conduction current and the magnetic field.

For the basic analysis the inner conductor will be assumed to be solid and the outer one to be *thick-walled.* This will mean that the wall thickness is so great that, for the frequencies of interest, the conduction-current density just within the outer surface of the outer conductor is negligible compared to that near its inner surface. (The thickness must be at least several times the skin depth δ, as defined in Eq. 8-83.) For mathematical application of boundary conditions, this is equivalent to considering the outer wall to be of infinite thickness.

If, at some frequency of interest, the skin depth is comparable to the thickness of the given outer conductor, that conductor may be termed "thin-walled." The appropriate boundary condition is given in Sec. B-4. Cumbersome expressions result for the fields within such a conducting region.

B-1. CONDUCTION-CURRENT-DENSITY FIELD

The conduction-current-density field will be predominantly longitudinal; for this approximation the radial component of that field will be neglected. Correspondingly, since $\boldsymbol{J} = \sigma \boldsymbol{E}$, the radial component of $\boldsymbol{E}$ within the conducting regions will be considered negligible in comparison to the longitudinal component.

a. Differential equation for density as a function of radius

A traveling-wave function in the phasor form will be postulated for $\boldsymbol{J}$. The geometry is as shown in Fig. 9-1. Because of circular symmetry one may assume that $\boldsymbol{J}$ is not a function of angle ϕ, but from the results in Sec. 8-2*d* variation with distance from the conductor surface (radially, in this instance) may be expected.

$$\boldsymbol{J}_1 = \text{Im}[f_J(r)\epsilon^{j(\omega t - \beta z)}]\boldsymbol{a}_z \tag{B-1}$$

[The symbol $f_J(r)$ was chosen rather than $J(r)$ to avoid possible confusion with Bessel functions of the first kind, which will be used here. It is anticipated that $f_J(r)$ may be complex.]

If Eq. B-1 is substituted successively in Maxwell's curl equations, an ordinary differential equation for $f_J(r)$ may be derived. Let Maxwell's equation in curl $\boldsymbol{E}$, Eq. 7-34, be multiplied by σ and $\boldsymbol{J}$ substituted:

$$\nabla \times \boldsymbol{J} = -\mu\sigma \frac{\partial \boldsymbol{H}_c}{\partial t} \tag{B-2}$$

The subscript c will be used with $\boldsymbol{H}$ to indicate that it is the magnetic field within one of the conductors. Subscripts a and b will be used instead when it is necessary to distinguish between the inner and outer conductors, and these subscripts will then be added to $\boldsymbol{J}$ and f_J.

When Eq. B-1 is inserted for $\boldsymbol{J}$, Eq. B-2 becomes

$$-\mu\sigma \frac{\partial \boldsymbol{H}_{1c}}{\partial t} = \text{Im}\left[-\frac{df_J(r)}{dr}\epsilon^{j(\omega t - \beta z)}\right]\boldsymbol{a}_\phi$$

Integration of the preceding equation with respect to t yields

$$\boldsymbol{H}_{1c} = \operatorname{Im}\left[\frac{1}{j\omega\mu\sigma}\frac{df_J(r)}{dr}\epsilon^{j(\omega t-\beta z)}\right]\boldsymbol{a}_\phi \qquad \textbf{(B-3)}$$

If Eq. B-3 is substituted in Maxwell's equation in curl $\boldsymbol{H}$, Eq. 7-32, and the displacement current and the radial component of curl $\boldsymbol{H}$ are neglected, the following is obtained:

$$\boldsymbol{J}_1 = \operatorname{Im}\left[\frac{1}{j\omega\mu\sigma r}\frac{d}{dr}\left(r\frac{df_J(r)}{dr}\right)\epsilon^{j(\omega t-\beta z)}\right]\boldsymbol{a}_z \qquad \textbf{(B-4)}$$

The right-hand side of Eq. B-1 may be substituted for $\boldsymbol{J}_1$ in Eq. B-4, and like terms cancelled:

$$f_J(r) = \frac{1}{j\omega\mu\sigma}\left[\frac{d^2f_J(r)}{dr^2} + \frac{1}{r}\frac{df_J(r)}{dr}\right] \qquad \textbf{(B-5)}$$

An ordinary differential equation of the second order has been obtained for the current-density phasor as a function of radius.

b. Solution of current-field equation: Bessel functions

Equation B-5 is a variation of Bessel's differential equation, one form of which is as follows:

$$\frac{d^2u}{dp^2} + \frac{1}{p}\frac{du}{dp} + u\left(1 - \frac{n^2}{p^2}\right) = 0 \qquad \textbf{(B-6)}$$

Agreement between Eq. B-5 and B-6 may be obtained by setting n equal to zero and making the following change of variable (see Problem B-1):

$$p = \sqrt{-j\omega\mu\sigma}\,r \qquad \textbf{(B-7)}$$

The general solution to Eq. B-6 is conventionally written

$$u(p) = A_nJ_n(p) + B_nY_n(p) \qquad \textbf{(B-8)}$$

As in Sec. 11-1b(2), $J_n(p)$ designates the Bessel function of the first kind, nth order; $Y_n(p)$ designates the Bessel function of the second kind, nth order; and A_n and B_n are constants which are determined for each application by the boundary conditions. Some comments on Bessel functions and their properties are in order.[2]

(1) FUNCTIONS OF THE FIRST KIND. The function of the first kind is obtainable by assuming, for the function $J_n(p)$, an infinite power series with undetermined coefficients and substituting it and its derivatives into Eq. B-6 in place of u, du/dp, and d^2u/dp^2. As an illustration, the zero-order case $n = 0$ will be considered. Let

$$J_0(p) = a_0 + a_1p + a_2p^2 + a_3p^3 + \cdots \qquad \textbf{(B-9)}$$

Equation B-9 is differentiated twice and substituted into B-6 after n has been set equal to zero:

$$2a_a + 6a_3p + 12a_4p^2 + \cdots + \frac{a_1}{p} + 2a_2 + 3a_3p + 4a_4p^2 + \cdots$$
$$+ a_0 + a_1p + a_2p^2 + \cdots = 0$$

Since the latter equation must be satisfied for all values of p, the coefficients of each power of p in the equation, when grouped together, must separately sum to zero:

$$\frac{a_1}{p} + (4a_2 + a_0) + (9a_3 + a_1)p + (16a_4 + a_2)p^2 + \cdots = 0$$

$$\begin{aligned} a_1 &= 0 \\ 4a_2 + a_0 &= 0 \\ 9a_3 + a_1 &= 0 \\ 16a_4 + a_2 &= 0 \end{aligned} \qquad \textbf{(B-10)}$$

The inclusion of higher-order terms in Eq. B-9 will yield additional equations for set B-10. In general,

$$k^2a_k + a_{k-2} = 0 \qquad \textbf{(B-11)}$$

And so $$J_0(p) = a_0\left(1 - \frac{p^2}{2^2} + \frac{p^4}{2^2 \cdot 4^2} - \frac{p^6}{2^2 \cdot 4^2 \cdot 6^2} + \cdots\right)$$

The constant a_0 might have any nonzero value; for the compilation of tables it has regularly been set equal to unity. It should be noted that the coefficients of all odd-power terms in p are zero. The preceding expression may be restated more conveniently as follows, where the k of the recurrence formula is replaced by $2i$:

$$J_0(p) = 1 - \left(\frac{p}{2}\right)^2 + \left(\frac{p}{2}\right)^4 \frac{1}{(2!)^2} - \left(\frac{p}{2}\right)^6 \frac{1}{(3!)^2} + \cdots + (-1)^i\left(\frac{p}{2}\right)^{2i} \frac{1}{(i!)^2} \qquad \textbf{(B-12)}$$

This series proves to be convergent for all values of p real or complex. The function $J_0(p)$ is plotted in Fig. B-1 along with three other Bessel functions.

The Bessel functions of the first kind with a real argument were encountered in the discussion of the circular wave guide (Chapter 11), and the zero-order functions of the first kind with a purely imaginary argument [modified Bessel function, $I_0(q) = J_0(jq)$] was used in Chapter 5 in the transient propagation of current along a lossy transmission line. At the moment the complex argument specified by Eq. B-7 is of interest.

Let $$m = \sqrt{\omega\mu\sigma} \qquad \textbf{(B-13)}$$

Hence $$\begin{aligned} p &= \sqrt{-jmr} \\ &= j^{3/2}mr \end{aligned} \qquad \textbf{(B-14)}$$

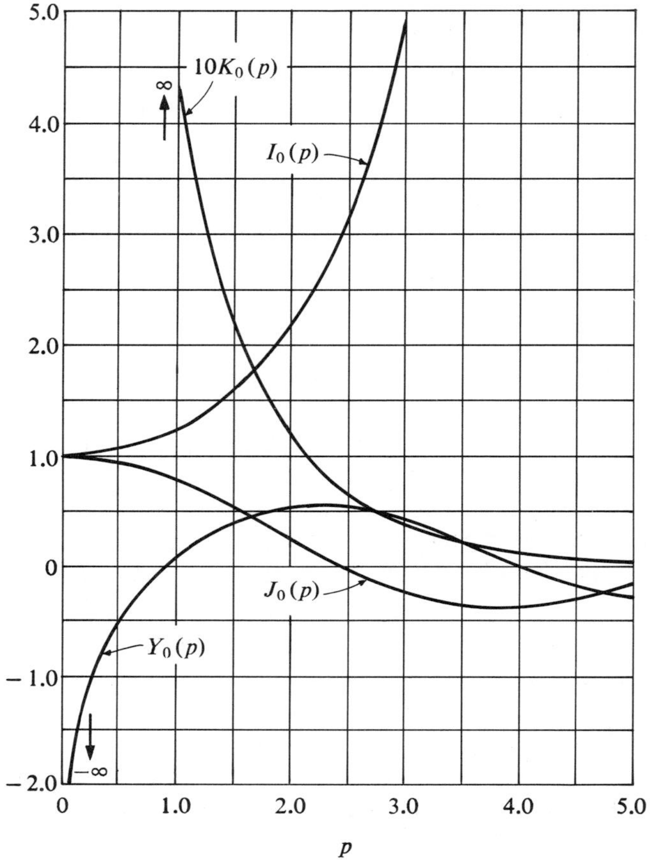

Figure B-1 Zero-order Bessel functions J, Y, I, and K [prepared from G. N. Watson, *Theory of Bessel Functions* (London: Cambridge University Press, 1944) pp. 666–713]

Substitution of Eq. B-14 in Eq. B-12 gives the following:

$$J_0(j^{3/2}mr) = 1 + j\left(\frac{mr}{2}\right)^2 - \left(\frac{mr}{2}\right)^4 \frac{1}{2^2} - j\left(\frac{mr}{2}\right)^6 \frac{1}{(3!)^2} + \cdots \quad \textbf{(B-15)}$$

The real and imaginary parts of the function may be renamed by defining two new functions, ber and bei:

$$J_0(j^{3/2}mr) = \text{ber}(mr) + j\,\text{bei}(mr) \quad \textbf{(B-16)}$$

These functions and the magnitude and angle of $J_0(j^{3/2}mr)$ have been tabulated.[2]

For large values of the argument ($mr \gg 1$), an asymptotic-series approximation[4] for this Bessel function is valid and convenient; the leading term (which is the first-order approximation) will be designated as $\tilde{J}_0(j^{3/2}mr)$:

$$\tilde{J}_0(j^{3/2}mr) = \frac{\epsilon^{[(mr/\sqrt{2})+j(mr/\sqrt{2})-j(\pi/8)]}}{\sqrt{2\pi mr}} \qquad \textbf{(B-17)}$$

Thus the zero-order Bessel function of the first kind with the complex argument $j^{3/2}mr$ approaches unity as mr approaches zero (Eq. B-15) and it approaches infinity in magnitude as mr approaches infinity (Eq. B-17).

(2) FUNCTIONS OF THE SECOND KIND. A second-order linear differential equation must have two linearly independent solutions. The derivation of the Bessel function of the second kind[4] is beyond the scope of this book, but some discussion of the function itself is appropriate. The form of solution credited to Weber [designated $Y_n(p)$ in Eq. B-8] has been generally adopted:

$$Y_0(p) = \frac{2}{\pi}\left[\gamma + \ln\left(\frac{p}{2}\right)\right]J_0(p) - \frac{2}{\pi}\sum_{r=1}^{\infty}\left[(-1)^r\left(\frac{p}{2}\right)^{2r}\frac{1}{(r!)^2}\right]\left[1 + \frac{1}{2} + \frac{1}{3} + \cdots + \frac{1}{r}\right] \qquad \textbf{(B-18)}$$

Here γ is Euler's constant, approximately 0.577216.

Any linear combination of independent solutions is also a solution, and this principle permits convenient latitude in the definition of the "function of the second kind." In particular it justifies a modification of the definition in Eq. B-18 when a complex argument is used.

The function $Y_0(p)$ "teams up" well with the function of the first kind when real arguments are used, a quality which is manifested by the fact that the leading terms of the respective asymptotic expansions are diminishing sinusoids which are bounded by the same envelope and which are in phase quadrature with each other.* $J_0(p)$ and $Y_0(p)$ both approach zero if the argument is purely real and it is made infinitely large.

With an imaginary argument or one proportional to $j^{3/2}$, Y_0 and J_0 both approach infinity in magnitude as the magnitude of the argument approaches infinity. For many applications the boundary conditions require a function which vanishes as the argument magnitude approaches infinity. The following linear combination of J_0 and Y_0 has this property for arguments proportional either to j or to $j^{3/2}$; it is customarily designated as a new function, K_0:

$$K_0(q) = \frac{j\pi}{2}\left[J_0(jq) + jY_0(jq)\right] \qquad \textbf{(B-19)}$$

* $J_0(p) \approx \sqrt{\dfrac{2}{\pi p}}\cos\left(p - \dfrac{\pi}{4}\right)$

$Y_0(p) \approx \sqrt{\dfrac{2}{\pi p}}\sin\left(p - \dfrac{\pi}{4}\right)$ $\qquad (p \gg 1)$

The following series defines $K_0(q)$:

$$K_0(q) = -\left[\gamma + \ln\left(\frac{q}{2}\right)\right] J_0(jq) + \sum_{r=1}^{\infty} \left[\left(\frac{q}{2}\right)^{2r} \frac{1}{(r!)^2}\right] \times \left[1 + \frac{1}{2} + \frac{1}{3} + \cdots + \frac{1}{r}\right] \quad \textbf{(B-20)}$$

Because of the logarithmic term, both Y_0 and K_0 will approach infinity in magnitude as their respective arguments approach zero.

For the complex argument which arises in this problem, the real and imaginary parts of the K_0 function have been designated as ker and kei:

$$K_0(j^{1/2}mr) = \ker(mr) + j\,\mathrm{kei}(mr) \quad \textbf{(B-21)}$$

These functions and the polar form of K_0 have been tabulated.[2]

The leading term of the asymptotic expansion for K_0 with a complex argument will be designated by $\tilde{K}_0(j^{1/2}mr)$:

$$\tilde{K}_0(j^{1/2}mr) = \frac{\sqrt{\pi}\epsilon^{[(-mr/\sqrt{2})-j(mr/\sqrt{2})-j(\pi/8)]}}{\sqrt{2mr}} \quad \textbf{(B-22)}$$

(3) General solution with complex arguments. The general solution for Eq. B-6, given in Eq. B-8 in the form appropriate for real arguments, may be rewritten for the complex arguments of this problem in terms of the functions J_0 and K_0 and new constants A_0' and B_0':

$$f_J(r) = A_0' J_0(j^{3/2}mr) + B_0' K_0(j^{1/2}mr) \quad \textbf{(B-23)}$$

c. Boundary conditions for current-density fields

Separate expressions for the current-density function for each conductor may be written by imposing the corresponding boundary conditions on Eq. B-23. Current density for the inner conductor $\boldsymbol{J}_{1a}$ is defined for $r \leqslant r_a$ and must be finite throughout that range. For the outer conductor (thick-walled), current density $\boldsymbol{J}_{1b}$ is defined for $r \geqslant r_b$, throughout which it must be finite. In view of the fact that $K_0(j^{1/2}mr)$ will approach infinity in magnitude as mr approaches zero and that $J_0(j^{3/2}mr)$ will approach infinity in magnitude as mr approaches infinity, the current-density functions are constrained to the following:

$$f_{Ja}(r) = A_0' J_0(j^{3/2}m_a r) \quad \textbf{(B-24)}$$

$$f_{Jb}(r) = B_0' K_0(j^{1/2}m_b r) \quad \textbf{(B-25)}$$

Here the constants A_0' and B_0' have yet to be determined, and the subscripts

a and b have been attached to m because the two conductors may be composed of different materials.

Equations B-24 and B-25 may be substituted into Eq. B-1.

$$\boldsymbol{J}_{1a} = \text{Im}[A_0' J_0(j^{3/2} m_a r)\epsilon^{j(\omega t - \beta z)}]\boldsymbol{a}_z \tag{B-26}$$

$$\boldsymbol{J}_{1b} = \text{Im}[B_0' K_0(j^{1/2} m_b r)\epsilon^{j(\omega t - \beta z)}]\boldsymbol{a}_z \tag{B-27}$$

The resultant currents within the conductors may be found by the following integrations over the respective cross sections. Let the current function be taken as $i_1(z,t)$, the same as for the derivation of the fields between the conductors, Sec. 9-1; the constants A_0' and B_0' of the preceding equations prove to be proportional to I_{1M}.

$$i_1(z,t) = \iint \boldsymbol{J}_{1a} \cdot \boldsymbol{dS} \tag{B-28}$$

$$-i_1(z,t) = \iint \boldsymbol{J}_{1b} \cdot \boldsymbol{dS} \tag{B-29}$$

Here $$\boldsymbol{dS} = r\,dr\,d\phi \boldsymbol{a}_z$$

$$i_1(z,t) = \text{Im}[I_{1M}\epsilon^{j(\omega t - \beta z)}] \tag{9-9}$$

Equations 9-9, B-26, and B-27 may be substituted in Eqs. B-28 and B-29, and the operator Im and the exponential cancelled from each term. This leads to

$$I_{1M} = \int_0^{2\pi}\int_0^{r_a} A_0' J_0(j^{3/2} m_a r) r\,dr\,d\phi \tag{B-30}$$

$$-I_{1M} = \int_0^{2\pi}\int_{r_b}^{\infty} B_0' K_0(j^{1/2} m_b r) r\,dr\,d\phi \tag{B-31}$$

The following integration formulas are applicable:

$$\int pJ_0(p)\,dp = pJ_1(p) \tag{B-32}$$

$$\int qK_0(q)\,dq = -qK_1(q) \tag{B-33}$$

Here $J_1(p)$ and $K_1(p)$ are functions of the first order, solutions to Bessel's differential equation, B-6, if n is equal to unity. The following specific values are needed when substituting limits in the integrals:

$$J_1(0) = 0$$

$$\lim_{q \to \infty} [qK_1(q)] = 0 \qquad \text{(providing the real part of } q \text{ is positive)}$$

Hence
$$I_{1M} = \frac{2\pi A_0'}{j^{3/2}m_a} r_a J_1(j^{3/2}m_a r_a)$$

or
$$A_0' = \frac{I_{1M} j^{3/2} m_a}{2\pi r_a J_1(j^{3/2}m_a r_a)} \qquad \textbf{(B-34)}$$

This result may be substituted into Eq. B-26 to give a complete expression for current density in the inner conductor in terms of the maximum value of the resultant current I_{1M}:

$$\boldsymbol{J}_{1a} = \text{Im}\left[\frac{I_{1M} j^{3/2} m_a J_0(j^{3/2}m_a r)}{2\pi r_a J_1(j^{3/2}m_a r_a)} \epsilon^{j(\omega t - \beta z)}\right] \boldsymbol{a}_z \qquad \textbf{(B-35)}$$

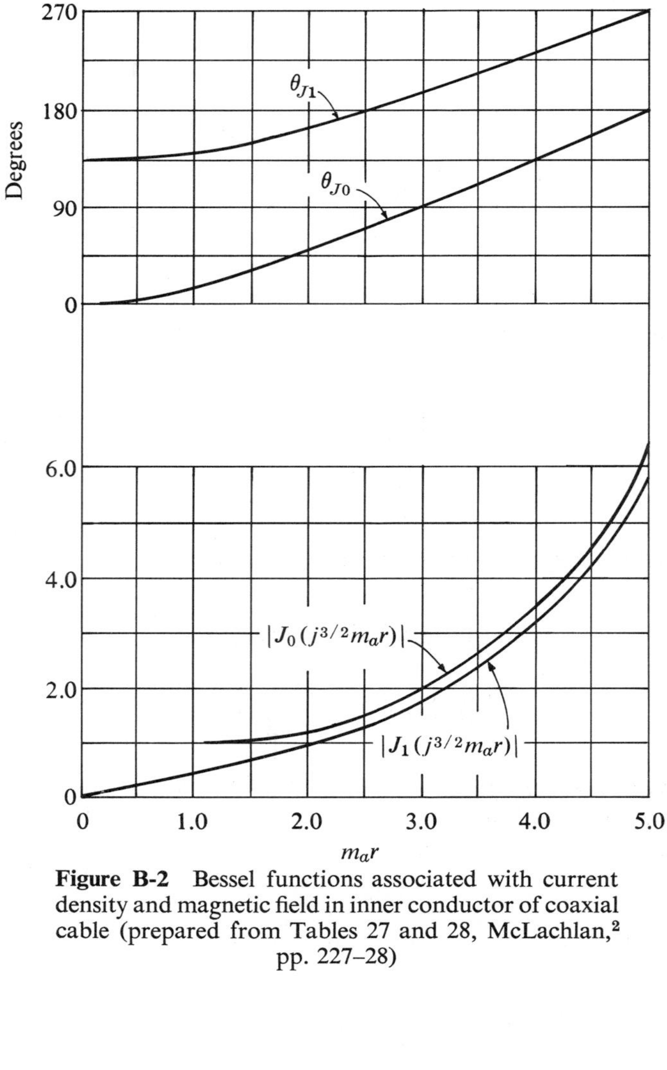

Figure B-2 Bessel functions associated with current density and magnetic field in inner conductor of coaxial cable (prepared from Tables 27 and 28, McLachlan,[2] pp. 227–28)

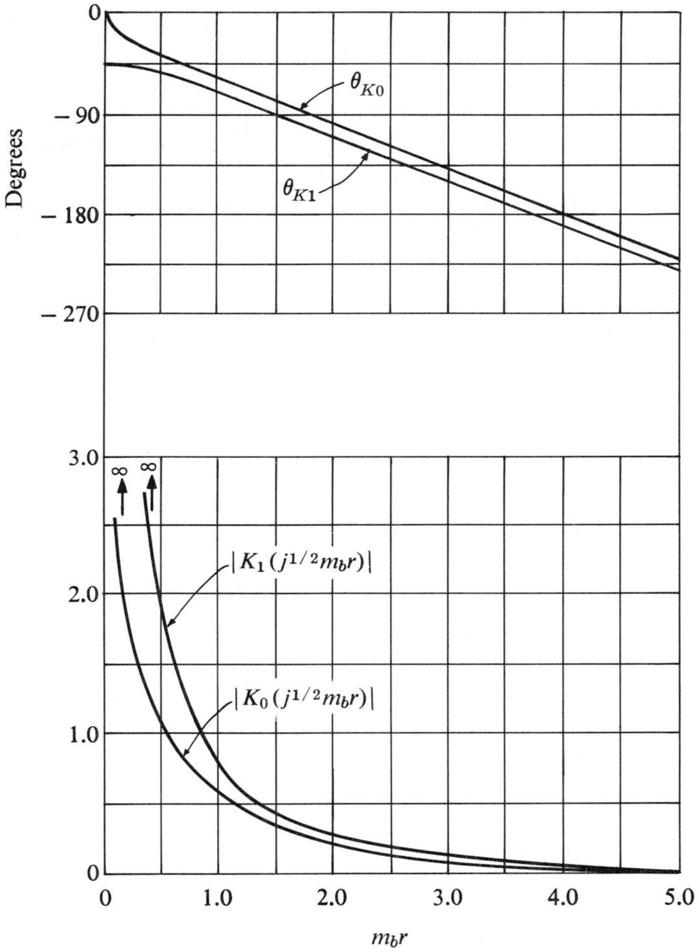

Figure B-3 Bessel functions associated with current density and magnetic field in outer conductor (thick-walled) of coaxial cable (prepared from Tables 29 and 30, McLachlan,[2] pp. 229–30)

Similarly,

$$\boldsymbol{J}_{1b} = \text{Im}\left[\frac{-I_{1M}j^{1/2}m_bK_0(j^{1/2}m_br)}{2\pi r_bK_1(j^{1/2}m_br_b)}\,\epsilon^{j(\omega t-\beta z)}\right]\boldsymbol{a}_z \qquad \textbf{(B-36)}$$

The Bessel functions indicated in Eqs. B-35 and B-36 are plotted in terms of magnitude and angle in Figs. B-2 and B-3. Current density as a function of radius in either conductor is directly proportional to the magnitude of the respective zero-order function. For the inner conductor, relative phase with respect to $i_1(z,t)$ is $\theta_{J0}(m_a r) - \theta_{J1}(m_a r_a) + 135°$; for the outer conductor, relative phase with respect to $-i_1(z,t)$ is $\theta_{K0}(m_b r) - \theta_{K1}(m_b r_b) + 45°$.

B-2. MAGNETIC FIELD WITHIN CONDUCTING REGIONS

The magnetic field within each conductor may be found by substituting f_J, as given by Eq. B-35 or B-36, in Eq. B-3. The following derivatives are needed:

$$\frac{dJ_0(j^{3/2}mr)}{dr} = -j^{3/2}mJ_1(j^{3/2}mr) \tag{B-37}$$

$$\frac{dK_0(j^{1/2}mr)}{dr} = -j^{1/2}mK_1(j^{1/2}mr) \tag{B-38}$$

For the inner conductor,

$$\boldsymbol{H}_{1a} = \text{Im}\left[\frac{I_{1M}J_1(j^{3/2}m_a r)}{2\pi r_a J_1(j^{3/2}m_a r_a)}\,\epsilon^{j(\omega t-\beta z)}\right]\boldsymbol{a}_\phi \tag{B-39}$$

For the outer conducting region the corresponding result is:

$$\boldsymbol{H}_{1b} = \text{Im}\left[\frac{I_{1M}K_1(j^{1/2}m_b r)}{2\pi r_b K_1(j^{1/2}m_b r_b)}\,\epsilon^{j(\omega t-\beta z)}\right]\boldsymbol{a}_\phi \tag{B-40}$$

Equations B-39 and B-40 may also be derived directly from Maxwell's equations, as suggested in Problem B-2.

The magnitude of $\boldsymbol{H}$ as a function of radius in either conductor is directly proportional to the respective first-order function in Figs. B-2 or B-3. Relative phase with respect to the field between the conductors is given by $\theta_{J1}(m_a r) - \theta_{J1}(m_a r_a)$ or $\theta_{K1}(m_b r) - \theta_{K1}(m_b r_b)$.

B-3. A-C RESISTANCE AND ADDITIONAL INDUCTANCE CAUSED BY FINITE CONDUCTIVITY

The expression for inductance of a coaxial cable derived earlier, Eq. B-4, took account only of flux between the conductors, and no derivation has been given for the resistance parameter. From the analysis of the preceding section it is apparent that unless the conductivity is infinite, some flux exists within the conductors, and this will increase the inductance beyond the value given in Eq. 9-24. Furthermore, because the conduction-current density varies both in magnitude and in relative time phase with radius, it may be expected that the resistive power loss will be greater than if the same resultant current were distributed uniformly over the transverse cross section of each conductor and was in time phase across each such cross section.

a. Derivation of component impedances

Consider the voltage rises around the closed path shown in Fig. B-4:

$$v(z_1,t) - \int_{z_1}^{z_1+\Delta z} \left(\frac{J_{1a}}{\sigma_a}\right)_z dz - v(z_1 + \Delta z, t) - \int_{z_1+\Delta z}^{z_1} \left(\frac{J_{1b}}{\sigma_b}\right)_z dz = -\oint E \cdot dL \quad \textbf{(B-41)}$$

The difference between the voltages at z_1 and $z_1 + \Delta z$ may be stated as follows:

$$v(z_1,t) - v(z_1 + \Delta z, t) = -\int_{z_1}^{z_1+\Delta z} \frac{\partial v(z,t)}{\partial z} dz \quad \textbf{(B-42)}$$

Equation B-42 may be substituted in Eq. B-41 and the integrals with respect to z consolidated:

$$\int_{z_1}^{z_1+\Delta z} \left[-\left(\frac{J_{1a}}{\sigma_a}\right)_z - \frac{\partial v(z,t)}{\partial z} + \left(\frac{J_{1b}}{\sigma_b}\right)_z\right] dz = -\oint \boldsymbol{E} \cdot \boldsymbol{dL} \quad \textbf{(B-43)}$$

Faraday's law may be substituted for the right-hand side:

$$\oint \boldsymbol{E} \cdot \boldsymbol{dL} = -\iint \frac{\partial \boldsymbol{B}}{\partial t} \cdot \boldsymbol{dS} \quad \textbf{(7-18)}$$

$$\boldsymbol{dS} = dr\, dz\, \boldsymbol{a}_\phi$$

$$\oint \boldsymbol{E} \cdot \boldsymbol{dL} = -\int_{z_1}^{z_1+\Delta z} \int_{r_a}^{r_b} \frac{\partial B_\phi}{\partial t} dr\, dz$$

The magnetic-field function between the conductors is given by Eq. 9-12; it may be substituted into the preceding equation and integration

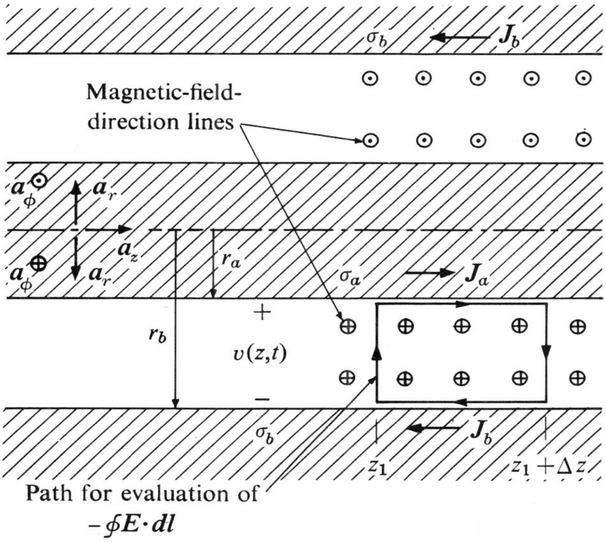

Figure B-4 Longitudinal cross section of coaxial line

performed with respect to r:

$$\oint \boldsymbol{E} \cdot \boldsymbol{dL} = -\mathrm{Im}\left[\int_{z_1}^{z_1+\Delta z}\int_{r_a}^{r_b} \frac{j\omega\mu I_{1M}}{2\pi r}\epsilon^{j(\omega t-\beta z)}\,dr\,dz\right]$$

$$= -\mathrm{Im}\left[\int_{z_1}^{z_1+\Delta z} \frac{j\omega\mu I_{1M}}{2\pi}\ln\left(\frac{r_b}{r_a}\right)\epsilon^{j(\omega t-\beta z)}\,dz\right] \quad \textbf{(B-44)}$$

The derivative of v with respect to z, which is used in Eq. B-43, may be put in terms of the current function $i_1(z,t)$ by substituting Eq. 9-9 in Eq. 2-3:

$$\frac{\partial v(z,t)}{\partial z} = -\mathrm{Im}[(\imath + j\omega l)I_{1M}\epsilon^{j(\omega t-\beta z)}] \quad \textbf{(B-45)}$$

Equations B-44 and B-45 may be substituted in Eq. B-43. Since every term is integrated with respect to z from z_1 to $z_1 + \Delta z$, and the location z_1 may be chosen arbitrarily on the line, the integrands must satisfy the corresponding equation. In addition, the Im operator, the term I_{1M}, and the exponential are common to each term, and they may be deleted. The following results:

$$(\imath + j\omega l) - \frac{j^{3/2}m_aJ_0(j^{3/2}m_ar_a)}{2\pi r_a\sigma_aJ_1(j^{3/2}m_ar_a)} - \frac{j^{1/2}m_bK_0(j^{1/2}m_br_b)}{2\pi r_b\sigma_bK_1(j^{1/2}m_br_b)} = \frac{j\omega\mu}{2\pi}\ln\left(\frac{r_b}{r_a}\right) \quad \textbf{(B-46)}$$

For mathematical convenience, the distributed inductance l may be split into three parts; thus

$$l = l' + l_a + l_b \quad \textbf{(B-47)}$$

Let

$$l' = \frac{\mu}{2\pi}\ln\left(\frac{r_b}{r_a}\right) \quad \textbf{(B-48)}$$

This definition corresponds to Eq. 9-24, the expression for the distributed inductance of a lossless coaxial line.

Also let

$$\imath = \imath_a + \imath_b \quad \textbf{(B-49)}$$

If one subtracts Eq. B-48 from Eq. B-46, the remaining terms may be apportioned as follows:

$$\imath_a + j\omega l_a = \frac{j^{3/2}m_aJ_0(j^{3/2}m_ar_a)}{2\pi r_a\sigma_aJ_1(j^{3/2}m_ar_a)} \quad \textbf{(B-50)}$$

$$\imath_b + j\omega l_b = \frac{j^{1/2}m_bK_0(j^{1/2}m_br_b)}{2\pi r_b\sigma_bK_1(j^{1/2}m_br_b)} \quad \textbf{(B-51)*}$$

* The real and imaginary parts of the zero-order functions have been tabulated as the ber, bei, ker, and kei functions, as noted in Eqs. B-16 and B-21. The first-order functions are expressible in terms of four other tabulated functions, ber′, bei′, ker′, and kei′, as follows:

$$j^{3/2}J_1(j^{3/2}mr) = -\mathrm{ber}'(mr) - j\,\mathrm{bei}'(mr)$$

$$j^{1/2}K_1(j^{1/2}mr) = -\mathrm{ker}'(mr) - j\,\mathrm{kei}'(mr)$$

These equations, together with Eqs. B-16 and B-21, may be substituted in Eqs. B-50 and B-51 and the resulting fractions rationalized to obtain separate expressions for the $\imath$'s and l's.

The component of impedance due to a nonideal inner conductor, Eq. B-50, may be divided by the resistance of that conductor to direct current to yield a dimensionless ratio:

$$r_{adc} = \frac{1}{\pi r_a^2 \sigma_a} \tag{B-52}$$

$$\frac{r_a + j\omega l_a}{r_{adc}} = \frac{j^{3/2} m_a r_a J_0(j^{3/2} m_a r_a)}{2J_1(j^{3/2} m_a r_a)} \tag{B-53}$$

The real part of Eq. B-54 is the *skin-effect-resistance ratio*, which is plotted in Fig. B-5.

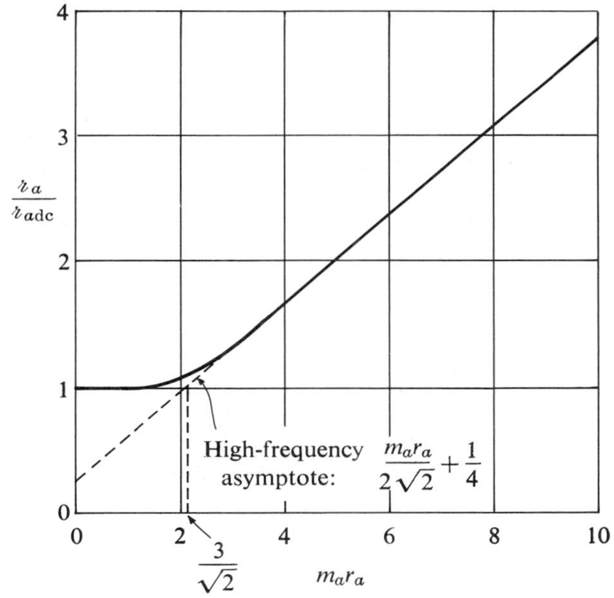

Figure B-5 Skin-effect-resistance ratio for circular conductor (prepared from Rosa and Grover,[3] pp. 226–28)

b. Asymptotes and approximations

"Inspectional analysis" of expressions such as Eqs. B-51 and B-53 is expedited by plots and by approximations for very small and very large values of the arguments.

(1) LOW-FREQUENCY APPROXIMATIONS FOR INNER CONDUCTOR. At low frequencies ($m_a r_a < 2.5$), power-series approximations are applicable[3]

(see Problem B-3):

$$\frac{r_a}{r_{adc}} \approx 1 + \frac{1}{12}\left(\frac{m_a r_a}{2}\right)^4 - \frac{1}{180}\left(\frac{m_a r_a}{2}\right)^8 \tag{B-54}$$

$$l_a \approx \frac{\mu}{8\pi}\left[1 - \frac{1}{24}\left(\frac{m_a r_a}{2}\right)^4\right] \tag{B-55}$$

Thus the skin-effect-resistance ratio has as its low-frequency asymptote the constant value of unity and departs from that as the square of frequency (m is proportional to $\sqrt{f}$, in accordance with Eq. B-13). Similarly, the incremental inductance due to internal flux linkages has a low-frequency asymptote of $\mu/8\pi$ henrys per meter and departs from this asymptote as the square of frequency.

(2) HIGH-FREQUENCY APPROXIMATIONS FOR INNER CONDUCTOR. High-frequency approximations derivable from asymptotic expansions of Bessel functions are valid if $m_a r_a \gg 1$. The first-order asymptotic approximation ($\tilde{J}_0$) for $J_0(j^{3/2}mr)$ was given in Eq. B-17; second-order asymptotic approximations for J_0 and J_1 are related to it as shown below (see McLachlan,[2] p. 152). The following change of variable will simplify the subsequent algebraic steps:

$$u = \frac{1}{8\sqrt{2}\, m_a r_a}$$

$$\begin{aligned} J_0(j^{3/2}m_a r_a) &\approx \tilde{J}_0(j^{3/2}m_a r_a)(1 + u)\epsilon^{-ju} \\ J_1(j^{3/2}m_a r_a) &\approx j\tilde{J}_0(j^{3/2}m_a r_a)(1 - 3u)\epsilon^{j3u} \end{aligned} \tag{B-56}$$

Substitution of these into Eq. B-53 gives the following:

$$\frac{r_a + j\omega l_a}{r_{adc}} \approx \frac{j^{3/2}m_a r_a(1 + u)\epsilon^{-j4u}}{2j(1 - 3u)} \tag{B-57}$$

The approximations in Eq. B-56 were valid to the first power in u and the same is true of Eq. B-57. Power-series expansions in u may be used to simplify Eq. B-57 (u approaches zero as $m_a r_a$ approaches infinity), but any resulting terms in u^2 or higher powers must be discarded:

$$\begin{aligned} \frac{1 + u}{1 - 3u} &\approx (1 + u)(1 + 3u) \\ &\approx 1 + 4u \end{aligned}$$

$$\epsilon^{-j4u} \approx 1 - j4u$$

$$j^{1/2} = \frac{1}{\sqrt{2}}(1 + j)$$

Substitution of these will reduce Eq. B-57 to the following:

$$\frac{r_a + j\omega l_a}{r_{adc}} \approx \frac{m_a r_a}{2\sqrt{2}}(1 + j)(1 + 4u)(1 - j4u)$$

$$\approx \frac{m_a r_a}{2\sqrt{2}}(1 + j + 8u)$$

Replacement of the variable u in terms of $m_a r_a$ gives the following result:

$$\frac{r_a + j\omega l_a}{r_{adc}} \approx \frac{m_a r_a}{2\sqrt{2}} + j\frac{m_a r_a}{2\sqrt{2}} + \frac{1}{4} \tag{B-58}$$

The real part of this is, of course, the skin-effect-resistance ratio:

$$\frac{r_a}{r_{adc}} \approx \frac{m_a r_a}{2\sqrt{2}} + \frac{1}{4} \tag{B-59}$$

This formula gives results within 1 per cent of the true value if $m_a r_a > 6$,* and is especially useful for radio-frequency calculations.

By taking the imaginary part of Eq. B-58, multiplying by r_{adc} (Eq. B-52), and dividing by ω, an approximation for l_a is obtained:

$$l_a \approx \frac{m_a}{2\sqrt{2}\,\pi r_a \omega \sigma_a}$$

Equation B-13 may be substituted for m_a:

$$l_a \approx \frac{1}{2\pi r_a}\sqrt{\frac{\mu_a}{2\sigma_a \omega}} \tag{B-60}$$

For those frequencies at which this approximation is valid, l_a is normally negligible compared to l'.

(3) RESISTANCE-RATIO FUNCTION IN RELATION TO ITS ASYMPTOTES. The high-frequency asymptote for r_a/r_{adc} described by Eq. B-59 is indicated in Fig. 9-6 with a dashed line. The intersection of this asymptote with the zero-frequency asymptote ($r_a/r_{adc} = 1.0$) is analogous to the "corner frequency" of plots of log amplitude versus log frequency used in control-system analysis;

* The following higher-order asymptotic approximation is given by Dwight[1] (p. 160):

$$\frac{r_a}{r_{adc}} \approx \frac{mr_a}{2\sqrt{2}} + \frac{1}{4} + \frac{3}{16\sqrt{2}mr_a} - \frac{63}{256\sqrt{2}m^3r_a^3} - \frac{27}{64m^4r_a^4}$$

The usefulness of the last three terms (and of any following terms which might be derived) is dubious; they improve the accuracy of the approximation at large values of the argument, where Eq. B-59 already gives results to engineering accuracy, but these terms render the series divergent at smaller values of mr_a.

the value of $m_a r_a$ at the intersection is $3/\sqrt{2}$:

$$\left[\frac{r_a}{r_{adc}}\right]_{m_a r_a = 3/\sqrt{2}} = 1.097 \qquad \textbf{(B-61)}$$

"Skin-effect-demarcation frequency," f_{skd}, is suggested as a name for the frequency which, for a given conductor, yields this value of $m_a r_a$. From Eq. B-17 and the foregoing,

$$f_{skd} = \frac{9}{4\pi\mu\sigma_a r_a^2} \qquad \textbf{(B-62)}$$

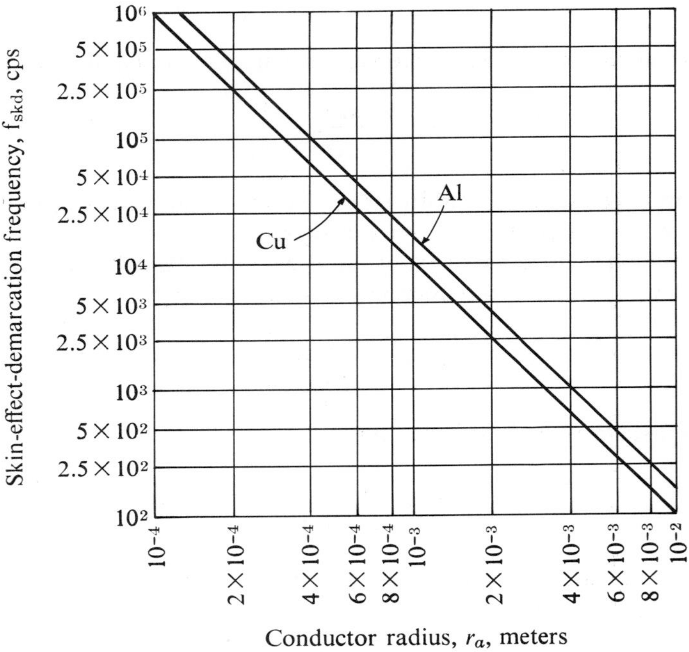

Figure B-6 Skin-effect-demarcation frequency of solid circular conductor as a function of radius (see Eq. B-62)

For the given conductor this frequency divides the spectrum into two regions which may be called, loosely, the region of negligible skin effect and the region of pronounced skin effect (see Problem 2-6). Fig. B-6 shows f_{skd} as a function of radius for solid conductors of copper and aluminum.

Equation B-59 for the high-frequency asymptotic approximation of the skin-effect-resistance ratio may be restated by substitution of Eq. B-62:

$$\frac{r_a}{r_{adc}} \approx \frac{3}{4}\sqrt{\frac{f}{f_{skd}}} + \frac{1}{4} \qquad \textbf{(B-63)}$$

(4) HIGH-FREQUENCY APPROXIMATION FOR OUTER CONDUCTOR. By means of asymptotic-approximation substitutions the following expressions for the resistance and internal-flux reactance per unit length of the outer conductor, valid at high frequencies ($m_b r_b \gg 1$), may be derived:

$$r_b + j\omega l_b \approx \frac{m_b}{2\sqrt{2}\,\pi r_b \sigma_b} - \frac{1}{4\pi r_b^2 \sigma_b} + j\,\frac{m_b}{2\sqrt{2}\,\pi r_b \sigma_b} \tag{B-64}$$

Asymptotic approximations may be applied to determine the conduction-current density and magnetic field within the conductors at high frequencies (see Problem B-5).

B-4. THIN-WALLED OUTER CONDUCTOR

The outer conductor of a physical coaxial line is necessarily of finite thickness; the case in which this is of the same order of magnitude as the skin depth for a particular operating frequency has more complicated boundary-value requirements than the thick-walled conductor just discussed. Figure B-7 shows the geometry.

The current-density function will be designated by J_{1bc}, and it is defined only for the region $r_b \leqslant r \leqslant r_c$. The Bessel functions J_0 and K_0 are both finite within the range, and hence are valid solutions. The following expression

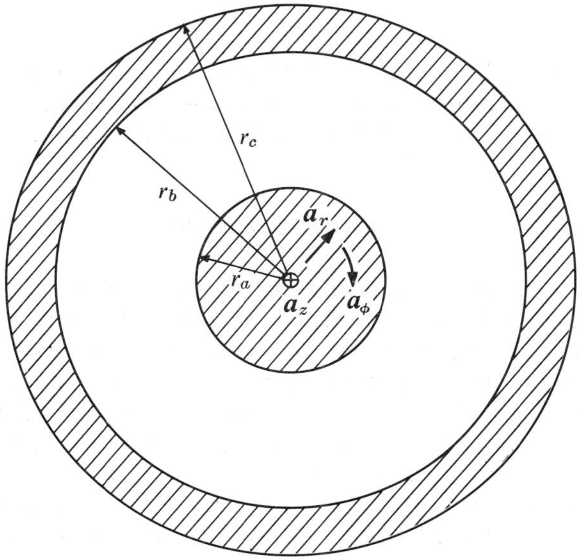

Figure B-7 Cross section of thin-walled coaxial line

parallels Eq. B-27:

$$\boldsymbol{J}_{1bc} = \mathrm{Im}[\{A_0''J_0(j^{3/2}m_b r) + B_0''K_0(j^{1/2}m_b r)\}\epsilon^{j(\omega t-\beta z)}]\boldsymbol{a}_z \qquad \textbf{(B-65)}$$

Two boundary conditions are needed to fix the constants A_0'' and B_0'': (1) the surface integral of $\boldsymbol{J}_{1bc}$ must equal the current in the outer conductor, $-i_1(z,t)$, as in Eq. B-29, and (2) the magnetic field must be continuous at $r = r_b$.

The surface-integral requirement reduces to the following, which should be compared with Eq. B-31 for the thick-walled conductor:

$$-I_{1M} = \int_0^{2\pi}\int_{r_b}^{r_c} [A_0''J_0(j^{3/2}m_b r) + B_0''K_0(j^{1/2}m_b r)]r\,dr\,d\phi \qquad \textbf{(B-66)}$$

The integrals given in Eqs. B-32 and B-33 are applicable (see Problem B-6).

The magnetic field in the outer conductor may be found by substituting Eq. B-65 in Eq. B-3.

$$\boldsymbol{H}_{1bc} = Im\left[\frac{-A_0''j^{3/2}m_bJ_1(j^{3/2}m_br) - B_0''j^{1/2}m_bK_1(j^{1/2}m_br)}{j\omega\mu\sigma_b}\epsilon^{j(\omega t-\beta z)}\right]\boldsymbol{a}_\phi \qquad \textbf{(B-67)}$$

The magnetic field between the conductors is the following whether the outer conductor is thick-walled or thin-walled:

$$\boldsymbol{H}_1 = \mathrm{Im}\left[\frac{I_{1M}}{2\pi r}\epsilon^{j(\omega t-\beta z)}\right]\boldsymbol{a}_\phi \qquad \textbf{(9-12)}$$

The right-hand sides of Eqs. B-67 and 9-12 may be set equal to each other if the r's are replaced by r_b's. The resulting equation and Eq. B-66 may be solved simultaneously for the constants A_0'' and B_0'', as called for in Problem B-6.

B-5. CONCLUSIONS

Finite conductivity in a coaxial line limits the current density to finite values and thereby causes it to be distributed continuously over the cross section of each conductor rather than concentrated on the surface closest to the other conductor. This in turn creates a magnetic field within each conductor. The current density is not uniform, however, unless the frequency approaches zero. This makes the effective resistance to alternating current higher than that to direct current.

For a solid, homogeneous inner conductor (or any solid, homogeneous circular conductor with a circularly symmetrical current distribution) the ratio of effective resistance to d-c resistance, or *skin-effect-resistance ratio* r_a/r_{adc} may be described by the parameter mr_a, where r_a is the conductor radius and

$m = \sqrt{\omega\mu\sigma}$. The *skin-effect-demarcation frequency* f_{skd} will be defined as the frequency at which $mr_a = 3/\sqrt{2}$:

$$f_{\text{skd}} = \frac{9}{4\pi\mu\sigma r_a^2} \tag{B-62}$$

The skin-effect-resistance ratio at $f = f_{\text{skd}}$ is about 1.097; it is essentially unity at lower frequencies, and for higher frequencies it quickly approaches the following asymptote:

$$\frac{r_a}{r_{adc}} \approx \frac{mr_a}{2\sqrt{2}} + \frac{1}{4} = \frac{3}{4}\sqrt{\frac{f}{f_{\text{skd}}}} + \frac{1}{4} \tag{B-63}$$

The function and its asymptotes are shown in Fig. B-5.

For usual telephone lines, voice-frequency transmission is largely in the range below the skin-effect-demarcation frequency, whereas carrier-frequency transmission is primarily in the range above that frequency.

PROBLEMS

B-1. Verify that the change of variables specified by Eq. B-7 will reduce Eq. B-5 to the form of Bessel's differential equation given in Eq. B-6.

B-2. Let $\boldsymbol{H} = \text{Im}[H(r)\epsilon^{j(\omega t - \beta z)}]\boldsymbol{a}_\phi$. By substitution in Maxwell's equations, derive a differential equation for $H(r)$ within the conducting regions of a coaxial cable. Change variables in accordance with Eq. B-7 and reduce to the form of Eq. B-6. [NOTE: The resulting equation will have n equal to unity rather than zero, as was the case with $f_J(r)$.] Write the general solution for $\boldsymbol{H}$. (*a*) Substitute the following boundary conditions for the inner conductor: (i) $\boldsymbol{H}$ vanishes at the center of the conductor, and (ii) the $\boldsymbol{H}$ field is continuous at the surface of the conductor. (Use Eq. 9-12 for $\boldsymbol{H}$ outside the conductor.) (*b*) Write the corresponding boundary conditions for $\boldsymbol{H}$ in the outer conductor (assuming it to be "thick-walled") and substitute in the solution for the differential equation. (Answers should agree with Eqs. B-39 and B-40.)

B-3. Verify the first terms of the approximations given in Eqs. B-54 and B-55 by means of Eq. B-12 and the following approximation:

$$J_1(p) \approx \frac{p}{2} - \left(\frac{p}{2}\right)^3 \frac{1}{2} \qquad (p \ll 1)$$

B-4. Compare the first-order asymptotic approximation for r_a as given in Eq. B-59 with the d-c resistance of a strip of thickness δ and width $2\pi r_a$. Also find r_a in terms of the surface resistance R_S as given by Eq. 8-79.

B-5. Find asymptotic, high-frequency approximations for the magnetic field and the conduction-current density inside the conductors of a coaxial line. Let $r = r_a - \Delta r_a$ for the inner conductor, and $r = r_b + \Delta r_b$ for the outer conductor. Compare these with the corresponding fields in a good conductor with a plane surface, caused by a normally-incident field, Eqs. 8-47 and 8-68, respectively.

B-6. Prepare a chart with the same ordinate variable as in Fig. B-6, but with the resistance to direct current, in ohms per meter, as the abscissa.

B-7. Evaluate the constants A_0'' and B_0'' for the current-density function in a thin-walled outer conductor of a coaxial line (Eq. B-65).

REFERENCES

1. DWIGHT, H. B., *Electrical Coils and Conductors*. New York: McGraw-Hill Book Company, Inc., 1945.
2. MCLACHLAN, N. W., *Bessel Functions for Engineers*, 2nd ed. London: Oxford University Press, 1961.
3. ROSA, EDWARD B. and FREDERICK W. GROVER, "Formulas and Tables for the Calculation of Mutual and Self Inductance," Sci. Paper 169, *Bull. Bureau of Std* (U.S.), 8, No. 1 (1912) pp. 1–237. (See pp. 173–77, 180.)
4. VON KARMAN, T. and M. A. BIOT, *Mathematical Methods in Engineering*, New York: McGraw-Hill Book Company, Inc., 1940.

Index

D

E